# FUNDAMENTALS OF *Electronics*

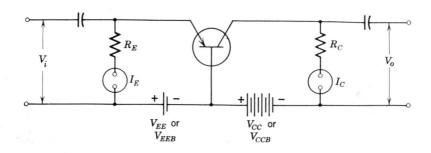

$$p_C = v_C i_C \qquad p_o = v_c i_c \qquad P_o = V_c I_c$$
$$V_i = h_i I_i + h_r V_o = V_1 = h_{11} I_1 + h_{12} V_2$$
$$I_o = h_f I_i + h_o V_o = I_2 = h_{21} I_1 + h_{22} V_2$$

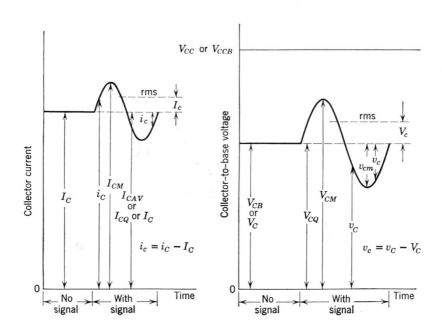

## Notes:

1. Lower-case symbols are instantaneous values.
2. Upper-case subscripts are d-c and total instantaneous values.
3. Lower-case subscripts are for varying component values.
4. If necessary to separate, for d-c use $av$ or $AV$, for maximum use $m$ or $M$, for effective use rms or RMS.
5. If necessary, use third upper-case subscript on electrode voltage to indicate reference; e.g. $V_{EE}$ or $V_{EEB}$.
6. Small-signal conditions: lower-case $p$, $h$, $y$, and $z$.
7. $z_{in}$ (lower-case) is input impedance when the external impedance is $Z_o$ (upper-case).
8. $z_{out}$ (lower-case) is output impedance when the external impedance is $Z_i$ (upper-case).

# FUNDAMENTALS OF

# Electronics

### E. NORMAN LURCH

*Aero-Space Technologist*
*Goddard Space Flight Center*
*National Aeronautics and*
*Space Administration*

New York · John Wiley & Sons, Inc.
London

# Preface

. . . . . . . . . . . . . . . . . . . . .

This book is planned to meet the need of the technician who is to work in the field of electronics. It is intended to provide the firm, solid background in fundamentals that is necessary for the study of the more specialized aspects of electronics: communications, industrial electronics, television, microwaves, or computer systems. A student using this book should have a working knowledge of d-c fundamentals and, if not prerequisite, he should be studying a-c circuits concurrently with Chapters 1 through 6 which deal with electron devices.

The level of the text material enables the student to solve such problems as gain calculations, power outputs, graphical solutions, and the determination of modulation applied to a carrier wave. It is not my intention, however, in this book to prepare the user to handle the design calculations and original derivations that are the premise of the electronic engineer. A student with a good working knowledge of algebra and right-angle trigonometry should not have difficulty with the solution of the problems.

In the development of the text material, I have assumed that the vacuum tube and the transistor are of equal importance. In the application chapters, for example Chapter 9 (Rectifiers) and Chapter 21 (Nonsinusoidal Oscillators), these elements are treated simultaneously. A unified, integrated treatment is necessary in light of the trend of current design and application.

The sequence of topics has been developed carefully from the preceding chapters to provide a logical and even flow of new material. I have found in my own classroom experience that students assimilate certain topics more rapidly than others. In this book, therefore, I have decreased the time spent on the easier subjects and increased the text material on the more difficult topics. For example, I have expanded the usual short presentation on decibels into a full chapter (Chapter 8).

A group of questions appears at the end of each chapter, the first in each group containing a list of at least ten newly introduced terms. All questions are designed to be answered orally and for use in stimulating classroom discussion. Quantitative problems involving slide-rule calculations have been supplied for the chapters that develop fundamental equations. Answers are given for approximately half the problems.

Various teachers may introduce the cathode-ray oscilloscope at different times in the study of electronics to meet their own course requirements. Accordingly, the chapter that deals with the oscilloscope is placed at the end of the book where it can be conveniently referred to without detracting from the continuity of the chapter sequence.

*October 1959*                                                 E. NORMAN LURCH

# Contents

• • • • • • • • • • • • • • • • • • • • • • • •

## Chapter 8 Decibels and Sound

## Chapter 9 Rectifiers

## Chapter 10 The Vacuum-Tube Amplifier

## Chapter 11 The Transistor Amplifier

## Chapter 12 Transformers and Transformer-Coupled Amplifiers

# Atoms, electrons, and current flow

• • • • • • • • • • • • • • • • • • • • • CHAPTER **1**

The study of d-c and a-c electric circuits, which is a prerequisite for this book, is usually introduced by an investigation into the basic structure and composition of matter (reviewed in Section 1–1). An understanding of the operation of electron tubes requires a further study of the atom. When transistors are encountered, it is necessary to take a number of the advanced theories of modern physics and streamline them to serve the needs of the technician. A discussion of internal atomic-energy levels (Section 1–2) paves the way for an understanding of the mechanism of current flow (Section 1–3) and of electron emission from a surface (Section 1–4). Concepts of the properties and the behavior of a crystalline structure (Section 1–5) and the extension to include $N$-type and $P$-type materials (Sections 1–6, 1–7, and 1–8) form the foundation for the study of transistors. The mechanism of current flow in a gas discharge (Section 1–9) has wide application in the field of electron tubes.

## Section 1–1   Composition of Matter

When a mass of a particular substance is examined, it is found that a division of this mass into small pieces does not affect the properties of the substance. We term the smallest piece which has the original properties the *molecule*. Molecules are so small that an individual molecule is invisible to the eye, even through a powerful microscope. A molecule, itself, may be divided into parts, but these parts do not

1

have the phsycial characteristics of the original substance. Now, these new small parts are called *atoms*.

Science has shown that all matter consists of combinations of one or more of the one-hundred-odd atomic elements. For instance, a molecule of water is composed of two hydrogen atoms combined with one oxygen atom. A molecule of an organic compound, such as aspirin or gasoline, is a very complex arrangement of many atoms. On the other hand, in many substances, such as carbon or copper, a single atom constitutes the molecule. Fortunately, in the field of electricity, we are concerned mainly with materials in which the molecule is the single atom.

### Section 1-2    Structure of the Atom

We have all become familiar with the symbol used by the government atomic agencies to represent the atom (Fig. 1-1). It is intended to represent a three-dimensional model wherein the electrons orbit about a central core called the *nucleus*. For purposes of clarity in understanding electronics, the three-dimensional concept is simplified to the two-dimensional forms of Fig. 1-2.

Elemental charged particles called *electrons* orbit around the nucleus in a manner similar to the movement of the planets about the sun. A breakdown of the nucleus shows that its major components are protons and neutrons. Advanced techniques of atomic physics indicate that there are other components in this nucleus, but they do not enter into the theory of electronic devices and may be disregarded. The

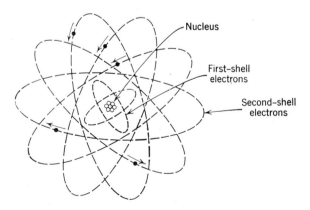

**Figure 1-1**    Three-dimensional model of an atom.

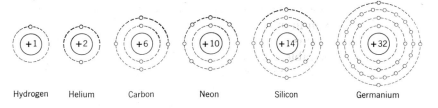

**Figure 1-2** Ring models of various atoms.

electron has a fixed electric charge, and, from its value, it has been determined that a flow of $6.24 \times 10^{18}$ electrons per second past a given point constitutes one ampere of electric current. The mass of an electron is incredibly small, $9.1 \times 10^{-31}$ kg. If the total weight of all the electrons in a steady current flow of 160 amperes past a fixed point for one year were measured, the result would be one ounce.

An atom itself in normal state is electrically neutral and without net charge. Since we have considered that each electron represents a certain fixed amount of negative charge, sufficient positive charges are necessary to balance the negative charges of the electrons. These positive particles of matter, located in the central region of the atom, are called *protons*. If a particular atom has 17 electrons in orbit, the nucleus must contain 17 protons to bring the total electric charge to zero. The nucleus also contains neutral components, without a specific charge, which are called *neutrons*. Both the proton and the neutron weigh about 1850 times as much as an electron. Thus the weight of a substance is determined primarily by the total weights of the protons and neutrons in the material.

Physically an atom then consists of a central nucleus with electrons orbiting around the core in much the same manner as the planets travel about the sun. The paths of the planets about the sun lie nearly in a single plane, whereas the orbits of the electrons about the nucleus follow a three-dimensional spherical pattern. The forces in the solar system are gravitational. In the atom, a stability of distance, revolution, and separation is maintained by the action of forces between the elemental charges of the electrons and the protons. If the hydrogen atom were enlarged to the size of a 3-foot sphere, the nucleus would be pinhead size at the center. The surface of the sphere would represent the range of possible orbits that the single electron, also pinhead size, might make around the nucleus. Thus, we see that the vast relative distance concepts in the solar system and in space are maintained within the atom.

Hydrogen has the simplest atomic structure. It has one proton with a single electron in orbit. We note that, as electrons are added, the number of protons (and neutrons) increases, making a heavier atom. The atomic table used in chemistry and physics is laid out on principles of orderly increasing numbers of electrons and protons. As examples, neon has 10 electrons, 10 protons, and 10 neutrons within the atom and copper has 29 electrons, 29 protons, and 34 neutrons in its atom.

Additionally, we find that electrons in orbits are confined to specific, finite distances from the atomic center. The innermost orbit, the $K$ orbit, may contain up to 2 electrons but no more than 2. The next orbit, the $L$ orbit, may contain up to 8 electrons. The third orbit, the $M$ orbit, may contain up to 18 electrons. The fourth orbit, the $N$ orbit, may contain up to 32 electrons. Succeeding orbits have, as maximum numbers of electrons, 18, 12, and 2 in that order. When these orbits are shown on paper for illustration, they are usually represented as concentric rings. As a result, the term *ring* is used quite freely in chemistry to describe many chemical reactions. Since, in physics, it is preferable to think of the atom in a three-dimensional concept, the term *shell* is used to describe the possible paths of orbits. Thus, a hydrogen atom has its electron in the $K$ shell. It has been observed that, for the simple atoms which are of interest electrically, an electron may exist in the $N$ shell only if the lower shells ($K$, $L$, and $M$) are completely filled. The atomic structures in Fig. 1–2 illustrate this orderly layout.

The outer shell, the *valence* shell, determines the chemical activity of the element. If the outer shell is filled in completely, the substance is inert and does not react chemically. Examples of this are neon, argon, and krypton. If the outer ring is incomplete, it may join in chemical bonds with other atoms to produce the effect of filled outer shells. This action produces molecules of stable chemical compounds, such as water and salt.

The shells are very definitely finite in character, and, for an electron to exist within an atom, the electron must exist within one of the specific shells. By this we mean that an electron cannot exist between shells. In order for an electron to move from one shell to another, energy must be supplied or extracted. In order for an electron to move from one shell to another, definite *discrete* amounts of energy, called *quanta*, are required. A quantum of energy is the least unit amount of energy that can be considered in the process. Furthermore, quanta must exist as whole numbers; fractions of a quantum do not exist. If the energy required to shift an electron from one shell to another were three quanta units, an energy level of two quanta would produce no shift. If the energy level were increased, then, suddenly, at a particular instant, the necessary three quanta would be available and the electron would abruptly shift from one shell to the next.

We have stated that the shells are described as finite orbits wherein electrons may travel. If we examine a particular shell carefully, we note that the $L$ shell consists of two very close subshells, the $M$ shell has three subshells, and the $N$ shell four subshells. Since the subshells are very close to each other within a particular shell, an electron may move between the subshells of a given shell with less energy-level changes required than as if they moved between shells. All this leads to describe electrons as existing in atoms at definite, *discrete* or *permissive* energy levels. The permissive energy levels are fixed and invariant. External addition or removal of energy may move an electron from one permissive level to another, but it cannot change the permissive levels. Less than permissive energy amounts can produce light and heat.

Perhaps a clearer concept of a discrete energy step can be obtained from the action of heat energy applied to a beaker containing a pound of water. A Btu (British thermal unit) is defined as the heat energy necessary to raise one pound of water one degree Fahrenheit. Successive Btu's raise the temperature of the water from room temperature to 212° F. We find at this point that the water accepts heat without raising its temperature at all. It requires about 970 Btu to evaporate the water into steam which is still 212° F. This large amount of heat is known as the latent heat of vaporization. If there are $10^x$ molecules of water in one pound, $1/10^x$ is the amount of heat as a fractional part of a Btu that is necessary to raise the molecule one degree in temperature. Let us call this basic amount of energy $q$. This $q$ is the equivalent energy to what we call a quantum for the electron. Each successive $q$ raises the energy one degree to 212° F. At 212°, the addition of $100q$ units of energy does nothing to the water. It takes 970$q$ to boil off the molecule. Any amount of energy less than 970$q$ does not produce steam. We can consider different water temperatures in degree steps of energy levels comparable to energy levels within a shell, and the large amount of energy, 970$q$, as the energy required to move from one shell to the next.

The electrons in the outer shell have a higher energy content than the electrons in the inner shells. External energy then will affect the electrons in the outer shell first. Application of energy in the form of heat will cause the electron to rise to outer permissive levels. Continued increasing heat energy can cause an outer electron to escape from the restraining forces of the atom. This effect is known as *electron emission* and will be discussed in detail in Section 1–4. Electrons from a free atom or molecule may secure enough energy for escape from the kinetic-energy transfer of collision or impact. A detailed discussion of this phenomenon appears in Section 1–9 as a *gas discharge*. The production of free electrons by radioactivity has a limited application to electronics, particularly for the needs of this text. When atoms are internally bound together to form the solid surface of a metal, electron release obtained by collision is termed *secondary emission* (Section 4–1). Electrons may be literally pulled out or ripped from the restraining forces of the atoms of a cold surface by means of a very high electric field. This is termed *high field emission* (Section 1–9). Light may be considered to consist of definite energy levels or quanta. Light also has the property that, as the frequency of the light increases (moving toward shorter wavelength), the energy content of the light per quantum increases. Certain materials are sensitive to light; that is, electron motion between permissive levels increases with incident light to the point where free electrons actually escape from the surface of the material. This is termed photoemission.

### Section 1–3    Electron Flow in Solids

Solid materials used in electrical work can be divided into three classes: conductors, semiconductors, and insulators. For a broad classification, let us assume that a cubic-inch block of each is available for tests and measurements. If the resistance between opposite faces of each cube is measured, we find that the insulator yields a resistance value of many megohms. The conductor will be measured in millionths of an ohm or micro-ohms. The semiconductor is a cross between the two, and we can expect to find its resistance value in the order of ohms. This method of classification is quite loose and very general as the boundaries between them often tend to be obscure.

In analyzing the properties of the three forms from the viewpoint of modern physics, we can obtain more satisfactory results if we consider permissive energy levels of the outer shell. The permissive energy bands at the outer surface form two groups. The outer group is known as the *conduction energy band*, and, separated from this energy band by a specific amount of energy, next comes, at a lower energy content, the *valence-bond energy band*. This is shown in Fig. 1–3. The valence-bond band contains the electrons that normally combine with valence-band electrons of other atoms to form molecules

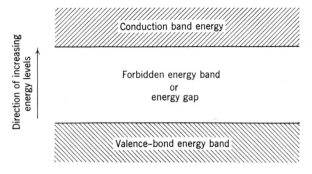

**Figure 1-3** Energy levels in the outer shell of an atom.

or compounds. Below the valence energy band exist other energy bands containing electrons. We have said that only the outer electrons can participate in chemical or electrical actions. The characteristic of the conduction-band which is of paramount importance electrically is that a flow of conduction-band electrons can be obtained from the influence of a weak external electric field or potential, whereas the valence-band electrons remain bound to the parent atom. The gap between the two represents a *forbidden-band* region where an electron cannot exist. This gap can be traversed by electrons which have the necessary energy-level change required to overcome the gap. This energy requirement is again measured in terms of quanta levels.

In an insulator, the conduction band is widely separated from the valence-bond band (Fig. 1-4). In order to have free electrons available in the conduction band, very large amounts of energy must be added to the electrons in order to get them to cross the gap into the

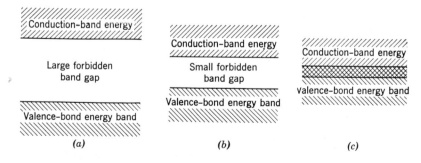

**Figure 1-4** Energy levels in the outer shells of different materials. (*a*) Insulator. (*b*) Semiconductor. (*c*) Conductor.

conduction band.   Thyrite, the material used in lightning arresters, at normal voltage levels, acts as an ideal insulator.   Under high-voltage surges, the stress of the high potential pulls electrons across the forbidden energy gap into the conduction band, and a protective shunting current is produced.   When insulators are operated at high temperatures, the increased energy of heat allows a crossing of electrons into the conduction band with less outside electric stress.   Thus, we note that many materials which are good insulators at low temperatures become conductors at high temperatures.

A semiconductor has a forbidden energy gap between the valence band and the conduction band, but it is not as great as in the insulator. Again, we note that a semiconductor which has certain operating characteristics at room temperatures may lose them at elevated temperatures because the additional heat energy causes too many electrons to cross over into the conduction band.

In a conductor, the conduction-band energy levels overlap the valence-band energy levels and effectively merge into one.   Thus, in a conductor, many of the valence-band electrons will move freely under the influence of external electric forces and so provide the large numbers of electrons necessary for what we term normal values of electric currents.

### Section 1-4   Emission

Free electrons are obtained to operate vacuum tubes and many forms of gas tubes by heating a surface called the *cathode*.   The cathode surface must have the property of being able to liberate the required quantity of electrons while meeting a number of other physical conditions.   The emission surface must be able to emit electrons at temperatures below its melting point.   It also must be mechanically strong enough to be stable under the conditions of its operation.   Also, its efficiency of emission must be high with respect to possible alternative materials.

The work required to extract an electron from a surface is termed its *work function* and is measured in *electron volts*.   One electron volt is defined as the kinetic energy acquired by the free fall of an electron in a potential difference of one volt.

Pure *tungsten* was one of the first materials to be used as a thermionic surface.   Tungsten operates at a temperature of about 4070° F with an emission rating of 2.7 amperes per square inch of surface.   The emission efficiency at this operating point is about 4 ma per watt of input heating power.   As with all other thermionic-emission materials, the characteristics vary greatly with small changes in the operating temperature. A "cold" tungsten filament at 3600° F produces negligible emission. Tungsten has a great advantage over other materials in its physical strength and in its ability to have an effective infinite emitting life. It is often used with very large tubes which are expensive to replace or with very tiny tubes where the cathode emitting surface is a fine wire.

In the experimental search for other useful emitting materials, *thoriated tungsten* was developed. A small percentage of thorium oxide is mixed with tungsten, and the material is then made into the necessary physical structure required for the tube. The emitter is then heated to just below the melting point. A monatomic layer of thorium oxide works to the surface and is converted to pure thorium. This combination has the advantage of the lower work function of the thorium together with the strength and higher operating temperature of tungsten. Pure thorium alone could not be used, as its melting point is too close to the required operating temperature. The emitter operates at a lower temperature of about 3000° F and has the very high emission value of about 7.6 amperes per square inch of surface. It also has the very high efficiency of about 70 milliamperes emission per watt of heating power. The pure thorium in time boils off, and the total emission becomes reduced. The surface may be reactivated by *flashing*. A higher heating power than normal is applied for a short time and drives some of the internally contained thorium oxide to the surface where it changes to pure thorium. Excessive or prolonged heating may cause the emitter to melt. The flashing process must be performed very carefully to prevent permanent damage to the tube.

The need for the third type of thermionic surface was brought about by the application of alternating current as a source of heating power in radio receivers. If alternating current is used on a tungsten emitter, electron emission will vary in accordance with the cycles of the alternating current. These fluctuations produce an a-c hum or interference on the electron output of the tube which in many applications is most undesirable. If it is necessary to develop heat for thermionic emission, an indirect method of heat transfer must be provided. Heat is produced by the alternating current in a resistance wire, and this heat is transferred through a nonmetallic heat conductor to an emitting surface. The thermal time lag through the heat conductor is slow enough to eliminate the effects of any instantaneous variation of heat production in the resistance wire. A device which, when heated by an electric current, produces emission itself is called a

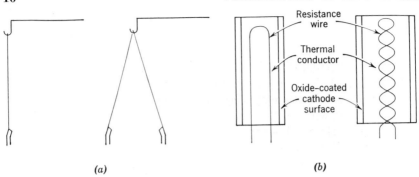

*(a)*                                                    *(b)*

**Figure 1–5**   The physical construction of typical thermionic emitters.   (a) Filament structures.   (b) Heater–cathode-structures.

*filament.*   When we have the indirect heating process, we call the wire which gets hot from the flow of current through itself the *heater* and the separate emitting surface the *cathode.*   Technically all emitting surfaces are cathodes, but we must be careful to distinguish a filament from the heater–cathode arrangement by the use of proper terminology.

Usually the heater wire is tungsten, and the cathode surface a combination of barium and strontium oxides.   This unit operates at a much lower temperature than the others.   At 1560° F, the emission current is 3 amperes per square inch of surface with an efficiency of the order of 300 ma emission per watt of heater power.   These heater–cathode structures are generally used for the small "receiving-type" tubes.   Typical structures are shown in Fig. 1–5.   The oxides are relatively fragile and tend to flake off with use.   The shorter life is compensated for by the fact that a replacement tube is inexpensive. When these oxide-coated surfaces are used directly as filaments, the efficiency increases by a factor of five or ten.   Thus, they would be

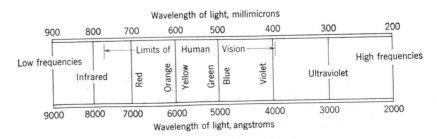

**Figure 1–6**   The spectral distribution of light energies.

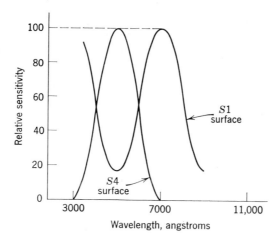

**Figure 1–7**   Spectral response of different cathode surfaces.   (*Courtesy RCA*)

used where available heating-power sources must be very conservative as in portable equipment.   The oxide-coated filament cannot take the stress of high electrode voltages.

An important method of obtaining electrons from surfaces is by *photoemission*.   Useful light ranges from low frequencies and long wavelengths (infrared), through the visible spectrum, to high frequencies and short wavelengths (ultraviolet).   The wavelength of light is measured in angstroms ($10^{-8}$ cm) or in microns ($10^{-6}$ m).   The relation between wavelength and color for light is shown in Fig. 1–6.   The energy, in quanta, which is available in a ray of light striking the emissive cathode surface, if sufficient, can cause the liberation of an electron.   Certain materials have been found and developed that have low enough work functions so as to be used as light-sensitive surfaces.   Some of these substances are indicated on the graph of Fig. 1–7 together with the response of the human eye.   It is seen that different materials are sensitive to different color ranges of light.

## Section 1–5   The Structure of a Crystal

In order to understand the operation of a transistor, it is necessary to go still deeper into atomic-structure theory, but only so far as it applies to crystals.   Fundamentally, a crystalline structure produces special properties which do not exist for the substance in the "ordinary" form.   An example may be taken as common carbon, where a special crystalline formation of carbon produces the diamond. Another example of application of crystalline structures is the field of metallurgy of steel where different heat-treating processes produce different crystalline formations. The different crystalline structures produce different characteristics, such as a surface hardening, an ability to withstand increased shearing stress, or the ability to be formed or machined. Many metal failures can be explained by the changes in their crystalline structures.

In transistor electronics, we are concerned with *single* crystals of silicon and germanium. Natural crystals usually are polycrystalline; that is, they comprise many individual crystals oriented in space in many different directions. The separate single crystals are joined to each other by *grain boundaries.* The primary difficulties faced by the manufacturers are, first, to produce single crystals which must not be polycrystalline, and, second, to maintain an extreme degree of purity in the germanium or silicon. The structures of the germanium and silicon atoms are shown in Fig. 1–2.

Transistor material is in the form of a *face-centered lattice.* In a face-centered crystal, each atom has four neighbors and all are equi-

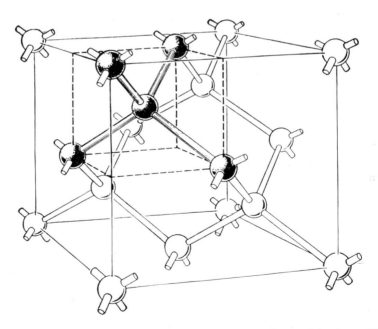

**Figure 1–8**   Three-dimensional model of a face-centered crystal lattice.   (*Courtesy Kittel, Introduction to Solid State Physics*)

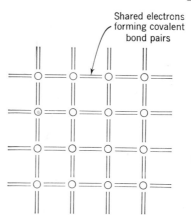

Figure 1–9 Two dimensional model of a face-centered crystal lattice.

distant from each other. The face-centered lattice arrangement is adaptable to both germanium and silicon, as the outer ring or shell contains four electrons. Thus, if the atoms in this crystal share electrons in their outer shells with their neighbors, the outer shells of all the atoms will be complete, since its own four electrons plus the four shared from the four neighbors make the complete number of eight electrons in the outer shell. Then, the material is now in a stable form. A three-dimensional model of this crystal is shown in Fig. 1–8. This model can be reduced to the two-dimensional representation of Fig. 1–9 for simplicity.

When we have closely placed atoms, as in the crystal, we may refer again to the permissive energy-band concept we used earlier in discussing insulators and conductors (Fig. 1–10). If the material is at the temperature of absolute zero, all electrons are contained in the valence-bond energy band; none are in the conduction band. Therefore, the material is an ideal insulator. When energy is applied to the system in the form of heat, electrons will leave the valence-bond band and jump across to the conduction band. The energy

Figure 1–10 Energy bands in the outer shell.

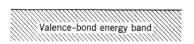

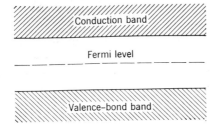

**Figure 1-11**   Energy-level diagram
showing the Fermi level.

required to jump the forbidden band is 0.7 electron volt for germanium
and 1.1 electron volts for silicon.   Further application of heat causes
more and more electrons to cross the energy gap into the conduction band.   This means that the resistivity characteristics of germanium and silicon (and carbon which also has four electrons in the
outer shell) show a decreasing resistance with an increase in temperature.   Both thermistors and Globars are direct applications of this
semiconductor characteristic.   Normally, however, transistors must
operate within definite temperature limits in order to control the
resistivity characteristics.

At room temperatures, then, electrons have crossed from the
valence-bond band into the conduction band.   The absence of the
electron in the valence band creates a *hole*.   In pure crystals, loose
electrons in the conduction band are balanced by an equal number of
holes in the valence band.   A pure crystal above absolute zero must
contain these combinatons which are called *electron-hole pairs*.   The
material that has this pairing is termed *intrinsic*.   Electrons are free
to move within the conduction band.   Correspondingly, if an electron
in the valence band moves to fill a hole, it leaves a hole where it was
before.   Thus, we can have not only current in the conduction band
but also an independent current within the valence band which is the
result of holes "jumping" from one atom to another.   The usual
currents that are encountered in electric circuits are normally conduction-band currents.

At this point we may also describe the region within the valence
band as being *ionized*.   An ionized atom no longer has a neutral
charge where protons are balanced by an equal number of electrons,
but has a net charge caused by the absence of an electron which
normally should be bound within the atom.   An ionized particle may
be termed *excited* since it is at an energy state different from that of
the ordinary neutral atom.

Another definition which must be noted is the term *Fermi level*.
The Fermi level is that energy level where the distribution of higher

energy levels equals the distribution of lower energy levels.    At room temperature the Fermi level is indicated for a semiconductor in Fig. 1–11.    When the ambient temperature is reduced, the Fermi level falls since conduction-band electrons lose their added energies and return to the valence band.    At higher ambient temperatures, more electrons cross into the conduction band, and the Fermi level rises since more electron-hole pairs are produced.

## Section 1–6    N-Type Material

When an impurity is introduced into pure germanium at the controlled rate of one part in ten million and when the face-centered lattice structure of pure germanium is maintained, N-type material is produced.    Atoms of arsenic or antimony (certain other atoms could also theoretically serve) have five electrons each in the outer shell, and, when they form part of this lattice structure, we find electrons available in excess of the number required for covalent bonds.    These extra electrons are only lightly bound to the parent atoms.    We may represent this new arrangement by Fig. 1–12.    The introduced impurities which add electrons to the crystal system are known as *donor* atoms. Now this N material inherently has more electrons than the pure intrinsic crystal, but it must be remembered that a block of this material is *definitely neutral* as far as over-all net charge is concerned. It has no charge any more than a piece of copper could have.

A very low amount of energy (0.05 electron volt) is required to release electrons into the conduction band.    This results in raising the Fermi level (Fig. 1–13).    Since a high energy level (0.7 to 1.1 electron volts) is required to break the covalent bonds, we can con-

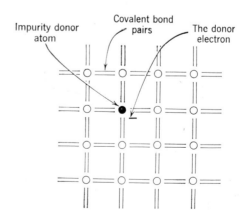

**Figure 1–12** Electron affinities within N material.

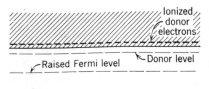

**Figure 1–13**    Energy levels within $N$ material.

sider that current flow in $N$ material is primarily the movement of these ionized electrons that have resulted from the donor atoms. We also have present, since the transistor material is above absolute zero, electron-hole pairs.   Now, in $N$ material, there are many more electrons in the conduction band than there are holes in the valence-bond band.  Obviously, there is a critical impurity concentration during manufacture which is that value that will produce a complete ionization of donor atoms at room temperature.   We term the electrons the *majority current carriers* and the holes the *minority current carriers* in $N$-type material.   At normal temperatures, there are many more electrons than holes.   If the temperature of the crystal is raised, more and more electron-hole pairs are formed.   At some temperature level, the number of donor electrons becomes negligible with respect to the number of electron-hole pairs, and the crystal is, for all practical purposes, intrinsic.   If the heat-generating source is removed, the material will settle back to normal.   However, there is a limit to the amount of heat that a crystalline substance can take without losing the lattice formation.   If the lattice pattern is destroyed by excessive temperatures, the device ceases to have the desired properties and must be replaced.

### Section 1–7    *P*-Type Material

Like $N$ material, $P$ material is formed by adding controlled amounts of impurity.   *Acceptor* atoms, indium, gallium, or aluminum, have three electrons each in the outer shell.   These impurities become an integral part of the crystal-lattice structure but leave certain of the covalent bonds short by one electron.   Again the shortage, or *hole*, is loosely attached to the parent atom (about 0.08 electron volt necessary for release), and at room temperature complete ionization of these acceptor atoms occurs.   The two-dimensional crystalline

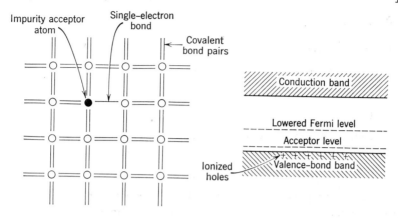

**Figure 1-14** Electron affinities and energy levels within $P$ material.

structure and the energy-level diagram with the lowered Fermi level are shown in Fig. 1–14. Now, in $P$ material, holes are the majority current carriers, and electrons are the minority current carriers. The few covalent bonds that break into electron-hole pairs establish the minority electron carriers in the conduction band. Current flow in $P$ material can be considered as a shift of holes from one atom to another atom within the valence-bond band.

As with $N$ material, excessive heat causes the number of created electron-hole pairs to overshadow the effect of the hole-producing acceptor atoms. The Fermi level will shift toward the center, and the substance will behave as intrinsic crystal.

## Section 1–8 Light on Crystals

We have stated that added energy on the pure crystal, on $N$ material, or on $P$ material can break down the covalent bonds into electron-hole pairs. A larger number of electron-hole pairs in a crystal means that, in it, a larger current will flow under the influence of an external potential source. In other words, we might state that the resistance of the crystal decreases. In this section we wish to investigate the photoconductive properties of the lattice.

We have repeated several times, for emphasis, that the breaking of a covalent bond is brought about by energy increments in discrete amounts, and that nothing will happen until the quanta energy requirements of the gap are reached. Earlier it was stated that, for a given light, the energy content per quantum increases with frequency (or,

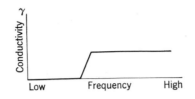

**Figure 1-15** The effect of varying light frequency on crystal conductivity.

rephrased, increases with a decrease in wavelength). Thus we can experimentally determine that a given light, which at low frequencies will not produce an electron-hole pair, will produce the electron-hole pair if only the frequency of the light is increased. Thus we find that the crystal which is *transparent* to low-frequency light is *opaque* to light at high frequencies. This action is shown in Fig. 1-15.

As the light intensity is raised from zero, the conductivity of the crystal increases (Fig. 1-16). The residual conductivity $\gamma_0$ exists because electron-hole pairs already exist normally at room temperatures which are produced by heat and not by light.

### Section 1-9   Mechanism of a Gas Discharge

In Section 1-2, we stated that electrons are produced from collision with a gas. In some electron tubes, initial velocities are produced by the presence of a hot-cathode surface. In others, the initial free electron is available because, in any volume of a gas, some degree of ionization is naturally present. If two plates have a voltage between them (Fig. 1-17), a free electron at point $A$ is attracted to the positive plate. The electron travels to the plate along the path $S$ shown by the arrow. At point $B$ it will collide with a gas molecule. If the kinetic energy at point $B$ is sufficient by virtue of having gained sufficient velocity, it liberates an electron from the outer shell of the gas molecule at $B$. Now, two electrons reach the plate, and the newly created positive gas ion at $B$ travels to the negative surface where it picks up an electron on contact and becomes a neutral gas molecule again. This process is cumulative, and the current resulting is limited

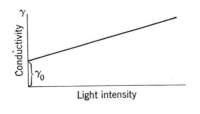

**Figure 1-16** The effect of varying light intensity on crystal conductivity.

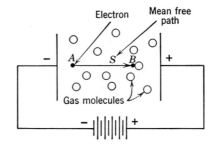

**Figure 1–17** The physical condition for ionization of a gas.

only by the resistance of the external circuit. The process of gas ionization is accompanied by formation of light energy. We find that different gases and gas combinations produce different colors.

A complete ionization occurs when all gas molecules or particles are ionized. If more input energy (from a higher voltage) is applied between the plates, *double ionization* may occur. Now each gas molecule delivers two electrons, and each gas ion must pick up two electrons at the negative surface. Further stages of *multiple ionization* are possible. A molecule which is subject to multiple ionization has a much greater force when striking the negative surface than has a singly ionized molecule. These stronger forces, referred to as *cathode bombardment, cathode sputtering,* or *ion bombardment,* often destroy a sensitive cathode surface by literally knocking it to pieces. The protection against this occurrence is to limit the permissible safe maximum current values by means of a properly selected value of external circuit resistance.

The average of all the lengths of the collision paths $S$ in Fig. 1–17 is called the *mean free path.* If the mean free path is greater or longer than the separation of the plates, the gas will not ionize. The presence of few gas molecules in a given volume results in a long mean free-path length; many gas molecules in the given volume allow for a very short mean free-path length. We stated earlier that, unless the energy content of the traveling electron is sufficient, the struck molecules will not ionize. In order to obtain ionization with a short mean free-path length, the applied voltage must be increased in order to get the electron up to the required speed within a shorter distance. These results have been summarized as *Paschen's law* and are plotted in Fig. 1–18. Assuming that electrons are not available from a thermionic source, let point $d$ represent the operating condition of a sparkplug gap in air. When the plug is subjected to the high-compression pressure of a piston, the actual firing point is at $e$ and is under much

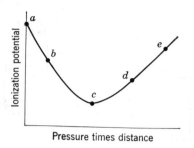

**Figure 1-18**   Graph illustrating
Paschen's law.

different conditions than were observed in open air.   If, for a fixed
gap, the pressure is decreased, we notice that the voltage necessary to
produce ionization falls until we reach a minimum at point $c$.   Further
reduction in pressure increases the length of the mean free path so that
a greater voltage is necessary to make use of the relatively few collisions.   Finally, at point $a$, there is a true vacuum.   Since the length
of the mean free path is infinite, the ionization potential is infinite.
A current is produced at point $a$ when the voltage is sufficiently high to
produce an electron flow by high field emission.

An interesting experiment can vividly illustrate the concept of the
mean free path.   In Fig. 1–19 there are two alternate paths, $x$ and $y$,
between plates $A$ and $B$.   If the pressure of a vacuum pump is adjusted
so that the product of pressure times distance around the long path $y$
falls at point $c$ in the curve of Fig. 1–18, the product of pressure times
distance $x$ must lie on the curve at $b$.   Thus, applying the least value of
ionization potential between plates $A$ and $B$ will produce light around
the long path $y$ but not across the short path $x$.

The volt-ampere characteristic of a gas diode which does not have a
thermionic source of electrons is shown in Fig. 1–20.   Note particularly that the current scale is not linear but logarithmic.   A small

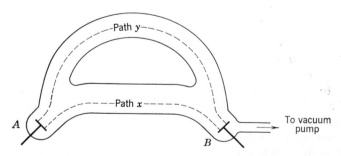

**Figure 1-19**   Demonstration apparatus to show the effect of mean free path.

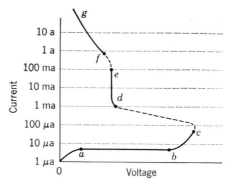

**Figure 1–20** The volt-ampere characteristic of a gas discharge.

voltage, point $a$, will collect the free electrons which are normally found within the gas. A further increase in voltage to $b$ does not increase the current flow since all the loose electrons have already been picked up at $a$. The current consists of *all* the electrons that are being produced naturally, and is termed *saturated*. This saturation current is also called *dark current* because it does not *produce* light.

When the voltage reaches point $b$, ionization causes an increase of current from $b$ to $c$. The region $0abc$ is the range of operation of vacuum and gas phototubes.

The characteristic is completely unstable between $c$ and $d$. Between points $d$ and $e$, we note that current is independent of voltage. This region is called the *glow-discharge* portion of the curve, and one of its main applications is in the field of light-producing devices such as neon lamps and sodium-vapor lamps. The region between $d$ and $e$ is also used for voltage-regulator tubes.

Again, the curve is somewhat unstable between $e$ and $f$. The portion of the curve between $f$ and $g$ is the arc-discharge region. An arc is generally associated with a very large current, and it has a negative-resistance characteristic wherein current increases with a decrease in voltage.

We might summarize this topic of gas discharges by stating a few facts and by making some definitions which were bypassed in order not to detract from the continuity of the discussion. A vacuum tube does not have a perfect vacuum, but has a residual gas pressure of the order of $10^{-8}$ to $10^{-6}$ mm of mercury. This results in a mean free-path length of the order of 40 meters. Thus, in a vacuum tube, ionization of the residual gas is practically impossible. In a gas tube, the pressure is of the order of $10^{-2}$ or $10^{-1}$ mm of mercury. Then, the mean free path is of the order of 0.1 mm.

There is a definite and finite *ionization time*. It is possible to reduce this ionization time to microseconds by proper gas combinations and by the use of high ionization potentials, but it is usually of the order of milliseconds. *Deionization time* is also a finite time, and it is necessarily longer than ionization time. A gas is ionized under the force and pressure of an external voltage. Deionization is a natural recombination of the ion and electron without the addition of external voltages. These finite times result in maximum upper-frequency limits in many applications.

Collisions between electrons and molecules take several forms. An *elastic* collision produces no results—it is merely a bouncing off of the two particles. If the collision causes a temporary increase in energy, the term *excited* is used. The excited molecule quickly loses this new energy in the form of light. A collision which causes an energy increase of longer duration produces a *metastable* state. A molecule in the metastable state, when struck again by another particle, will produce complete ionization. Naturally, if the colliding electron hits with sufficient energy, *complete* ionization is immediately developed.

When a gas is ionized, the gas exists as a mixture of electrons, ions, and ordinary neutral-gas molecules. This region, called the *plasma*, extends across the tube between the plates. The plasma region acts electrically as if it were a conductor, with the electrons moving to the positive plate and the ions moving to the negative plate. Most of the voltage drop occurs right off the negative plate or cathode. This abrupt potential drop is termed *cathode fall*. The light distribution is uniform along the plasma, but drops off markedly both at the positive plate, the anode, and the cathode. Also, near the cathode, other dark bands of low light intensity are found.

#### . . . . Suggested References for Further Study

1. T. S. Gray, *Applied Electronics*, 2nd ed., Chapters 2 and 3, John Wiley & Sons, New York, 1954.
2. W. G. Dow, *Fundamentals of Engineering Electronics*, 2nd ed., Chapters 7, 10, and 12, John Wiley & Sons, New York, 1952.
3. K. R. Spangenberg, *Vacuum Tubes*, Chapter 4, McGraw-Hill Book Co., New York, 1948.

#### . . . . QUESTIONS

1. Define or explain each of the following terms: (*a*) neutron, (*b*) photoemission, (*c*) forbidden band, (*d*) work function, (*e*) flashing, (*f*) donor atom,

(g) grain boundary, (h) electron-hole pair, (i) mean free path, (j) cathode fall.

2. Name the component parts of an atom.
3. Under what conditions will the L shell be the valence shell?
4. Distinguish between the terms photoemission and photoconductivity.
5. Explain how a semiconductor acts as a conductor at high temperature.
6. Explain how wood acts as a conductor when struck by lightning.
7. What are the properties of a useful thermionic emitter?
8. What is meant by the Fermi level?
9. What are the main current carriers in N material? In P material?
10. Why are acceptor atoms so called?
11. What is an opaque crystal?
12. Describe what occurs to produce multiple ionization in a gas.
13. Explain by Paschen's law the effect of a high-compression engine on the firing of a spark plug.
14. Why is deionization time longer than ionization time?
15. Show the difference between the elastic, the excited, the metastable, and the ionized states of a gas molecule.

# Two-element
# electron devices

A discussion of space charge and saturation provides the foundation for understanding the operation of vacuum-tube diodes (Section 2–1). A number of other basic principles of diodes can be brought out in the application of the diode to a simple rectifier circuit (Section 2–2). Semiconductors are also very important in diode form (Section 2–3). Cold-cathode gas diodes (Section 2–4) and hot-cathode gas diodes (Section 2–5) have special characteristics which make them useful for applications for which other diodes may be unsuited.

### Section 2–1   The Vacuum Diode

A vacuum diode consists of two elements: the plate or anode and a cathode. The thermionic cathode may be either a filament surface or a heater–cathode combination. For simplicity, the illustrations and discussions are confined to a diode in which the plate and the cathode are parallel planes of finite dimensions (Fig. 2–1). Actually, we do not often encounter this physical arrangement in practice. The plates are usually rectangular in cross section surrounding the cathode or take the shape of a cylinder wall. Also the emitter is usually one of the forms shown in Fig. 1–5.

Figure 2–1 shows that a cloud of electrons exists in space just off the cathode surface. This is known as a *space charge*. If we assume the plate potential to be zero, when electrons are emitted or "boiled off" the cathode, the small velocities obtained in the emitting process carry

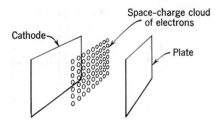

**Figure 2-1** The basic structure of a diode.

the electrons away from the cathode in a slow drift which diffuses throughout the tube envelope. If a milliammeter is connected from the plate to the cathode, forming a complete circuit, the electrons that reach the plate from this small initial velocity return to the cathode, giving an indication of a small current flow on the meter. This is known as the *Edison effect*. If electrons are "boiled off" the cathode, the cathode is left with a positive charge. The tendency of the cathode is then to seek back electrons to cancel this positive charge. Accordingly, electrons striking and entering the plate return to the cathode through the external circuit, causing a deflection on the meter.

Another consequence of the resulting positive charge on the cathode is that the cathode draws back into itself a great many of the electrons that it has emitted. Thus, in the process of emission, there is a heavy "rain" of electrons back on the emitting surface. We noted that, during this process, there is a drift of electrons across the tube. These electrons have a negative charge and tend to repel back into the cathode the next group of electrons that are emitted. The over-all result is that there exists in the space just off the cathode a cloud of electrons which is called the *space charge*.

If an external voltage source is connected to a diode so that the plate is negative with respect to the cathode (Fig. 2-2), the meter which

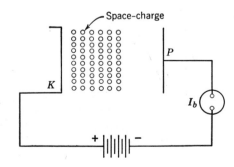

**Figure 2-2** Reverse voltage on a diode.

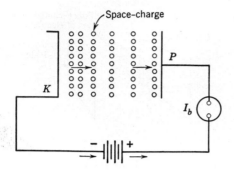

**Figure 2–3**   Forward voltage on a diode.

reads plate current $I_b$ indicates zero.   The negative voltage on the plate not only prevents electrons from reaching the plate but also forces the drift electrons back into the space-charge cloud.   If the external battery is reversed (Fig. 2–3) so that the anode is positive with respect to the cathode, a plate current results.   The positive anode attracts electrons from the space charge.   Those electrons that are removed from the space charge are replaced by further emission from the cathode surface.   When the anode potential is increased, the plate current increases.   The space charge is reduced as the plate current increases.   Eventually, we find that the number of "stored" electrons in the space charge is reduced to zero, and the electrons that are emitted are directly swept to the plate.

When plate current comes from the reservoir of the space charge, the space-charge cloud is actually serving as the cathode of the tube as far as the plate is concerned.   The term *virtual cathode* is used to describe this function of the space charge.   Also, at those current levels where a space charge exists, the term *space-charge-limited* is used to describe the operation of the tube.   When the plate collects all the electrons, a *plate saturation* exists.

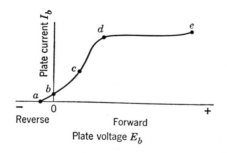

**Figure 2–4**   Plate characteristic of a diode.

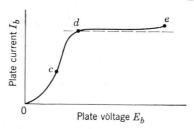

**Figure 2–5** Simplified plate characteristic of a diode.

If the relation between plate current and plate voltage is plotted, the curve of Fig. 2–4 results. The plate current at point $b$ is the Edison-effect value. A small reverse negative voltage $a$ is required to counteract the initial velocities of emission which produce the Edison-effect current. The current increases from $b$ to $c$ to $d$ with an increasing positive plate potential. At point $d$, we reach plate saturation. From what we have said so far, it would seem that no further current increase would be noted between $d$ and $e$. Actually, the current does rise slightly from $d$ to $e$, and this rise may be explained by the *Schottky effect*. Between $d$ and $e$ all the emitted electrons go immediately to the plate. The higher plate voltage at $e$ exerts a greater force on the still bound-in electrons within the emitter than the voltage at $d$. This increased force results in a slightly decreased work function at the cathode. The lowering of the work function slightly produces the slight increase in plate current between $d$ and $e$.

The magnitude of the Edison effect is so small that, except in certain special applications, it may be neglected, and the curve may be redrawn as Fig. 2–5. By several different mathematical methods, an equation may be established for the space-charge-limited region of the curve, $0cd$:

$$I_b = KE_b^{3/2} \qquad (2\text{–}1)$$

This equation is known as the *three-halves power law*, *Child's law*, the *Langmuir–Child law* or the *space-charge equation*. If one set of readings is experimentally determined, the value of $K$ may be found by calculation, and then other values of $I_b$ and $E_b$ worked out for this value of $K$. $K$ is proportional to the area of the plate and inversely proportional to the square of the distance between the cathode and plate. In actual tubes the exponent may not be exactly $\frac{3}{2}$. The $\frac{3}{2}$ value of the exponent is only approximately correct for actual tubes.

If the amount of space charge is controlled by setting different levels of emitter heating power (different filament or heater voltages), we find that we obtain different values of plate currents at plate satura-

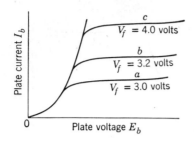

Figure 2–6  Effect of different filament voltages on the plate characteristic.

tion.  In Fig. 2–6, plate-current saturation values increase as the filament voltage is increased from $a$ to $c$.  Normally, a vacuum tube is operated at levels of plate current that are considerably below the saturation point.  However, in diodes, the maximum peak current, which is the saturation value, is important in rectifier circuits and is always listed for the diode in the tube manual.  For a typical space-charge-limited diode plate characteristic (Fig. 2–8), point $P$ on the curve is established when the plate voltage $E_b$ is 12 volts.  The plate voltage $E_b$ causes a 300-ma plate current $I_b$.  If we divide the value of $E_b$ by $I_b$, we obtain 40 ohms.  This is the equivalent value of resistance which the tube presents to $E_b$, and, since these values are direct current, it is called the $d$-$c$ *plate resistance* or *static resistance*, using the symbol $R_p$:

$$R_p = \frac{E_b}{I_b} \qquad (2\text{–}2a)$$

If the plate voltage increases a small amount, we move from $P$ to $P'$ on the curve.  Correspondingly, the plate current increases a small amount.  If $P'$ moves closer and closer to $P$, the direction of change from $P$ to $P'$ approaches the slope of the tangent drawn to the curve at point $P$.  Now we can use the slope of the tangent to determine

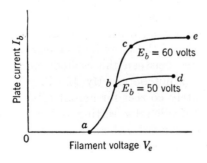

Figure 2–7  Variation of plate current
with filament voltage.

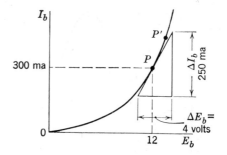

**Figure 2–8** Method of determining the static resistance $R_p$ and dynamic resistance $r_p$ for a diode.

the ratio of a small change in $E_b$ to the resulting small change in $I_b$. This ratio value is resistance, and, since its definition is based on *small changes*, it must be an a-c resistance. The symbol $r_p$ is used to designate this *a-c plate resistance*.

It is seen from Fig. 2–8 that, if a change in plate voltage along the tangent is taken as $\Delta E_b$, the corresponding change in plate current is $\Delta I_b$. Then the a-c plate resistance $r_p$ is defined as

$$r_p = \frac{dE_b}{dI_b} \approx \frac{\Delta E_b}{\Delta I_b} \qquad (2\text{–}2b)$$

The symbols $\Delta$ and $d$ are both used in mathematics to be read as "a change in." Other terms often used for $r_p$ are *dynamic plate resistance* or *variational plate resistance*.

We must very carefully note that $R_p$ is a d-c value and that $r_p$ is an a-c value. Also they are different numerically. Solving for $R_p$ at point $P$, we obtain 12/0.3 or 40 ohms, whereas the value for $r_p$ is 4/0.250 or 16 ohms. In order for the d-c value of resistance to equal the a-c value, the volt-ampere curve would have to be a straight line going through the origin.

### Section 2–2   The Simple Rectifier

If an a-c source is applied to the series circuit formed by a diode and a load resistance, we obtain the simple rectifier circuit of Fig. 2–9. The applied voltage waveform is sinusoidal having a peak value of $E_m$ volts and an effective or rms value of $E$ volts. When $m$ is positive, $n$ is negative. This makes the plate of the diode positive with respect to the cathode. Electrons are drawn to the plate, and a current flows through the entire series circuit. This current develops a load-resistance voltage drop with the polarity shown on the circuit diagram. When $n$ is positive and $m$ is negative, the plate is negative with respect

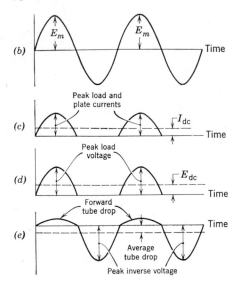

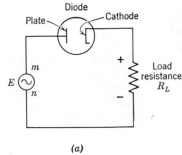

(a)

**Figure 2–9** Circuit and wave form for the basic rectifier. (*a*) Basic circuit. (*b*) Applied alternating voltage wave. (*c*) Load- and tube-current wave. (*d*) Load-voltage wave. (*e*) Voltage wave across tube.

to the cathode. No current can flow in the circuit, and the entire voltage appears across the diode. Thus, the only voltage that can exist across the load resistance exists when *m* is positive. The diode is serving as a rectifier. A rectifier is a device or circuit arrangement which makes one-direction (unidirectional) current or voltage from a two-direction or a-c source.

From the discussion on the diode in Section 2–1, it is obvious that, when plate current flows through a diode, there must be an accompanying plate-voltage drop. This is shown in waveform *e* as the tube drop. The current, waveform *c*, must be a half sine wave, always positive, as is the load-voltage drop, waveform *d*, assuming the diode curve is a straight line. The whole alternating voltage on the negative half-cycle appears across the diode since no current can flow in the circuit (waveform *e*). We note on waveform *e* that the *peak inverse voltage* is, for this circuit, the peak of the alternating line voltage $E_m$.

If the magnitude of the supply voltage $E$ is large, the small forward tube drop may be neglected. Then, effectively, the peak voltage across the load is $E_m$, and the peak load current is $E_m/R_L$. By means of calculus, we can show that the average value of a *half* of a sine wave over a *full* a-c cycle is the peak value divided by $\pi$. Then, the average load current is the peak load current divided by $\pi$, and the average load voltage is the peak value of the line voltage divided by $\pi$. Remembering that the peak values and the effective values are related by $\sqrt{2}$ for sinusoidal waveforms, we have

$$E_{dc} = \frac{E_m}{\pi} = \frac{\sqrt{2}\,E}{\pi}$$

$$(2\text{--}3)$$

and

$$I_{dc} = \frac{E_m}{\pi R_L} = \frac{\sqrt{2}\,E}{\pi R_L} = \frac{E_{dc}}{R_L}$$

We should note from the waveforms that, if the load-voltage wave $d$ is added point by point to the diode-voltage wave $e$, the sum must, by Kirchhoff's voltage law, be the applied voltage wave $b$. Likewise, since the d-c value of a sine wave is zero, the direct voltage across the load, $E_{dc}$, plus the average tube voltage must be zero. In other words, if the load voltage is called positive, the average tube drop is equal and negative.

If the value of the load resistance $R_L$ changes, the only change in the waveforms is a change in the amplitude of the current flowing in the load if the tube drop is neglected.

## Section 2–3   The Semiconductor as a Diode

A semiconductor is formed into a diode by the creation of a junction between $P$ material and $N$ material within a crystal during the process of manufacture. The theory of the operation of the transistor diode becomes an investigation into the properties of the $P\text{--}N$ junction. In Fig. 2–10$a$ and $b$, we repeat the energy-level diagram for the $N$ material with a raised Fermi level and the energy-level diagram for the $P$ material with a lowered Fermi level. When the two materials come together at a $P\text{--}N$ junction (Fig. 2–10$c$), by definition the Fermi

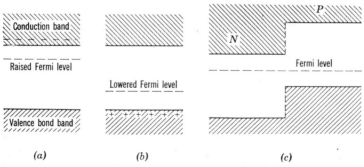

**Figure 2–10**   Energy-level diagrams in semiconductors.   ($a$) $N$ material.   ($b$) $P$ material.   ($c$) $N\text{--}P$ junction.

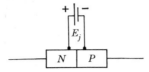

**Figure 2–11**  Barrier potential in an $N$–$P$ junction.

level must be one and the same for the entire crystal.   We see that there appears to be an abrupt discontinuity in energy levels from the $N$ material to the $P$ material.   This abrupt discontinuity in level creates forces between the two materials at the junction.   In the conduction band, ionized electrons in the $N$ material move across the junction to the $P$ material.   Holes in the valence-bond band move across the junction from the $P$ material to the $N$ material.   This movement of electrons and holes takes place at the time when the junction is formed and is then an inherent characteristic of the diode.   Another approach which may be taken to an understanding of this action is to consider that, in order to have stable conditions at the junction, the $P$ material must gain some high-level energy bands from the $N$ material and lose some of its low-level energy bands to the $N$ material.   We must again stress that a $P$–$N$ junction is not polycrystalline.   It is not made up of an $N$ crystal and a $P$ crystal, but it is a single crystal, part of which has donor atoms and part has acceptor atoms.

The movement of holes into the $N$ and the movement of electrons into the $P$ are both additive in polarity to develop an emf across the barrier surface.   The $P$ material at the barrier has acquired electrons making it "minus," and the $N$ material has acquired holes making it "plus."   We represent this emf diagrammatically in Fig. 2–11 where we show it as the junction potential equivalent to the battery voltage $E_j$.   In Fig. 2–12, an external battery $E_{bb}$ is connected with leads to the $N$ material and to the $P$ material.   It is obvious that the junction emf is opposing or bucking $E_{bb}$.   In Fig. 2–13, $E_{bb}$ is acting in the same direction as or aiding the junction emf.   The connection of Fig. 2–12

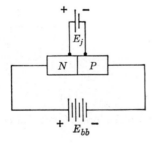

**Figure 2–12**  Reverse bias.

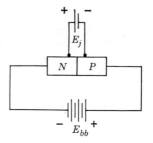

**Figure 2-13**   Forward bias.

will produce less current than the connection of Fig. 2–13. The external connection of Fig. 2–12 which discourages current flow is called *reverse bias*. The external connection of Fig. 2–13 which encourages current is called *forward bias*. If we call the positive terminal of the external battery $P$ and the negative terminal of the external battery $N$, we can state that reverse bias is a connection of $P$ to $N$ and of $N$ to $P$. Forward bias is a connection of $N$ to $N$ and of $P$ to $P$. This quick method gives a simple approach for determining proper battery polarity connections for transistor circuits.

If we represent the $N$–$P$ junction in Fig. 2–14 as a barrier, showing holes on the $N$ side of the barrier, and electrons on the $P$ side of the barrier, a forward-bias voltage causes more electrons to cross the barrier from $N$ to $P$. This action lowers still further the energy-level differences between the $N$ and the $P$ materials. A reverse bias will *deplete* the junction of these majority current carriers, making the energy-level difference between the $N$ and $P$ greater. We can now sketch energy-level diagrams for the forward- and reverse-bias conditions (Fig. 2–15).

We very explicitly developed the existence of both majority and minority current carriers in Section 1–6. The number of majority

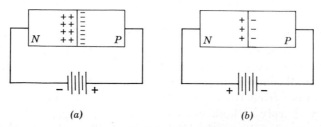

(a)                              (b)

**Figure 2-14**   Action of holes and electrons at the junction under forward and reverse bias. (a) Forward bias. (b) Reverse bias.

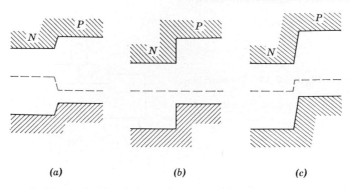

(a)            (b)            (c)

**Figure 2–15**   Energy levels of an $N$–$P$ junction.   (a) Forward bias.   (b) Without bias.   (c) Reverse bias.

current carriers under normal conditions overshadows the number of minority current carriers present.   When reverse bias is applied to a $P$–$N$ junction, a current is produced by the minority current carriers in the same manner as forward current in the forward direction.   This minority current-carrier flow is called *back current, reverse current* or *cutoff current* and is often designated as $I_{co}$.

Figure 2–16 is a summary of the tube manual information on a typical germanium diode, the 1N34.   At 25° C, when the forward voltage is 1.2 volts, the forward current is 10 ma.   Using these figures, the power dissipation is 12 mw, and the d-c resistance is 120 ohms.   In the reverse direction, 50 volts causes a back current of 500 $\mu$a.   This corresponds to 25 mw dissipation and a d-c resistance value of 100,000 ohms.   If we consider these two points on the diode curve, the front-to-back current ratio is 10 ma/500 $\mu$a or 20/1, and the front-to-back resistance ratio is 120/100,000 or 1/800.   If any other two points on this curve are used, these ratios would naturally change. We can use an ohmmeter to check out a diode quickly, but the reliable method is to apply a known voltage and note the current flow in each direction.

The symbol representing a semiconductor diode (Fig. 2–17) uses an arrowhead to show the direction of *conventional* current flow.   It should be noted very carefully that the *electron* flow opposes the arrowhead as in all semiconductor symbols.

We can see from the characteristic curve that the inverse current rises very sharply at high values of reverse voltage.   At a particular value of reverse voltage, the back current will reach very high values. This breakdown potential is the point at which the covalent bonds are

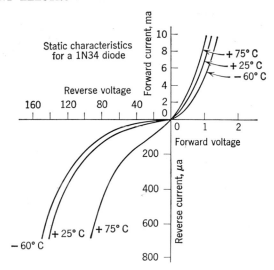

**Figure 2–16**  Characteristics of a typical germanium diode.

Limit ratings

| | |
|---|---|
| Peak reverse voltage | 75 |
| Operating reverse voltage | 60 |
| Average forward current | 40 ma |
| Recurrent peak current | 150 ma |
| Reverse current at 10 volts | 50 μa |
| Reverse current at 50 volts | 500 μa |

completely disrupted (creating an avalanche of electrons flowing in a manner similar to the cumulative action in a gas discharge) and is termed the *Zener* potential.  Usually, at this point, the transistor action is ruined, and the diode must be replaced.  Certain structures are designed to take repeated applications of Zener voltages and are termed *Zener diodes*.

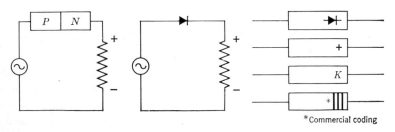

**Figure 2–17**  Circuit using a *P–N* junction as a diode rectifier and several methods of marking diodes to show polarity.

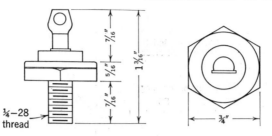

**Figure 2-18**  Characteristics of a typical power silicon rectifier.  Ratings for U. S. Dynamics Corp. rectifier type USD-5091-B.

*Maximum Ratings*

| | |
|---|---|
| Maximum average forward current | 5 amperes |
| Peak recurrent inverse voltage | 100 volts |
| Maximum rms voltage | 70 volts |
| Peak recurrent forward current | 22 amperes |
| Maximum average inverse current | 3 ma |
| Minimum operating case temperature | $-65\ °C$ |
| Maximum operating case temperature | 275 °C |

*Typical Characteristics*

| | |
|---|---|
| Efficiency at full ratings | 99% |
| Forward dynamic resistance | 0.005 ohm |
| Forward current at 0.8 volt | 4 amperes |
| Forward current at 1.0 volt | 6 amperes |
| Forward current at 1.2 volts | 10 amperes |
| Forward current at 1.4 volts | 20 amperes |

The silicon diode has a $P\text{–}N$ junction just like the germanium diode, but uses silicon as the base material instead of germanium.  Silicon, as a diode, was developed quite some time after germanium diodes were first used commercially.  Silicon diodes have a much greater range of operating temperatures and can handle very much greater currents than the germanium diodes.  Silicon diodes are available for handling the large currents required in arc welding.  The data for a typical power silicon diode are shown in Fig. 2-18.

It appears at present that silicon diodes will displace the bulkier and less efficient *dry-disk* or *metallic* rectifiers, the copper oxide, the selenium and the magnesium–copper sulfide types.

The construction of a single-cell dry-disk rectifier is shown in Fig. 2-19 along with the various commercial forms.  The simplest approach to take to understand their operation is to assume that the semiconductor is $N$ material and that the blocking layer formed between the active metal plate and the semiconductors is $P$ material.  This approach is quite close to the actual theory of operation since forward and reverse currents come about from a difference in the energy levels of the two materials in a fashion very similar to the $P$–$N$ junction.

In order to secure large inverse-voltage ratings, the cells are stacked so that the total inverse voltage is the sum of the inverse-voltage ratings of the individual cells. The current depends on the cross-sectional area of the active surface. Very large units have an active cross section of a square foot or more. A fin is usually provided at each cell to assist in heat dissipation. These three disk rectifiers have a higher forward power loss and a lower inverse voltage per cell than the very much smaller silicon diodes.

The copper oxide rectifier, which was the very first of the semiconductors in development and application, has a low inverse-voltage rating per cell of about 10 volts and is very sensitive to temperature change. An increase in operating temperature lowers the forward power losses, but the inverse current rises sharply. Copper oxide rectifiers are noted for a very long life and can handle current in the

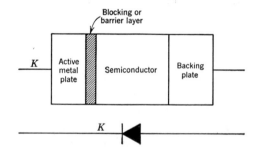

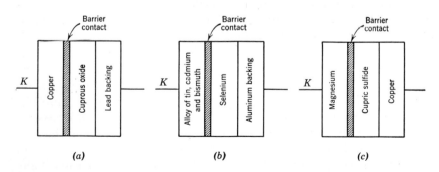

**Figure 2–19** Dry-disk metallic-rectifier cells. (*a*) Copper oxide cell. (*b*) Selenium cell. (*c*) Magnesium–copper sulfide cell.

order of an eighth of an ampere per square inch of active cross section. The cost of these units is relatively low.

The selenium rectifier can handle almost unlimited values of currents and inverse voltages. The selenium-rectifier inverse voltage is about three times the rating of the copper oxide cell. The forward current rating is of the order of one-half to one ampere per square inch of active area. These rectifiers may be operated over a wider temperature range than the copper oxide units, with less variation in the characteristic. The selenium unit is a little more expensive than the copper oxide unit, but its ruggedness more than compensates for the cost differential.

The magnesium–copper sulfide rectifier has a very high operating-current value, over 10 amperes per square inch, but it has a very low inverse-voltage rating, about 5 volts. The unit can withstand high-current overloads, but its efficiency is low owing to large reverse currents. The cell cannot withstand excessive inverse voltages, and it does not have the very long life of the other types. Its principal use is for applications where high currents at low voltages are required such as battery chargers.

### Section 2–4   Cold-Cathode Diodes

Cold-cathode diodes are designed to operate in the region of $d$ to $e$ of Fig. 1–20. Over this part of the characteristic, the voltage drop across the tube is constant for different values of current. In the construction of the OD3 (Fig. 2–20), a small tip $S$ is welded to the rod which serves as the plate. The distance from the end of the starter $S$ to the cathode is much less than the distance from the cathode to the plate. As a result, ionization starts from $S$ to the cathode. As more and more current flows through the tube, the area of the glow on the inner cathode surface spreads. When the glow covers the cathode completely, the tube is fully ionized at the single ionization level. For the OD3, the tube drop is 150 volts. In order to initiate ionization, a slightly higher voltage, point $a$, is required. This overvoltage causes the current to shift abruptly from point $a$ to point $b$ upon ionization of the gas. Point $c$ is the point at which ionization is complete. A further increase of current causes a state of double ionization accompanied by an increasing voltage drop across the tube. When the current is reduced below the value at $b$, the voltage drops a few volts before the tube goes out (the current falls to zero and visible light ceases . . . hence, the generally accepted expression for gas tubes; "goes out").

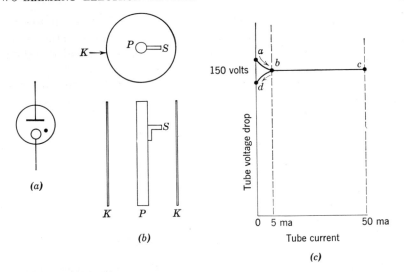

**Figure 2–20** Construction and electrical characteristic for an 0D3 voltage-regulator tube. (*a*) Symbol (the solid dot indicates a gas tube). (*b*) Physical structure. (*c*) Electrical characteristics.

An important application of the cold-cathode diode is its use as a voltage regulator. In the circuit of Fig. 2-21, a constant-output voltage is maintained over the normal operating range of the diode. If the 0D3 is used, the useful range of diode currents is from 5 ma to 50 ma. Assume, for example, that the diode current is $27\frac{1}{2}$ ma in this circuit when the load current is 80 ma. If the load current demand falls by $22\frac{1}{2}$ ma to $57\frac{1}{2}$ ma, the excess current will go into the voltage-regulator tube, increasing its current by $22\frac{1}{2}$ ma to 50 ma. In the same manner, if the load current increases to $102\frac{1}{2}$ ma, the regulator tube current falls to 5 ma. If the load does not change, but, if the supply voltage either increases or decreases within these limits, the voltage regulator can either take the increased current or deliver more to the load, while maintaining the load voltage at the constant value.

**Figure 2–21** The application of the cold-cathode gas diode in a voltage-regulator circuit.

$$I_{in} = I_{VR} + I_L$$

$$R = \frac{E_{in} - E_{out}}{I_{in}}$$

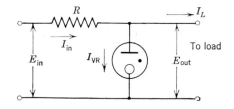

In each case, if the regulator tube current falls below 5 ma, it goes out, and the load voltage is no longer maintained at the constant value. If the regulator current exceeds 50 ma, the tube is overloaded and may burn out by excessive heating.

A neon lamp operates in the same manner, but its characteristic is not as flat as the OD3. The voltage across the neon lamp can vary from 55 to 65 volts over its operating current range. If a neon lamp is to be used as an indicator on 117 volts alternating current, a resistor must be connected in series with it to limit the peak current. Both neon lamps and argon lamps are available with standard household-type lamp bases. The internal leads to the base contacts are made from very high-resistance wire.

### Section 2–5   Hot-Cathode Gas-Filled Diodes

A hot-cathode gas-filled diode combines the action of a gas discharge with the advantages of thermionic emission. In Fig. 2–22, a typical vacuum tube has the plate characteristic $0ab$. If gas is introduced into the envelope, the initial plate current from $0a$ is produced from thermionic emission. At point $a'$, ionization takes place. The plate voltage drops slightly and the current increases from $a$ to $c$ without a further increase in plate voltage.

At a plate current of 200 ma, the gas tube drop is in this example 15 volts, whereas the corresponding vacuum-tube plate voltage is 60 volts. Thus, the plate dissipation of the gas tube is 3 watts, whereas the corresponding plate dissipation of the vacuum tube is 12 watts.

It is apparent that the gas tube will be used for high-power levels whereas the vacuum-tube diode has its main function in low-power

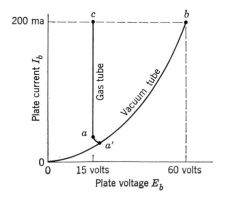

**Figure 2–22**   Comparison of a gas and a vacuum hot-cathode diode.

applications.   There are a number of distinct disadvantages of the gas tube.   The presence of a gas requires that the inverse-voltage rating must be lower than that of a vacuum tube lest *arcback* or *flash-back* take place within the tube during that part of the cycle when the plate is negative and the cathode is positive.   The possibility of cathode bombardment or cathode sputtering in a gas tube demands a stronger and a more expensive cathode than the vacuum tube.   The motion and velocity of the ions and electrons within a plasma are random.   This means that, if we consider the velocity and travel of a particular random particle, we can describe its motion as the period of an a-c cycle.   Thus, energies of all frequencies are generated within a plasma discharge.   This energy can cause serious radio-frequency interference requiring adequate shielding for the tube.   As a result, we find that gas tubes are not often used in communication equipment.

We discussed in Section 2–1 the space-charge cloud in a thermionic vacuum tube.   In the gas-tube version, the space charge is neutralized by the plasma, allowing greater currents at lower voltages.   When an ion approaches the cathode, its positive charge offsets the negative charge of an electron in the space charge, making possible extra useful emission from the cathode surface.   The pressure of the gas in the envelope reduces the rate of vaporization of the cathode surface material, permitting operation of the cathode at higher temperatures to secure a greater emission from a given cathode.

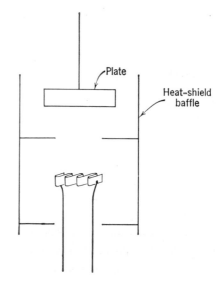

**Figure 2–23**   Typical high-emission cathode and heat baffle used in mercury-vapor diodes.

In many high-power mercury-filled gas tubes, the cathode structure is very complex (Fig. 2–23) in order to form a very large emission surface. To keep the cathode at the proper operating temperature, heat baffles are used so that the cathode is effectively contained within an oven. Also, in these tubes, adequate warm-up time must be allowed for the mercury to vaporize. If sufficient vapor is not available, a high order of multiple ionization takes place on the few mercury gas molecules available, and serious cathode sputtering takes place.

Certain tubes are hybrid; that is, they are at once hot- and cold-cathode types. The OZ4, which has been widely used in automobile receivers, starts as a cold-cathode gas diode. Positive-ion bombardment creates a hot spot on the cathode surface which produces electrons by thermionic emission. A fluorescent lamp is started by operating filaments at the ends of the tube. Once the discharge starts, emission is maintained from hot spots by ion bombardment. The function of the starter is to turn on the filaments for only the length of time needed to initiate the gas-discharge action.

### . . . . Suggested References for Further Study

1. D. DeWitt and A. L. Rossoff, *Transistor Electronics*, Chapter 2, McGraw Hill Book Co., New York, 1957.
2. W. G. Dow, *Fundamentals of Engineering Electronics*, 2nd ed, Chapter 1, John Wiley & Sons, New York, 1952.
3. J. Millman, *Vacuum-Tube and Semiconductor Electronics*, Chapters 4, 5, and 6, McGraw-Hill Book Co., New York, 1958.

### . . . . QUESTIONS

1. Define or explain each of the following terms: (*a*) Edison effect, (*b*) virtual cathode, (*c*) average voltage, (*d*) reverse bias, (*e*) ionization potential, (*f*) cutoff current, (*g*) Zener potential, (*h*) arcback, (*i*) heat baffle, (*j*) positive-ion bombardment.

2. What factors determine the number of electrons in the space charge?

3. What are the effects of plate saturation and of space-charge-limited current on the space charge itself?

4. Under what conditions is a static resistance equal to a dynamic resistance?

5. What is the result of the Schottky effect on plate current?

6. Distinguish carefully between *inverse voltage* and *peak inverse voltage*.

7. Explain the transfer of holes and electrons when a *P–N* junction is formed.

8. Explain how a reverse bias depletes the majority current carriers at the junction.

9. How are the effects of minority current carriers apparent at a junction?

10. Compare silicon and germanium diodes.

11. What materials form the P–N junction in the copper oxide, in the selenium, and in the magnesium–copper sulfide rectifiers?

12. What is the significance of the arrowhead on the symbol for a semiconductor diode?

13. Compare the current and voltage ratings of the copper oxide, the selenium, and the magnesium–copper sulfide rectifiers.

14. Explain and account for the potential difference between points $a$, $b$, and $d$ in Fig. 2–20c.

15. How is space charge neutralized in a hot-cathode gas-filled rectifier?

16. What are the results of positive ion bombardment?

# . . . . PROBLEMS

1. Using the 25° C characteristic of the 1N34 diode (Fig. 2–16), plot curves of $R_p$ and $r_p$ against forward and reverse voltage as the independent variable.

2. Using the characteristic of the 1B3 in the tube manual, plot curves of $R_p$ and $r_p$ against the plate voltage as the independent variable.

3. Using the characteristic of the OD3 given in the text and the circuit shown in Fig. 2–21, determine the value of $R$ when the average load current is 130 ma and the supply voltage is 200 volts. Over what range of load-current variation is regulation obtained?

4. Solve problem 3 for a load current of 110 ma and a supply voltage of 165 volts.

5. In a particular diode, when the plate voltage is 75 volts, the plate current is 58 ma. What is the plate current when the plate voltage is 60 volts? When the plate voltage is 35 volts? When the plate voltage is 15 volts?

# Three-element
# electron devices

• • • • • • • • • • • • • • • • • • • • • • • CHAPTER 3

The material in this chapter concerns the basic electronic amplifying devices. The theory of the triode (Section 3–1) and an understanding of the triode curves (Section 3–2) and the triode parameters (Section 3–4) lead to the operation of the triode in a basic amplifier circuit (Section 3–5). Junction transistors (Section 3–6) may be used in either grounded-base circuits (Section 3–7) or in grounded-emitter circuits (Section 3–8). Also, as with the triode, a simple transistor amplifier is considered (Section 3–9). Limitations of both the vacuum tube (Section 3–3) and the transistor (Section 3–10) are discussed in order to give a better understanding of their function as amplifiers. Discussions of the control action of the cold-cathode gas triode (Section 3–11) and of the thyratron (Section 3–12) complete the chapter.

### Section 3–1   The Action of a Grid in a Triode Vacuum Tube

The invention of the control grid by De Forest in 1907 initiated the development of today's vast electronics industry. The action of a control grid enables large energies in a plate circuit to be controlled by a very small energy at the control grid. This tube, which consists of a cathode emitting surface, a plate, and a grid, is called a *triode*. Typical physical arrangements for a triode are shown in Fig. 3–1. The considerations given to the design and operation of the cathode and of the plate of the diode in Section 2–1 are also valid for the triode.

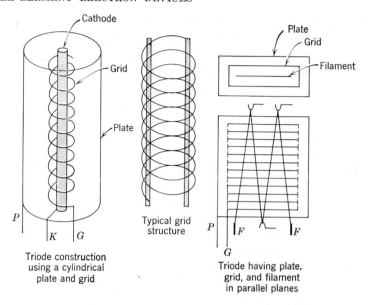

**Figure 3–1**   Internal mechanical structure of typical triodes.

The grid wires are fine, and the grid assembly is usually placed close to the cathode and far from the plate.

If the action of the grid is neglected, the plate current is that value which is determined by Child's law.   If the grid is maintained at a negative potential (Fig. 3–2), the grid structure is charged negatively. This negative charge creates an electric field which opposes and diminishes the flow of electrons from the cathode to the plate.   If

**Figure 3–2** Supply voltage connections to the elements of a triode.

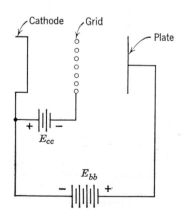

the negative voltage is sufficiently large, no electrons at all flow from the cathode to the plate.   This condition is called *cutoff*.   When the negative grid field is weaker than the cutoff value, current flows to the plate.   When the potential on the grid is negative, the grid cannot pick up electrons from the electron stream, and grid current is zero. Thus, in a vacuum tube, a negative grid potential controls plate current without itself taking power (that is, the product of grid voltage times grid current is zero).   In many applications, sources that have very low energy levels can be arranged to control a much larger power in the plate circuit of the triode in order to secure an amplification or gain.   When the grid is positive, it collects electrons which produce a grid current.   A positive grid also tends to move the space-charge cloud out toward the plate, resulting in a further increase in plate current.   If the grid structure forms a fine mesh close to the cathode, it has a much greater control over the plate current than if the mesh were coarse and near the plate.

### Section 3–2   Triode Curves

In Fig. 3–3, a triode is connected to a variable voltage source for the plate potential $E_b$ with the grid connected to a variable potential source $E_c$.   The cathode is the common reference point of the two applied potential circuits and, as such, is often called "ground." It is customary to omit the actual heater circuit in schematic diagrams since the heater only serves the purpose of bringing the cathode up to the proper operating temperature.   The cathode symbol is retained in the schematic diagram as the cathode itself contributes the electron stream for the tube.   In this circuit, when the grid is negative ($I_c$ is zero), there are three possible independent variables, $E_c$, $E_b$, and $I_b$.

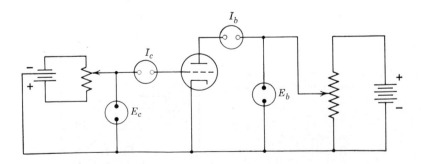

**Figure 3–3**   Test circuit for triode characteristics.

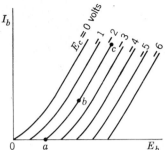

**Figure 3-4** Plate characteristics of a triode.

When the grid is positive, there are four independent variables, $E_c$, $E_b$, $I_c$, and $I_b$.

Several combinations of these variables are conventionally used to show the interdependence of these four quantities because the results must be plotted on graph paper which allows only two variables to be used as the axes. If the plate voltage is varied as the independent variable, and if the grid voltage is held at a constant value, plate current is the dependent variable. This curve is called a *plate family* or a *plate characteristic*. When the plate voltage is held constant, a variation in grid voltage, as the independent variable, produces changes in the plate current, the dependent variable. This set of curves is called the *transfer characteristic*, or the *mutual characteristic*. When the plate current is held constant, the grid voltage is plotted against the plate voltage to give *constant-current curves*. Since these curves are all for the same tube, it is possible to develop one curve from the other.

The plate family of a triode is shown in Fig. 3-4. When the grid voltage is zero, the current takes the same form as the diode plate characteristic. A negative grid voltage requires a larger plate voltage in order to overcome the negative repelling effect of the grid field on the electron stream attracted to the plate. Further increasing amounts of negative grid voltage requires that the plate voltage be increased accordingly. Thus the curves are effectively the diode curve shifted in uniform steps to the right with increasing negative grid voltage. Point $a$, for example, on the characteristic is a typical cutoff value. The curve is nonlinear from $a$ to $b$, but it is very close to a straight line between $b$ and $c$. These curves for constant grid potentials are, for all purposes, parallel.

Figure 3-5 shows the region of the plate characteristic for positive values of grid voltage. When the grid is positive, it extracts electrons from the electron stream which would ordinarily go to the plate.

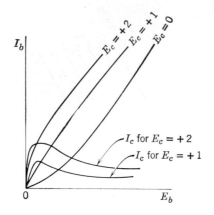

**Figure 3–5** Plate characteristics of a triode in the positive grid region.

Thus, we note a change in the curvature of the characteristics. At the same time a grid current is produced. For a constant positive grid voltage, as the plate voltage increases, fewer electrons go into the grid wires, and more electrons go on to the much greater plate potential. Thus the grid-current curves, which are also plotted on this plate family, decrease with increasing plate voltage.

The grid family or transfer characteristic shows the grid voltage as the independent variable and the plate current as the dependent variable, using constant plate voltages as the parameter (Fig. 3–6). The curve shows that, for a particular plate voltage, a grid voltage that becomes more negative allows less plate current to flow. The curves in the negative region are again essentially parallel. The curvature is more pronounced between cutoff, point $a$, and point $b$.

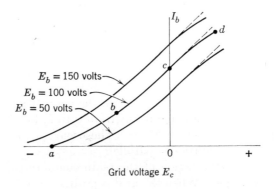

**Figure 3–6** Transfer characteristics of a triode.

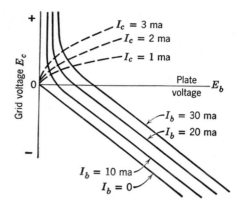

**Figure 3-7** Constant-current curves for a triode.

The curve is fairly straight between $b$ and $c$.   When the grid is positive, some of the electron stream transfers to the grid as a grid current, and the plate-current curves tend to drop off from the straight-line extension of the negative grid region.

Constant-current curves are plotted in Fig. 3-7.   We show the curve with $E_b$ as the independent variable and $E_c$ as the dependent variable.   The axes could very well be inverted, using $E_c$ as the independent variable and $E_b$ as the dependent variable.   The practice varies between the different tube manufacturers.   The curves are linear in the negative grid region.   The line representing zero plate current is the locus of the combinations of $E_b$ and $E_c$ which cut off the tube.   This line is called the *cutoff line*.

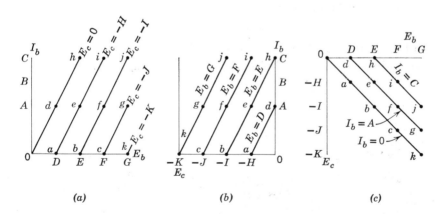

**Figure 3-8** Common points to show interrelation of the various tube characteristics.   (*a*) Plate family.   (*b*) Mutual characteristic.   (*c*) Constant-current characteristics.

If any one of the curves is available, it is possible to draw the other two without the need of actually taking further laboratory data. The correspondence between the points of the three characteristic curves is shown in detail in Fig. 3–8. All corresponding points are labeled with lower-case letters and all corresponding voltages and currents are labeled with capital letters.

### Section 3–3  Limitations of a Triode

The region of maximum allowable operation of a triode is shown graphically in a plate characteristic (Fig. 3–9). Line $0a$ is the maximum emission that the tube can have from Child's law. Actually in practice, the limit is $0c$, which is determined not by Child's law but by the maximum allowable grid current. If the grid current exceeds a certain value, the heat developed in the grid wire will damage or even melt the grid structure. Line $cb$ is the maximum allowable plate current for the tube, which is the saturation value. The product of $E_b$ times $I_b$ is the *plate dissipation* of the tube. If the rated value of plate heating is exceeded, the tube will be damaged. The maximum allowable plate dissipation is the curved line between $b$ and $d$. If the plate voltage exceeds $de$, the plate may arc over to the grid wires. Line $mn$ is the maximum allowable negative grid voltage to prevent arcing or breakdown either from the grid to the cathode or from the grid to the plate. Thus the allowed region of operation of the tube is within the shaded area, $0cbdnm0$.

### Section 3–4  Determination of the Dynamic Coefficients of a Triode

In Fig. 3–10, point $P$ is shown on each of the three basic tube curves. If the plate current is held constant, we move through $P$ from $A$ to $B$.

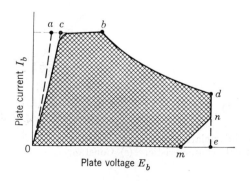

**Figure 3–9**  Limitations on the operation of a triode.

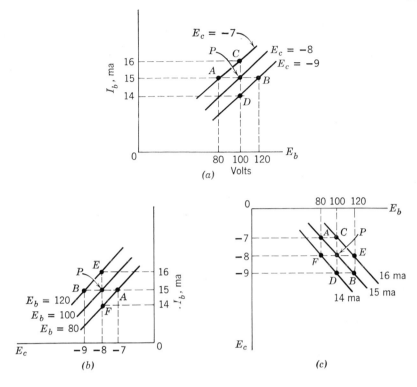

**Figure 3-10** Graphical determination of $\mu$, $r_p$, and $g_m$. (a) On plate family. (b) On grid family. (c) On constant-current curves.

For the numerical values we have indicated, this means that a change in plate voltage of 40 volts (120 − 80) is obtained from a change of 2 volts on the grid. The ratio of this change, 40/2 or 20, is termed the *amplification factor* or $\mu$ (Mu) of the tube. It is this property of the tube that makes it so useful as an amplifying device. A small change on the grid (2 volts in this case) produces a large change (40 volts) on the plate for a fixed plate current. We may express this definition as an equation:

$$\mu = -\frac{\partial E_b}{\partial E_c} \approx -\frac{\Delta E_b}{\Delta E_c} \qquad (I_b \text{ is constant}) \qquad (3\text{-}1a)$$

For the given numerical values:

$$\mu = \tfrac{4\,0}{2} = 20$$

This number or ratio $\mu$ is dimensionless since it is a ratio of two voltages.

We can obtain this value of $\mu$ from either the plate characteristic or the transfer characteristic directly.  If we must find it from the constant plate-current curves, we must take increments *along* the constant current line through $P$ (the 15 ma curve).

If we consider the change from $C$ to $D$ through point $P$, we obtain a change in plate current for a change in grid voltage with a constant plate voltage.  Making this a ratio, we have

$$g_m = \frac{\partial I_b}{\partial E_c} \approx \frac{\Delta I_b}{\Delta E_c} \qquad (E_b \text{ is constant}) \qquad (3\text{--}1b)$$

This ratio has the units of conductance, mhos, but it is usually expressed in micromhos.  Since the term relates plate current to grid voltage, it is termed *mutual conductance* or *transfer conductance* or *grid-plate transconductance.*

We can obtain this value of $g_m$ directly from either the plate characteristic or the constant plate-current family as

$$g_m = \frac{2 \text{ ma}}{2 \text{ volts}} = 0.001 \text{ mho} = 1000 \text{ micromhos}$$

If the value is determined from the transfer characteristic, increments must be taken along the constant-voltage line for a plate voltage $E_b$ of 100 volts.

If we consider the change from $E$ to $F$ through point $P$, the increments obtained are a change in plate voltage and a change in plate current for constant grid voltage.  This, as a ratio, is the *dynamic plate resistance $r_p$* of the triode at point $P$:

$$r_p = \frac{\partial E_b}{\partial I_b} \approx \frac{\Delta E_b}{\Delta I_b} \qquad (E_c \text{ is constant}) \qquad (3\text{--}1c)$$

$r_p$ may be found directly from the mutual characteristic and from the constant plate-current curves, but increments must be taken along the constant grid-voltage curve through $P$ in the plate family.  From the values we have assumed, the plate resistance is

$$r_p = \frac{40 \text{ volts}}{2 \text{ ma}} = 20,000 \text{ ohms} = 20 \text{ kilohms}$$

If we take the definitions for $g_m$ and $\mu$ and multiply them together, we find

$$g_m \times r_p = \frac{\Delta I_b}{\Delta E_c} \times \frac{\Delta E_b}{\Delta I_b} = \frac{\Delta E_b}{\Delta E_c}$$

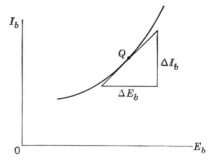

**Figure 3–11** Determination of $r_p$ from the plate family by the slope method.

But this is the defined value of $\mu$; so we may write an expression to relate these three dynamic characteristics:

$$-\mu = r_p g_m \qquad (3\text{--}1d)$$

This equation is very useful in determining tube characteristics from graphs. If two are known, the third may be calculated.

Very often it is necessary to determine all three characteristics from one characteristic curve. For instance, the evaluation of $r_p$ from the plate family requires that increments are to be taken *along* the constant grid-voltage line. If the $r_p$ at point $Q$ (Fig. 3–11) is required, the procedure, as with the determination of $r_p$ in a diode, is to erect a tangent to the curve at $Q$ and to use the slope of the tangent as the slope of the curve at point $Q$. In this manner it is easy to determine $g_m$ from a transfer curve and $\mu$ from a constant plate-current curve.

The variation of the values of these dynamic characteristics with plate current is shown in Fig. 3–12. The amplification factor is almost constant as it is primarily a geometrical factor involving the shape of the grid structure and its placement with respect to the cathode and to the plate allowing a certain ratio of control over the plate current. The transconductance increases with increasing plate

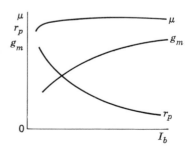

**Figure 3–12** Variation of the dynamic characteristics with plate current.

current, whereas naturally the plate resistance decreases with increasing plate current. In a complex amplifier circuit, the over-all amplification is a function of all these factors (Chapters 10, 12, and 13).

We may also develop an equation for a triode by the mathematical processes used to derive Child's law:

$$i_b = K(\mu E_c + E_b)^n \qquad (3\text{--}2)$$

For triodes, $n$ is very close to the value 3/2 used in Child's law. $E_c$ is normally a negative number, and $\mu$ is used in the equation as a positive number. The equation is only valid for three variables; it cannot be used for positive grid voltages since there will be grid current (the fourth variable). From the equation, it is seen that $\mu$ is a ratio of the effectiveness of the grid voltage in relation to the plate voltage. Also for constant values of plate current the term $(\mu E_c + E_b)$ must be constant. Then, on constant-current curves, for negative grid voltages, the plots of $E_c$ against $E_b$ must be straight lines with a slope of $\mu$.

### Section 3–5   The Triode as a Simple Amplifier

The details of waveforms, of the standard nomenclature, and of the process for handling the load resistance $R_L$ of the circuit of Fig. 3–13 are left completely to Chapter 10. Only enough information is used in this section to provide an understanding of the operation of the triode as a simple amplifying device. The battery supplies, $E_{cc}$ and $E_{bb}$, establish a particular operating point on the tube characteristic curve. A direct plate current flows causing an $I_b R_L$ drop in the load resistance. The operating plate potential $E_b$ is less than $E_{bb}$ by the amount of the $I_b R_L$ drop in the load resistance. Assume that the operating plate current of the triode is 10 ma, that $R_L$ is 10 kilohms, and that the plate supply voltage is 250 volts. Without signal, the $I_b R_L$ drop is 100 volts, and $E_b$ is then 150 volts. Also assume that the grid supply voltage $E_{cc}$ is $-10$ volts.

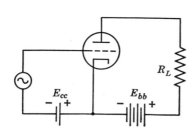

**Figure 3–13**   Basic triode amplifier circuit.

The total instantaneous grid voltage on the tube varies in accordance with the signal. When the signal is $+1$ volt, the total grid signal is $-10 + 1$ or $-9$ volts. Now the plate current increases, causing an increased drop in $R_L$. The new plate current is, say, 15 ma. The $I_bR_L$ drop is now 150 volts, and the plate voltage is 100 volts. When the signal is $-1$ volt, the total grid voltage is $-10 - 1$ or $-11$ volts. Assume that the plate current is now 5 ma. The $I_bR_L$ drop is 50 volts, and the plate voltage is 200 volts. These results are summarized in Table I.

TABLE I

| Signal Voltage | $I_b$ | $I_bR_L$ | $E_b$ | Plate Voltage Relative to the No-Signal Condition |
|---|---|---|---|---|
| 0 | 10 | 100 | 150 | — |
| $+1$ | 15 | 150 | 100 | $-50$ |
| $-1$ | 5 | 50 | 200 | $+50$ |

Now it can be seen that the total change of 2 volts in the signal produces a change of 100 volts at the plate of the tube. Thus the *voltage amplification* of the vacuum-tube circuit with the load resistance is 50. Also it is very important to note that, when the signal goes positive or increases, the plate voltage decreases or goes negative. When the signal goes negative, the plate voltage increases or goes positive. We make the very important conclusion that not only does this circuit give an amplification to the signal but it also produces, for a resistive load, a *phase inversion* or a *phase shift of 180°* on the signal.

## Section 3–6   Junction Transistors

The junction transistor is the result of the development which sought to find a solid substance for use as an amplifying device. The junction transistor does not have a thermionic emitting surface. This saving of power by not requiring a heater current and voltage is very useful in many applications. The life expectancy of a transistor properly designed into a circuit is many thousands of hours, whereas the vacuum-tube cathode surface normally vaporizes after one or two thousand hours of use. The small size and weight of the junction transistor in comparison to the comparable vacuum tube offers many advantages.

A junction transistor (Fig. 3–14) consists of two $P$–$N$ junctions in one crystal. Thus, the crystal may be considered a "sandwich" of $P$

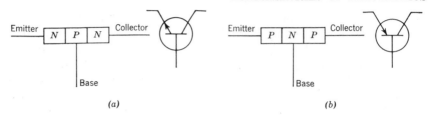

**Figure 3–14**  Methods of representing transistors.  (*a*) *NPN* transistor and symbol.  (*b*) *PNP* transistor and symbol.

material between two *N*'s or of *N* material between two *P*'s.  The nomenclature, *base, emitter* and *collector*, refers to the three impurity regions.  The base and emitter are considered the input or signal circuit for the transistor in the same manner as the grid–cathode circuit in a vacuum tube.  Likewise, the collector may be considered the output section of the transistor in the same way that the plate is the output in the vacuum-tube amplifier.

### Section 3–7   The Grounded-Base Transistor

In our discussion of the semiconductor diode (Section 2–3), we analyzed its operation from the viewpoint of a discussion of the action of the *P–N* junction.  In this junction transistor, we have not one, but two *P–N* junctions.  A transistor is operated with forward bias on the emitter (with respect to the base) and reverse bias on the collector.  In Fig. 3–15, the battery $V_{EE}$ provides forward emitter bias, and the battery $V_{CC}$ provides reverse collector voltage.  The magnitude of the collector supply is usually, but not necessarily, greater than the emitter bias supply.  In the block form of the circuits in Fig. 3–15, arrows are drawn showing the direction of *conventional current flow*.  These arrows are carried to the transistor symbol and are placed in the emitter lead.  The collector lead does not have an arrowhead.  The direction of the arrowhead on the symbol distinguishes between an *NPN* and a *PNP* transistor.

If we sketch the energy-level diagrams for an *NPN* unit, we obtain Fig. 3–16*a* for the transistor without electrode voltages and Fig. 3–16*b* with the biasing voltages in the circuit.  As we recall from Section 2–3 (Fig. 2–15), a forward bias lowers the energy-level differences across a *P–N* junction and a reverse bias increases the energy-level differences across the junction.  In this case, for the *NPN* transistor, a forward bias injects electrons from the emitter into the base, reducing the number of holes in the base. The action of the reverse bias on the base-collector junction is to deplete the base of its electrons, thus creating excess holes. If the holes at the emitter-base junction are filled by injected electrons, holes diffuse from the base-collector junction to try to keep the hole density uniform throughout the base material. If the "density" of holes in the $P$ material is reduced near the base-collector junction by this drift, the reverse bias will create new and additional holes within the $P$ material at the base-collector junction. Thus we find that the current in the collector is caused by the hole drift or hole current in the base. If there is no hole drift or hole current in the base, there can be no current in the collector circuit. We have shown that hole current in the base is produced by forward-bias current in the emitter. Hole drift to the base can only take place if there are injected electrons from an emitter current. In conclusion, a collector current can exist only if there is an emitter current and in an amount that cannot be greater than the emitter current. Also, we may state that the collector current is controlled by the majority current-carrier movement in the base. This discussion suggests that a transistor is a *current-operated* device, whereas we discussed the action of the grid in a triode solely from the voltage concept.

When we considered the depletion of holes in the base caused by the

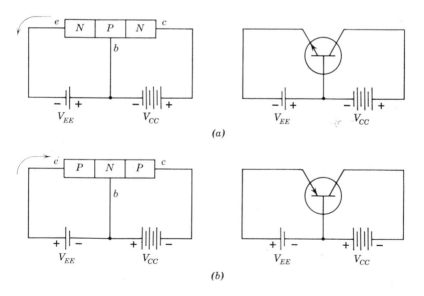

**Figure 3–15** Transistor bias connections. (*a*) *NPN* transistor. (*b*) *PNP* transistor.

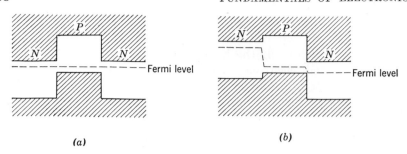

**Figure 3–16**  Energy levels in the *NPN* transistor.  (*a*) Without bias voltages. (*b*) With proper biasing voltages.

emitter current, we said that the collector, under the conditions of reverse bias, will accept electrons moving across the base-collector junction in order to bring the number of holes in the base back to "normal." It is also possible for the base connection to accept some electrons from the *P* material of the base. As this is the case in an actual transistor, the number of electrons injected into the base from the emitter must be greater than the number of electrons taken from the base by the collector. Thus, in the junction transistor, the collector current $I_c$ is always less than the emitter current $I_e$. If we define $\alpha$, *current gain*, as this ratio, in terms of small current changes we have

$$\alpha = \frac{\Delta I_c}{\Delta I_e} \quad \text{and} \quad \alpha < 1 \tag{3–3}$$

Minority current carriers create a collector current without assistance from a forward emitter current. If the emitter voltage is zero and if the emitter current is zero, such current that exists in the collector circuit is the same back current that exists in a crystal diode unit with reverse voltage and is produced by the minority current carriers. As we recall from Section 2–3, a bias that is reverse for the majority current carriers is a forward bias for the minority current carriers. Any current in the collector is the sum of the reverse-bias current plus the normal current produced by forward bias on the emitter. For example, in a new transistor, let us assume that the emitter current is 5 ma and the collector current is 4.8 ma. If the transistor has been overloaded, we note that the collector current is 5.6 ma when the emitter current is 5 ma. Thus a *back current* or *cutoff current* $I_{co}$ of 0.8 ma is produced by these undesired minority current carriers.

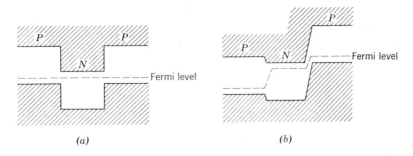

(a)                                          (b)

**Figure 3-17**   Energy levels in the *PNP* transistor.   (*a*) Without bias voltage.
(*b*) With bias voltages.

If a *PNP* transistor were used in the preceding discussion, the same
approach would be taken, except that the majority current carriers
in the base are electrons instead of holes.   Then the process would be
a depletion of electrons within the base material.   Figure 3–17 gives
the energy-level diagrams for the *PNP* transistor.

If the circuit of Fig. 3–15*a* is modified so that the emitter and collector potentials may be varied to produce data for characteristic
curves, we have the circuit of Fig. 3–18.   If the emitter voltage is
reduced to zero, the emitter current is zero.   Ideally, when the collector voltage is raised from zero to maximum, the collector current
remains at zero.   However, there must be some reverse current $I_{co}$
due to the ever-present minority current carriers in transistor material.
In a "good" transistor, the value is very low, often negligible.   In a
"poor" transistor, the value is high.   $I_{co}$, the back current, is plotted
in Fig. 3–19.

Now, let us maintain the emitter current at 3 ma.   Since the emitter
has forward bias, the voltage $V_E$ required is very low, say 0.1 volt.
We established that the collector current is produced by the action of
emitter current, and it cannot exceed 3 ma, but it is almost 3 ma for
all values of collector voltage.   This is shown on the curve from *d* to *e*.

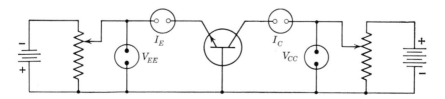

**Figure 3-18**   Test circuit for grounded-base *NPN* transistor.

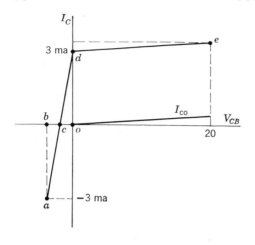

**Figure 3–19** The transistor collector characteristic.

Almost all the rise in collector current from $d$ to $e$ may be attributed to $I_{co}$. A small "reverse" voltage is necessary on the collector to reduce the collector current to zero, point $c$ on the curve. If the "reverse" voltage on the collector is increased to $b$, the current will rise to point $a$ which is 3 ma but is in the direction reverse from normal.

Let us assume that the point $e$ corresponds to 20 volts on the collector and that point $c$ is $-0.1$ volt and point $b$ is $-0.2$ volt. The 20 volts is a normal reverse bias on the collector, so that the voltages at points $b$ and $c$ are actually forward voltages on the collector. If the voltage from $c$ to $b$, 0.1 volt, produces 3 ma, the full collector volt-

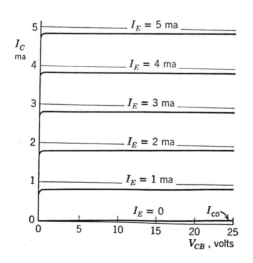

**Figure 3–20** Common-base collector characteristic.

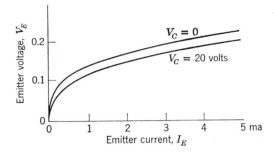

**Figure 3-21**    Emitter characteristic for common-base amplifier.

age applied to the transistor connected backward would produce $3 \times (20/0.1)$ or 600 ma in the collector. This 600 ma current flow would surely destroy the crystalline structure of the transistor. Thus we must be very careful not to make improper battery connections to transistor circuits. With vacuum tubes we often save the tube after an improper connection is made since saturation limits the current, but with the transistor we can get no such second chance.

We normally do not use any part of the transistor curve except the first quadrant. The complete collector characteristic is drawn in Fig. 3-20, using the emitter current as the parameter. For an *NPN* transistor, both the collector voltage and the collector current are positive. For a *PNP* transistor, the collector current and the collector voltage are both negative, but the usual practice is to plot the results in the first quadrant in spite of the negative values of $I_C$ and $V_{CB}$.

The emitter characteristic (Fig. 3-21) indicates that the emitter voltage and current relation is very nonlinear. It also indicates the order of the small forward-bias voltage required. The slope of these curves shows that we are dealing with resistances of the order of 100 ohms or less.

### Section 3-8    The Grounded-Emitter Transistor

In the previous section, the common return for the bias supplies was the base. The connection of the circuit showing the bias supplies using the emitter as the common return point is given in Fig. 3-22. In this circuit for an *NPN* transistor, the emitter is negative with respect to the base and provides forward bias. Since the base-to-emitter voltage $V_{BE}$ is so very small numerically, the collector-to-

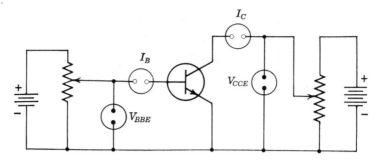

**Figure 3-22**   Test circuit for grounded-emitter *NPN* transistor.

emitter voltage $V_{CE}$ is effectively the same as the collector-to-base voltage, $V_{CB}$. Very often the second subscript letters are omitted from the collector voltage designations and $V_C$ is used indiscriminately. In this circuit the collector is positive, providing the required reverse bias. For a *PNP* transistor both supply batteries are reversed.

In the grounded-base connection, the base current is the difference between the emitter current and the collector current. In this circuit, the base current is held to a fixed value while the collector voltage is varied to obtain the collector characteristic. Since the base current does not directly control the collector current, we do not find the same degree of linearity that we have in the common-base characteristics. The base currents are measured in microamperes (Fig. 3-23) when the

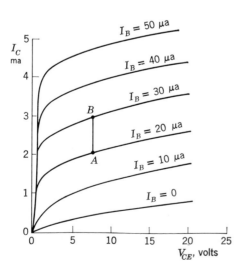

**Figure 3-23**   Common-emitter collector characteristic.

emitter and collector currents are in milliamperes. The base current is in milliamperes when the order of magnitude of the emitter and collector currents is in amperes. Here again the sense of collector current when the base current is zero is that of a reverse current $I_{co}$.

In Fig. 3–23, we note that a change of 10 $\mu$a in the base current from $A$ to $B$ produces a corresponding collector current change of 1 ma. In the grounded-base circuit, a change of current in the emitter produced a change of smaller amount in the collector. Here, the change in the collector is much greater than the change in the base current required to produce it. We use the term $\beta$ to define this current-gain ratio:

$$\beta = \frac{\Delta I_C}{\Delta I_B} \tag{3–4}$$

$\beta$ is normally greater than unity and, for the example we have used, $\beta$ is 1 ma/10 $\mu$a or 100. We note that

$$I_B = I_E - I_C$$

and, substituting this in Eq. 3–4, we have

$$\beta = \frac{\Delta I_C}{\Delta I_B} = \frac{\Delta I_C}{\Delta I_E - \Delta I_C}$$

Dividing all terms by $\Delta I_E$:

$$\beta = \frac{\Delta I_C/\Delta I_E}{1 - \Delta I_C/\Delta I_E}$$

But $\Delta I_C/\Delta I_E$ is defined as $\alpha$. Then

$$\beta = \frac{\alpha}{1 - \alpha} \tag{3–5a}$$

Solving this equation for $\alpha$:

$$\beta(1 - \alpha) = \alpha$$

$$\beta - \beta\alpha = \alpha$$

$$\beta = \alpha + \beta\alpha$$

$$\beta = (1 + \beta)\alpha$$

or
$$\alpha = \frac{\beta}{1 + \beta} \tag{3–5b}$$

These equations (3–5a and 3–5b) relate the two basic current gains of the transistor in much the same manner as the equation $-\mu = r_p g_m$ ties together the dynamic characteristics of the vacuum tube.

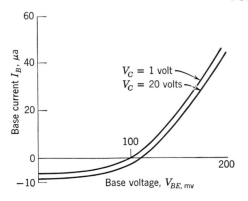

**Figure 3–24** Typical base-input characteristic for a common-emitter circuit.

A full discussion of transistor dynamic characteristics must be delayed until the equivalent circuits for transistor connections are analyzed. They are termed *hybrid parameters* and are discussed at length in Chapter 11.

The action of the input circuit in the grounded-emitter transistor circuit (Fig. 3–24) behaves somewhat differently from the input curves for the grounded-base circuit. Because of the action of the back current, a reverse current flows through the base lead at very low base voltages. This curve indicates that the input resistance to the base is about 100 mv/50 $\mu$a or 2000 ohms as contrasted to the input resistance of about 100 ohms in the grounded-base circuit.

### Section 3–9   The Transistor as a Simple Amplifier

In a grounded-base circuit (Fig. 3–25) let us assume that $V_{EE}$ is 0.15 volt and produces an emitter current $I_E$ of 2 ma. A signal produces a swing of 0.05 volt plus and minus, causing $I_E$ to vary between 1 ma and 3 ma. If we assume for purposes of a simplified discussion that $\alpha$ is unity, the static value of collector current is 2 ma, and, with signal, it will range between 1 ma and 3 ma, in accordance with the

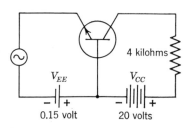

**Figure 3–25** The transistor in a simple grounded-base amplifier.

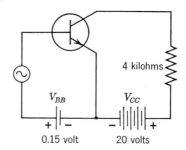

**Figure 3–26** The transistor in a simple grounded-emitter amplifier.

emitter current. A 4000-ohm load resistance, at 2 ma current, has a voltage drop of 8 volts. Since the collector supply is 20 volts, the collector voltage is 12 volts. When the collector current increases to 3 ma, the drop in the load is 12 volts, and the collector voltage is 8 volts. When $I_C$ decreases to 1 ma, the drop in the load is 4 volts, and $V_C$ is 16 volts. Thus, a total change of 0.10 volt in the input results in a change in the output of 8 volts. The voltage gain in the circuit is 8/0.10 or 80. Thus, as with the vacuum-tube amplifier, this circuit will amplify a signal to a greater level. The current gain is unity; so the power gain, which is the product of the voltage gain times the current gain, is, for this example, 80 also.

We note in the circuit (Fig. 3–25) that the operating bias voltage on the emitter is negative and that it is positive on the collector. A positive incoming signal makes the emitter *less* negative and *reduces* the emitter current. The collector current accordingly *decreases*, and the collector voltage, or output signal, *increases* in the positive direction. This circuit, the grounded-base amplifier, has gain but does not give phase inversion; the input and output signals are *in phase*.

In the grounded-emitter circuit (Fig. 3–26), assume that the operating conditions for the circuit are: collector current 2 ma, base current 30 $\mu$a, and base voltage 0.15 volt. Also assume that an input signal of plus and minus 10 $\mu$a is produced by a base voltage change of plus and minus 0.05 volt. A 10-$\mu$a increase in base current increases the collector current 1 ma from the operating point of 2 ma to 3 ma, lowering the collector voltage from 12 volts to 8 volts. A decrease in base current of 10 $\mu$a decreases the collector current from 2 ma to 1 ma, thus raising the collector voltage to 16 volts. Thus, for this example, the voltage gain is 8 volts/0.10 volt or 80, and the current gain is 2 ma/20 $\mu$a or 100. The power gain of the circuit is 80 $\times$ 100 or 8000.

We see from this example that we obtain much greater power gains from the grounded emitter circuit than from the grounded base circuit.

In practice, we find that most transistor-circuit connections are of the grounded-emitter form, in order to obtain this greater power gain.

In Fig. 3–26, a positive signal increases the base voltage. This increase in base voltage increases the base current which controls the collector current. The collector supply voltage is positive; so an increasing collector current causes the collector voltage to be less positive. This less positive condition is negative as far as the signal is concerned. Thus a grounded emitter circuit produces *phase inversion* as did the vacuum-tube circuit of Section 3–5.

**Section 3–10   Limitations of a Transistor**

The limits of operation of a transistor can be established by referring to a collector characteristic curve (Fig. 3–27). In the transistor circuit, we can actually operate up to and along the $I_C$ axis, $0a$. A point located along this line is termed *saturated* since the curves drop off very sharply here. The maximum value of $I_C$ that is permitted is $ab$. Limiting the collector current to the maximum allowable current density in the junction automatically establishes a limit on the emitter current and on the base current. The curve $bc$ is the product of $I_C$ times $V_C$ and represents the maximum allowable collector heat dissipation. The product of voltage and current in the input is so small that it may be neglected with respect to the very much greater heating in the collector. If the collector dissipation is exceeded, the excessive heat will permanently damage the crystalline structure. The limit $cd$ is the maximum allowable reverse voltage on the collector. A collector voltage exceeding this value may cause a Zener breakdown within the transistor.

An increase in operating temperature breaks down the covalent bonds and produces a larger back current $I_{co}$. If this back current is large, all the curves will rise sharply with increasing collector voltage.

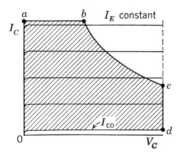

**Figure   3–27**   The   limits   of operation of a transistor.

The severity of this rise depends on the increase in the operating temperature.   It should be noted that it is unsafe to exceed power ratings for transistors for even short periods of time because of the small size of the active part and the consequent low ability of the unit to absorb heat without the temperature rise being excessive.

These factors, then, limit the operating range of the transistor to the shaded region, 0abcd0.

We stated that transistors have a very long life of many thousand hours.   The original developmental models indicated that the life expectancy was of the order of 70,000 hours, or about 8 years' continuous service.   Improvements in manufacturing processes have extended this time considerably.   A number of random causes of a very short life have been eliminated.   The main problems appear to be metallurgical changes produced by heating the lattice structure.   Occasionally transistors do fail in service from metallurgical failure, and occasionally transistors are received in inoperative condition although they were carefully tested in production.   It is noted, however, that the replacement of transistors in properly designed circuits is a negligible problem.

### Section 3–11   The Cold-Cathode Gas-Filled Triode

The cold-cathode gas-filled triode is not a triode in the same sense as a vacuum-tube triode with a grid, but it has an auxiliary or starter anode which controls the gas discharge between a main plate and the

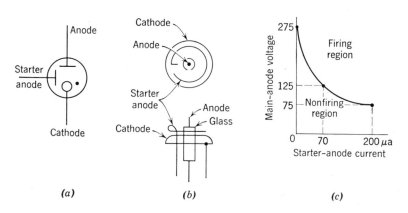

**Figure 3–28**   Characteristics of the 0A4G tube.   (*a*) Symbol.   (*b*) Physical structure.   (*c*) Transfer characteristics.

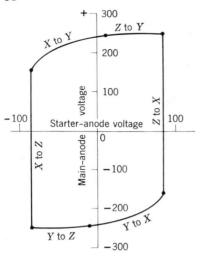

**Figure 3–29**  Breakdown characteristics for different electrode polarities for the 0A4G tube.

X – Starter anode
Y – Main anode
Z – Cathode

cathode.  The tube has applications as a relay or control tube and, in the form of a light-producing device, is the Strobotron.  Figure 3–28 shows the physical structure of this tube.  The main anode is far from the cathode while the starter anode is very close to the cathode.

It is easy to start ionization between the starter anode and the cathode.  If the main-anode voltage is sufficiently large, the ionization initiated by the starter anode will transfer to the main plate.  A low ionization level at the starter anode requires a high main-anode potential, whereas a high ionization level at the starter transfers to the main anode at much lower voltages.  The relation between the starter-anode current (degree of initial ionization) and the potential at the main anode required for transfer is shown in Fig. 3–28c.  Because of this transfer action, the tube is known as a relay tube.

Once the main anode has fired across to the cathode, the starter anode can regain control only if the ionization in the tube ceases for the required deionization time.

It is possible for firing to occur between any two elements of the tube.  Also, *any* one element can serve as the positive plate for this discharge action while *either* of the other two can serve as the cathode. The combination of possible discharges is shown in Fig. 3–29.

## Section 3–12    The Hot-Cathode Gas-Filled
## Triode—the Thyratron

The term *thyratron* is universally accepted as the name for a hot-cathode gas-filled triode. Small thyratrons, such as the 884, are similar in construction with triodes of the same size. The presence of gas molecules in the tube in addition to a negative grid voltage effectively prevent electrons from reaching the plate. When the plate potential is sufficiently increased, electrons from the space charge gain sufficient velocity and kinetic energy to produce ionization. The action of ionization is cumulative as in the gas diode, and plate current is limited only by the external plate-circuit resistance. The plate voltage, upon ionization, falls to a very low value, from 10 to 20 volts. Different ionizing plate potentials are required for different values of negative grid voltage. When the grid has a high negative voltage, a very large plate voltage is required to produce ionization. Typical characteristics of a small thyratron are given in Fig. 3–30.

Once a thyratron is fired, the grid loses control. The negative potential on the grid attracts ions, and the ions, surrounding the grid wires in the form of a sheath, neutralize the effect of the negative grid voltage. Electrons from the grid leave the grid wires to neutralize the surrounding positive ions. Since this grid current is formed in the process of neutralizing ions, the term *ion current* or *ionic current*

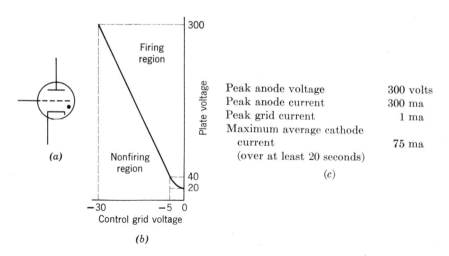

**Figure 3–30**   Ratings of a typical small thyratron. (*a*) Symbol. (*b*) Control characteristic. (*c*) Typical ratings.

is used to describe this action. In order to limit the grid current to a safe value (for the 884, 1 ma peak), an external resistance must be placed in series with the grid. This current in the negative grid cannot occur in the high vacuum tube.

If the peak anode voltage rating is exceeded, there is a gas discharge between the grid and the plate in the manner of the cold-cathode gas diode. If the peak anode current rating is exceeded, multiple ionization occurs and the cathode is subjected to the ion bombardment which shortens its life. When the tube fires, the plate voltage is about 16 volts. If the maximum allowable average current is 75 ma, the product of 16 volts times 75 ma is 1.2 watts, which is the maximum allowable plate dissipation for the tube.

The tube can handle 75 ma plate current indefinitely. It can handle larger plate current only for so long a time as the average over 20 seconds will not exceed 75 ma. For example, if the peak anode current of 300 ma is maintained for 5 seconds, the current must be zero for 15 seconds so that the average current over this interval will not exceed 75 ma. If the duration of flow of the 300 ma is greater than 5 seconds, the average over the 20-sec period exceeds the average plate-current rating.

Once ionization takes place, the grid loses control completely, and it can only regain control by one of several means:

1. Turnoff the plate supply for at least the time required for the tube to deionize.

2. Make the plate voltage negative for at least the deionization time. This may be accomplished by using an a-c wave for the plate supply or by applying a negative pulse to the plate.

3. Reduce the plate current by means of an external resistance to such a low value that recombination takes place within the plasma faster than ionization does.

The data in Fig. 3–31 are for a medium-power mercury-vapor thyratron. The considerations given to the maximum ratings in the data are very much the same as for the low-power 884. The surge current rating is for a fuse or circuit breaker which must operate within the specified 0.1 second if it is to protect the tube. Since the gas used is mercury vapor, the control of firing is quite sensitive to temperature. Thus, instead of having the sharply defined firing line of the 884, we have the extended plot of Fig. 3–31b for the range of mercury condensation temperatures.

In the higher-power thyratrons, the function of the grid becomes solely the control between firing and nonfiring conditions. It is

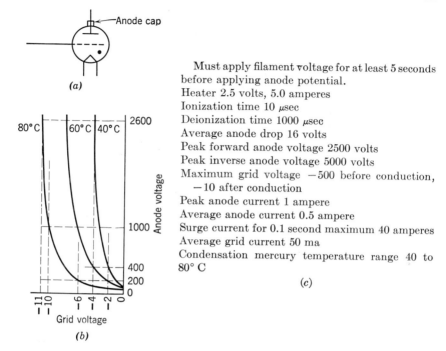

Must apply filament voltage for at least 5 seconds before applying anode potential.
Heater 2.5 volts, 5.0 amperes
Ionization time 10 μsec
Deionization time 1000 μsec
Average anode drop 16 volts
Peak forward anode voltage 2500 volts
Peak inverse anode voltage 5000 volts
Maximum grid voltage −500 before conduction, −10 after conduction
Peak anode current 1 ampere
Average anode current 0.5 ampere
Surge current for 0.1 second maximum 40 amperes
Average grid current 50 ma
Condensation mercury temperature range 40 to 80° C

(c)

**Figure 3–31** Tube manual data on the 5557/FG17, a typical mercury-vapor thyratron. (*Courtesy RCA*) (a) Symbol. (b) Control characteristics. (c) Typical operating characteristics.

important that the grid structure give a heavy shielding action between the cathode and the plate. Then the grid can serve the dual function of a control shield and a heat baffle. Representative grid structures are shown in Fig. 3–32.

Very high-power thyratrons (peak anode voltages of the order of 10,000 volts and maximum average anode currents of 25 amperes) require a very large spacing between the cathode and anode and a grid structure similar to Fig. 3–32c. These large physical dimensions carry the control curves from the negative grid region to the positive grid region. In a typical large thyratron, in order to fire the tube at 6000 volts on the plate, a grid potential of +4 volts is required. The heating time required to secure an adequate number of mercury-vapor molecules before application of anode voltage may be several minutes.

In a great many applications, the thyratron is used as a grid-controlled rectifier. In order to keep the material of this textbook in

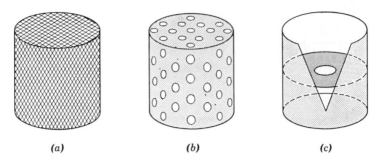

(a)                    (b)                    (c)

**Figure 3–32** Typical heavy-duty thyratron grid structures. (a) Wire mesh. (b) Solid surface with holes. (c) Solid cylinder with internal disk acting as grid and heat shield.

orderly sequence, Section 9–12 in the rectifier chapter is devoted to the circuitry and action of the thyratron as a rectifier in detail. For those who have the need and the immediate interest, Section 9–10 may be taken up at this point by first going over the operation of the single-phase half-wave and full-wave rectifiers with resistive load (Section 9–1 and 9–2).

. . . . **Suggested References for Further Study**

1. W. G. Dow, *Fundamentals of Engineering Electronics*, 2nd ed., John Wiley & Sons, New York, 1952.
2. K. R. Spangenberg, *Vacuum Tubes*, Chapters 5 and 7, McGraw-Hill Book Co., New York, 1948.
3. A. Coblenz and H. L. Owens, *Transistors*, McGraw-Hill Book Co., New York, 1955.

. . . . **QUESTIONS**

1. Define or explain each of the following terms: (a) cutoff, (b) ground, (c) transconductance, (d) phase inversion, (e) back current, (f) emitter, (g) base, (h) collector, (i) starter anode, (j) ionic current.
2. Explain the difference in the control of plate current in a triode by the use of a grid structure with coarse spacing and with fine spacing.
3. Explain the curvature of the plot of grid current in Fig. 3–5.
4. Explain the curvature of the plot of plate current in Fig. 3–6.
5. Explain the curvature of the plot of plate current in Fig. 3–7.
6. Account for the limitations of points a, b, c, d, m, and n in Fig. 3–9.

7. Define $\mu$, $g_m$, and $r_p$.

8. How are $\mu$, $g_m$, and $r_p$ related?

9. Explain why phase inversion takes place in a triode amplifier.

10. What symbols are used for the battery and electrode voltages and currents in a triode amplifier?

11. What is meant by the term *diffuse* in the operation of a transistor?

12. What is the interpretation of the arrow in the transistor symbol?

13. Show how improper polarity of the collector supply battery can destroy a transistor.

14. What is the effect of reverse bias on the emitter of a transistor?

15. What is the current-gain symbol for a grounded-base transistor?

16. Show how the current gain must be less than unity in a grounded-base transistor.

17. Compare the input resistances for a transistor when used in the grounded-base and in the grounded-emitter connections.

18. Show how the input and the output voltages are in phase for the common-base connection of a *PNP* transistor.

19. Show how the input and the output voltages are out of phase for the common-emitter connection of a *PNP* transistor.

20. What are the symbols used for the currents and voltages in a simple transistor amplifier?

21. What happens to the collector characteristic with an increase in operating temperature?

22. Explain how a cold-cathode triode acts as a relay tube.

23. Referring to Fig. 3–29, state how each tube element acts for each point on the characteristic.

24. Why does the grid lose control when a thyratron fires?

25. What are three ways to stop plate current in a thyratron once it fires?

26. Why must both the average and the peak plate currents of a thyratron be given?

27. Explain why there are different curves for different temperatures in Fig. 3–31b.

28. Why are the grid structures shown in Fig. 3–32 unsuited for vacuum tubes?

29. Why may a positive grid voltage be necessary to fire a large thyratron?

# . . . . PROBLEMS

1. Using the tube manual curves for the 6AV6, by transferring the points on the plate characteristic, construct the grid family and the constant current family.

2. On each of three different plate characteristics in the tube manual, locate the point on the curves established under "characteristics and typical operation." At this point, by using the slope method, determine $\mu$, $r_p$, and $g_m$.

3. The data in Table A are for four points on a plate characteristic.

TABLE A

| Point | A | B | C | D |
|---|---|---|---|---|
| $I_b$ ma | 17 | 23 | 20 | ? |
| $E_c$ volts | 0 | 0 | −1 | −2 |
| $E_b$ volts | 100 | 125 | 150 | 175 |

From these data evaluate the coefficients in Eq. 3–2, and determine the missing value of current.

4. From the curve given in Fig. 3–21, plot values of d-c and a-c emitter input resistances ($R_e$ and $r_e$) against emitter current.

5. From the curve given in Fig. 3–24, plot the values of d-c and a-c base resistances ($R_b$ and $r_b$) against base current.

# Multigrid tubes

◆ ◆ ◆ ◆ ◆ ◆ ◆ ◆ ◆ ◆ ◆ ◆ ◆ ◆ ◆ ◆ ◆ ◆ ◆ ◆ ◆ ◆ ◆ ◆ CHAPTER 4

The function of a second grid in reducing interelectrode capacitance is discussed (Section 4–1). The tetrode (Section 4–2), the pentode (Section 4–3), and the beam-power tube (Section 4–5) make use of this second grid. Remote-cutoff grid structures (Section 4–4) are used primarily with multigrid tubes. A gas tube, the thyratron, also is available with two grids (Section 4–6). The action of an electron-ray indicator is considered both from the operation of the tube and from circuit application (Section 4–7). A short discussion of miscellaneous tube characteristics (Section 4–8) completes the chapter.

## Section 4–1  Interelectrode Tube Capacitance

If two conductors are separated by a dielectric medium, by definition of the term, a capacitance is said to exist. In a triode vacuum tube (Fig. 4–1), capacitances exist between the grid and cathode $C_{gk}$, between the grid and plate $C_{gp}$, and between the plate and cathode $C_{pk}$. These capacitances are small, in the order of a few micro-microfarads. If the value of the capacitance is 5 $\mu\mu$f, the reactance at 1 Mc is about 30,000 ohms; at 10 Mc, it is about 3000 ohms. Thus, as the frequency of operation is increased, the effect of these capacitances becomes more and more important. In particular, an a-c circuit exists for energy transfer from the plate back into the grid through $C_{gp}$. We established in Section 3–5 that the output of an amplifier is 180° out of phase with the grid signal. The signal which is fed from the plate back to the grid through $C_{gp}$ is, then, 180° out of phase with the input, and it tends to cancel or to counteract the signal at the grid.

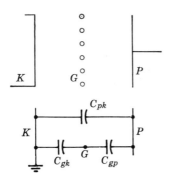

**Figure 4–1**  Interelectrode capacitance in a triode.

In the early years of the vacuum tube, most of the applications were in the field of communications.  As the need for higher and higher frequencies developed, the more apparent it became that the triode was, because of this capacitive effect between the grid and the plate, very limited in application.  We will find later (Section 13–4) that this capacitive energy transfer often adversely affects the gain of multistage amplifiers which are found in many applications of electronics.

The next step in vacuum-tube development was the attempt to reduce or eliminate this energy-transferring capacitance.  If a grounded electrostatic shield is placed between the control grid and the plate, capacitance exists between the control grid and ground (the shield), and between the plate and ground (the shield), but not between the grid and the plate.  In order to have this shielding, the shield would have to be large and solid.  It is necessary in vacuum-tube action to have an electron flow from the cathode to the plate.  This means that the shield cannot be a solid plate, but it must be an open-wire mesh of the same form as the control grid.  When we make this shield or *screen* in the form of a mesh, it loses some of its shielding ability.  We find that the actual mesh design of this shielding grid is a compromise between electron flow and satisfactory shielding.  As an illustration, with a screen used as an electrostatic shield, $C_{gp}$ is reduced from 3 $\mu\mu$f to 0.007 $\mu\mu$f.

### Section 4–2   The Tetrode

The tetrode (Fig. 4–2) is a vacuum tube which has four elements: a cathode, a control grid, a screen or shield grid, and a plate.  The functions of the cathode, the control grid, and the plate are the same as the three elements of the triode.  For the second grid or screen grid to serve as a shield, we found that it must be operated at ground

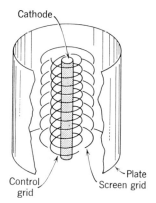

**Figure 4–2** Mechanical structure of a tetrode.

potential. This statement may be modified to include its operation at a fixed d-c potential which is adequately and sufficiently shunted to ground with a bypass capacitor. We find that, if the screen were directly connected to the ground or to the cathode, it would be impossible to obtain any plate current at normal tube voltages. Thus, it is found necessary to operate the screen in the vacuum tube at a fixed positive potential of the order of one-third to full plate voltage.

The conventional test circuit used for obtaining the characteristic curves of a tetrode is shown in Fig. 4–3. The screen voltage is maintained at a fixed value, and the grid and plate voltages are allowed to vary. For the plate characteristic, the grid voltage is adjusted and held to a specific negative value. When the plate voltage is zero, the positive voltage on the screen attracts electrons from the space-charge cloud. Most of these electrons go to the screen wires, paths $a$ and $b$ of Fig. 4–4. Some of the electrons pass through the screen-wire

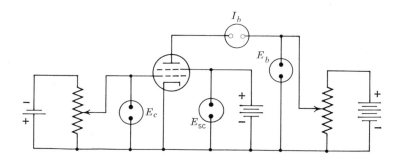

**Figure 4–3** Test circuit for a tetrode.

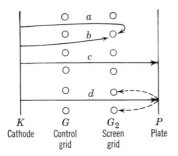

**Figure 4–4** Secondary emission in a tetrode.

mesh and continue on until they hit the plate, producing a plate current, path $c$ of Fig. 4–4. As the plate voltage is raised from zero, an increasing number of electrons are drawn away from the paths to the screen and go to the plate. This increase in plate current causes a corresponding decrease in the screen current. This action is shown in that part of the plate characteristic curves which lies between $m$ and $n$ (Fig. 4–5).

As the voltage on the plate increases, the kinetic energy of the electrons which reach the plate increases. This increasing kinetic energy now produces a sufficient striking force on impact at the plate to cause *secondary emission.* Electrons are literally knocked out of the surface of the plate by the impact to produce the secondary emission, path $d$ of Fig. 4–4. The electrons produced by secondary emission are thrown into the space between the screen and the plate. They go to the electrode which is at the higher potential, the screen. This means that, as secondary emission increases, the net plate current which is the incoming electrons less the secondary emission, decreases, whereas the screen current increases by the amount that the plate current goes down. If the nature of the plate surface is such that it produces a

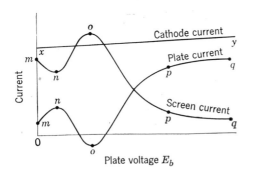

**Figure 4–5** The plate characteristic of a tetrode.

large secondary emisssion, the quantity of electrons of secondary emission can exceed the number of incoming electrons to the plate from the cathode. In this case, the plate current goes negative. This effect shows on the plate characteristic as the region between $n$ and $o$ (Fig. 4–5).

After a certain critical value is reached, point $o$ of Fig. 4–5 an increasing plate voltage recaptures more and more of the secondary electrons. The plate current increases, and the screen current decreases. This is shown on Fig. 4–5 from point $o$ to point $p$. When the plate voltage equals and exceeds the screen voltage, point $p$ to point $q$, all the secondary emission is drawn back into the plate. The plate current rises somewhat while the screen current continues to decrease.

Over the whole characteristic, the total number of electrons that are involved is determined by the value of the negative grid voltage. The total current, the cathode current, $xy$ of Fig. 4–5, is essentially constant. This total current divides between the two positive electrodes, the screen and the plate, in accordance with their relative voltages and the effects of secondary emission, as we have discussed. The slight rise of cathode current from $x$ to $y$ is caused by the Schottky effect (Section 2–1).

The region of the plate characteristic between $n$ and $o$ indicates a negative resistance. An increasing voltage produces a decreasing current. We will find in subsequent chapters that a negative-resistance characteristic in a vacuum tube can very adversely affect its operation as an amplifier, but it does have many applications in triggering and counting circuits and in oscillators. Normally the useful range of the tube as an amplifier is limited to the flat portion of the curve between $p$ and $q$. The discussion of this tube from this point on in the chapter assumes that its operation is confined to this linear region.

The slope of the curve between $p$ and $q$ shows that there is a very small change in plate current for a large change in plate voltage. For a typical small tetrode, a change in plate voltage of 100 volts produces a change in plate current of 0.5 ma. Dividing 100 volts by 0.5 ma gives a plate resistance $r_p$ of 200,000 ohms. A high value of plate resistance is characteristic of multigrid vacuum tubes, whereas plate resistances of triodes are relatively low. Since the control grid controls cathode current in the same manner as in a triode, the order of magnitude of the transconductance $g_m$ is the same for tetrodes as for triodes. Then, by use of the relation $-\mu = g_m \times r_p$, we note that tetrodes have much higher amplification factors than triodes. An amplifier stage using a tetrode gives a much higher gain than a

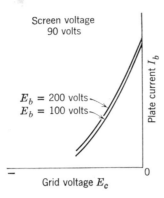

Screen voltage
90 volts

$E_b$ = 200 volts

$E_b$ = 100 volts

Plate current $I_b$

Grid voltage $E_c$

0

**Figure 4–6** Transfer characteristic for a tetrode.

triode stage.  Thus, we find that the tube which was developed to reduce the undesirable effects of a large grid-to-plate capacitance also provides an increased voltage amplification.

The operation of the tetrode as an amplifier is normally confined to the linear part of the plate characteristic.  In view of this, transfer characteristics for the tube are only given for values of plate-voltage parameters which do not involve secondary-emission interaction between the screen and the plate.  The mutual characteristic is shown in Fig. 4–6.

### Section 4–3   The Pentode

The useful part of the plate characteristic of the tetrode is limited to that region where the plate voltage exceeds the screen voltage. Although the tetrode resolves the problem of grid-to-plate capacitance satisfactorily, vacuum-tube development was continued to find a means of extending the useful range of the tube to include the whole

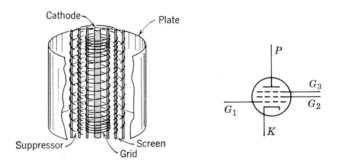

Cathode

Plate

$P$

$G_3$

$G_1$

$G_2$

$K$

Suppressor

Screen
Grid

**Figure 4–7** Mechanical structure of a pentode.

characteristic. The pentode (Fig. 4–7) was the outgrowth of this development. A third grid structure, called the suppressor, is located between the screen and the plate.

The screen is held at the same positive voltage as in the tetrode. This positive screen attracts electrons in the same fashion detailed in the discussion of the tetrode. The suppressor which is held at cathode potential is less positive than the screen and exerts a repelling effect on the electron flow. When the plate voltage is zero, because of this repelling effect, comparatively few electrons coast on to the plate. When the plate is slightly positive, the attracting force of this plate voltage overcomes the repelling effect of the suppressor, and electrons

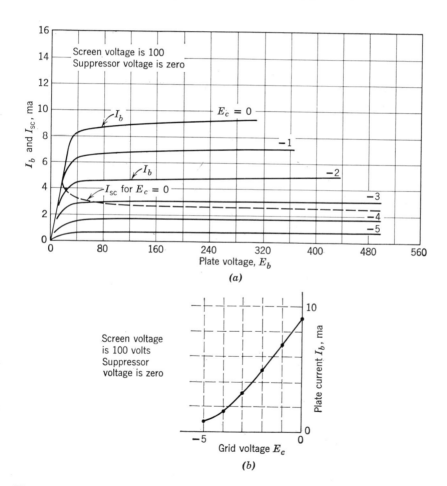

**Figure 4–8** Characteristic curves for a pentode. (*a*) Plate characteristics. (*b*) Transfer characteristic. (*Courtesy RCA*)

do get through to the plate.   As the plate voltage increases, electrons strike the plate to produce secondary emission as in the tetrode. Now, however, the secondary-emission electrons which have a low velocity do not go to the screen because of the intervening suppressor-grid electric field which tends to repel electrons.   The secondary electrons are driven back into the plate because the plate is at a higher potential than the suppressor.   The action of the suppressor is then *not* to eliminate secondary emission but to prevent the electrons produced by secondary emission from reaching the screen.

In the pentode, at very low plate voltages, most of the electrons go to the screen.   As the plate voltage is increased, more and more of this electron stream is diverted from the screen to the plate.   At a relative low plate voltage, the plate current reaches its final value.   The plate and the transfer characteristics are shown in Fig. 4–8.   The slight rise of plate current along the "flat" part of the characteristic may be explained by a slight decrease in screen current and the increased total cathode current caused by the Schottky effect.   Now in the pentode we have *two* shield grids between the control grid and the plate instead of the one shield grid of the tetrode.   These two shield grids reduce the control grid-to-plate capacitance still further.   We used 0.007 $\mu\mu$f as a typical value for the grid-to-plate capacitance of the tetrode.   The additional screening action of the suppressor grid reduces this value to 0.005 $\mu\mu$f in a pentode.

The pentode characteristics are distinctly "flatter" than the tetrode curves.   This results in still higher values of plate resistance.   Since the transconductance is a function of the control grid and screen potentials, the transconductance is substantially the same as the values for a tetrode.   Therefore, the values of $\mu$, the amplification factor, are still higher for pentodes than for tetrodes.   A résumé of the characteristics of typical vacuum tubes is given in Table I.

TABLE I

|  | Triode | | Tetrode | Pentode |
|---|---|---|---|---|
|  | 6SN7 | 6SL7 | 24A | 6SJ7 |
| $C_{gk}$, $\mu\mu$f | 3.0 | 3.4 | 5.3 | 6.0 |
| $C_{gp}$, $\mu\mu$f | 4.0 | 2.8 | 0.007 | 0.005 |
| $C_{pk}$, $\mu\mu$f | 1.2 | 3.2 | 10.5 | 7.0 |
| $r_p$, ohms | 7.7K | 44K | 400K | 700K |
| $g_m$, micromhos | 2600 | 1600 | 1000 | 1600 |
| $\mu$ | 20 | 70 | 400 | 1120 |

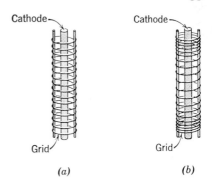

**Figure 4–9** Grid structures for sharp and remote-cutoff tubes. (*a*) Sharp-cutoff control grid. (*b*) Remote-cutoff control grid. (*Courtesy RCA*)

The suppressor by extending the useful working range of the tube has caused the tetrode to become essentially obsolete except for certain special applications. We do find tetrodes frequently used as very high-power tubes, but they are used only rarely in preference to pentodes as voltage amplifiers.

### Section 4–4   Remote-Cutoff Tubes

Up to this point we have considered vacuum-tube grid structures as being formed of uniformly spaced wires made in the form of a spiral or helix. A second structural form (Fig. 4–9) consists of a close spacing at the top and bottom and a gradual spreading toward the center. In the discussion of the operation of the control grid of the triode, we brought out the fact that a fine-wire mesh produces an effective low grid-voltage control over the plate current whereas a wide-grid mesh results in less control of the plate current by the grid voltage.

In a vacuum tube using this variable spacing in the control grid construction, a small negative grid voltage cuts off the plate current at the ends of the helix. As the grid is made more negative, the region of cutoff approaches the center. In a vacuum tube with a uniformly spaced grid, cutoff takes place over the whole axial length at once. A comparison between the two grid arrangements can best be shown on the transfer characteristic (Fig. 4–10). The curve for the uniform grid structure is essentially a straight line producing a *sharp cutoff*. The variable grid spacing results in a transfer characteristic which is sharply curved with an indefinite cutoff point. The transconductance $g_m$ of the tube is affected in the same manner since the transconductance is defined as the slope of the transfer curve [$g_m = (\Delta I_b/\Delta E_c)$ for $E_b$ constant]. Because of this, the tube employing this special grid is termed *remote cutoff, supercontrol,* or *variable-mu*.

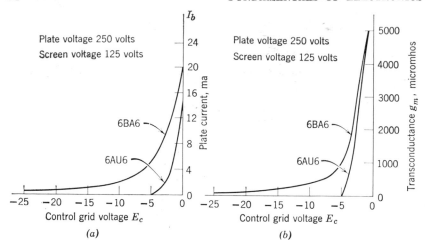

**Figure 4–10**   Electrical characteristics of a sharp (6AU6) and a remote (6BA6) cutoff tube.   (*Courtesy RCA*)

The use of the variable-control grid spacing has been confined, with only a few exceptions, to multigrid tubes.   The supercontrol tube has its major application in radio-receiving equipment.   We do, however, find the remote cutoff tube used in special industrial electronic circuits to the extent that the operation and functioning of the tube must be understood by all students of electronics.

### Section 4–5   The Beam-Power Tube

The effect of a suppressor grid reduces the power efficiency of a pentode, and the limited range of linear operation reduces the efficiency of the tetrode.   The beam-power tube is the result of developmental efforts seeking to combine into one tube structure the best features of each.   Because of this similarity, the circuit symbols used for the beam-power tube can be any of several forms (Fig. 4–11).

In the beam-power tube, the grid wires of the control grid and of the screen grid are carefully aligned so that the electron flow from cathode to plate is in planar bunches or beams (Fig. 4–11).   The suppressor grid is omitted, but there are solid beam-directing plates which are electrically tied to the cathode.   Since these beam-directing plates are at cathode potential and located in the area of the tube which is subject to the high screen and plate voltages, these plates repel the electron stream and keep it within tight concentrated paths to the

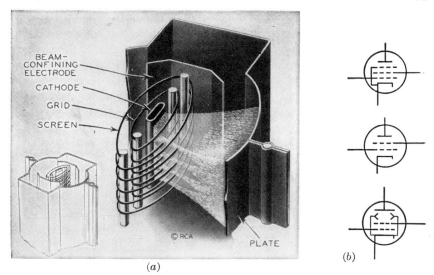

(a)

(b)

**Figure 4–11** Mechanical structure of a beam-power tube. Zone of negative space charge. (a) Mechanical structure. (b) Symbols in use for beam-power tube. (*Courtesy RCA*)

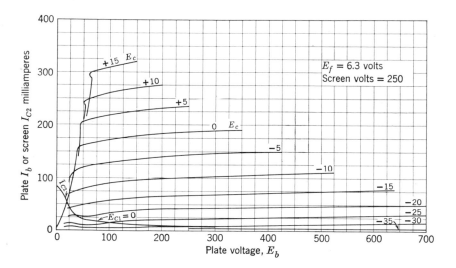

**Figure 4–12** Plate characteristic of a beam-power tube. (*Courtesy RCA*)

plate. This concentration of electrons in a compact path between the screen and the plate produces a negative field just as a concentration of electrons in the space charge produces a negative field. The negative-field effect of the beam serves to push the electrons of secondary emission which are produced from impact at the plate back into the plate. The concentration of electrons then acts on secondary emission in the same manner as the suppressor grid in the pentode. The term *virtual suppressor* is used to describe this action of having a suppressor action without actually having the physical structure.

This virtual suppressor action functions only for the high plate-current levels which are found in tubes intended, not as voltage amplifiers, but as power amplifiers. In the plate characteristics for a beam-power tube (Fig. 4–12) the curves are not exactly uniformly spaced, but the very steep, sharp rise at low plate voltages before the curves flatten enables a useful operating range to be obtained which encompasses nearly the full quadrant.

### Section 4–6   The Shield-Grid Thyratron

The concept of a second grid is also incorporated into thyratron tube design. When a second grid is used, the accepted terminology used is either *shield-grid thyratron* or *tetrode-type thyratron*. In a thyratron, a second grid is used to give the tube a more flexible range of operating

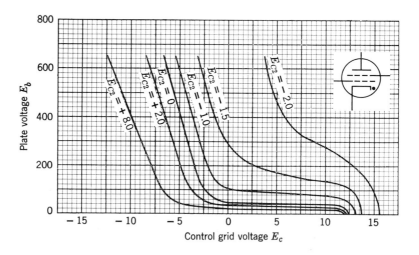

**Figure 4–13**   Firing characteristics of a typical screen-grid thyratron. (*Courtesy RCA*)

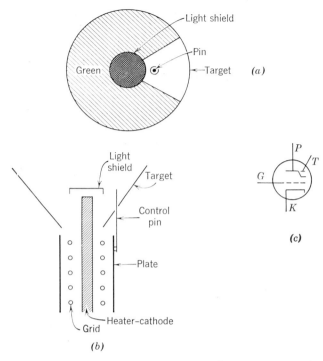

**Figure 4-14** Mechanical structure of the electron-ray indicator. (*a*) **Top view.** (*b*) Cross section. (*c*) Symbol.

control (Fig. 4–13). The tube may be fired by a signal on the control grid, by a signal on the shield grid, or by a proper combination of signals on both grids. The firing characteristics show that a negative shield-grid potential requires a positive control grid for firing, whereas a positive voltage on the shield grid is fired with a negative control-grid voltage. As may be seen from the typical data, the operating voltages of a shield grid in a thyratron are quite different from the screen voltages used in a vacuum tube.

## Section 4–7   The Electron-Ray Indicator

The construction of the electron-ray indicator is shown Fig. 4–14. The triode section is conventional, and a small pin welded to the plate extends above the conical target through a clearance hole. The target is held at a high positive voltage. Electrons leave the upper part of the cathode structure and travel radially out to the surface of the target.  The surface of the conical target is coated with a fluorescent material which glows green when struck by electrons.  *Fluorescence* is that property of a material which converts part of an impact kinetic energy into visible light.  The entire target glows with visible light. When the voltage on the plate of the triode section is less than the target voltage, the pin is negative with respect to the target.  In this case, electrons will avoid the region of the pin, preferring the higher voltage of the rest of the target.  Accordingly, the area around the pin will be dark.  The width of this dark sector depends on the difference between the target voltage and the pin voltage.  When the voltage on the pin is close to target potential, the shadow angle is small.  When the voltage on the pin is considerably below the target voltage, the shadow angle is large.  The black button serves as a light shield so that an observer cannot see the orange glow of the heater.  This button together with the circular shape of the green target has caused the terms *tuning-eye tube* or *magic-eye tube* to be popular.

The pin is physically closer to the cathode than the target.  Accordingly, when the pin is at the same voltage as the target, a greater density of electrons flows toward the region of the pin than to the rest of the target.  This causes the phenomenon of what appears to be an overlap of the green.  An exact zero shadow angle is obtained only when the plate pin is slightly negative with respect to the target.

The target we have described in this discussion is circular.  The tuning-ray indicator is also made with a rectangular target operating along the same principles.  One version of the tube incorporates two complete units with two rectangular targets.  This tube is used in circuitry where one shadow is compared visually with the other.

The circuit of Fig. 4–15 illustrates the operation of the tuning-ray indicator.  The direct voltage on the grid controls the triode current. When the plate is cut off, the plate current is zero, and the drop in the

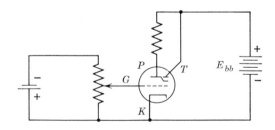

**Figure 4–15**   Circuit for the electron-ray indicator.

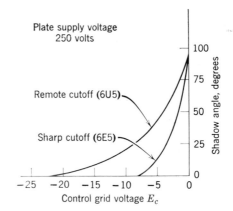

**Figure 4–16** Electrical characteristics of the electron-ray indicator.

load resistance $R_L$ is also zero. Then the plate and the pin are at the same potential $E_{bb}$. The shadow angle is zero (or may overlap). When the grid is less negative, a plate current flows, producing a voltage drop in $R_L$. Now the plate voltage is less than $E_{bb}$. Since the target is directly connected to the supply $E_{bb}$, the plate pin is negative with respect to the target, causing a definite angle of shadow. When the grid is made still less negative, the shadow angle increases. The characteristic curves for typical tuning-ray indicators (Fig. 4–16) show curves for both a sharp-cutoff and a remote-cutoff form of triode construction.

These tubes are widely used for tuning circuits and as visual indicators in electronic equipment. If the grid is maintained at a fixed value of d-c bias to give a certain fixed shadow angle, an alternating voltage introduced in series with the grid causes the shadow angle to fluctuate rapidly at the a-c frequency rate about the d-c or static point. This rapid fluctuation produces a "fuzziness" or an indeterminate edge to the green. When the circuit is used as an a-c bridge-balance indicator, at balance the fuzziness disappears, and the shadow has a sharply defined edge.

### Section 4–8    Miscellaneous Characteristics of Tubes

Figure 4–17 illustrates a number of different physical forms of tubes. When using tubes, it is very necessary to have at hand a tube manual. Not only does the manual give details on the electrical characteristics. but also it lists the mechanical data for the tube. The physical size,

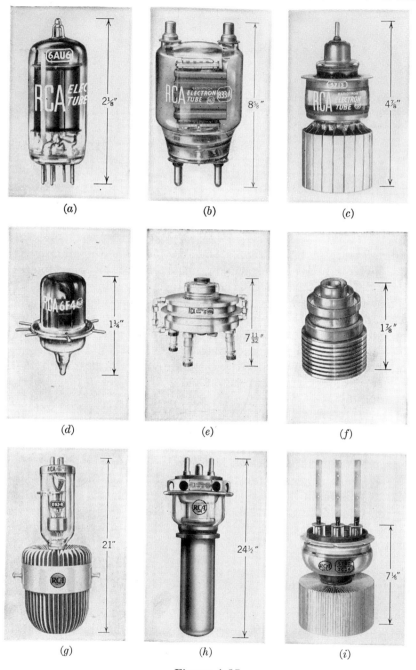

(a)       (b)       (c)

(d)       (e)       (f)

(g)       (h)       (i)

**Figure 4–17**

the type of envelope, the socket requirements, the identification of the leads at the base and of special plate or grid caps if used are all part of this necessary information. Many of the large tubes have special cooling problems. A certain volume of forced cooling air or water is required for normal operation. All these data are part of the tube manual, and all students of electronics must have a copy of one of the several available commercial publications issued by the different tube manufacturers.

We have discussed at length the operation of the diode, the triode, the tetrode and the pentode. Vacuum tubes are also made with four grids (*hexodes*) and five grids (*heptodes* or *pentagrid tubes*). These tubes were developed for special applications in communications. Multipurpose tubes are very common. For instance, a 6AL5 has two plates and two cathodes with a common heater. The 6SN7, the 6SL7, and the 6J6 are examples of tubes that have two separate triodes contained in one envelope with a common heater circuit. The 6AQ5 and 6AV6 are examples of high-$\mu$ triodes combined with two diodes in one envelope, using a common heater and a common cathode for all three sections. Very evidently these multipurpose vacuum tubes satisfy a need of economy where one tube and one base can serve satisfactorily in place of two or more separate tubes.

Many special types of tubes, such as lighthouse tubes, klystrons, magnetrons, and traveling-wave tubes, are used primarily in high-frequency microwave communications systems. A discussion of these tubes does not properly fit a textbook on basic electronics and electronic circuits. Accordingly, reference should be made for them to any one of the numerous advanced texts in this specialized field.

. . . . **Suggested Reference for Further Study**

K. R. Spangenberg, *Vacuum Tubes*, Chapter 10, McGraw-Hill Book Co., New York, 1948.

**Figure 4–17** (*page 90*)  Miscellaneous vacuum tubes. (*a*) 6AU6, pentode, 7-pin miniature-type receiving tube. (*b*) 833A, triode, natural or forced-air cooled (to 1600 watts output at 30 Mc). (*c*) 5713, triode, forced-air-cooled (to 290 watts output at 220 Mc). (*d*) 6F4, triode, small acorn type (to 1200 Mc). (*e*) 6806, beam power, water-cooled (to 28 kw output at 550 Mc). (*f*) 6816, beam-power tube, forced-air-cooled (to 180 watts output at 1200 Mc). (*g*) 892-R, with radiator, triode, forced-air-cooled (to 14 kw output). (*h*) 5770, triode, water- and forced-air-cooled (to 105 kw ouput at 20 Mc). (*i*) 5762/7C24, triode, forced-air-cooled (to 7 kw at 30 Mc). (*Courtesy RCA*)

## . . . . QUESTIONS

1. Define or explain each of the following terms: (a) screen voltage, (b) secondary emission, (c) suppressor, (d) sharp cutoff, (e) remote cutoff, (f) virtual suppressor, (g) ionization, (h) fluorescence, (i) hexode,(j) heptode.

2. Why is a shield grid effective?

3. Explain why the plate current follows $m$, $n$, $o$, $p$, and $q$ in Fig. 4–5.

4. What is meant by a negative resistance?

5. Why is the screen of a tetrode held at a lower potential than the plate?

6. Explain the action of secondary emission in a pentode.

7. Why is plate current substantially independent of plate voltage in Fig. 4–6?

8. Describe the construction of a grid structure that produces a remote-cutoff pentode.

9. Explain how the beam-forming plates in a beam-power tube prevent secondary-emission effects.

10. Explain why there are different control-grid curves for different screen-grid voltages in the characteristic of a shield-grid thyratron.

11. Explain the reason for using each mechanical element shown in Fig. 4–14.

12. Explain why an overlap can occur on an electron-ray indicator tube.

13. How does the "eye" of the electron-ray indicator tube react when it is used in an a-c bridge circuit?


## . . . . PROBLEMS

1. Using Fig. 4–5, sketch a plot of $R_p$ and $r_p$ against $E_b$ as the independent variable.   (If a curve for a tetrode is available, the problem can be done for numerical values).

2. Using the zero control-grid voltage curve from a set of plate characteristics (1S5 or 6AK5 or 12AC6 or 12AF6 from the tube manual), repeat problem 1.

# Special transistors

The first decade of transistor development has produced a great many basic forms and types. The industry has not stabilized its designs, with the result that a transistor manual is not available which gives the same coverage to the field that a vacuum-tube manual does to the electron-tube industry. New transistors constantly replace those that become obsolete. One objective of the industry is to develop a closer quality control while new transistors are being introduced. Many of the types discussed in this chapter are as yet not in common use because of their high cost, but they are used for special purposes. Naturally, as the cost is reduced, their use will become more widespread. Junction transistors (Section 5–1), the field-effect transistor (Section 5–2), the tetrode transistor (Section 5–3), and other types (Section 5–4) are considered. The features of special diodes (Section 5–5) and of the controlled rectifier (Section 5–6) are discussed. The chapter concludes with a review of the point-contact transistor (Section 5–7).

## Section 5–1  Junction Transistors

Several forms of transistors which are, in a broad sense, called junction transistors have special names which result from the manufacturing process. In the earlier chapters, we have considered the transistor as being formed of three layers, the emitter, the base, and the collector. We have also stated that the base layer is thin and that it has large surface dimensions compared to its thickness.

To manufacture *rate-grown* junction transistors, a *bar* or ingot of germanium is slowly drawn from the mold, and, by a combined process

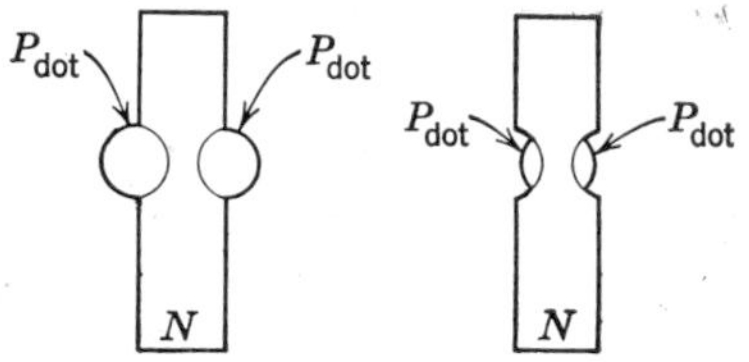

**Figure 5-1** Diffused-alloy transistors.

of impurity control called *doping* and of critical temperature control, thin layers of $P$ material are formed between slabs of $N$ material. The resulting bar is sawed up into small pieces of $NPN$ material about 0.01 by 0.01 by 0.10 inch for transistor construction. The process can also be made to produce small pieces of $PNP$ material. The transistors manufactured by this process have a low collector capacitance and are used up to several megacycles.

The *meltback* process used for special transistor types is similar to the method of manufacturing rate-grown junction transistors. A bar of $N$-type germanium is cut into small pieces of the size mentioned above. The end of it is melted and refrozen quickly, and, by a doping method, a thin layer of $P$ material is produced within the $N$ material.

The capacitance between the emitter and the collector is a limiting factor in the high-frequency use of the transistor. Another limitation is the transit time for majority current carriers to flow through the base. On one hand, if the thickness of the base is reduced, the capacitance between the emitter and the collector increases. On the other hand, an increase in base thickness increases the transit time although it does decrease the capacitance. The objective in the design of high-frequency transistors is to find a way to escape from these simultaneous limitations.

The *diffused-alloy* junction transistor is one of the first successful attempts to circumvent these limitations. Holes are drilled into the base material which is $N$-type material in Fig. 5–1. Small pellets or *dots* of $P$-type germanium are placed in the holes. A short pulse of high current between the pellet and the base melts the contact surfaces, and they weld or fuse together. The application of heat is not sufficient to destroy the basic characteristic of the $N$ and the $P$ materials. This process is also applied to the manufacture of diffused-alloy $NPN$ transistors.

The separation between the emitter and the collector is reduced, reducing the transit time through the base. The capacitance between the emitter and the collector is actually decreased because, although the separation is reduced, the surface area of the pellets is much less than the surface area of the emitter and the collector in a cut bar transistor.

When we discussed the basic concepts of crystalline structures, we were very careful to state that the conditions concerned the center of the crystal and *not* the surfaces. The action of forces and energy levels at the surface is quite complex, but, for the purposes of this discussion, a simplified approach can be taken.

When $N$-type surfaces are exposed to air or to vacuum (Fig. 5–2a), a *surface-barrier layer* of electrons crowds the surface in a state of equilibrium. Just below the barrier layer is a "layer" of holes which has been attracted by the negative charge of the surface-barrier layer, but these holes do not combine with the surface electrons. A small contact can be made to this surface (Fig. 5–2b) without disturbing the barrier layer. In the *surface-barrier transistor*, indentations are made on the base $N$ material by an electrochemical etching process. The separation between the bottoms of the identations is very small. Electrodes serving as the emitter and collector are electroplated within the identations. A reverse bias on one electrode serving as the collector causes the surface-barrier layer to thicken. The other electrode is forward-biased to serve as the emitter. The emitter injects holes into the base, and these holes cause a neutralization of the surface barrier, allowing a collector current to flow to the extent of the neutralization of the surface barrier. This transistor has a lower capacitance and a shorter transit time than the diffused-alloy junction transistor, and it was developed specifically for high-frequency applications.

### Section 5–2  The Field-Effect Transistor

The *field-effect transistor* operates on very different principles from ordinary transistors. A block of $N$ material has two plates, one at each end. The plate that is positive is called the *drain D*, and the

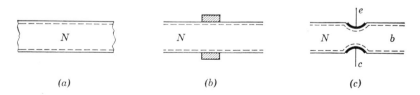

(a)          (b)          (c)

**Figure 5–2**  Surface-barrier transistors. (a) Barrier layers. (b) Barrier layer with small electrode plates. (c) With etched wells.

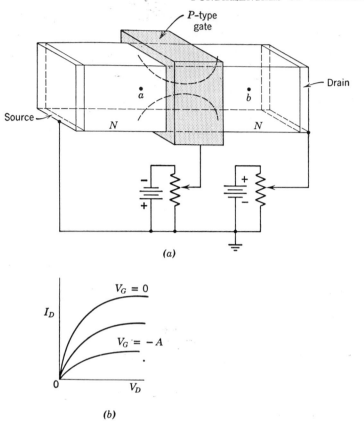

**Figure 5-3**  The field-effect transistor.  (*a*) Test circuit.  (*b*) Characteristic.

plate at the lower potential is called the *source S*.   A third plate, called
the *gate G*, encircles the $N$ material.   The gate is $P$ material and forms
a $P$–$N$ junction with the body of the transistor.

When a positive voltage $V_D$ is applied between the drain and the
source, a current $I_D$ flows.   If $a$ and $b$ are two points within the
$N$ material, by the ordinary concept of a voltage drop, $b$ is more positive than $a$ with respect to the source.   When the gate is reverse-
biased and is negative, there is a greater difference of potential between
the gate and point $b$ than between the gate and point $a$.   Since the
gate is reverse-biased, there is a greater tendency to inhibit flow of
current at $b$ than at $a$.   When the gate has reverse bias, it can be said
to deplete the region shown by the dotted lines of majority current
carriers.   When the drain voltage is zero, this depletion area is uni-

form around the region of the gate. When the drain is positive, the depletion effect is greater near $b$ than near $a$, causing the depletion area to shift toward the drain. If the gate is sufficiently negative, the dotted regions meet, and the drain current falls to zero. This condition is termed *pinchoff voltage*.

When the depletion region becomes large, the cross-sectional area of the drain-current flow becomes very small in the region between $a$ and $b$ and the capacitance between the source and the drain is reduced. The characteristic for this transistor is shown in Fig. 5–3$b$.

### Section 5–3   The Tetrode Transistor

The *tetrode transistor* is fundamentally an ordinary junction transistor with a second base connection $b_2$ added to the base portion of the unit. The transistor functions in the normal manner when the "tetrode" base voltage is zero. When a voltage of proper polarity is applied to the base $b_2$, the majority current carriers are forced down toward $b_1$. In this manner, the cross-sectional area of the base is materially decreased, reducing the interelement capacitance between the base and the collector. This reduction in the capacitance enables the transistor to be used at much higher frequencies than would otherwise be possible.

The displacement of the majority current carriers toward $b_1$ reduces the value of $\alpha$ for the transistor to approximately 0.8. This sacrifice in gain is offset by an improvement in the upper-frequency limits. These transistors can be used up to 100 or 200 Mc.

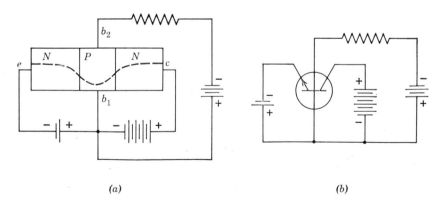

(a)                                                             (b)

**Figure 5–4**   The tetrode transistor.   (a) Physical construction.   (b) Schematic diagram.

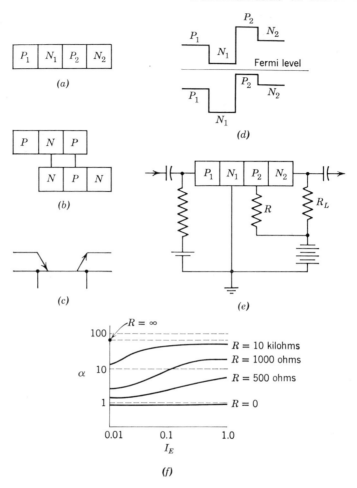

**Figure 5–5** The *PNPN* transistor. (*a*) Physical arrangement. (*b*) Two-transistor equivalent. (*c*) Symbol. (*d*) Energy-level diagram. (*e*) Circuit. (*f*) Characteristics.

## Section 5–4   Special Transistors

The *PNPN* (or *NPNP*) *transistor* is an arrangement that is used to obtain current gains greater than unity in junction transistors. The four sections of the *PNPN* can be considered the equivalent (Fig. 5–5*b*) of two junction transistors. $N_1$ serves simultaneously as the base of the first unit and the emitter of the second. By this reasoning, a current gain is immediately apparent.

In the symbol (Fig. 5–5c), two base leads are indicated. The emitter and collector leads are both indicated by arrows. Accordingly, the terminology *double-base transistor* and *double-emitter transistor* is used to describe the unit in the literature.

Figure 5–5d shows the energy-level diagram for this transistor. The third section $P_2$ causes a loop or *hook* in the energy levels. This unit is often called a *hook transistor*. The hook "traps" holes, and these trapped holes tend to neutralize the junction created between $P_2$ and $N_2$, allowing a large collector current to flow in the load. These trapped holes are the semiconductor equivalent of a space charge. The majority current carriers from the first equivalent transistor establish this space-charge effect of holes, and the collector current is effectively coming from this charge of holes.

When $R$ is zero in the circuit of Fig. 5–5e, the unit acts as an ordinary three-element junction transistor with a current gain less than unity. When $R$ is raised from zero, holes are allowed to accumulate in the hook, the junction between $P_2$ and $N_2$ becomes neutralized, and the current gain increases. The limit on current gain with no connection to $P_1$ is of the order of 50 to 100.

When a $PNP$ (or $NPN$) transistor is formed, the effect of the formation of barrier junction potentials *depletes* the adjacent region to the barrier of majority current carriers (Fig. 5–6a). When forward bias is applied to the emitter, this region of depletion decreases and a reverse bias on the collector increases the depletion region (Fig. 5–6b). The large depletion region around the base-to-collector barrier extends into the collector and increases the distance that the majority current carriers must travel in order to be effective. This increased distance produces a greater transit time and a consequent decrease in the upper operating-frequency limit. This limitation is characteristic of the junction transistor.

In order to gain an increased frequency response, an intrinsic region $I$ is added between the base and the collector (Fig. 5–6c). The transit time of current carriers in the intrinsic material is much shorter than in either $N$ or $P$ material because there are no retarding forces created by donor or acceptor atoms. These transistors are known as $PNIP$ (or $NPIN$) units.

The *drift transistor* is a special junction transistor which is equivalent to the $PNIP$ transistor in operation. In a $PNP$ transistor the base of $N$ material is specially processed. At the junction between the emitter and base, the $N$ material has a high conductivity, and it gradually changes until it is almost intrinsic material at the base-to-collector junction. The change in voltage gradient across this non-

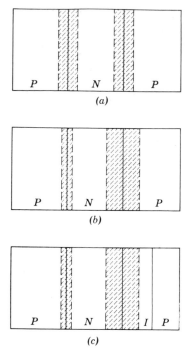

(a)

(b)

**Figure 5–6**  Effect of depletion regions.  (a) Without electrode voltages.  (b) With normal electrode biasing.  (c) The *PNIP* transistor.

(c)

uniform base causes the current carriers to travel faster through the base than they do across a uniform base and thus reduce transit time. The drift transistor is also manufactured in the *NPN* form.

When the emitter and the collector electrodes are manufactured by the process used for the surface-barrier transistor, the resulting transistor is called a *microetched diffused transistor*.

### Section 5–5  Special Diodes

The normal operation of a *P–N* junction is in region *aoz* of the characteristic (Fig. 5–7).  In diodes that are used as rectifiers, the forward characteristic *oa* produces the load current, and the reverse characteristic *oz* is the inverse voltage on the diode during the negative half of the voltage cycle.  The inverse voltage on rectifiers must be kept at a potential lower than *x* which is the Zener breakdown point.  *Zener diodes* are designed to allow circuit operation in the region between *x* and *y* without overheating.  The resistance between *o* and *x* is of the order of megohms, and the resistance between *x* and *y* is of the order of ohms.  The cross-over point *x* is the *breakdown potential* of the

Zener diode.   The change in voltage between $x$ and $y$ usually does not exceed 1%.   Zener diodes are available in many different combinations of breakdown voltage and maximum current ratings.

In Section 5–4 we showed that a depletion area at a junction (Fig. 5–6) can vary in accordance with the reverse voltage across the junction.   *Capacitance diodes* are designed to take advantage of this characteristic.   When the depletion region is large, the capacitance between the $P$ and the $N$ is small, and, when the depletion region is small, the capacitance is large.   For example, the characteristics of a typical diode show that, when the reverse bias is 5 volts, the capacitance is 10 $\mu\mu$f, and, when the reverse bias is 30 volts, the capacitance is 5 $\mu\mu$f.

The *double-based diode* or *unijunction transistor* (Fig. 5–8) has a small rod of $P$ material extending into the block of $N$ material which serves as a $P$–$N$ junction.   Two bases are welded to the $N$ block without creating new junctions.   The electrode $B1$ is the common return for the circuit.   When a positive voltage is applied to $B2$, there is a uniform potential drop to ground through the $N$ material which has a linear *interbase* resistance of several thousand ohms.   By a voltage-divider action, the emitter $E$ is located at a point in this potential drop which is $\eta V_{BB}$.   The coefficient $\eta$ is called the *intrinsic standoff ratio*. When the potential on the emitter is raised sufficiently to develop a forward bias, holes are injected into the base material.   These holes reduce the resistance of the $N$ material to current flow in the double-base circuit.   The characteristics of this unit show a negative-resistance effect which makes the device very useful in oscillator circuits.

**Figure 5–7**   Characteristic of the Zener diode.

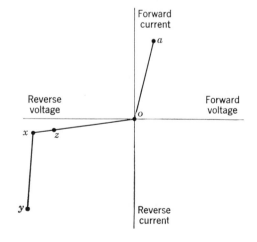

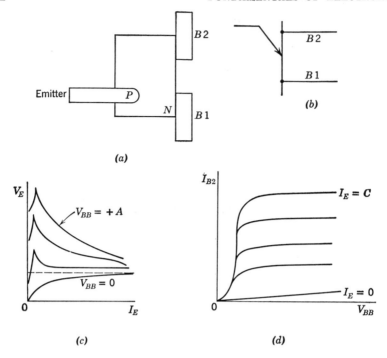

**Figure 5–8** Double-based diodes. (*a*) Physical structure. (*b*) Symbol. (*c*) and (*d*) Characteristics.

## Section 5–6   The Controlled Rectifier

A four-section silicon diode (Fig. 5–9a) can be used as a controlled rectifier in which the *gate* serves to control the main-anode current as the grid controls plate current in a thyratron.   Normal operation of this device is confined to the first quadrant of the characteristic; that is, the device is biased in the forward direction with the anode positive and cathode negative.   Under these conditions, junctions 1 and 3 (Fig. 5–9a) are biased in the forward direction, and junction 2 is reverse-biased.

When a positive voltage is applied to the gate, the injection of holes into the $P$ material neutralizes reverse junction 2, and a large current flows between the anode and the cathode.   The transfer point is called the *break-over* point.   $I_{bo}$ is the break-over current and $E_{bo}$ is the break-over voltage.   When break-over occurs, the gate loses control.   The minimum current that maintains this break-over condition is called the *holding current* $I_H$.

The gate can regain control over the main-anode current by any one of the following ways:

(a) Reduction of the anode voltage to zero.
(b) Reversal of the anode voltage (a negative anode potential).
(c) Reduction of the anode current below the holding value.

An application of this rectifier is shown in Fig. 5–9d. The operation of this circuit is left as an exercise.

These rectifiers are manufactured with current ratings up to 15 amperes and 150 amperes peak. The transfer time is of the order of one microsecond.

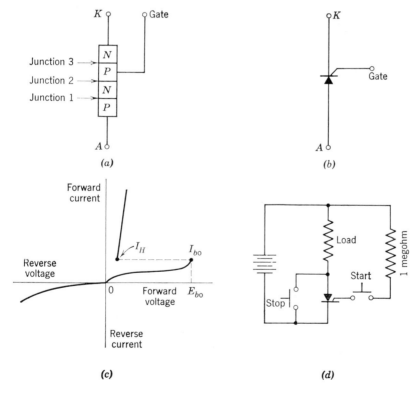

Figure 5–9 The controlled-diode rectifier. (a) Physical characteristics. (b) Symbol. (c) Characteristic. (d) Application.

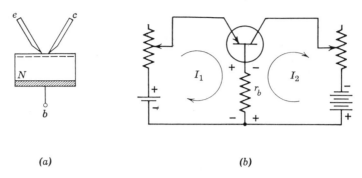

*(a)*                                              *(b)*

**Figure 5–10**   The point-contact transistor.   *(a)* Physical structure.   *(b)* Basic circuit.

## Section 5–7   The Point-Contact Transistor

A *point-contact transistor* is constructed by placing two sharp pointed electrodes which serve as *cat's whiskers* in contact with the surface of $N$ material.   The contact points are placed very close to each other.   We showed in Section 5–1 (Fig. 5–2$a$) that a surface barrier exists at the face of the $N$ material.   A positive voltage on the emitter injects holes into the $N$ material, and, since the collector electrode is very close physically, part of the potential barrier which is acting as a reverse barrier is neutralized.   Current flow between the collector and the base electrode is limited only by the number of surface-barrier electrons remaining and by the resistance of the collector circuit itself.   A small emitter current injects few holes, and a large emitter current injects many holes.   The collector current is dependent on the emitter current, but it is not limited to the value of the emitter current.   Large current gains can be obtained from this unit.

Actually, in the manufacture of the point-contact transistor, small areas of $P$ material are formed at the contact points of the cat's whiskers.   When the contact separation is small, there is a high capacitance between the emitter and the collector.   When the spacing is large, the control of the collector current by the emitter is poor.

In the circuit shown in Fig. 5–10$b$, the internal base resistance $r_b$ is given as an external resistance.   There are voltage drops in $r_b$ which are produced by $I_1$ and by $I_2$, but the polarities of these voltage drops are subtractive.   Since the current gain of the point-contact transistor is greater than unity, the value of $I_2 r_b$ is usually greater than $I_1 r_b$.   When $I_2 r_b$ exceeds $I_1 r_b$ by a certain amount (determined by the complex transistor analysis), the circuit becomes unstable and is not suitable for use as an amplifier. This condition of instability can be brought about in three ways:

1. Decreasing $R_1$.
2. Increasing $r_b$ (or a resistor in series with $r_b$).
3. Decreasing $R_2$.

The instability of the point-contact transistor has caused it to become almost obsolete, and it is used only in special applications. It is of interest since it was the first transistor.

#### . . . . Suggested References for Further Study

1. W. D. Bevitt, *Transistors Handbook*, Prentice-Hall, Inc., Englewood Cliffs, N. J., 1956.
2. D. DeWitt and A. L. Rossoff, *Transistor Electronics*, McGraw-Hill Book Co., New York, 1957.
3. L. P. Hunter, editor, *Handbook of Semiconductor Electronics*, McGraw-Hill Book Co., New York, 1956.
4. *General Electric Transistor Manual* 3rd ed., General Electric Co., Syracuse, N. Y., 1958.
5. Transistor Manufacturer's Data Sheets and Technical Literature.

#### . . . . QUESTIONS

1. Define or explain each of the following terms: (*a*) rate-grown, (*b*) meltback, (*c*) dot, (*d*) bar, (*e*) pinch-off, (*f*) hook, (*g*) interbase, (*h*) breakdown, (*i*) break-over, (*j*) holding current.
2. Explain how a diffused-alloy transistor is formed.
3. What is a surface-barrier layer?
4. Explain the operation of the field-effect transistor.
5. Show how a tetrode transistor reduces the emitter-to-collector capacitance.
6. Explain the operation of a double-emitter transistor.
7. What is meant by the depletion of majority current carriers?
8. What is the principle of operation of a Zener diode?
9. Explain the operation of a capacitance diode.
10. Show how current is controlled in a double-base diode.
11. Explain the operation of a controlled diode rectifier.
12. Show how the circuit given in Fig. 5–9d functions.
13. Show how current gain is established in the point-contact transistor.

# Auxiliary components
# in electronic circuits

•   •   •   •   •   •   •   •   •   •   •   •   •   •   •   •   •   •   • CHAPTER **6**

The study that is prerequisite or corequisite to the study of electronics is usually concerned with the theory of d-c and a-c circuit analysis. It is natural to expect that in these preliminary courses only a small amount of time is devoted to the various features of circuit elements which are designed to meet the specialized needs of the electronic application. It is the intent of this chapter, not to introduce the elements, but to point out certain available types and forms that are useful in vacuum-tube and transistor circuits. Resistors (Section 6–1), potentiometers (Section 6–2), inductances (Section 6–3), transformers (Section 6–4), capacitors (Section 6–5) and relays (Section 6–6) are considered in this chapter.

## Section 6–1  Resistors

Resistors are used freely in electronic circuits to serve as specific current paths and to serve as circuit elements which either provide a means of reducing a voltage or provide a means of securing a specific voltage drop. The calculation of resistance from the various forms of Ohm's law is very familiar from d-c and a-c circuit analysis. In electronics, the determination of the power rating of a resistor is just as important as the calculation of the resistance value itself. A specification for a resistor is meaningless and incomplete if this power rating in watts is not included. Let us assume that the rating for a resistor is 3.65 watts by calculation. The nearest available com-

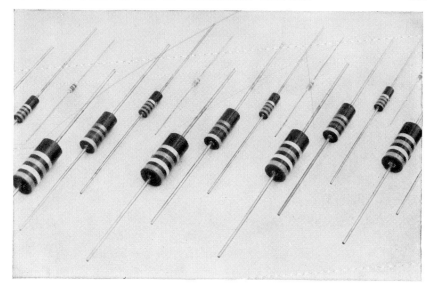

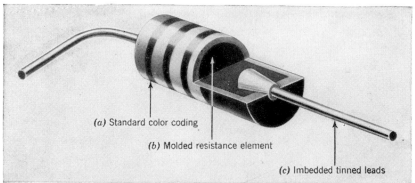

*(a)* Standard color coding

*(b)* Molded resistance element

*(c)* Imbedded tinned leads

**Figure 6–1** Typical carbon resistors. (*Courtesy Allen-Bradley Co.*)

mercial resistor having the necessary power rating is, say, 5 watts. The significance of a 5-watt rating is that this unit can safely dissipate 5 watts if it is in free space with an unrestricted air circulation. Also, the temperature of the "cooling" air cannot exceed that specified by the manufacturer. When this resistor is wired into the underside of a chassis, the power rating is *derated* so that the surface temperature of the resistor does not exceed its maximum permissible value. Derating factors of five or ten are necessary under extreme conditions.

In most applications, fixed carbon resistors (Fig. 6–1) are suitable. A mixture of carbon in a binder is formed into a short rod. Con-

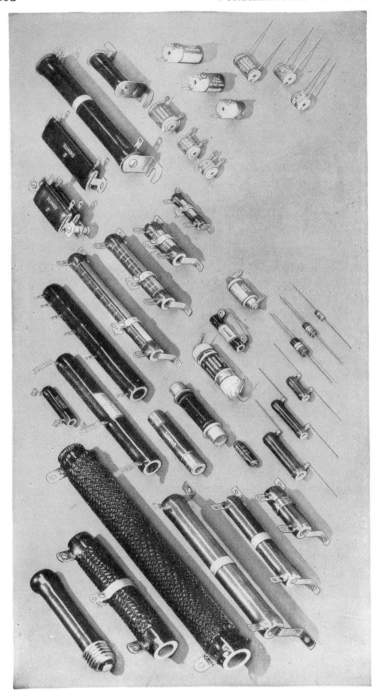

**Figure 6–2** Typical wire-wound resistors. *(Courtesy Ohmite Manufacturing Co., Skokie, Ill.)*

nection pigtails are placed on the ends of the resistance element. A ceramic form encases the carbon element to keep it protected from humidity and from mechanical damage. The units are made in several sizes capable of dissipating 2 watts, 1 watt, $\frac{1}{2}$ watt or $\frac{1}{4}$ watt. The resistance values, which depend on the carbon mixture, range from a fraction of an ohm to about 22 megohms. Special forms of deposited carbon on glass extend this range to much higher values.

Although carbon has a negative temperature coefficient, the properties of the resistance element have been developed to produce a substantially constant value of resistance over normal temperature variations extending from about $-40°$ C to $+80°$ C. The carbon resistor has the very important property of being noninductive. This means that, when a carbon resistor is used in a high-frequency circuit, its impedance effectively does not change with frequency.

Carbon resistors are normally not available for handling powers in excess of 2 watts. Wire-wound resistors are used for these higher powers. The wire-wound resistor is made from one of several forms of alloy resistance wire such as Nichrome. The wire is coiled on a hollow ceramic tube (Fig. 6–2), and lugs are placed at each end. The whole unit is covered with a heat-resistant ceramic compound and baked. Standoff mounting brackets must be used with the larger units to prevent contact of the resistor with the chassis or with other circuit components. These resistors are manufactured with power-handling capacities from 4 or 5 watts to several hundred watts.

As can be seen from Fig. 6–2, these units are available in two forms in addition to the totally enclosed element. Some have additional fixed lugs which serve as taps. On others the lug is adjustable and can be moved along the length of the resistor to provide taps where needed.

Wire-wound resistors are normally inductive and are used in d-c circuits where the inductance of a great many turns has no effect. If they are used in high-frequency circuits, the inductance of the turns and the capacitance between turns makes the calculation of the net impedance of the unit very complex.

### Section 6–2    Potentiometers

A *rheostat* is a continuously variable two-terminal resistance, and a *potentiometer* is a continuously variable three-terminal resistance. A potentiometer can be used as a rheostat, but a rheostat cannot be used as a potentiometer. The circuit connections of these units are shown in Fig. 6-3. The rheostat serves as a device to control and limit the

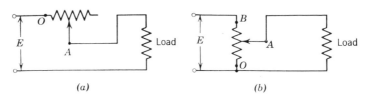

*(a)*                    *(b)*

**Figure 6–3**  Circuits using continuously variable resistors.  (*a*)  Rheostat circuit.
(*b*)  Potentiometer circuit.

load current.  As the slider is moved toward $O$, the resistance is *cut
out*, and the load current increases.  As an example, consider a
rheostat that is 100 ohms total resistance and has a power rating of
100 watts.  When the entire resistance is in the circuit, 100 ohms, it
has a current rating of one ampere.  If the rheostat is made of uniform
wire, the wire cannot handle more than one ampere even though the
slider is set so that there is only one ohm between $O$ and $A$.  In the
potentiometer circuit, the load current and load voltage increase as
the slider is moved from $O$ toward $B$.  In this circuit, there is a current
flow through the potentiometer at all times.  This shunting current
reduces the amount of current that may be available for the load.
For example, if a 100-ohm 100-watt potentiometer is used across a
100-volt source, *any* current taken by the load overloads the potentiometer.  In this case, the potentiometer may only be used to serve
as a variable-voltage source which does not supply load current.  In
general a rheostat serves to control current within a certain range,
whereas a potentiometer is generally used as a voltage divider,
giving a range of voltages from zero to maximum, the applied
voltage.

In physics, a potentiometer is generally considered as a long resistance wire across which a voltage is placed.  A sliding tap picks off a
proportional part of this voltage measured from the tap to the common
end.

A wire-wound potentiometer or rheostat (Fig. 6–4) is manufactured
to handle a high-power dissipation ranging from several watts to several hundred watts.  As the resistance is cut out in a rheostat, the load
current increases.  In order to handle larger currents at low-resistance
settings, the unit is often made with different-size wire, so that, as
the resistance of the rheostat is reduced, a larger-gage wire section is
used for the larger currents.

For low-power ratings up to 2 or 4 watts and for high values of
resistance which cannot be obtained satisfactorily with a wire-wound

unit, a carbon resistance element is used (Fig. 6–5). The carbon control also has the advantage of being noninductive. These potentiometers are available with several *tapers*. The resistance between one end terminal and the wiper arm varies directly with rotation in a *linear-taper* potentiometer. As an example of a *nonlinear* taper, a potentiometer which has a total resistance of one megohm at full rotation has a resistance of 500,000 ohms at three-fourths rotation, 250,000 ohms at one-half rotation, and 125,000 ohms at one-fourth rotation. Representative available tapers are illustrated in Fig. 6–5. The carbon potentiometer is usually adapted so that a power line switch may be mounted on the back of the control. An example is the volume control on a radio receiver which is used also as an on–off switch.

Conventional practice requires that the rheostat or potentiometer be connected in a circuit so that a clockwise rotation produces an *increase* in whatever is being controlled and a counterclockwise rotation produces a *decrease*.

Wire-wound potentiometers can be made with a very high precision. They also are available with high-power ratings and can be made with very low-resistance values. Tapered wire-wound units are expensive

**Figure 6–4** Wire-wound potentiometer. (*Courtesy Ohmite Manufacturing Co., Skokie, Ill.*)

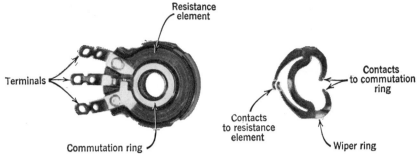

Terminals

Resistance element

Commutation ring

Contacts to resistance element

Contacts to commutation ring

Wiper ring

(a) Internal construction of the type Q control.

whereas tapers are obtained easily in the carbon type. Carbon potentiometers are available only with low-power ratings, but they can be manufactured to resistance values of the order of megohms. The carbon control has a shorter life than the wire-wound unit since the carbon resistance surface tends to wear off when subject to the scraping action of the contact wiper arm. When this happens, small

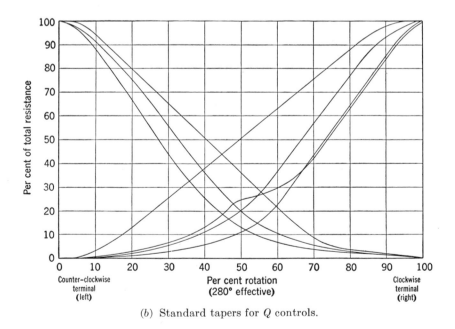

(b) Standard tapers for Q controls.

**Figure 6–5**  Carbon potentiometer and tapers. (*Courtesy International Resistance Co.*)

arcs form in the carbon element and the control becomes noisy.  This effect is quite noticeable in a worn volume control in a radio receiver.

### Section 6-3   Inductance

The fundamental *definition* of inductance is given by

$$L = \frac{N\phi}{I} 10^{-8} \tag{6-1}$$

where $N$ is the number of turns, $\phi$ is the lines of flux, and $I$ is the current.

This definition of inductance can be expressed in words as *flux linkages per ampere*.  The phenomenon of a changing current in a coil producing an emf is given in equation form by Lenz's law:

$$e = L \frac{di}{dt} = L \frac{\Delta I}{\Delta T} \tag{6-2}$$

If the inductance is of such value that a current change of one ampere in one second produces an emf of one volt, the unit of inductance is one henry.  From magnetic-circuit analysis, the magnetic equivalent of Ohm's law states that the flux is the magnetomotive force divided by the reluctance:

$$\phi = \frac{\mathcal{F}}{\mathcal{R}} \tag{6-3a}$$

The magnetomotive force is

$$\mathcal{F} = 0.4\pi N I \tag{6-3b}$$

and the reluctance of the magnetic path is

$$\mathcal{R} = \frac{l}{\mu A} \tag{6-3c}$$

where $l$ is the length of the magnetic path, $A$ is the cross-sectional area of the magnetic circuit, and $\mu$ is the permeability.  It should be pointed out that this value of reluctance $\mathcal{R}$ is an equivalent reluctance for the whole magnetic circuit and that the actual calculation of the reluctance for a particular coil can be a very complex procedure.

Substituting these values of $\mathcal{F}$ and $\mathcal{R}$ in Eq. 6–3a, we have

$$\phi = \frac{0.4\pi N I}{(l/\mu A)} = \frac{0.4\pi N I \mu A}{l}$$

and, using this expression for $\phi$ in Eq. 6-1, we find

$$L = \frac{N\phi}{I} \, 10^{-8}$$

$$L = \frac{N}{I} \left( \frac{0.4\pi N I \mu A}{l} \right) 10^{-8}$$

$$L = \frac{0.4\pi N^2 A}{l} \, \mu 10^{-8} = k\mu N^2$$

Several general considerations can be formed from this last relation. For a coil in which the permeability is unity, such as an air-core coil, the inductance is strictly a geometric concept dependent on the number of turns and the physical design. A handbook gives formulas for the value of inductance for many types of coils as a function of the turns and the dimensions. If the length of a solenoidal coil is increased without changing the number of turns, the inductance decreases. A larger cross section results in a larger value of inductance than a coil

**Figure 6-6**  Typical magnetic tuning cores.  (*Courtesy Arnold Engineering Co.*)

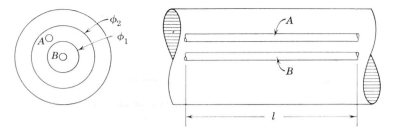

**Figure 6–7** Conditions in a wire showing skin effect.

of small cross section since the inductance is directly proportional to $A$. The inductance of a coil with a magnetic core is proportional to the permeability of the magnetic path.

When a magnetic material is introduced into the core of a coil, the flux is increased, and the value of inductance is increased. Since the resonant frequency of a tuned circuit is determined by the relation

$$f_0 = \frac{1}{2\pi \sqrt{LC}}$$

an increased inductance lowers the resonant frequency. Adjustable magnetic cores are manufactured (Fig. 6–6) which can be lowered into or removed from a coil to change the permeability of the coil, thus changing its resonant frequency. These cores, called *tuning cores*, are manufactured of a powdered iron pressed in a binder to give the mixture a mechanical strength and stability. These cores or *slugs* can be cast or machined to provide threads and slots for adjustment by a plastic screwdriver called an *alignment tool*.

The effect of a nonmagnetic metallic tuning core, such as brass or aluminum, is to act as a short-circuited turn on the secondary winding of a transformer (Section 12–1). The short-circuited turn reduces the inductance of the coil. Thus, the introduction of a brass core into a coil, by reducing the inductance, *increases* the resonant frequency of a tuned circuit in contrast to the powdered iron core which *decreases* the resonant frequency.

A very elemental application of the definition of inductance is its use in developing the explanation for *skin effect*. Let us consider a conductor (Fig. 6–7) in which the *current density* throughout the cross section is uniform. Now consider two filaments or threads extending axially along the wire of equal cross section. One of these threads of the conductor $B$ is located near the center of the wire, and the other $A$

is located nearer the outside of the conductor. The flux $\phi_1$ circles or links $B$ but does not link $A$. The flux $\phi_2$ circles around and links both $A$ and $B$. Since this wire is in a complete electric circuit carrying current, we consider the circuit to be one turn. Then the flux linkages about $B$ are greater than the flux linkages about $A$, or

$$N\phi_B > N\phi_A$$

The self-inductances of $B$ and $A$ from Eq. 6–1 are

$$L_B = \frac{N\phi_B}{I_B} 10^{-8} \quad \text{and} \quad L_A = \frac{N\phi_A}{I_A} 10^{-8}$$

In the original premise, we specified that the current density is uniform over the conductor and that the cross-sectional areas of $A$ and $B$ are equal. Then the current in $A$ equals the current in $B$. Then the inductance of $B$ is greater than the inductance of $A$ or

$$L_B > L_A$$

In an a-c circuit for a finite length $l$ we have

$$Z_A = R + j\omega L_A$$

and $$Z_B = R + j\omega L_B$$

As $L_B$ is greater than $L_A$,

$$Z_B > Z_A$$

Since we have specified equal current through $A$ and $B$, the voltage drop along $B$ is greater than the voltage drop along $A$ for the same length of conductor. This creates an impossible situation, and we must conclude that the voltage drops *must* be equal. Therefore, $I_A$ cannot equal $I_B$. The current distribution cannot be uniform over the cross section of the conductor, but the current density must be greater on the surface than within the wire. This phenomenon is called *skin effect* since the current in an a-c circuit tends to travel toward the outside surface of the conductor.

As the frequency increases, this effect is more pronounced. At high frequencies it is not necessary to have a solid conductor. The conductor can be a hollow tube. At extremely high frequencies, the current is confined to the polished plating on the surface of the base material.

Let us assume that the resistances of $A$ and $B$ are each 2 ohms and that, since a direct current flows in the wire, the current is 3 amperes in $A$ and 3 amperes in $B$. Since the effect of inductance on a steady-state current flow is zero, there is no skin effect. The power loss in $A$, by the relation $I^2R$, is 18 watts and in $B$ is 18 watts, or a total of 36 watts. The total current is 6 amperes, and the equivalent resistance of $A$ and $B$ in parallel is 1 ohm. Now, assume that by the uneven current distribution caused by skin effect, there is an alternating current in $A$ of 4 amperes and in $B$ of 2 amperes. The power loss in $A$ is $4^2 \times 2$ or 32 watts and the power loss in $B$ is $2^2 \times 2$ or 8 watts. The total loss for the a-c condition is 40 watts whereas the same current, 6 amperes, caused a loss of only 36 watts without regard to skin effect. This means that there is an *apparent* rise in the resistance of the conductor. This new equivalent resistance is called the *a-c effective resistance*. In the numerical example, the a-c resistance is $40/6^2$ or 1.11 ohm, whereas the d-c resistance is 1 ohm.

The remedy to minimize skin-effect losses is to provide as great a surface area as possible. A special stranded wire, *litz wire*, is often used in which each strand is insulated from the other. The strands are properly *transposed* so that each wire is on the outside and in each strand position for the same length as each of the other strands. Stranded wire usually consists of either three strands or seven strands to maintain a geometric symmetry.

The figure of merit or $Q$ of a coil is defined as the ratio of the inductive reactance to the effective resistance:

$$Q = \frac{2\pi fL}{R} = \frac{X_L}{R} \tag{6-4}$$

The reactance of the coil is directly proportional to the frequency, and the skin effect, as we have explained, depends on the frequency. If the value of the reactance increases faster than the effective resistance, the $Q$ increases with an increase in frequency, curve $a$ in Fig. 6-8. If the increase in reactance is in the same proportion as the

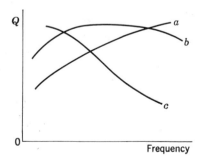

**Figure 6–8**  Variation of $Q$ with frequency.

increase in the effective resistance, the $Q$ of the coil is fixed over a wide range in frequency, curve $b$. There is a capacitance between turns of a coil since the turns are near each other. This capacitive action tends to cancel part of the inductive reactance of the coil, and this canceling effect increases with an increase in frequency. Thus, the $Q$ of the coil decreases (curve $c$) with an increase in frequency when this capacitive shunting effect is appreciable. The exact curve of variation of the $Q$ of a coil with frequency is a function of the size of the wire and the geometric design of the coil. Again, the function of the handbook is to provide the necessary equations for the calculation of the $Q$ of a particular coil at different frequencies.

In order to keep the capacitance between the turns as low as possible, the turns of a coil that is layer-wound cannot be parallel. The winding method is to weave the wire back and forth from side to side as the turns are added in a specific pattern. The characteristic pattern of this *universal winding* can be seen in Fig. 6–9.

Coils with complete steel cores are used to provide high values of inductance of several or many henrys. The steel-core inductor is usually called a *choke*. Two forms of chokes are used in electronic applications. The *audio choke* is used in low-frequency electronic circuits as a circuit element, and a *filter choke* is used in power-supply circuits to aid in the conversion of a-c power into d-c power to operate other electronic circuits.

The saturation curve for a choke, shown in Fig. 6–10, is the relation between the current $I$ in a choke and the flux $\phi$ which this current produces. As the current increases, the core saturates, and the increase in $\phi$ is small compared to the increase in $I$. If the core did not saturate, the curve would rise from 0 to $B'$. Since the core

**Figure 6–9**   Air core choke.

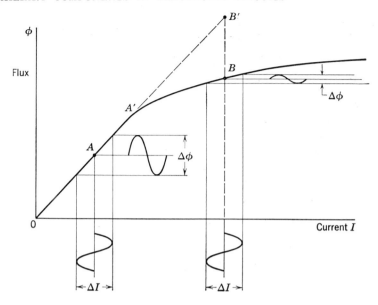

**Figure 6-10**    The saturation curve for a choke.

saturates, the curve starts to bend at the *knee* of the curve $A'$, and the maximum possible flux is only slightly greater than the flux at $B$.

The change of flux at $A$ for a given current change $\Delta I$ is greater than the change of flux at $B$ for the same incremental current change. By Eq. 6–1, the inductance at $B$ is less than the inductance at $A$. The operating point, $A$ or $B$, is established by the amount of fixed direct current through the choke. Thus, in order to specify the inductance of a choke, the value of the direct operating current at which the inductance is measured must be specified.

### Section 6–4    Transformers

The electrical analysis of a steel-core transformer is considered in detail in Section 12–1 through Section 12–4, and the air-core transformer in Section 7–4 through Section 7–6. The ratings for power transformers used in electronic circuits are specified in terms of the voltage and current ratings for each secondary winding. The voltage rating of the primary winding is also given. Volt-ampere ratings are also specified for many electronic transformers. Power transformers are usually designed for a line frequency of 50 to 60 cycles. Aircraft

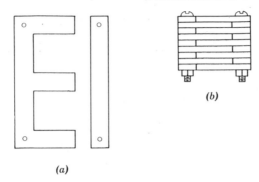

(a)

(b)

**Figure 6–11** Typical transformer cores. (a) Typical *E–I* lamination. (b) Method of stacking laminations.

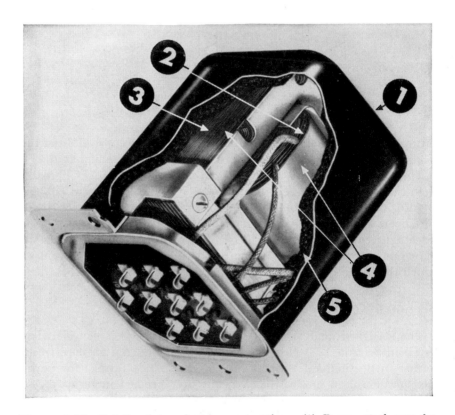

**Figure 6–12** Details of transformer construction. (1) Drawn steel case for magnetic and electrostatic shielding. (2) Coil structure. (3) Laminations. (4) Core and coil are vacuum-impregnated with varnish. (5) Moisture-resistant compound. (*Courtesy Chicago Standard Transformer Co.*)

equipment operates on 400 to 2400 cycles, and special transformers are available for these frequencies.

The core of a power transformer is formed by stacking insulated laminations (Fig. 6-11) in the same fashion as the core for a choke coil. Alternate laminations are reversed in order to keep the effect of the air gap at a minimum. The laminations are stamped from special transformer steels.

A copper electrostatic shield serving as a Faraday screen is often placed between the primary and the secondary windings. This shield is a full turn of a copper sheet. The ends of the sheet overlap, but they are separated from each other by insulation to prevent the shield from acting as a short-circuited turn. A tab from this sheet extends and is clamped between the laminations to ground the shield. The use of the shield prevents energy transfer from the primary to the secondary winding by capacitive coupling. A cut-away view of a transformer showing construction details is shown in Fig. 6-12.

### Section 6-5  Capacitance

A capacitor is formed when two parallel surfaces are separated by a dielectric. The basic equation for computing the value of the capacitance is

$$C = \frac{0.2448\kappa S}{t} \, \mu\mu f \tag{6-5}$$

where $S$ is the total parallel surface area in square inches, $\kappa$ is the dielectric constant of the separating medium, and $t$ is the distance between the active surfaces in inches.

The ideal capacitor has a perfect dielectric which has no losses. Actually, any dielectric indicates a measureable power loss if the applied a-c frequency is increased sufficiently. When a capacitor is measured on an a-c bridge, the result of the test gives the values for a series circuit (Fig. 6-13b). Some bridges measure susceptance and conductance, resulting in equivalent parallel arrangements. In many circuit calculations it is necessary to have an equivalent circuit which shows the resistance in parallel with the capacitance (Fig. 6-13c). When a capacitor is checked for leakage on an ohmmeter, the measurement of the ohms is a parallel resistance and not a series resistance. In order to determine the conversion between the series resistance and the parallel resistance, it is assumed that the power factor and the power losses of the capacitor are small.

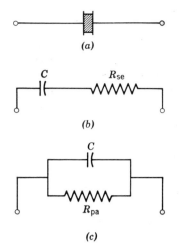

(a)

(b)

(c)

**Figure 6–13** Equivalent circuit of a capacitor. (a) Capacitor with losses. (b) Series equivalent circuit. (c) Parallel equivalent circuit.

In the series circuit, if the power factor is less than 10%, the current produced by an applied voltage $E$ is

$$I = \frac{E}{X_C}$$

The power dissipation in the series resistance is

$$P_{se} = I^2 R_{se} = \frac{E^2}{X_C^2} R_{se}$$

The power dissipation in the parallel equivalent circuit is determined directly by the applied voltage $E$ and the parallel resistance $R_{pa}$:

$$P_{pa} = \frac{E^2}{R_{pa}}$$

If these two circuits are to be equivalent, the powers are equal

$$P_{se} = P_{pa}$$

$$\frac{E^2}{X_C^2} R_{se} = \frac{E^2}{R_{pa}}$$

$$R_{pa} R_{se} = X_C^2 = \frac{1}{(2\pi f C)^2}$$

$$R_{pa} = \frac{X_C^2}{R_{se}} \tag{6–6a}$$

$$R_{se} = \frac{X_C^2}{R_{pa}} \tag{6–6b}$$

It is evident from Eq. 6–6 that a large parallel resistance is equivalent to a small series resistance. In an ideal capacitor, the parallel resistance is infinite and the series resistance is zero.

The dielectric used in a capacitor must have low losses and a high-voltage breakdown rating. The voltage breakdown rating is called the *dielectric strength* and is usually measured in volts per mil (0.001 in.) thickness. Dielectrics that are commonly used in commercial capacitors are mica, ceramic material such as titanium dioxide, paper, aluminum oxide, and air.

Sheets of metal foil separated by strips of mica form *mica capacitors*. The capacitor is enclosed in a plastic housing which keeps the unit both mechanically rigid and waterproof. Mica has very excellent characteristics at high frequencies and is used in large capacitors only when the increased cost is justified by the need of a very low power factor. Usually micas are manufactured in sizes less than 0.01 μfd.

The *ceramic capacitor* is manufactured by depositing directly on each side of the ceramic dielectric silver coatings which serve as the plates.

**Figure 6–14**  Typical fixed capacitors.  (*Courtesy Cornell Dubilier Electric Corp.*)

The advantage of a ceramic dielectric is that the substance has a very high dielectric constant which can be as great as 500 or 600. The dielectric constant of mica is 6 or 7. By using ceramic dielectrics instead of mica, it is possible to reduce the required plate area by a factor of about 100 for the same capacitance value. These ceramic capacitors are very popular because of their small size.

The paper capacitor is manufactured by rolling long narrow sheets of alternate aluminum foil and wax-impregnated paper into compact rolls. The completed unit is sealed to moisture-proof the capacitor. The aluminum sheet which is on the outside should be connected to the lower a-c potential and the inside sheet to the higher a-c potential for good shielding qualities. The lead which is connected to the outside foil is marked "outside foil" or "ground." Paper capacitors are often enclosed in a metal can which is filled with oil. The oil improves the breakdown characteristic of the dielectric.

A special capacitor which can only be used on a unidirectional potential is called an *electrolytic* capacitor. An aluminum electrode serves as the positive plate, and an alkaline electrolyte serves as the negative plate. The dielectric is an aluminum oxide film formed on the surface of the aluminum. This film is extremely thin, and, from Eq. 6–5, the capacitance per unit volume is very high. Often the surface of the aluminum is *etched* to produce corrugations which further increase the working area of the capacitor. The electrolytic has an inherent high leakage current and cannot be used in an application in which a low power factor is required. When the applied voltage on an electrolytic is reversed, its resistance drops toward zero and short-circuits the circuit to which it is connected. The electrolytic capacitor does not function at high frequencies. As a result, the primary application of the electrolytic is to maintain a pure direct voltage such as a bypass capacitor or as a power-supply filter capacitor.

*Air-dielectric capacitors* (Fig. 6–15) are used as tuning capacitances. The capacitance of the air-dielectric units can be varied either by changing the meshing areas of the plates or by changing the spacing between the plates. The *tuning capacitor* is varied by rotating the *rotor* section. The rotor is grounded to the frame through the shaft and the bearings. The *stator* plates are insulated from the frame.

Since air has a dielectric constant of unity and the spacing between the plates is greater than is found in a capacitor in which the dielectric is a thin sheet of mica, the capacitance per unit volume for the variable is less than for other forms. The rating of the variable capacitor is given in terms of both its maximum capacitance and its minimum

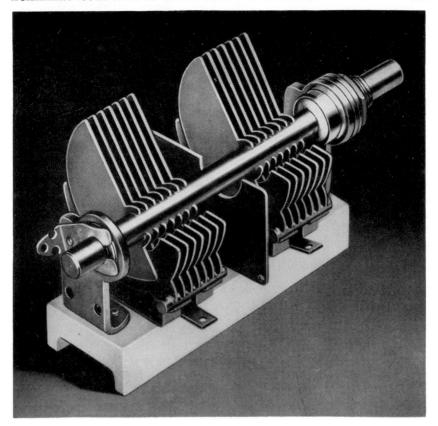

**Figure 6–15** Typical air-dielectric variable capacitor. (*Courtesy Hammarlund Manufacturing Co.*)

capacitance. Small two- or three-plate capacitors are approximately 3 to 15 μμf, whereas larger units of about 30 to 40 plates have correspondingly higher values of capacitance, for example 30 to 350 μμf.

A *trimmer* or *padder* capacitor is usually made of metal plates separated by a mica dielectric. The capacitance is varied by changing the plate separation by adjusting a machine screw which compresses the plates together. These capacitors are small, usually introducing not more than 150 μμf and often only about 20 μμf into the circuit. They are usually used in parallel with variable capacitors or placed in parallel with coils to allow the circuit to be adjusted to resonance at a fixed frequency.

## Section 6-6   Relays

A relay is a device used to control a circuit operation by energizing a coil and performing a mechanical operation. The basic relay (Fig. 6–16) consists of an energizing coil, a magnetic core, an armature, and a set of contacts. When sufficient current flows through the coil, the magnetic flux becomes strong enough to overcome the force of the spring and to attract the armature down to the magnetic core and to operate the contacts. The contact points are made of tungsten, silver, or platinum to prevent pitting. When a pair of contacts closes, a wiping action is required to remove the oxidation or the pitting which takes place on the contact surfaces when a circuit carrying current is broken. When a circuit is broken, an arc occurs between the points. This arc or spark ionizes the air in the vicinity of the spark. When a d-c circuit is broken, the separation of the points must be sufficient to prevent an arc discharge between the points. When an a-c circuit is broken, the arc is extinguished, normally, when the alternating voltage passes through zero. Thus a contact has a higher alternating current and voltage rating than for a direct current. For example, a particular relay contact is rated for 5 amperes alternating current but only two amperes direct current.

The arrangement of the contacts is a mechanical problem. In a simple relay, the actuated relay opens or closes a pair of contacts. Relays used in telephone circuits often have a great many contacts operating as many as 20 circuits. In a relay with multiple contacts,

**Figure 6–16**   D-c relay.   (*Courtesy C. P. Clare & Co.*)

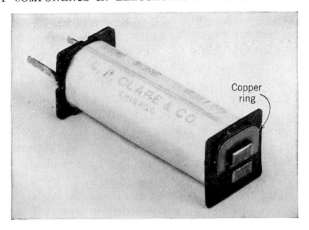

**Figure 6-17**   A-c relay coil assembly.   (*Courtesy C. P. Clare & Co.*)

a set of contacts may close *before* another set opens.   The arrangement can be, alternatively, that one circuit closes *after* the other set opens. Obviously, an infinite variety of contact combinations can be made.

When a relay armature is open and the coil is de-energized, the air-gap is large.   Let us assume that a coil current of 60 ma is required to develop sufficient flux to close the relay.   When the armature of the relay comes in contact with the core of the coil, the air gap is at a minimum, and a much greater flux passes through the magnetic circuit, assuming there is no saturation.   When the current in the coil is reduced toward zero, at some particular value of current the relay opens.   The value of release current is much less than 60 ma, say 20 ma, because of the reduced air gap.

The a-c operated relay (Fig. 6-17) is quite similar in construction to the d-c relay.   If a d-c relay is used on alternating current, at the instant that the flux wave passes through zero the armature releases, and then is pulled back to the coil when the flux increases on the next half-cycle.   This causes a loud *chattering*.   An a-c relay must provide a means of preventing the flux from falling completely to zero.   A copper ring or *shaded pole* is part of the end of the magnetic core. This short-circuited turn causes an inductively lagging current to flow in the turn.   The flux from this phase-displaced current is about 120° behind the main flux, and it is not zero when the main flux is zero. Thus, the armature does not release, and chattering is prevented.

The time-delay relay (Fig. 6-18) has a large copper slug in the form of a cylinder around the magnetic core.   The very large cross section of the copper provides a very high $Q$ for its inductance. When the relay coil is connected to a power source, the flux through the magnetic core rises from $O$ to $A$ to $B$. The relay operates at $A$, and the armature moves in to decrease the reluctance of the magnetic path. When the coil is de-energized at the time $C$, the flux through the magnetic path is maintained by the induced current in the copper slug. The relay remains closed until this flux decays to the dropout point $D$. The time interval between $C$ and $D$ represents the time-delay action of the relay. The physical location of the slug on the relay can vary this action and cause the relay to be slow to close, slow to open, or just slow.

A common variation in relay construction is the relay that can operate on direct but not on alternating current (Fig. 6–19). The relay coil has two windings, $L_A$ and $L_B$. The winding $L_A$ is energized from a control-voltage source $E$, and the winding $L_B$ is short-circuited. When the control voltage is alternating, $L_B$ creates the condition of a

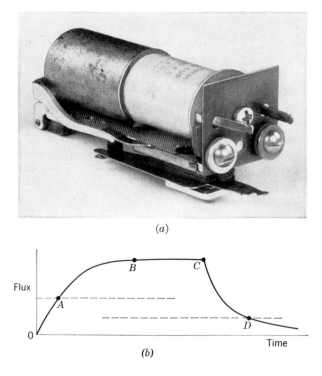

(a)

(b)

**Figure 6–18**  Time-delay relay.  (a) Typical relay.  (b) Operating characteristic.  (*Courtesy C. P. Clare & Co.*)

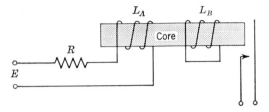

**Figure 6–19**   Relay operating on direct current but not on alternating current.

short-circuited transformer, and, since $R$ limits the current, the flux in the core is at a low value, and the relay does not operate.   On direct current, the only action of $L_B$ is a time delay, and the flux in the core does build up to the necessary value to operate the relay. A simple application is the remote-control whistle in a model train. The driving motor of the locomotive operates on either alternating or direct current.   In order to blow the whistle, d-c energy is supplied to the track by switching at the control box from normal a-c operation over to half-wave rectification.

Time-delay relays are extensively used in telephone-dial switching circuits.

**. . . . Suggested References for Further Study**

1. H. Henney and C. Walsh, *Electronic Components Handbook*, McGraw-Hill Book Co., New York, 1957.
2. F. E. Terman, *Radio Engineer's Handbook, Section 2*, McGraw-Hill Book Co., New York, 1943.
3. F. Langford-Smith, *Radiotron Designer's Handbook*, 4th ed., Chapters 5, 9, 10, and 11, RCA, Harrison, N. J., 1953.
4. J. F. Blackburn, editor, *Components Handbook*, Vol. 17, Radiation Laboratories Series, McGraw-Hill Book Co., New York, 1949.

**. . . . QUESTIONS**

1. Define or explain each of the following terms: (*a*) derating, (*b*) taper, (*c*) magnetomotive force, (*d*) reluctance, (*e*) permeability, (*f*) transposed, (*g*) lamination, (*h*) outside foil, (*i*) trimmer, (*j*) chattering.

2. Why is it necessary to determine the power rating of a resistor?

3. Why is a carbon resistor noninductive?

4. Describe the method of obtaining tapers on rheostats and on carbon potentiometers.

5. Define inductance by both words and formula.

6. How does inductance vary with permeability and with turns?

7. What is the permeability of copper? Of glass? Of brass? Of wood? Of air?

8. Explain how an inductance is changed by means of a magnetic tuning core. By a brass tuning core.

9. Describe the cause and result of skin effect.

10. What is a universal winding?

11. Define $Q$.

12. Explain why, for a particular coil, the $Q$ may decrease with an increase in operating frequency?

13. Explain how a direct operating current can reduce the inductance of a choke.

14. How are multiple windings on a transformer distinguished from each other?

15. Why is an electrostatic shield used in a power transformer?

16. In Fig. 6–14, point out the different types of capacitors.

17. Distinguish between *dielectric* and *dielectric strength*.

18. Describe the operation and characteristics of an electrolytic capacitor.

19. Differentiate between the rotor and the stator of a variable capacitor.

20. Name the parts of a relay.

21. Why are different d-c and a-c ratings given to a particular set of relay contacts?

22. Why does a shaded pole stop chattering on an a-c relay?

23. Describe the operation in detail of a time-delay relay.

24. Explain the operation of a relay which functions on a direct current but not on an alternating current.


## . . . . PROBLEMS

1. The voltage across a 39-ohm resistor is 15 volts. Using a derating factor of 3, what is the power rating of the resistor?

2. A 15,000-ohm bleeder resistor is placed across 300 volts. Using a derating factor of $2\frac{1}{2}$, what is the power rating of the unit? What is the nearest commercial size?

3. A 10,000-ohm 100-watt rheostat is set at 3600 ohms in a particular application. What is the maximum voltage that can be placed across the terminals?

4. A 15,000-ohm 70-watt potentiometer is used in a voltage-divider circuit. The supply voltage is 80 volts. What is the maximum current that can be drawn from the slider when it is set at the midpoint?

5. A coil has 480 turns and is wound on a core which has a permeability of 60. The inductance is 1.3 henrys. The core is removed, and 120 turns are taken off the coil. What is the inductance of the coil?

6. A wire-wound resistor is measured by an ohmmeter, and the resistance is found to be 75 ohms. When this unit is placed across a 400-cycle 120-volt a-c circuit, the unit takes 110 watts at a power factor of 0.8. Determine the percentage increase in resistance caused by skin effect.

7. A coil is 300 $\mu$h at 5000 cycles and is 310 $\mu$h at 100,000 cycles. Assume that the true value of inductance is given at 5000 cycles. Neglect the resistance of the coil, and determine the equivalent shunting capacitance across the turns.

8. A tuning capacitor has 11 stator plates and 12 rotor plates. The plates are semicircular with a diameter of one inch each. The plates are 0.016 inch thick and the over-all length of the rotor section is 0.500 inch. Determine the maximum capacitance of this unit.

9. When a paper capacitor is unrolled, each sheet is found to be 3 yards long. The foil plates are 0.003 inch thick and 1.75 inches wide. The paper is 0.008 inch thick and has a dielectric constant of 7.5. Determine the original capacitance of the unit.

10. At 1000 cycles, a Wheatstone-type a-c bridge gives values for the capacitance and series resistance of a particular capacitor of 4300 $\mu\mu$f and 3.4 ohms. What is the equivalent shunt resistance, and what is the power factor at 1000 cycles?

11. A particular capacitor, when placed across 300 volts alternating current at 18 Mc, draws 2 amperes, and its heating is equivalent to 15 watts. Determine both the series and the parallel equivalent circuits.

12. A 0.001-$\mu$f capacitor is rated at 400 volts alternating current when it is used in a circuit where the frequency is 1000 kc. What are the voltage ratings at 5 Mc and at 10 Mc? If the direct voltage rating is 2000 volts, at what frequency can this capacitor be used to obtain a maximum alternating voltage rating?

# A-c circuits in electronics

• • • • • • • • • • • • • • • • • • • • CHAPTER **7**

The objective of this chapter is to review and to present certain basic circuit arrangements from a-c theory which form the foundation of electronic circuit analysis. Series (Section 7–1) and parallel (Section 7–2) tuned circuits are discussed from the viewpoint of their response to different frequencies. The tuning of these circuits by varying the inductance or the capacitance is also considered. The nature of the term, bandwidth, is investigated (Section 7–3). The discussion of general coupled circuit theory (Section 7–4) leads to consideration of the single-tuned air-core transformer (Section 7–5) and the double-tuned air-core transformer (Section 7–6). Filters (Section 7–7), harmonics (Section 7–8), and certain network theorems (Section 7 -9) have major applications in electronics. A knowledge of four-terminal network theory (Section 7–10) is a prerequisite for transistor circuit analysis.

### Section 7–1  Series Circuits

A series a-c circuit can be reduced to three elements; resistance $R$, inductance $L$, and capacitance $C$, in series with a source of emf $E$ (Fig. 7–1). The equations for this circuit which do not have any

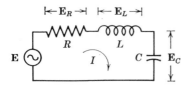

**Figure 7–1**  The series circuit.

restrictions or assumptions for sinusoidal waveforms are

$$\mathbf{E} = \mathbf{E}_R + \mathbf{E}_L + \mathbf{E}_C$$

$$Z = R + j2\pi fL - j\frac{1}{2\pi fC}$$

$$= R + jX_L - jX_C$$

$$= R + j\left(2\pi fL - \frac{1}{2\pi fC}\right)$$

$$= R + j(X_L - X_C)$$

and

$$\mathbf{I} = \frac{\mathbf{E}}{Z}$$

The $Q$ of the circuit is defined as $2\pi fL/R$ or $X_L/R$.

In the first four sections of this chapter, there are certain equations in which the currents and voltages must be explicitly expressed as phasor quantities in order to prevent any confusion. At these places, the phasors are shown in boldface type. In a-c theory, it is a general policy to designate that all currents and voltages are phasors and should be in this boldface type unless specifically expressed as magnitudes. Electronic literature does not rigidly adhere to this rule. For instance, Eq. 7–12 should be written in phasor terminology in order to be technically correct. In this textbook we follow the loose interpretation with the understanding that the a-c equations have their main application in electronics to resistive circuits and that they are valid for complex impedances, should the need arise.

When a constant emf is applied to the circuit and when frequency is the only variable, at some one particular frequency, which is defined as the resonant frequency $f_0$, the inductive reactance equals the capacitive reactance. The circuit impedance is a minimum and is equal to the resistance $R$. The sum of $(X_L - X_C)$ is zero and is indicated as the condition of resonant frequency in Fig. 7-2.

As the frequency increases from zero (direct current), the inductive reactance $X_L$ increases linearly, and the capacitive reactance $X_C$ becomes smaller. The current is a maximum at resonance, and the voltage across the resistance equals the applied emf $E$, since $E_C$ and $E_L$ are equal but 180° out of phase at resonance. $E_C$ reaches a peak value just before resonance, and $E_L$ reaches its maximum value at a frequency just greater than resonance. When the $Q$ of the circuit is high, these peaks are so very close to resonance that for all purposes they may be considered to be at resonance.

$$Z = R + j(X_L - X_C)$$

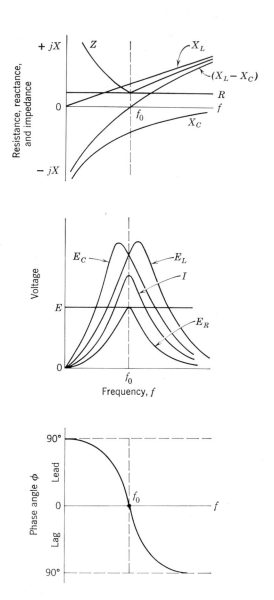

**Figure 7–2**    Response of the series circuit—variable frequency.

At resonance $\quad\quad\quad X_L = X_C$

or $\quad\quad\quad\quad\quad 2\pi f_0 L = \dfrac{1}{2\pi f_0 C}$

Then $\quad\quad\quad\quad\quad f_0{}^2 = \dfrac{1}{4\pi^2 LC}$

and the resonant frequency is

$$f_0 = \frac{1}{2\pi \sqrt{LC}} \qquad\qquad (7\text{--}1)$$

At resonance $\quad\quad\quad Z = Z_o = R + j0 = R$

the current at resonance is

$$I_0 = \frac{E}{Z_o} = \frac{E}{R}$$

The voltage across the inductance at resonance is

$$V_{L0} = I_0 X_L = \frac{E X_L}{R}$$

But $Q$ is defined as $X_L/R$. Then

$$V_{L0} = EQ$$

The voltage across the capacitor at resonance is

$$V_{C0} = I_0 X_C = \frac{E X_C}{R}$$

Since, at resonance, $X_L = X_C$,

$$V_{C0} = \frac{E X_L}{R} = EQ$$

or the voltage either across the inductance or across the capacitor in series resonance is $EQ$:

$$V_{L0} = V_{C0} = EQ \qquad\qquad (7\text{--}2)$$

By this derivation, in a series circuit, the voltage across the capacitor and the voltage across the inductance (if pure) are both equal in magnitude and equal to $QE$. For example, consider a series-resonant circuit in which the applied emf is 3 volts, $R$ is 10 ohms and $X_L$ and $X_C$ are each 220 ohms. The $Q$ is 220/10 or 22. The voltage across

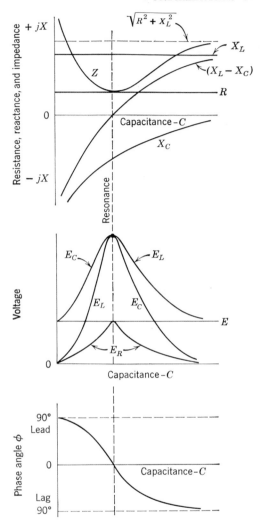

**Figure 7–3**   Response of the series circuit—variable capacitance.

the capacitor is, then, $QE$ or $22 \times 3$ or 66 volts. This rise of voltage across the inductance or capacitor at resonance is often termed the *Q gain* of a series-resonant circuit.

At low frequencies the circuit is primarily capacitive, and the phase angle of the circuit is leading at almost 90°. At high frequencies, above resonance, the circuit is inductive with a power angle of almost 90° lagging. At resonance, the power factor is unity, and the phase angle is zero. The transition from frequencies just below resonance to frequencies just above resonance shows that the change of phase angle is linear with the change in frequency. A high-$Q$ circuit has a greater linear range than a low-$Q$ circuit.

If we consider a series circuit in which the coil, the resistance, the applied voltage, and the frequency are fixed, the only variable is the capacitance. The analysis of this circuit is shown in Fig. 7–3. $E$, $R$, and $X_L$ are constant with changes in $C$. As $C$ is increased, the value of $X_C$ decreases. At some value of $C$, $X_C$ equals $X_L$. This value is the point of resonance. At resonance, $Z$ is a minimum and is equal to $R$. $E_C$ and $E_L$ are maximum ($E_C = E_L = QE$), and the voltage across the resistance equals the applied voltage $E$. As $C$ increases still further, the value of $X_C$ falls toward zero, and the circuit acts as if it were made up of the two elements $R$ and $L$ alone. The magnitude

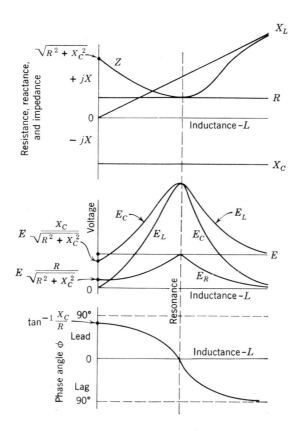

**Figure 7–4** Response of the series circuit—variable inductance.

of the impedance is then $\sqrt{R^2 + X_L{}^2}$, and the line voltage divides vectorially across $R$ and $L$. Then the $Q$ is high, the limiting value of the impedance is $X_L$, and the voltage across the inductance approaches the line voltage $E$. The phase-shift variation is very similar to the phase-shift curve in Fig. 7-2.

If the inductance is the only variable, and if we consider a high-$Q$ circuit only, the results are shown on Fig. 7-4. The value of $X_L$ increases directly with an increase in inductance $L$. Again, resonance occurs when $X_L = X_C$. At this point the impedance is a minimum, and the voltage across the inductance and the capacitor are maximum. As $L$ increases, the values of $R$ and $X_C$ are small in comparison with $X_L$, and the value of the circuit impedance approaches $X_L$. Then the voltage across the inductance is the applied voltage $E$.

### Section 7-2   Parallel Circuits

The basic parallel circuit is shown in Fig. 7-5. In electronic circuits, the capacitors used are usually of such quality that the resistance of the capacitor can, for all practical purposes, be assumed zero. The relations in the circuit are, from basic a-c circuit theory:

$$\mathbf{I} = \mathbf{I}_L + \mathbf{I}_C$$

$$Z_L = R_L + j2\pi fL$$

$$= R_L + jX_L$$

$$= \sqrt{R_L{}^2 + X_L{}^2} \; \underline{/\tan^{-1} X_L/R_L}$$

$$Z_C = R_C - j\frac{1}{2\pi fC}$$

$$= R_C - jX_C$$

$$= \sqrt{R_C{}^2 + X_C{}^2} \; \underline{/-\tan^{-1} X_C/R_C}$$

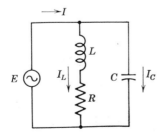

Figure 7-5   The parallel circuit.

When $R_C$ is zero, $Z_C$ becomes

$$Z_C = -j\frac{1}{2\pi f C} = -jX_C = X_C\underline{/-90°}$$

$$I_L = \frac{E}{Z_L}, \qquad\qquad I_C = \frac{E}{Z_C}$$

$$Z_T = \frac{Z_C Z_L}{Z_L + Z_C} = \frac{(-jX_C)(R_L + jX_L)}{R_L + jX_L - jX_C}$$

Let $\qquad\qquad X_C = X_L = X \quad\text{and}\quad R = R_L$

Then $\qquad\qquad Z_T = \dfrac{-jX(R + jX)}{R} = \dfrac{X^2}{R} - j\dfrac{RX}{R}$

$$= \frac{X^2}{R} - jX$$

but $Q$ is $X/R$. Then

$$Z_T = QX - jX$$

$$= X(Q - j1)$$

If $Q$ is equal to or greater than 10, the last relation may be written with negligible error as

$$Z_T = QX - j0 = QX \quad\text{where}\quad Q \geq 10 \qquad (7\text{–}3)$$

This expression for $Z_T$ is resistive and not reactive. The fundamental definition of resonance states that, at resonance, the power factor of the circuit is unity. Thus, when we specify a circuit in which the $Q$ is not less than 10, we have the same relation for resonance in a parallel circuit that we had in the series circuit:

$$X_L = X_C$$

and $\qquad\qquad f_0 = \dfrac{1}{2\pi \sqrt{LC}} \qquad\qquad (7\text{–}4)$

In a series circuit, the impedance at resonance is resistive and equal to $R$, whereas, in the high-$Q$ parallel circuit, at resonance, the circuit is resistive and its impedance is $QX$.

If we have circuits where the $Q$ is less than 10, we must use the rather laborious methods that have been studied in formal a-c circuit theory.

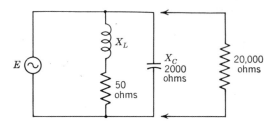

**Figure 7-6** The parallel circuit with shunt loading.

This relation of parallel impedance as $QX$ at resonance is very useful in many applications of electronic-amplifier circuits. In the circuit of Fig. 7-6 at resonance, $X_L$ equals $X_C$ or 2000 ohms. Then the $Q$ of the coil is 2000/50 or 40. The impedance at resonance is $QX$ or $40 \times 2000$ or 80,000 ohms pure resistance. If a 20,000-ohm resistor is connected in parallel with the resonant circuit, we have at resonance two

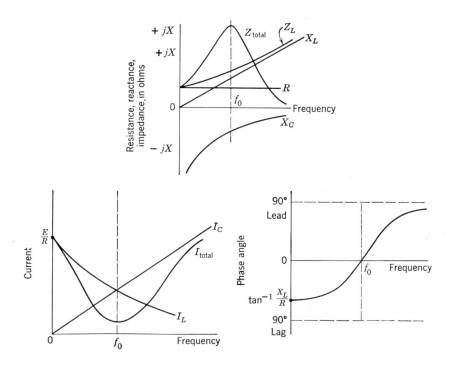

**Figure 7-7** Response of the parallel circuit—variable frequency.

resistances in parallel:

$$R'_T = \frac{R_1 R_2}{R_1 + R_2} = \frac{80,000 \times 20,000}{80,000 + 20,000}$$

$$= \frac{80,000}{100,000} \, 20,000 = 16,000 \text{ ohms}$$

The total impedance of the circuit is now 16,000 ohms. This total impedance is the effective $Q$, $Q'$, times the reactance:

$$R'_T = Q'X$$

$$16,000 = Q' \times 2000$$

$$Q' = 8$$

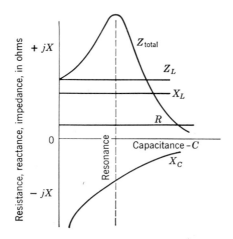

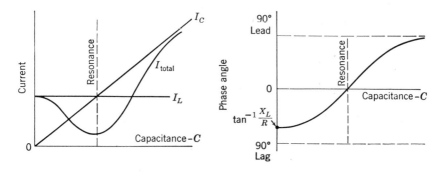

**Figure 7–8** Response of the parallel circuit—variable capacitance.

Thus, placing a resistance in parallel with the tuned circuit effectively reduces the circuit $Q$. This *loading resistance* may be adjusted to obtain a particular over-all circuit $Q$ which is required for an application.

In Section 6–5, we treated an actual capacitor as being equivalent to a pure capacitor in parallel with its leakage resistance. If it is necessary to consider the resistance of the capacitor, the calculation should be first made for the ideal capacitor and then the leakage resistance considered as a shunt loading resistor which lowers the circuit $Q$ and the circuit impedance.

The response of this circuit to a varying frequency is shown in Fig. 7–7. The current in the circuit at zero frequency (direct current) is determined by the values of $E$ and $R$. As the frequency increases, the current through the capacitance increases linearly, and the current through the inductive branch decreases to zero. At resonance, the

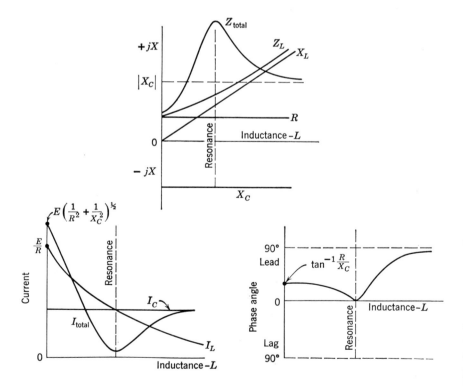

**Figure 7–9**   Response of the parallel circuit—variable inductance.

impedance is the maximum value $QX$, and the current is at a minimum value $E/QX$.

The effects of changing the inductance or the capacitor are shown in Fig. 7-8 and Fig. 7-9. The applied voltage and the frequency are held constant.

## Section 7-3   Bandwidth

If we consider the current-response curve of a series-resonant circuit (Fig. 7-10), the current has a peak value of $I_0$ at the resonant frequency $f_0$. Let $I_1$ and $I_2$ be equal to $I_0/\sqrt{2}$ or 70.7% of $I_0$. The current value $I_1$ occurs at $f_1$, and the current value $I_2$ occurs at $f_2$. Now we define the *bandwidth* BW as $(f_2 - f_1)$.

When considerations of bandwidth are involved in circuit applications, the $Q$ of the coil is assumed constant over the frequency range (Section 6-3). Not only is this true of the frequencies used in communications, but it is also true of industrial electronic applications where we may have, for instance, an iron-core coil operating at a resonant frequency of 1300 cycles with a bandwidth of 50 cycles. If the $Q$ is constant and, since $Q$ equals $2\pi fL/R$, the resistance $R$ of the coil must vary directly with frequency. This assumption is valid since the bandwidth is small with respect to the resonant frequency. In the series circuit at resonance, the current is

$$I_0 = \frac{E}{R_0}$$

At any frequency, the current is

$$I = \frac{E}{R + j(X_L - X_C)}$$

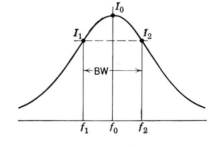

**Figure 7-10**   Bandwidth of a resonant circuit.

Expressing this as a ratio:

$$\frac{I_0}{I} = \frac{R + j(X_L - X_C)}{R_0}$$

At any frequency,

$$R = R_0 \frac{f}{f_0}$$

Then

$$\frac{I_0}{I} = \frac{R_0 \dfrac{f}{f_0} + j(X_L - X_C)}{R_0}$$

If we assume that $(X_L - X_C) = R_0 \dfrac{f}{f_0}$

Then

$$\frac{I_0}{I} = \frac{R_0 \dfrac{f}{f_0} + j R_0 \dfrac{f}{f_0}}{R_0}$$

$$= \frac{f}{f_0} \frac{1 + j1}{1}$$

The magnitude of the ratio is

$$\left| \frac{I_0}{I} \right| = \frac{f}{f_0} \sqrt{2}$$

and the phase angle is 45°.

If $f_1$ and $f_2$ are sufficiently close to $f_0$, this ratio then is $\sqrt{2}$. Now, to summarize what has been done up to this point, the bandwidth was defined as the interval between the 70.7% dropoff points, and these dropoff points occur when

$$R_0 \frac{f}{f_0} = X_L - X_C$$

The next step is to insert $f_1$ and $f_2$ into the relation and to solve the result for a final equation in terms of $f_1, f_2, f_0,$ and $Q$. We have called $f_2$ the higher frequency and $f_1$ the lower frequency. Now, at $f_2$, $X_L$ is greater than $X_C$ and $(X_L - X_C)$ is positive. At $f_1$, $X_C$ is greater than $X_L$ and $(X_L - X_C)$ is negative. Making this substitution, we have

For $f_1$:

$$-R_0 \frac{f_1}{f_0} = 2\pi f_1 L - \frac{1}{2\pi f_1 C}$$

And for $f_2$:

$$R_0 \frac{f_2}{f_0} = 2\pi f_2 L - \frac{1}{2\pi f_2 C}$$

If the first equation is multiplied through by $f_0/f_1$, and the second by $f_0/f_2$ and then if the resulting equations are divided through by $R_0$, $Q$ may be substituted for $2\pi f_0 L/R_0$. When the resulting equations are simplified and one is subtracted from the other, we find

$$2\pi R_0 C(f_2{}^2 - f_1{}^2) = f_0 \left( \frac{1}{Q-1} - \frac{1}{Q+1} \right) = f_0 \frac{2}{Q^2 - 1}$$

Since $Q$ is at least 10, $(Q^2 - 1)$ may be taken as $Q^2$. Then

$$2\pi R_0 C(f_2{}^2 - f_1{}^2) = \frac{2f_0}{Q^2}$$

Factoring,

$$2\pi R_0 C(f_2 + f_1)(f_2 - f_1) = \frac{2f_0}{Q^2}$$

but $(f_2 + f_1)/2$ is very close to $f_0$, and $(f_2 - f_1)$ is the bandwidth BW:

$$2\pi f_0 C R_0 \text{BW} = \frac{f_0}{Q^2}$$

Since $2\pi f_0 C = 1/2\pi f_0 L$ by the definition of resonance, we have an expression of the bandwidth in terms of the $Q$ and the resonant frequency:

$$\text{BW} \frac{R_0}{2\pi f_0 L} = \frac{f_0}{Q^2}$$

$$\frac{\text{BW}}{Q} = \frac{f_0}{Q^2}$$

or

$$f_2 - f_1 = \text{BW} = \frac{f_0}{Q} \tag{7-5}$$

By a similar but considerably more lengthy algebraic process, we may show that Eq. 7–5 is also valid for high-$Q$ parallel circuits.

### Section 7–4   Coupled Circuit Theory

When a signal is transferred through a network, the signal is said to be *coupled* from one point to another. The concepts of a coupled circuit are shown in Fig. 7–11a. A signal $\mathbf{E}_1$ develops a voltage $\mathbf{V}_2$

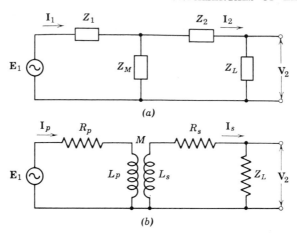

**Figure 7-11** Basic coupled circuits. (*a*) General circuit. (*b*) The air-core transformer.

across the load impedance $Z_L$.  The impedance that is common to the input and the output circuits is called the *mutual* or *coupling impedance* $Z_M$.  This coupling impedance can be made with any circuit element— a resistor, a capacitor, an inductance, or a transformer.  The circuit analysis in this section and in the next two sections is devoted to the *air-core transformer* (Fig. 7-11*b*), used as the coupling device between the source and the load.

In the fundamentals of d-c and a-c circuit theory, certain definitions are made and basic relations established for transformer-coupled circuits.  When two coils are linked by a common or mutual flux, the *coefficient of coupling* $k$ is the ratio of the flux linking the second coil from the first coil to the total flux of the first coil.  From this relation and from the definition of inductance, we can show that

$$M = k \sqrt{L_1 L_2}$$

where $M$ is the mutual inductance between two coils which have self-inductance values, $L_1$ and $L_2$, and a common linking flux determined by $k$.

In an iron-core transformer, the objective of the design is to make $k$ as close to unity as possible.  In air-core transformers, the values of $k$ are much less than unity and are usually of the order of 0.01 to 0.10 (1% to 10%).

In the air-core transformer, a voltage is induced in the secondary winding by the mutual flux that is created from current flow in the primary winding. This induced voltage lags the current which produces it by 90° and may be expressed as

$$\mathbf{E}_s = -j\omega M \mathbf{I}_p \qquad (7\text{-}6)$$

It should be noted from Fig. 7–11b that $\mathbf{V}_2$ equals $\mathbf{E}_s$ only when the transformer secondary circuit is open ($Z_L$ is infinite). If $Z_s$ is the total impedance of the secondary circuit including $R_s$, $j\omega L_s$, and $Z_L$, then

$$\mathbf{E}_s = \mathbf{I}_s Z_s \qquad (7\text{-}7a)$$

and

$$\mathbf{V}_2 = \mathbf{I}_s Z_L \qquad (7\text{-}7b)$$

When there is a current in the secondary circuit, a voltage $-j\omega M I_s$ is induced by this current back into the primary winding. This back voltage opposes the source voltage. The primary circuit voltage equation is

$$\mathbf{E}_1 = \mathbf{I}_p Z_p + j\omega M \mathbf{I}_s \qquad (7\text{-}8)$$

Substituting Eq. 7–7a in Eq. 7–6, we have

$$\mathbf{I}_s Z_s = -j\omega M \mathbf{I}_p$$

$$\mathbf{I}_s = \frac{-j\omega M \mathbf{I}_p}{Z_s}$$

and, placing this in Eq. 7–8,

$$\mathbf{E}_1 = \mathbf{I}_p Z_p + \frac{(\omega M)^2}{Z_s} \mathbf{I}_p$$

$$\mathbf{E}_1 = \mathbf{I}_p \left[ Z_p + \frac{(\omega M)^2}{Z_s} \right] \qquad (7\text{-}9)$$

From these five fundamental equations of coupled circuits, we can describe the operation of an air-core transformer. When a voltage is applied across the primary terminals of the transformer, a voltage is induced in the secondary winding. The secondary voltage is a function of both the primary current and the mutual inductance. The current that flows in the secondary circuit is limited by the total series impedance $Z_s$ of the secondary circuit.

The total primary impedance is $Z_p + (\omega M)^2/Z_s$. The term $(\omega M)^2/Z_s$ is the reflected impedance of the secondary into the primary. When the secondary circuit is open-circuited, its impedance is infinite and the reflected impedance is zero. When the secondary circuit is resistive, $R + j0$, the impedance reflected into the primary is resistive.

This coupled or reflected resistance lowers the input $Q$ of the transformer. When the secondary circuit impedance is inductive, $R_s + jX_s$, the reflected value of the impedance into the primary circuit is proportional to the reciprocal of $Z_s$. Upon rationalization, we find

$$\frac{(\omega M)^2}{R_s + jX_s} = \frac{(\omega M)^2}{R_s{}^2 + X_s{}^2} R_s - j \frac{(\omega M)^2}{R_s{}^2 + X_s{}^2} X_s$$

The second term or reactive part of this expression is "$-j$". This means that an inductive reactance in the secondary circuit reflects into the primary circuit as a "negative inductive reactance" which acts as if it were a capacitive reactance in the circuit calculations. Correspondingly, a capacitive reactance in the secondary circuit reflects back into the primary circuit as a "positive capacitive reactance" acting as an inductive reactance in the calculations. In describing the operation of transformers, we will say for simplicity that an inductive secondary impedance reflects into the primary circuit as a "capacitive reactance" and that a capacitive reactance reflects as an "inductive reactance." We will retain the quotation marks around these terms to distinguish them from the concept of a literal inductance or capacitance.

The currents and voltages in the air-core transformers are phasors which have both direction and magnitude. Accordingly, they are placed in boldface type in this section. Since, in most practical applications, we are concerned only with the magnitudes of currents and voltages in the transformer circuit, we will follow the usual electronic circuit notation and place them in ordinary type face in Sections 7–5 and 7–6. It should be remembered that these currents and voltages are phasors although we do not keep the boldface notation.

### Section 7–5    Air-Core Transformers—Untuned Primary, Tuned Secondary

The untuned-primary, tuned-secondary air-core transformer (Fig. 7–12) has many applications in that range of high frequencies which are referred to as RF (radio frequencies). At that frequency which resonates the secondary, the impedance of the secondary is resistive and is a minimum. The secondary current is then at maximum and the voltage across the capacitance, $E_{out}$, is a maximum.* When the coefficient of coupling $k$ is very low, the mutual inductance $M$ is low,

---

* An exact analysis of this circuit shows that the maximum value of $E_{out}$ occurs at a frequency that is very close to the resonant frequency of the secondary and that the error is negligible when it is assumed they occur at the same point in a high-$Q$ circuit.

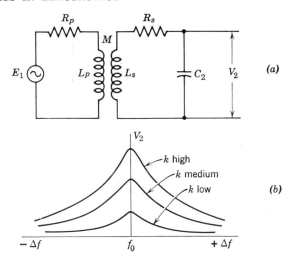

**Figure 7–12**   The air-core transformer—untuned primary, tuned secondary. (*a*) Circuit.   (*b*) Response.

and the secondary output voltage $E_{out}$ is low.   As $k$ is increased, this output voltage increases.   The limitation on the output voltage is determined by the closest physical spacing that may be obtained with the particular coil structure.

The development of the resonant curves shown in Fig. 7–12*b* is quite complex but they have the shape of the bandpass characteristics of the simple resonant circuits.   When data for a particular circuit are given, the curves can be computed by point-to-point calculations, using Eq. 7–6 through 7–9.

When the circuit is used to feed power into or to *drive* an electronic device (such as a class-C amplifier), $C_2$ is adjusted to resonance. That is, it is tuned to produce a maximum output voltage $E_{out}$ at the resonant frequency.   Then, the coefficient of coupling $k$ is adjusted to produce the required output voltage for optimum operation of the circuit that is being driven.   Typical curves showing the variation of the output voltage for different couplings at frequencies above and below resonance are given in Fig. 7–12*b*.

### Section 7–6   Air-Core Transformers—Tuned Primary, Tuned Secondary

In Fig. 7–13, we show both the primary and the secondary as series circuits.   In most applications of this transformer, the primary is a

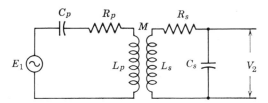

**Figure 7–13**   The air core transformer—tuned primary, tuned secondary.

parallel-resonant circuit and the secondary is a series-resonant circuit. We will show later in the application of this circuit in an amplifier (Section 22–2) that an equivalent series circuit can be established by Thévenin's theorem from the actual parallel-resonance circuit. This transformer could be analyzed for a parallel-resonant circuit in the primary, but the algebra is much simpler when the primary and the secondary are both taken as series-resonant circuits.

Each coil $L_p$ and $L_s$ must be adjusted independently to resonate at the same frequency. At resonance the total secondary circuit is resistive, and the secondary impedance couples back into the primary as a reflected resistance, $(\omega M)^2/R_s$. As the coupling is increased from a very low value, the total resistance in the primary, $R_p + (\omega M)^2/R_s$, increases and the primary current decreases. As $k$ increases, $(\omega M)$ increases from zero and the magnitude of the secondary voltage $\omega M I_p$ must increase from zero. However, since the secondary voltage is also proportional to $I_p$, it will reach a maximum value and then decrease back to zero. Since the output voltage $E_{\text{out}}$ is $I_s X_{Cs}$, it has the same response (Fig. 7–14).

In Fig. 7–14, we show $k_x$ as that value of coupling which is the physical limit of closeness of coupling. That value of coupling which produces the maximum output is the *critical coupling $k_c$*. In terms of circuit components, the critical coupling is

$$k_c = \frac{1}{\sqrt{Q_p Q_s}} \qquad (7\text{--}10)$$

and, if $Q_p = Q_s = Q$, then $k_c = 1/Q$.

When the value of the coefficient of coupling is less than or equal to the critical coupling $k_c$, the frequency-response curves (Fig. 7–15) are similar to the untuned-primary, tuned-secondary transformer curves. As the coefficient of coupling increases, the bandwidth decreases. When the circuit is overcoupled, the output at the resonant

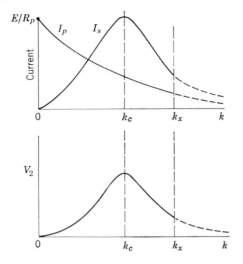

**Figure 7–14**  Response of the double-tuned transformer with variable coupling.

frequency is reduced.  In the overcoupled circuit, when the frequency is increased above resonance, the primary and secondary circuit impedances are both inductive because they are both series circuits. However, the inductive effect in the secondary reflects back into the primary as a "capacitance" and re-resonates the circuit at a new frequency $f_b$.  Likewise, below resonance, the two circuits are capacitive. The capacitive secondary reflects back into the primary as an "inductance," causing a second resonance at $f_a$.  Thus, in an overcoupled circuit, two points of apparent resonance are produced, $f_a$ and $f_b$.

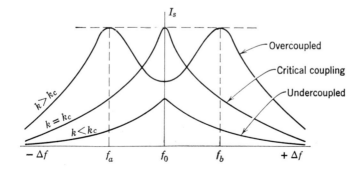

**Figure 7–15**  Secondary-current variation with frequency.

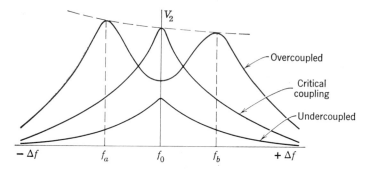

**Figure 7–16**   Secondary-voltage variation with frequency.

Since $X_{Cs}$ decreases with frequency, the value of $E_{out}$ which is $I_sX_{Cs}$ shows the effect of this variation of $X_{Cs}$ with frequency (Fig. 7–16). From a lengthy analysis of the circuit, we can show for identical overcoupled circuits in which $Q_p$ equals $Q_s$ that

$$\frac{f_a}{f_0} = 1 - \frac{k}{2}, \qquad \frac{f_b}{f_0} = 1 + \frac{k}{2} \qquad (7\text{--}11a)$$

At the resonant frequency the output voltage is given by

$$V_2 = \sqrt{\frac{L_s}{L_p}} \frac{k}{k^2 + \dfrac{1}{Q_pQ_s}} E_1 \qquad (7\text{--}11b)$$

When the primary and secondary circuits are identical, $L_s$ equals $L_p$ and $Q_p$ equals $Q_s$, and, using Eq. 7–10, we have

$$V_2 = \frac{k}{k^2 + k_c{}^2} E_1 \qquad (7\text{--}11c)$$

and, for critical coupling ($k$ is $k_c$), this equation simplifies to

$$V_2 = \frac{1}{2k_c} E_1 \qquad (7\text{--}11d)$$

which is the maximum possible output voltage at resonance occurring when the coupling is the critical value.

Let us assume that a typical double-tuned transformer is manufactured with a coefficient of coupling of 5%. Also assume that the $Q$ of both the primary and the secondary is 40. Then, the critical coefficient of coupling by Eq. 7–10 is 1/40 or 2.5%. It is evident that the transformer is overcoupled. In a normal resonant circuit, the usual procedure for tuning (varying either $L$ or $C$) is to adjust the circuit for a maximum output-voltage reading. In this overcoupled transformer, we find that neither a peak nor a dip secures the proper tuning. If, by loading the primary and secondary circuits with shunt loading resistors which are noninductive, we can reduce the effective $Q$ from 40 to 20 or less, the whole transformer is now operating at or below critical coupling. Now the primary and secondary circuits may be adjusted for a maximum reading of $E_{\text{out}}$. When the procedure of tuning is complete, the loading resistors are removed. If the shunt resistors are noninductive, the tuning is unchanged and the alignment is correct for the overcoupled condition.

### Section 7–7    Filters

Electric-wave filters may be divided into four classes, Fig. 7-17:

1. Low pass,
2. High pass,
3. Band pass, and
4. Band reject.

In the low-pass filter, the series path $A$ to $C$ offers a low impedance to the low frequencies. As the frequency increases, the impedance between $A$ and $C$ increases. At low frequencies, the impedance of the shunt path $A$ to $D$ through the capacitance is very high, and, as the frequency increases, this shunting impedance becomes lower and lower in value. The high-pass filter functions in the same manner except that, as the frequency increases, the impedance of the series path $A$ to $C$ decreases, and the impedance of the shunting path increases. In the band-pass and band-reject filters, the series circuits present a high impedance off resonance and a very low impedance at resonance. The parallel circuit presents at resonance a very high impedance and away from resonance a very low impedance. In the band-pass circuit, the series path $A$ to $C$ at resonance is a low impedance, and the shunt path is a very high impedance, allowing the energy at or near resonance to pass through the filter. The band-stop or band-reject filter offers a high-impedance series path and a low-impedance shunt path at resonance, preventing energy at or near resonance from transferring through the filter network.

A low-pass filter allows the low frequencies to pass and rejects or *attenuates* the high frequencies. In the simple rectifier, both alternating and direct current are present in the output. A low-pass filter

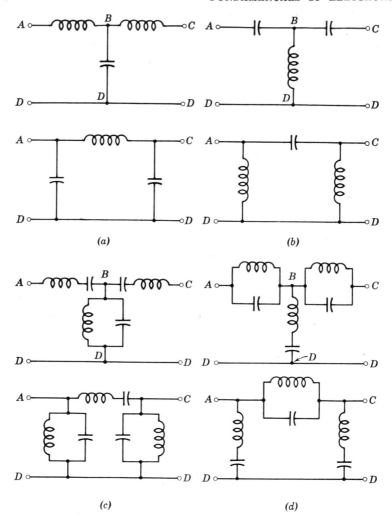

**Figure 7–17** Basic T and $\pi$ filters. (*a*) Low pass. (*b*) High pass. (*c*) Band pass. (*d*) Band reject.

allows the direct current to transfer to the load and rejects the a-c ripple. In telemetering, a signal frequency of several thousand cycles is transmitted over a 60-cycle power line. At the receiving end a high-pass filter allows the telemetering signal to pass into the receiving device while it keeps the low-frequency 60-cycle energy out of the receiver. Band-pass filters have infinite application in radio and television circuits where they allow a particular station to be selected while rejecting all the rest which would otherwise create interference. A band-reject filter is commonly used in series with an antenna to suppress interference from a particular station or from a group of stations in a particular frequency band. For instance, a trap is often used on a television receiver to prevent interference from an amateur radio transmitter.

Each filter may be represented as a T network wherein the parts are physically arranged as the arms of the letter T. An alternate arrangement is to lay out the components in the form of a $\pi$. Filters may be made in these basic forms, or, if the filtering problem is not critical, the network may be simplified considerably (Fig. 7–18). On the other hand, if the filtering requirements are very stringent, a composite filter is required which may comprise several complex and matched forms of T and $\pi$ sections, together with L-type end sections at the input and at the output.

Let us examine three representative filtering problems:

*Case 1.* In a rectifier power supply, the 60-cycle ripple must be separated from the direct current (zero frequency).

*Case 2.* In a telemetering system, the signal frequency is 3000 cycles superimposed on a 60-cycle power line.

*Case 3.* A receiver that is tuned to a station at 1000 kc must reject a strong interfering station at 1010 kc.

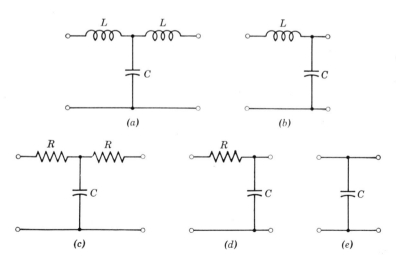

**Figure 7–18**   Simplified filter arrangements.   (*a*) Basic filter.   (*b*) L filter.   (*c*) T filter.   (*d*) L filter.   (*e*) Capacitor filter.

If we take a ratio of the two frequencies in each case, keeping the ratio larger than unity, we have:

*Case 1.*    $\dfrac{60}{0} = \infty$

*Case 2.*    $\dfrac{3000}{60} = 50$

*Case 3.*    $\dfrac{1010}{1000} = 1.01$

When this ratio is very large, the frequency to be rejected is very far from the wanted frequency as in case 1. Under these circumstances, the filtering problem is simple, and it is often not necessary to use formal combinations of $\pi$ and T networks. The simpler modifications shown in Fig. 7–18 can satisfactorily meet the requirements. In case 2, the filter needs are more stringent, but it may be possible to use an $RC$-type L or T filter if the values of the component parts are properly taken. In case 3, the filtering problem is very difficult. In an actual radio receiver, it is necessary to use many tuned circuits acting as band-pass filters in order to pass the desired station satisfactorily while having sufficient rejection for the undesired station. This ratio then can give a quick method of determining whether the filtering problem is simple, very difficult, or intermediate.

### Section 7–8    Harmonics

A basic a-c circuits course is primarily concerned with the theory, the calculations, and the applications of sinusoidal waveforms. In practice, in electronic circuits, pure sinusoidal waveforms are not common. The waveforms as shown on an oscilloscope may be square waves, triangular waves, pulses or completely nonrepetitive waveforms. Usually, we analyze the electronic circuit on the basis of sine-wave signal sources and tests and then apply this analysis to the nonsinusoidal waveforms. It is necessary to develop an understanding of harmonic content in order to consider these irregular shapes in terms of a sine-wave analysis. Later, the topic is extended to include a discussion of distortion and distortion analysis in amplifiers (Section 10–5).

The basic repetitive period of a wave establishes its form and its *fundamental* frequency. If we use a 20-cycle square wave, we mean that, over one second, 20 full cycles are completed. If two sine waves

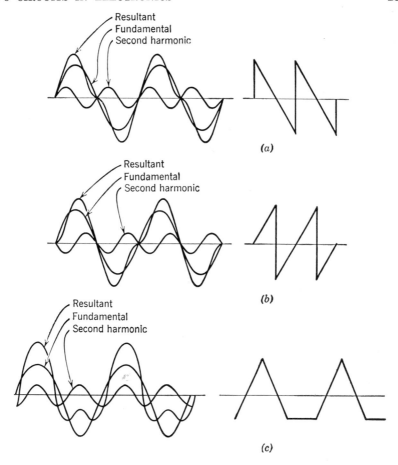

**Figure 7–19** Fundamental with even harmonics. (*a*) Fundamental with even harmonics starting in phase. (*b*) Fundamental with even harmonics starting 180° out of phase. (*c*) Fundamental with even harmonics starting at a 90° lag.

are added, one at a fundamental frequency $f$, and the other at double the fundamental frequency or at the *second harmonic* $2f$, we obtain the results shown in Fig. 7–19. If the amplitude of the second harmonic is correct with respect to the amplitude of the fundamental and if proper amounts of the 4th, the 6th, the 8th, etc., harmonics are added, we get the sawtooth waveforms shown. In order to obtain a pure sawtooth from mathematics, an infinite number of harmonics is required. Practically, we consider the waveform pure if all harmonics up to about the 10th or 12th are included.

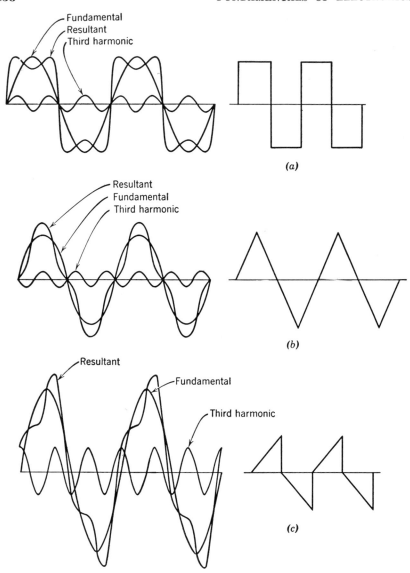

**Figure 7–20**   Fundamental with odd harmonics.   (*a*) Fundamental with third harmonic starting in phase.   (*b*) Fundamental with third harmonic starting 180° out of phase.   (*c*) Fundamental with third harmonic starting at a 90° lead.

**Figure 7–21** A general waveform
used to show harmonic content.

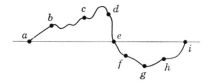

It is obvious from Fig. 7–19 that not only is the relative amplitude
of the harmonic to the fundamental important, but also the phase
angle of the phase relationship is very critical. The three different
waveforms are produced, not by a change in amplitude, but by a
change in phase-angle relationship only.

Figure 7–20 shows the results of adding odd harmonics to a fundamental. Again a phase difference radically affects the resultant
waveform.

In Fig. 7–21, one cycle of a generalized irregular waveform is given.
The positive half-cycle is *abcde*, and the negative half-cycle is *efghi*.
If we use the results obtained from Fig. 7–19 and Fig. 7–20, we can
often make a very useful analysis of the waveform under study (Fig.
7–21). If the negative half of the cycle repeats the positive half of
the cycle in the same order, that is, if the negative loop is − (*abcde*)
in that order, the wave contains odd harmonics only. This is known
as a *complete symmetry*. If the negative half of the waveform repeats
the positive half in the reverse order, that is, if the negative half is
− (*edcba*), we have *mirror symmetry*. A wave with mirror symmetry
must contain even harmonics. A wave may contain all harmonics.
An example of this is a square wave with even harmonics which combines Fig. 7–20*a* with Fig. 7–19*a*:

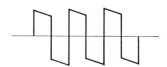

This waveform shows mirror symmetry, thereby having an even-
harmonic content.

An important aspect of harmonics is the consideration of the con-
verse to our analysis. In circuits that are tested with square-wave
signal sources, if the output waveform is not square, the circuit has
either failed to pass the harmonic content or it has changed the amplitude and phase relations of the harmonics. If the output of a circuit
is not a sine wave when a sine-wave generator is used at the input, the
circuit has introduced harmonics into the wave which were not present

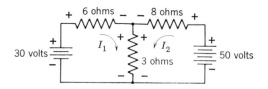

**Figure 7–22**   Network used to illustrate Kirchhoff's voltage law.

in the incoming signal.   In other words, the electronic circuit introduces and develops *distortion*.   Often from an examination of the symmetry characteristics of the output waveform, a quick analysis may be made of the kind of distortion that is being produced (Fig. 15–2 and Fig. 15–3).

### Section 7–9   Network Theorems

The solution of networks by solving equations is usually first presented in an elementary d-c course.   A sufficient review can be accomplished by solving the circuit of Fig. 7–22.   If the resistances are polarized with plus and minus signs to indicate the signs of the $IR$ drops, the equations for the two outside loops may be written immediately as

$$30 = 6I_1 + 3(I_1 + I_2)$$

$$50 = 8I_2 + 3(I_1 + I_2)$$

Collecting terms, we have

$$9I_1 + \ 3I_2 = 30$$

$$3I_1 + 11I_2 = 50$$

When we simplify and solve for $I_1$ and $I_2$, we obtain

$$I_1 = 2 \text{ amperes}$$

$$I_2 = 4 \text{ amperes}$$

and                     $$I_1 + I_2 = 6 \text{ amperes}$$

The voltage drop across the 3-ohm resistance is 18 volts.

To show the *nodal method* of analysis, Fig. 7–22 is drawn in a simplified form for discussion (Fig. 7–23).   There are four junction points, $A$, $B$, $C$, and $D$.   $D$ is taken as the reference point of measurement. Between $A$ and $D$ and between $C$ and $D$ are fixed emf's $E_1$ and $E_2$.

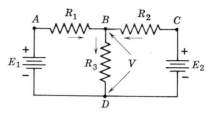

**Figure 7–23**  Network used to illustrate the nodal method.

These two points *A* and *C* are *dependent nodes* since the voltage between them and the reference is at all times fixed. The voltage between *B* and the reference depends on the circuit currents and the values of the circuit elements. This is an *independent node*. *B* is the only independent node in this circuit. In nodal analysis, for the solution of a network, we need as many equations as there are independent nodes. Kirchhoff's law states that the sum of the currents into a junction is zero:

$$\frac{E_1 - V}{R_1} + \frac{E_2 - V}{R_2} - \frac{V}{R_3} = 0$$

Substituting values from Fig. 7–22, we have

$$\frac{30 - V}{6} + \frac{50 - V}{8} - \frac{V}{3} = 0$$

Simplifying, using 24 as the least common denominator:

$$(120 - 4V) + (150 - 3V) - 8V = 0$$

Then                                $V = 18$ volts

and                        $$I_1 = \frac{30 - 18}{6} = 2 \text{ amperes}$$

$$I_2 = \frac{50 - 18}{8} = 4 \text{ amperes}$$

and                   $I_1 + I_2 = 6$ amperes

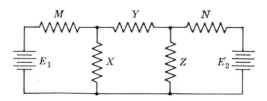

**Figure 7–24**  A general network problem.

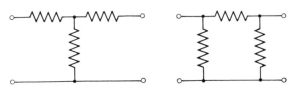

**Figure 7–25**    Equivalent T and $\pi$ circuits.

The use of the nodal method can often simplify the solution of a network considerably. In Fig. 7–24, a solution by Kirchhoff's loop equations requires three unknowns and three equations, whereas, since there are only two independent nodes, $A$ and $B$, only two unknowns and two equations are involved in the solution in nodal form.

By using the sometimes laborious $\Delta$–Y or $\Delta$–star conversion formulas developed in d-c theory, one can convert from a T network to a $\pi$ network or from a $\pi$ network to a T network at will (Fig. 7–25). The network of Fig. 7–24 can be reduced by transforming the elements $X$, $Y$, and $Z$ which are in the form of a $\pi$ into a T. The arms of the T combine with $M$ and $N$ to give the reduced forms of Fig. 7–25. A very important general circuit theorem states that any network that contains passive elements only (not active elements which are voltage or current sources) can be reduced to an equivalent $\pi$ or T. By use of this very valuable circuit theorem, if we prove or demonstrate a new theorem by using a T network, we have automatically accomplished a valid general proof.

*Thévenin's theorem* states that an electrical network may be replaced by an emf in series with an impedance. The emf is the open-circuit voltage of the network. The series impedance is the impedance measured back into the network with all the emf's reduced to zero, but the internal impedances of the generators are left in the circuit for this measurement. An example can serve to illustrate Thévenin's theorem. In the circuit of Fig. 7–26, it is required to find the current through the 1.6-ohm load resistance. If the load is removed, the voltage across $AB$ is the open-circuit voltage. It is equal to the voltage

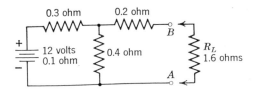

**Figure 7–26**    Network used to show Thévenin's theorem.

drop across the 0.4-ohm resistance:

$$I = \frac{12}{0.1 + 0.3 + 0.4} = \frac{12}{0.8} = 15 \text{ amperes}$$

$$V_{oc} = 15 \times 0.4 = 6 \text{ volts}$$

The impedance measured between $A$ and $B$ is

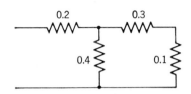

$$Z = 0.2 + \frac{0.4(0.3 + 0.1)}{0.4 + 0.3 + 0.1} = 0.4 \text{ ohm}$$

The final equivalent circuit by Thévenin's theorem is

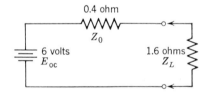

Now the load current is

$$I = \frac{6}{0.4 + 1.6} = 3 \text{ amperes}$$

The reader can solve this problem by the other two methods to check this result. If this problem had required the load currents for a number of different values of load resistance, the time saved by using the method of Thévenin's theorem is considerable.

*Norton's theorem* states that a network may be replaced by a constant-current generator in parallel with an impedance. The current in the constant-current generator is the short-circuit current of the network, and the parallel impedance is the same back impedance that we used in Thévenin's theorem.

The problem used to illustrate Thévenin's theorem is now solved by Norton's theorem. The load presented to the generator with the

output terminals short-circuited is

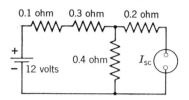

$$Z = 0.1 + 0.3 + \frac{0.4 \times 0.2}{0.4 + 0.2} = 0.533 \text{ ohms}$$

The battery current is

$$\frac{12}{0.533} = 22.5 \text{ amperes}$$

The voltage drop across $AB$ is

$$22.5 \times 0.133 = 3.00 \text{ volts}$$

Now the short-circuit current is

$$\frac{3.00}{0.2} = 15 \text{ amperes}$$

The final equivalent circuit by Norton's theorem is:

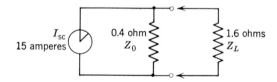

The current from the source $I_{sc}$ divides between $Z_0$ and $Z_L$. The load current through the 1.6-ohm resistance is

$$I_L = I_{sc} \frac{Z_0}{Z_0 + Z_L} = 15 \frac{0.4}{0.4 + 1.6} = 3 \text{ amperes}$$

This is the same result as obtained from Thévenin's theorem.

By checking the numerical values, we can see that $E_{oc}$ equals $I_{sc}Z_0$ and that $I_{sc}$ equals $E_0/Z_0$. We, therefore, could obtain the equivalent circuit for Norton's theorem directly from the results of Thévenin's theorem. Conversely, if the circuit for Norton's theorem is known,

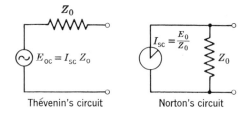

**Figure 7-27** The equivalence of Thévenin's and Norton's theorems.

Thévenin's circuit      Norton's circuit

the circuit for Thévenin's theorem can be set up directly (Fig. 7-27). This equivalency is very useful in vacuum-tube and transistor-circuit analysis. It may be very easy to establish one form, but the other form may be more useful in developing the derivation of a particular equation.

The *maximum power-transfer theorem* establishes the conditions under which the load impedance is such that a maximum output power is dissipated in or delivered to the load. The source network may be reduced to a single emf in series with an internal impedance by Thévenin's theorem. When $Z_o$ (or $Z_g$) is resistive and $Z_L$ is resistive, the power computed for different values of load is plotted in Fig. 7-29. Either graphically or by means of calculus, we may show that the maximum load power occurs when the load resistance equals the internal resistance. Also, at the point of maximum power transfer, the $IR_g$ drop equals the load voltage $IR_L$. This means that, under conditions of maximum power transfer, the load voltage is one-half the source emf. The load power at point $A$ is

$$\left(\frac{E_{oc}}{2R_g}\right)^2 R_0 = \frac{E^2_{oc}}{4R_g} = \frac{E^2_{oc}}{4R_L}$$

and the over-all efficiency is 50%.

If the internal impedance is complex (resistance and reactance), the maximum power transfer occurs when the load impedance is the conjugate of the internal impedance. For instance, if the internal impedance is $6 + j8$, maximum power transfer occurs when the load

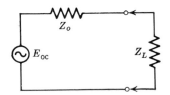

**Figure 7-28** Circuit illustrating the maximum power-transfer theorem.

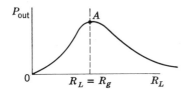

**Figure 7–29** The response of the circuit showing maximum power transfer.

impedance is $6 - j8$ ohms. Actually, in this case of conjugate impedances, the circuit is in series resonance. In electronic circuits, it is often necessary to deliver power into a resistive load from an inductive source. To obtain maximum power transfer under these conditions, the load resistance should be equal to the magnitude of the input impedance. For example, if the internal impedance of the source is $6 + j8$ ohms, the proper resistive loading for maximum power transfer is $\sqrt{6^2 + 8^2}$ or 10 ohms.

When a circuit is adjusted for maximum power transfer, the circuit is considered to be *matched*. In filter circuit design, matching is not generally done on a conjugate impedance basis.

### Section 7–10   Four-Terminal Networks

In many electronic circuit applications, a generator $E_g$ with an internal impedance $R_g$ is the input to a circuit which produces a voltage $E_2$ across a load resistance $R_L$. The generator is connected to the input terminals $A$ and $B$, and the load is connected across the terminals $C$ and $D$ (Fig. 7–30). The internal circuit between $A$ and $B$ and between $C$ and $D$ may be a very complex network consisting of resistances, inductances, capacitances, transformers, vacuum tubes, and transistors. This internal circuit has no limit as to its complexity. It is often referred to as a *black box* since the nature of its components may be unknown. In order to analyze this circuit, we make two con-

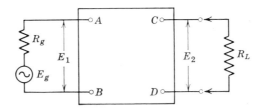

**Figure 7–30** A four-terminal network.

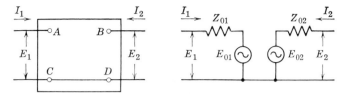

**Figure 7–31** The black box and its equivalent circuit.

ditions on the circuit of the black box. First, there must be a direct connection between one input terminal and one output terminal which is the common ground. Second, all elements within the black box—resistances, inductances, capacitances, transformers, emf's and current sources—must be linear elements.

The black box itself (Fig. 7–31) may be reduced to an equivalent circuit by Thévenin's theorem. The input circuit between $A$ and $C$ is replaced by one equivalent circuit by Thévenin's theorem, and the output circuit between $B$ and $D$ is replaced by a second equivalent circuit. This complete equivalent circuit is often called a *two-terminal-pair* network. Very obviously $E_{01}$ must be related to $E_{02}$ since, in a linear network, a change in the input voltage produces a proportional change in the output voltage.

The circuit of Fig. 7–31, although it is suitable for vacuum-tube analysis, must be modified to serve for transistor-circuit analysis.

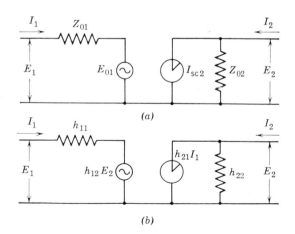

**Figure 7–32** Equivalent circuits for four-terminal networks. (*a*) Using resistances. (*b*) Using hybrid parameters.

The output equivalent circuit is converted from the Thévenin form to the constant-current form of Norton's theorem (Fig. 7–32a). If we refer to the black box of Fig. 7–31 and short-circuit the output, the short-circuit current is evidently determined by the magnitude of either $E_1$ or $I_1$. We can then replace $I_{sc,2}$ by $h_{21}I_1$ where $h_{21}$ is a dimensionless constant of proportionality. When the input is open-circuited, there is a voltage in the input, $E_{01}$, which is directly determined by the value of $E_2$. Then $E_{01}$ may be replaced by $h_{12}E_2$ where $h_{12}$ is another dimensionless constant of proportionality. If $Z_{01}$ is called $h_{11}$ and $h_{22}$ is defined as $1/Z_0$, the dimension of $h_{11}$ is resistance in ohms, and the dimension of $h_{22}$ is conductance in mhos. Making these substitutions, we obtain the circuit of Fig. 7–32b. The two equations from this new circuit are

$$E_1 = h_{11}I_1 + h_{12}E_2 \qquad (7\text{–}12)$$

and

$$I_2 = h_{21}I_1 + h_{22}E_2 \qquad (7\text{–}13)$$

This equivalent circuit has one voltage equivalent circuit and one current equivalent circuit. This mixed combination is a *hybrid* form, and the symbols, $h_{11}$, $h_{12}$, $h_{21}$ and $h_{22}$ used in this circuit and in the equations are termed *hybrid parameters*. Since $h_{11}$ is in ohms, $h_{22}$ is in mhos, and $h_{12}$ and $h_{22}$ are dimensionless, this combination of different units for the different $h$'s also gives rise to the term hybrid parameters.

From Eq. 7–12 and Eq. 7–13, we may readily define these hybrid parameters in terms of $E_1$, $I_1$, $E_2$, and $I_2$.

$$h_{11} = \frac{E_1}{I_1} = Z_1 \quad \text{when} \quad E_2 = 0 \qquad (7\text{–}14)$$

$$\text{(output short-circuited)}$$

$$h_{12} = \frac{E_1}{E_2} \qquad \text{when} \quad I_1 = 0 \qquad (7\text{–}15)$$

$$\text{(input open-circuited)}$$

$$h_{21} = \frac{I_2}{I_1} \qquad \text{when} \quad E_2 = 0 \qquad (7\text{–}16)$$

$$\text{(output short-circuited)}$$

$$h_{22} = \frac{I_2}{E_2} = \frac{1}{Z_2} \quad \text{when} \quad I_1 = 0 \qquad (7\text{–}17)$$

$$\text{(input open-circuited)}$$

The significance of these definitions is that, by making a series of open- and short-circuit measurements on a four-terminal network, the equivalent circuit for the complex network may be established and evaluated.

## . . . . Suggested References for Further Study

1. MIT Electrical Engineering Staff, *Electric Circuits*, John Wiley & Sons, New York, 1940.

2. F. E. Terman, *Electronic and Radio Engineering*, 4th ed., Chapter 3, McGraw-Hill Book Co., New York, 1955.

3. Cruft Electronics Staff, *Electronic Tubes and Circuits*, Chapters 7 and 8, Mc-Graw-Hill Book Co., New York, 1947.

4. H. H. Skilling, *Electric Transmission Lines*, McGraw-Hill Book Co., 1951. (Filters)

## . . . . QUESTIONS

1. Define or explain each of the following terms: (a) resonance, (b) Q gain, (c) shunt loading, (d) bandwidth, (e) coefficient of coupling, (f) critical coupling, (g) attenuate, (h) mirror symmetry, (i) independent node, (j) matched.

2. Are there any assumptions in establishing the formula for series resonance as $f_0 = 1/2\pi \sqrt{LC}$?

3. Are there any assumptions in establishing the formula for parallel resonance as $f_0 = 1/2\pi \sqrt{LC}$?

4. What is the relation between bandwidth and Q?

5. What are the essential characteristics of a series-resonant circuit?

6. What are the essential characteristics of a parallel-resonant circuit?

7. What is the effect of a secondary impedance on the primary winding of a coupled circuit?

8. On what factors does the secondary voltage depend in a coupled circuit?

9. Why does the output of a double-tuned circuit decrease at resonance when the coupling exceeds the critical value?

10. Explain the process of tuning an overcoupled double-tuned transformer.

11. What are the characteristics of the four basic filter circuits?

12. What filter configuration best describes the characteristic of a crystal which is either transparent or opaque depending on the light frequency?

13. When are harmonics useful, and when should they be avoided?

14. Distinguish between complete symmetry and mirror symmetry.

15. Describe the method of circuit analysis, using Kirchhoff's laws.

16. Describe the method of circuit analysis, using the nodal method.

17. Describe the method of circuit analysis, using Thévenin's theorem.

18. Describe the method of circuit analysis, using Norton's theorem.

19. State the maximum power-transfer theorem.

20. In a four-terminal network using hybrid parameters, what are $h_{11}$, $h_{12}$, $h_{21}$, and $h_{22}$?

## . . . . PROBLEMS

1. A series circuit consisting of a 10-$\mu h$ coil in series with a 25-ohm resistance is placed across a 30-volt source. The frequency is varied. Plot current and coil voltage against frequency.

2. A series circuit consisting of a 100-$\mu h$ coil in series with a resistance is placed across a 4-volt 2.5-Mc source. The resistance is varied. Plot current and phase angle against resistance.

3. A coil has an inductance of 65 $\mu h$ and a resistance of 24 ohms. The coil is resonated with a parallel capacitor at 2.75 Mc. What size capacitor is required, and what is the impedance of the tuned circuit at resonance?

4. A 230-$\mu\mu f$ capacitor resonates with a coil at 2.4 Mc. The $Q$ of the coil is 45. What shunting resistance reduces the $Q$ to an effective value of 34? What is the bandwidth of the circuit?

5. A coil has a $Q$ of 70 and is resonant with an 80 $\mu\mu f$ capacitor at 460 kc. The capacitor used has a power factor of 0.006. What is the resulting circuit impedance at resonance? What is the bandwidth?

6. A parallel-tuned circuit is shunted with a 90,000-ohm resistor. The circuit resonates at 760 kc with a 200-$\mu\mu f$ capacitor. The bandwidth is 12 kc. What is the $Q$ of the coil itself?

7. In the circuit shown, $L_1$ has a $Q$ of 40 and an inductance of 30 mh. $L_2$ has a $Q$ of 50 and an inductance of 45 mh. The coefficient of coupling is 60%. The frequency is 6000 cycles, and the load is a 50-ohm resistor. If the applied voltage is 10 volts, determine the input current.

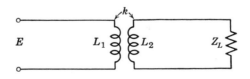

**Prob. 7–7**

8. Solve problem 7 if the load is a 0.01-$\mu$f capacitor.

9. Solve problem 7 if the load is a capacitor which resonates the secondary circuit.

10. Using Kirchhoff's laws, solve the network shown for the battery currents when

$$E_1 = 70 \text{ volts}, \quad R_1 = 15 \text{ ohms}, \quad R_2 = 4 \text{ ohms}$$

$$E_2 = 90 \text{ volts}, \quad R_3 = 14 \text{ ohms},$$

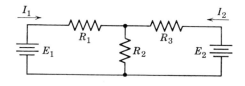

**Prob. 7–10**

11. Solve problem 10 if

$$E_1 = 8 \text{ volts}, \quad R_1 = 12 \text{ ohms}, \quad R_2 = 3 \text{ ohms}$$

$$E_2 = -6 \text{ volts}, \quad R_3 = 7 \text{ ohms}$$

12. Using the nodal method of analysis, solve the circuit for the current through $R_2$ and for the voltage drop across $R_4$ when

$$E_1 = 120 \text{ volts}, \quad R_1 = 40 \text{ ohms}, \quad R_3 = 60 \text{ ohms}, \quad R_5 = 50 \text{ ohms}$$

$$E_2 = 200 \text{ volts}, \quad R_2 = 25 \text{ ohms}, \quad R_4 = 20 \text{ ohms}$$

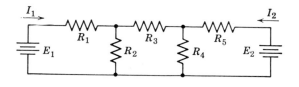

**Prob. 7–12**

13. Solve problem 12 if the polarity of $E_2$ is reversed.

14. Remove the battery $E_2$ from the circuit given in problem 10, and determine the equivalent circuit by Thévenin's theorem.

15. Remove the battery $E_2$ from the circuit given in problem 12, and determine the equivalent circuit by Thévenin's theorem.

16. Remove the battery $E_1$ from the circuit given in problem 10, and determine the equivalent circuit by Norton's theorem.

17. Remove the battery $E_1$ from the circuit given in problem 12, and determine the equivalent circuit by Norton's theorem.

18. In the equivalent circuit obtained in problem 14, what is the output power when the circuit is matched to a load.

19. In the equivalent circuit obtained in problem 15, what is the output power when the circuit is matched to a load?

20. In the circuit given for problem 10, assume that $R_1$, $R_2$, and $R_3$ are contained in a black box. What are the values for the hybrid parameters for the black box?

21. In the circuit given for problem 12, assume that $R_1$, $R_2$, $R_3$, $R_4$, and $R_5$ are contained in a black box. What are the values for the hybrid parameters for the black box?

# Decibels and sound

The consideration that the ear is not linear in its response (Section 8–1) points out the need of decibels as a logarithmic means of having a physical response and an electrical characteristic represented to the same scale (Section 8–2). A review of logarithms (Section 8–3) preceeds actual calculations using the decibel (Section 8–4). A general discussion of loudness and intensity of sound (Section 8–5) leads to the meaning of the rating of a microphone (Section 8–6). The operation of a sound-level meter (Section 8–7) completes the chapter.

### Section 8–1  The Need for a Nonlinear System of Measurement

Human sensory response is nonlinear. As an example showing this nonlinearity, a single match, when suddenly ignited in a dark room, produces a lasting glare. In bright sunlight, the same-size match, when struck, does not give off noticeable light. As another example, the noise of an insect can disrupt the calm of a still summer's night. On the other hand, it would take millions of these insects to be heard over the roar of a passing railroad train. In a dark room, two lighted matches give twice the effect of one match on the response of the human eye. In broad daylight, it would take two suns to give twice the effect of one on human vision. These facts would indicate that a true response would be of the order:

| Steps of equal response | 1 | 2 | 3 | 4 | 5 | 6 | 7 | 8 | 9 |
|---|---|---|---|---|---|---|---|---|---|
| Quantity of cause | $\frac{1}{16}$ | $\frac{1}{8}$ | $\frac{1}{4}$ | $\frac{1}{2}$ | 1 | 2 | 4 | 8 | 16 |

Each successive step doubles the previous quantity, but the change in response is uniform.

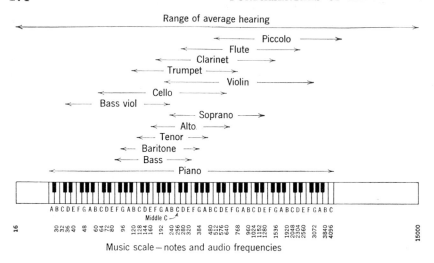

Figure 8–1    Range of frequencies in music.

A further indication of the usefulness of such a scheme is given by the system used in music. In music, an increase in one octave doubles the pitch or frequency. The reference frequency used is "middle C" at 256 cycles. If the relative pitch is plotted on a linear axis, as the keys on a piano, Fig. 8–1 shows that the frequency scale is nonlinear.

The nonlinear responses to these and all sensory responses have been generalized under what is called the Weber-Fechner law.

In mathematics the process of taking logarithms of numbers converts a nonlinear scale, such as the musical scale, into a linear scale. Since each octave in the musical scale is a multiplication of the frequency of the preceding octave by two, the spread of one octave on a logarithmic scale is *log 2* and it is the same number for any one octave.

In showing graphs of frequency response where the independent variable is frequency, the frequency is plotted as the logarithm to the base 10 of the frequency. Since this is the standard conventional practice, graph paper is available called *semilogarithmic* paper in which one axis is logarithmic and the other axis is linear. If we were to use ordinary graph paper for frequency-response curves, it would be necessary to calculate the logarithms of the different frequencies used. In semilogarithmic graph paper, the engraved printing plate is designed so that it is laid out proportionally to the logarithms on one axis scale. When this paper is used, there is no need to calculate logarithms; that work was done in the original design of the graph paper.

If it is desired to represent 20 to 20,000 cycles, the required logarithmic axis would be 10 to 100 to 1000 to 10,000 to 100,000 or four-cycle semilogarithmic paper. To represent 20 to 8000 cycles, one would need a logarithmic axis of 10 to 100 to 1000 to 10,000 or three-cycle semilogarithmic paper. Figure 8–3 is drawn on four-cycle semi-logarithmic paper.

### Section 8-2  The Decibel

In honor of Alexander Graham Bell, the logarithm to the base 10 of the ratio of two powers is defined as a *bel:*

$$\text{Number of bels} = \log_{10} \frac{P_2}{P_1}$$

where $P_2$ and $P_1$ represent the two powers that are being compared.

The bel as a unit is cumbersome for general use and for problem solution. In order to have numerical results for problems and applications as numbers which are normally larger than unity, we define the *decibel* as one tenth of a bel:

$$\text{Number of decibels} = 10 \log_{10} \frac{P_2}{P_1} \tag{8–1}$$

In audio work, a change in power level of one decibel is barely perceptible to the ear. A change of two decibels is slightly apparent.

### Section 8-3  Logarithms

Since the decibel is defined as a logarithm, the technique of the mathematical process of taking logarithms must be studied. In working with decibels, there is a slight variation from the normal mathematical procedure which greatly simplifies the final numerical result. All the work done in taking logarithms is to the base 10. Thus, no subscripts will be used when writing *log;* the 10 is understood.

$$\log 10,000 = 4$$
$$\log 1000 = 3$$
$$\log 100 = 2$$
$$\log 10 = 1$$
$$\log 1 = 0$$

The numbers, 4, 3, 2, 1, and 0, are known as the *characteristic*. The characteristic numerically is one less than the number of digits in the number to the left of the decimal point. If the number were 834.24, the characteristic is 2. This means that the logarithm of the number lies between 2 and 3. If the number were 8342.4, the logarithm would have the characteristic 3 and lie between 3 and 4. The exact decimal of the logarithm is called the *mantissa*. The mantissa for 834.24 is the same as the mantissa for 8342.4. It is also the same for 8,342,400 or 8.3424. The mantissa is determined by the sequence of the digits and not by the decimal point. The placement of the decimal point in the original number determines the characteristic. In general, the characteristic is determined by visual inspection, and the mantissa is determined by the use of a slide rule. Some examples are:

$$\log 834{,}240 = 5.921$$

$$\log 74 \times 10^5 = 6.870$$

$$\log 231 = 2.364$$

$$\log 3.85 = 0.586$$

A table of logarithms could be used in lieu of a slide rule, but the slide rule has the advantage of saving time while maintaining sufficient accuracy for most problems.

A formal mathematical definition may be given to a logarithm. If a number $N$ is expressed in the form of the $x$ power of 10, the logarithm of $N$ to the base 10 is $x$.

If $$N = 10^x$$

then $$\log_{10} N = x$$

When a number $M$ is less than 1, it may be written

$$M = \frac{1}{10^y}$$

where $y$ is a positive number greater than zero. Then

$$M = 10^{-y}$$

and by the definition of the logarithm

$$\log_{10} M = -y$$

This approach for a number $M$, which is less than one but greater than zero, is a little different from the usual method of determining logarithms for calculation of numerical problems in mathematics but is the approach that *must* be taken when working with decibels. For example, to find the logarithm of 0.1, convert 0.1 to the fraction 1/10. Then

$$\log 0.1 = \log \frac{1}{10} = -\log 10 = -1$$

Similar examples are

$$\log 0.001 = \log \frac{1}{1000} = -\log 1000 = -3$$

$$\log 0.20 = \log \frac{1}{5} = -\log 5 = -0.700$$

$$\log 0.375 = \log \frac{1}{2.667} = -\log 2.667 = -0.426$$

$$\log 0.023 = \log \frac{1}{43.5} = -\log 43.5 = -1.638$$

As a general rule, *take logarithms only of numbers that are greater than 1.*

In taking antilogarithms, the method is directly the inverse process used for finding logarithms. Some examples are as follows:

If $\log x = 4$,  $x = 10,000$

If $\log x = 2$,  $x = 100$

If $\log x = 0.254$,  $x = 1(\text{antilog } 0.254) = 1(1.795) = 1.795$

If $\log x = 3.621$,  $x = 1000(\text{antilog } 0.621)$

$$= 1000(4.18) = 4180$$

If $\log x = -2.00$, $\dfrac{1}{x} = 100(\text{antilog } 0) = 100(1) = 100$

$$x = 0.01$$

If $\log x = -4.854$, $\dfrac{1}{x} = 10,000(\text{antilog } 0.854) = 10,000(7.13)$

$$= 71,300$$

$$x = 0.0000140$$

In working with decibels, we need to evaluate the logarithm of zero.

If
$$0 = \frac{1}{\infty}$$

then
$$\log 0 = \log \frac{1}{\infty} = -\log \infty = -\infty$$

or
$$\log 0 = -\infty$$

Thus, the logarithm of zero is equal to minus infinity.

### Section 8-4    Decibel Calculations

In Section 8–2, we defined the decibel as

$$\text{db} = 10 \log \frac{P_2}{P_1} \tag{8-1}$$

Properly speaking, a decibel is a measure of a power ratio, but very often the measurements are taken in terms of voltage, current, or impedance. In a general case,

$$P_1 = \frac{E_1{}^2}{Z_1 \cos \theta_1} \quad \text{and} \quad P_2 = \frac{E_2{}^2}{Z_2 \cos \theta_2}$$

Then
$$\text{db} = 10 \log \frac{P_2}{P_1} = 10 \log \frac{E_2{}^2/Z_2 \cos \theta_2}{E_1{}^2/Z_1 \cos \theta_1}$$

$$\text{db} = 10 \log \frac{E_2{}^2 Z_1 \cos \theta_1}{E_1{}^2 Z_2 \cos \theta_2} = 10 \log \left(\frac{E_2}{E_1}\right)^2 \left(\frac{Z_1}{Z_2}\right) \left(\frac{\cos \theta_1}{\cos \theta_2}\right)$$

$$\text{db} = 20 \log \frac{E_2}{E_1} + 10 \log \frac{Z_1}{Z_2} + 10 \log \frac{\cos \theta_1}{\cos \theta_2}$$

In most instances of application, it may be assumed that the two impedances are purely resistive. For pure resistance the power factor $\cos \theta$ is unity, and, as the logarithm of one is zero, the expression simplifies to

$$\text{db} = 20 \log \frac{E_2}{E_1} + 10 \log \frac{R_1}{R_2} \tag{8-2}$$

When the two resistances are equal or refer to the same resistance, $R_1/R_2$ becomes unity. The resistance correction term, $10 \log (R_1/R_2)$, is zero, and the decibel relation becomes

$$\text{db} = 20 \log \frac{E_2}{E_1} \tag{8-3}$$

If this decibel relation is evaluated in terms of currents instead of voltages, we have

$$P_1 = I_1{}^2 R_1 \quad \text{and} \quad P_2 = I_2{}^2 R_2$$

Then

$$db = 10 \log \frac{I_2{}^2 R_2}{I_1{}^2 R_1}$$

$$db = 20 \log \frac{I_2}{I_1} + 10 \log \frac{R_2}{R_1} \tag{8-4}$$

As an example assume that the voltage across a loudspeaker is 2.3 volts, and, when the volume control is advanced, the speaker voltage becomes 4.8 volts. The decibel increase in gain is

$$db = 20 \log \frac{V_2}{V_1}$$

$$db = 20 \log \frac{4.8}{2.3} = 20 \log 2.09$$

$$= 20 \times 0.320 = 6.4$$

$$db = +6.4 \quad \text{(gain)}$$

We did not use the correction factor, $10 \log (R_1/R_2)$ because both measurements are taken across the same loudspeaker.

In another example, the input to a transmission line is 64 volts, and the output voltage is 18 volts. Since the output is less than the input, we have a loss in gain:

$$db = 20 \log \frac{E_2}{E_1} = 20 \log \frac{18}{64} = -20 \log \frac{64}{18}$$

$$= -20 \log 3.55 = -20 \times 0.550 = -11.1$$

$$db = -11.1 \quad \text{(loss)}$$

When the impedance is not specified, it must be assumed that the two values are the same and that the correction term, $10 \log (R_1/R_2)$, accordingly is zero. It is standard practice in decibel calculations to insist that the sign + or − be associated with the numerical value. A *+7 db* means a gain or increase in level of 7 decibels whereas *−4 db* means a decrease in level or a loss of 4 decibels. Sometimes these figures are expressed as "7 db up" and "4 db down." In filter work a +db value ordinarily means loss and a −db means gain.

Certain decibel values shown in Table I are very convenient to use and should be memorized as they represent whole number ratios.

When the voltage ratio is 2, we find db = 20 log 2 = +6 db. When the voltage ratio is $\frac{1}{2}$, db = −6. If the power ratio is 2, db = 10 log 2 = +3 db. If the power ratio is $\frac{1}{2}$, db = 10 log $\frac{1}{2}$ = −10 log 2 = −3 db. As the power in a resistive circuit varies directly as the square of the voltage, a voltage ratio of 2 or $\frac{1}{2}$ corresponds to a power ratio of $\sqrt{2}$ or $1/\sqrt{2}$.

TABLE I

| Decibels | Voltage Ratio | Power Ratio |
|----------|---------------|-------------|
| −6 | $\frac{1}{2}$ or 0.500 | $\frac{1}{4}$ or 0.250 |
| −3 | $1/\sqrt{2}$ or 0.707 | $\frac{1}{2}$ or 0.500 |
| 0 | 1 | 1 |
| 3 | $\sqrt{2}$ or 1.414 | 2 |
| 6 | 2 | 4 |

As an example of the use of these special values, assume that an initial power level of 60 mw is subject to a +28 db gain. The approximate result is as follows.

0 db is 60 mw.

+6 db gain (power ratio of 4) raises the power level to 240 mw or 0.24 watts.

Another +6 db, a total of +12 db, increases the power level by 4 to 0.96 watts.

Another +6 db, a total of +18 db, increases the power level by 4 to 3.84 watts.

Another +6 db, a total of +24 db, increases the power level by 4 to 15.36 watts.

Another +3 db, a total of +27 db, increases the power level by 2 to 30.72 watts.

Another +3 db, a total of +30 db, increases the power level by 2 to 61.44 watts.

If the last three-decibel steps were linear, the result would be about 41 watts. The result by slide-rule calculation is 37.8 watts. This method is often very useful for giving a rapidly obtained approximate result without the use of a slide rule or tables.

**Problem.** Let us assume that a microphone delivers 36 mv at 300 ohms into an amplifier which delivers 15 watts into a 16-ohm speaker system at full power. To find the decibel gain of the amplifier, we may use either the power equation or the voltage equation.

**Solution 1.** The power in the microphone is

$$P_1 = \frac{E_1{}^2}{R_1} = \frac{0.036^2}{300} = 4.32 \times 10^{-6} \text{ watts}$$

$$\text{db} = 10 \log \frac{P_2}{P_1} = 10 \log \frac{15}{4.32 \times 10^{-6}}$$

$$= 10 \log 3.48 \times 10^6 = 10 \times 6.541$$

$$\text{db} = +65.41 \text{ gain}$$

**Solution 2.** The voltage at the speaker is

$$P_2 = \frac{E_2{}^2}{R_2}$$

$$15 = \frac{E_2{}^2}{16}$$

$$E_2 = 15.48$$

$$\text{db} = 20 \log \frac{E_2}{E_1} + 10 \log \frac{R_1}{R_2}$$

$$\text{db} = 20 \log \frac{15.480}{0.036} + 10 \log \frac{300}{16}$$

$$\text{db} = 20 \log 430 + 10 \log 18.75$$

$$\text{db} = 20 \times 2.634 + 10 \times 1.273$$

$$\text{db} = 52.68 + 12.73 = +65.41 \text{ gain}$$

Very often it is very useful to have a meter that is calibrated to read directly in decibels. Since the definition of the term decibel stated that the decibel is a power ratio, a wattmeter with a new scale could be used. However, wattmeters are prohibitively expensive for this use. An a-c voltmeter ordinarily serves as a decibel meter subject to certain restrictions. As 12 volts across 30 ohms is not the same power as 12 volts across 4000 ohms, the decibel meter needs the additional specification that its scale is accurate only when the meter is used on the specified impedance for which the instrument was calibrated. Three standard zero references are in common use:

*Electronics Industry:* The zero decibel reference is a 6-mw power dissipated in a 500-ohm resistive load.

*Radiobroadcasting Industry:* The zero decibel reference is a 1-mw power dissipated in a 600-ohm resistive load. This reference is abbreviated *dbm* to distinguish it from the first reference value.

*The Volume Unit (VU):* The volume unit reference is a 1-mw power dissipated in a 600-ohm resistive load. The volume unit is used only to read power levels in complex waves such as program lines carrying speech or music. When the meter is used on pure sine-wave signals, the reading should be taken as *dbm*. A zero volume unit means that a complex wave has the same average power that a 1-mw sine-wave signal set at 1000 cycles would indicate.

Thus, if the VU meter is used to measure decibels, it does not give a true reading without a correction factor. The reference impedances and the reference powers are different. A correction factor must be *subtracted* from the readings of the VU meter to give the reading in decibels. The conversions between the references are left as an exercise to the reader.

The reference for 0 db at 6 mw in 500 ohms is, by calculation, a specific voltage value:

$$P = \frac{E^2}{R}$$

$$0.006 = \frac{E^2}{500}$$

$$E^2 = 3$$

$$E = \sqrt{3} = 1.73 \text{ volts}$$

If the 0- to 3-volt scale of a meter is calibrated in decibels, then 0 db is located at 1.73 volts. The scale marking of −6 db corresponds to a half-voltage ratio, 1.73/2, or 0.865 volts. The scale reading of −3 db is at $1.73/\sqrt{2}$ or 1.225 volts. Likewise, +3 db corresponds to $1.73\sqrt{2}$ or 2.45 volts and +4 db to 2.74 volts; +5 db is 3.08 volts and is slightly off scale. The zero on the 3-volt scale is evaluated as $-\log \infty$ or $-\infty$ db. The two scales are shown in Fig. 8–2.

All these concepts can be illustrated in the solution of a problem which is commonly encountered in the measurement of audio fre-

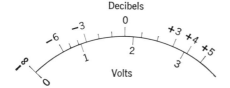

**Figure 8–2** Scale of a decibel meter.

quencies. In working with decibels, we often find more than one approach may be taken to determine the final result.

**Problem.** A multirange a-c meter has a 0- to 3-volt scale which is calibrated in decibels (reference: 0 db is 6 mw in a 500-ohm load) as shown in Fig. 8-2. The 0- to 60-volt scale is not calibrated in decibels. The meter reads $-4.5$ db, but the voltage-range selector switch is set on the 60-volt range. The load impedance across which the meter is connected is 4500 ohms. Determine the meter reading in decibels, the true decibel value, and the load power.

**Solution 1.** The scale-range factor, 60/3 or 20, is an increase in voltage and power level. The scale-correction factor introduced by switching to a higher-voltage range is

$$db = +20 \log 20 = +26 \text{ db}$$

If the 60-volt scale were marked in decibels also, it would read for this meter deflection:

$$-4.5 + 26 = +21.5 \text{ db}$$

The meter is calibrated for 500 ohms, but it is used across 4500 ohms. For the same voltage reading, the power dissipated in 4500 ohms must be less than if the meter were connected to the 500 ohms for which it is calibrated. Therefore, the impedance correction factor is negative:

$$db = -10 \log \tfrac{4500}{500} = -9.54 \text{ db}$$

The true level is the meter reading plus the impedance correction factor:

$$21.5 - 9.54 = +11.96 \text{ db}$$

The true power is

$$db = 10 \log \text{ (power ratio)}$$

$$11.96 = 10 \log \text{ (power ratio)}$$

$$\log \text{ (power ratio)} = 1.196$$

$$\text{Power ratio} = 15.70$$

Since the true power is a $+$db, and since the zero reference level of the meter scale is 6 mw, the true power is $6 \times 15.70$ or 94.2 mw. (If the true power level were $-11.96$ db, we would divide 6 by 15.70 instead of multiplying.)

**Solution 2.** The reference level of 0 db corresponds to 1.73 volts. The $-4.5$-db reading indicates that the meter is reading less than 1.73 volts.

$$4.5 = 20 \log \text{ (voltage ratio)}$$

$$\log \text{ (voltage ratio)} = 0.225$$

$$\text{Voltage ratio} = 1.68$$

Therefore the meter reads:

$$\frac{1.73}{1.68} = 1.03 \text{ volts}$$

As the conversion from the 3-volt scale to the 60-volt scale is a factor of 20, the true load voltage is

$$1.03 \times 20 = 20.6 \text{ volts}$$

The true load power is

$$P_L = \frac{E_2{}^2}{R_L} = \frac{20.6^2}{4500} = 0.0942 \text{ watts}$$

$$= 94.2 \text{ mw}$$

The true decibel value is

$$\text{db} = 10 \log \frac{P_2}{P_1} = 10 \log \frac{94.2}{6}$$

$$= 10 \log 15.7 = +11.96 \text{ db}$$

The meter reading is the true decibel value *plus* the impedance correction factor of 9.54 db or $+21.5$ db.

## Section 8–5    Loudness

H. Fletcher and W. A. Munson presented in the October 1933 issue of the *Journal of the Acoustical Society of America* the results of their lengthy research in sound, "Loudness, its definition, measurement and calculation." In this paper they presented a graph (Fig. 8–3) which relates frequency, decibels, and *phons*. A phon is the logarithmic sound-intensity-level unit which corresponds to the decibel in the electrical scale. Phons are numerically equal to decibels at 1000 cycles. Zero phons is the lower limit of audibility; 120 phons is a loudness level which is the threshold of feeling and pain. Zero phons at 1000 cycles is established as the reference level of sound pressure which is $10^{-16}$ watts per square centimeter or 0.0002 dyne/cm$^2$.

From these curves, we note that, in order to have threshold audibility at 100 cycles, we must have a $+38$-db increase in power at 100 cycles over the power required for threshold hearing at 1000 cycles. One of the important results of this research was to show that, as the sound level increases, the curves tend to flatten out. Very often the term phon is dropped, and the term decibel is used in its place. This tends to become confusing, but usually the context determines which is being considered. Thus, a 60-db sound level refers not to the driving power, but to a phon level of 60.

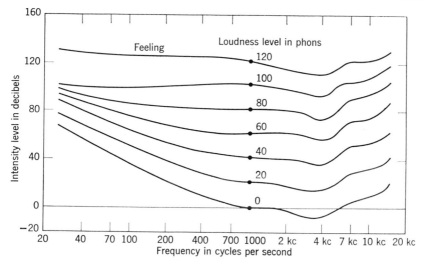

**Figure 8-3**  Equal-loudness contours.  (Reference: 0 db = $10^{-16}$ watt/cm² at 1 kc)

## Section 8-6  Microphone Ratings

Manufacturers of microphones have found that it is very convenient to use some form of the decibel to specify the output. The method of rating is not completely uniform and some typical microphone ratings are:

(*a*)  58 db below 1 mw per 10 microbars signal at 50 ohms impedance.

(*b*)  56 db below 1 volt per microbar.

(*c*)  50 db below 1 volt/dyne/cm².

(*d*)  −54 db where 0 db is 1 volt/dyne/cm² for high impedance. A 500-ohm impedance output is available.

The part of the rating that reads "58 db below 1 mw" or "56 db below 1 volt" refers to the method of decibel calculations that we have used up to this point.  The *bar* is a unit of sound pressure equal to 1,000,000 dynes per square centimeter.  A *microbar* is one dyne per square centimeter.  As we have defined the phon as a pressure of 0.0002 dyne/cm² at the threshold of hearing, the microbar equals

$$20 \log \frac{1}{0.0002} = 20 \log 500 = +54 \text{ phons} \quad \text{(or db)} \quad \text{at 1000 cycles}$$

Ten microbars is then

$$54 + 20 \log \frac{10}{1} = +74 \text{ phons} \quad (+74 \text{ db at } 1000 \text{ cycles})$$

The noise level of ordinary conversation at 3 feet, the noise level of a large office, or the noise level of a large store averages $+65$ db. Busy street traffic is about $+70$ db, and a riveter at 35 feet averages $+97$ db.

If a high-impedance microphone is rated at $-54$ db based on a zero reference level of one volt per microbar, the open-circuit voltage at this sound level is

$$\text{db} = 20 \log(\text{voltage ratio})$$

$$54 = 20 \log(\text{voltage ratio})$$

$$\text{log (voltage ratio)} = \frac{54}{20} = 2.70$$

$$\text{Voltage ratio} = 500$$

$$E = \frac{1}{500} = 0.002 \text{ volts} = 2 \text{ mv output}$$

If this microphone were available to match a 500-ohm load impedance, under the conditions of maximum power transfer (Section 7–9), the load voltage is one-half the value of the open-circuit emf. This means that there is an additional 6 db loss in the impedance transfer circuit, since the half-voltage corresponds to $-6$ db. Now the microphone would be rated at $-60$ db instead of $-54$ db to include this coupling network loss. If a microphone is specifically listed as being designed to work into a load and to develop a given power in that load, this correction factor of $-6$ db is not needed.

### Section 8–7   Sound-Level Meters

A sound-level meter is an instrument with a microphone, an amplifier, and an output meter which reads the noise level and is usually calibrated in decibels. Simple sound-level meters have response curves which follow the Fletcher–Munson equal-loudness contours (Fig. 8–3). If the over-all frequency response of the contour of the meter, the amplifier, and the microphone is adjusted for the 40-phon sound level, it is most accurate for low sound intensities. A meter set for the 70-phon contour is most accurate for medium sound levels and a flat response is most accurate at high sound intensities. These three response levels are accepted as the standards for sound-level

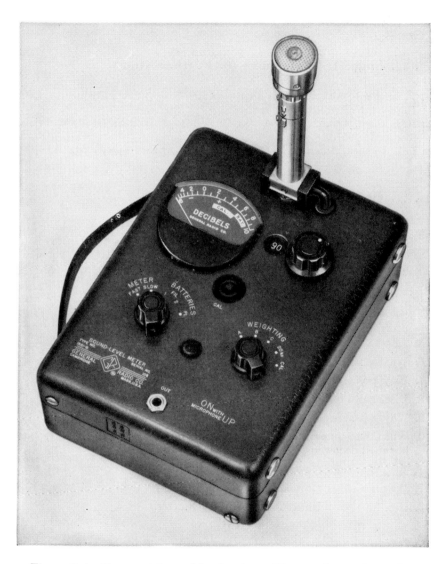

**Figure 8–4** Commercial sound-level meter. (*Courtesy General Radio Co.*)

measurements. The meter may be highly damped to read average sound level or be lightly damped to show peaks. Figure 8–4 shows a typical commercial sound-level meter.

. . . . **Suggested References for Further Study**

1. F. Langford-Smith, *Radiotron Designer's Handbook*, 4th ed., Chapter 19, RCA, Harrison, N. J., 1953.
2. H. F. Olsen, *Acoustical Engineering*, Chapter 12, D. Van Nostrand Co., Princeton, N. J., 1957.
3. L. L. Beranek, *Acoustics*, McGraw-Hill Book Co., New York, 1954.

. . . . **QUESTIONS**

1. Define or explain each of the following terms: (a) Weber–Fechner law, (b) Fletcher–Munson curves, (c) semilog graph paper, (d) octave, (e) decibel, (f) mantissa, (g) characteristic for log, (h) VU, (i) phon, (j) microbar.

2. Explain why decibels are used.

3. Why is the plus sign used in decibel terminology?

4. As a voltage ratio, what is 0 db? −3 db? −6 db? +3 db? +6 db?

5. As a power ratio, what is 0 db? −3 db? −6 db? +3 db? +6 db?

6. What is the logarithm of zero?

7. Why are correction factors necessary when decibel meters are used?

8. Distinguish between dbm and VU.

9. Why is it necessary to introduce the term "loudness"?

10. When the volume of a record player is increased, should the bass response be raised or lowered? The treble?

11. Why is a meter movement lightly damped?

12. Why is a meter movement heavily damped?

13. Give four possible uses for a sound-level meter.

. . . . **PROBLEMS**

1. Determine the logarithms of the following numbers: (a) 2650, (b) 132, (c) 756,000, (d) 1.46, (e) $294 \times 10^{16}$, (f) 0.0023, (g) 0.874, (h) $\frac{1}{16}$, (i) $\frac{3}{64}$, (j) $84 \times 10^{-6}$.

2. Determine the numbers for which the logarithms are: (a) 2.46, (b) 6.92, (c) 14.20, (d) 23.3, (e) 0.024, (f) −5.78, (g) 0, (h) −27.4, (i) $\frac{1}{16}$, (j) 7.23.

3. The gain of an amplifier is +46 db. The amplifier delivers 3 watts into a 4-ohm load. The amplifier input resistance is 150,000 ohms. What input voltage is necessary to produce full output power?

4. The input resistance to an amplifier is 175 ohms, and the output resistance is 3000 ohms. The amplifier gain is +18 db. What is the apparent voltage gain of the amplifier?

5. An amplifier drives a 16-ohm load. The hum-level rating of the amplifier is 70 db below the full power-output rating which is 25 watts. What is the hum level in the load in milliwatts, and what voltage does the hum produce across the load?

6. The input resistance of an amplifier is 75 ohms, and the input current is 6 ma. The output resistance is 2300 ohms, and the output voltage is 16 volts. What is the amplifier voltage gain, and what is the power gain? Express both in decibels.

7. The output of an amplifier decreases from 15 watts to 6 watts when a new input cable is used. What is the increase in attenuation of the new cable compared to the old cable?

8. The input to a 1400-foot 72-ohm transmission line is 64 volts. The output is 12 volts when the load is matched. What is the loss of the transmission line expressed in decibels per hundred feet?

9. A phonograph pickup develops 15 mv across a 35-ohm input. A 15-watt speaker system has an impedance of 8 ohms. What minimum amplifier gain is necessary to produce full power output?

10. What is the conversion factor when a decibel meter calibrated for 6 mw across 500 ohms is used as a VU meter on a 600-ohm line?

For the following three problems, the decibel meter is calibrated to a 6-mw 500-ohm standard (0 db). The meter scale (Fig. 8–2) is marked in decibels for the 0- to 3-volt range.

11. The meter is placed across a 4500-ohm load and reads +2.5 db. The scale-range switch is set to the 30-volt scale. What is the true load power, and what is the true decibel value?

12. The meter is placed across a 75-ohm load and reads −5.5 db. The scale-range switch is set on the 60-volt scale. What is the true load power, and what is the true decibel value?

13. The meter is placed across a 1200-ohm load and reads +3 db. The scale-range switch is set on the 300-volt scale. What is the true load power, and what is the true power in VU?

14. A microphone is rated at 50 db below one volt per microbar. The rated output impedance of the microphone is 500 ohms. What amplifier gain is necessary to develop 6 watts of audio power from ordinary conversation around a conference table?

15. Solve problem 14 if the only change is that the microphone is rated −55 db where 0 db is 1 volt/dyne/cm².

# Rectifiers

•••••••••••••••••••••• CHAPTER 9

The half-wave rectifier (Section 9–1), the full-wave rectifier (Section 9–2), and the bridge rectifier (Section 9–3) are the three basic rectifying circuits in general use in power supplies. Their salient features are compared in Section 9–4. In order to decrease the amount of ripple in the rectifier output, the capacitor filter (Section 9–5), or the choke filter (Section 9–6), or the $\pi$ filter (Section 9–7) is used. Voltage doublers (Section 9–8) and mechanical-vibrator power supplies (Section 9–9) are used for special applications. The thyratron rectifier (Section 9–10) as a controlled-grid rectifier has many applications in industrial electronics.

The electronic-regulated power supply is analyzed in Section 17–9. Transistors are often used as a source of a-c power in conjunction with these rectifier circuits. The topic of transistor power supplies is considered in Section 21–8.

### Section 9–1   The Half-Wave Rectifier

The basic action of the half-wave rectifier with a resistive load was considered in Section 2-2 as an application of the vacuum-tube diode. The basic circuit and the fundamental waveforms for an ideal diode in which the forward tube drop is zero are redrawn in Fig. 9–1 for convenience. It should be noted that, for this circuit, the frequency of the a-c variation in the load-voltage waveform is the same as the frequency of the applied alternating voltage.

If $E$ is the rms or effective value of the transformer secondary voltage, and if $E_m$ is its peak value, we have, from Eq. 2–3:

$$E_{\text{dc}} = \frac{E_m}{\pi} = \frac{\sqrt{2}\,E}{\pi} = 0.318E_m = 0.450E$$

and $\quad I_{\text{dc}} = \dfrac{I_m}{\pi} = \dfrac{E_m}{\pi R_L} = \dfrac{\sqrt{2}\,E}{\pi R_L} = \dfrac{E_{\text{dc}}}{R_L} = 0.318I_m = 0.450\,\dfrac{E}{R_L}$ $\quad$ (9–1)

where $\qquad\qquad\qquad E_m = \sqrt{2}\,E.$

In Fig. 9–2, when waveform $b$ is added point by point to waveform $a$, the result is waveform $c$. $E_A$ is a direct voltage and $E_B$ is the rms value of the wave $b$. If $E_C$ represents the rms value of the total wave $c$, then, by fundamentals of a-c circuit theory, we may write

$$E_A{}^2 + E_B{}^2 = E_C{}^2$$

If the waveform of Fig. 9–2c represents the output of a rectifier circuit, then $a$ is the direct current in the output, and $b$ is the alternating current in the output. The a-c component of the output is called the *ripple*. The ratio of the amount of ripple to the d-c value is called the *ripple factor*, and, when it is expressed in per cent, it is called

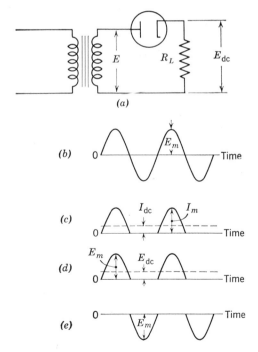

**Figure 9–1** The half-wave rectifier. (*a*) Circuit. (*b*) Input voltage. (*c*) Tube and load current. (*d*) Load voltage. (*e*) Tube voltage.

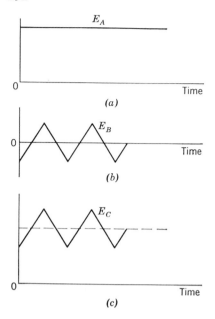

**Figure 9–2**   Superimposed d-c and a-c waves.

the *per cent ripple*.   The value of this ripple factor then is a measure of the effectiveness of the circuit in rectifying.   A d'Arsonval-type d-c instrument reads $E_A$ directly.   An a-c meter which reads true effective values such as an electrodynamometer movement or an iron-vane movement will read $E_C$.   A blocking capacitor placed in series with the a-c meter keeps out the direct current and allows a reading of $E_B$ to be made directly.   A rectifier-type instrument is calibrated for sinusoidal waveforms only and cannot give a true reading for $E_C$ at all, but it is often accurate enough to be used to read $E_B$.   If we know the values for $E_A$ and $E_C$, then the ripple voltage $E_B$ is

$$E_B{}^2 = E_C{}^2 - E_A{}^2$$

$$E_B = \sqrt{E_C{}^2 - E_A{}^2}$$

$$\text{Ripple} = \frac{E_B}{E_A} = \frac{\sqrt{E_C{}^2 - E_A{}^2}}{E_A}$$

The load-voltage waveform for the half-wave rectifier (Fig. 9–1c) is the positive half of the sine wave.   Since only the half sine-wave contributes, its rms value must be $\sqrt{\tfrac{1}{2}}$ times the rms value of a normal sine wave or $E_m/2$.   The average or d-c value of this rectified wave is

$E_m/\pi$. If we let the rms value of the ripple voltage be denoted by $E_R$, we have

$$\left(\frac{E_m}{2}\right)^2 = \left(\frac{E_m}{\pi}\right)^2 + (E_R)^2$$

$$E_R{}^2 = \frac{E_m{}^2}{4} - \frac{E_m{}^2}{\pi^2} = \left(\frac{1}{4} - \frac{1}{\pi^2}\right)E_m{}^2$$

$$E_R = \sqrt{\frac{1}{4} - \frac{1}{\pi^2}}\, E_m = 0.386 E_m = 0.545 E \qquad (9\text{-}2)$$

From Eq. 9–1 the direct voltage in the output is

$$E_{\text{dc}} = 0.318 E_m$$

Then

$$\text{Ripple factor} = \frac{E_R}{E_{\text{dc}}} = \frac{0.386 E_m}{0.318 E_m} = 1.21 \qquad (9\text{-}3)$$

The conclusion we may draw from this is that, for a half-wave rectifier with resistive load, the amount of alternating current in the output is greater than the amount of direct current in the output.

Since the current and voltage in a resistive load are proportional by Ohm's law, if the rms value of load voltage is $E_m/2$, the rms value of load current is $E_m/2R_L$. The total power delivered to the load by the transformer is $(E_m/2) \times (E_m/2R_L)$ or $E_m{}^2/4R_L$. The direct load voltage is $E_m/\pi$ and the direct load current is $E_m/\pi R_L$. Then, the d-c load power is $(E_m/\pi) \times (E_m/\pi R_L)$ or $E_m{}^2/\pi^2 R_L$. The *ratio of rectification* is defined as the ratio of the d-c power delivered by the rectifier circuit to the a-c input power delivered to the circuit:

$$\text{Ratio of rectification} = \frac{E_m{}^2/\pi^2 R_L}{E_m{}^2/4R_L} = \frac{4}{\pi^2} = 0.406 \qquad (9\text{-}4)$$

The ratio of rectification cannot be truly considered an efficiency since it does not include the losses of the diodes and of the transformer. It is an efficiency in the sense that the over-all operating efficiency of a half-wave rectifier with a resistive load cannot be greater than 40.6%.

The rating of the secondary winding is $E$ or $E_m/\sqrt{2}$ volts and the actual alternating current is $E_m/2R_L$, giving an a-c power equal to $E_m/\sqrt{2} \times E_m/2R_L$ or $E_m{}^2/2\sqrt{2}\,R_L$ watts. The d-c load power has been determined as $E_m{}^2/\pi^2 R_L$ watts. The ratio of these two powers is the *transformer utilization factor:*

$$\text{Transformer utilization factor} = \frac{E_m{}^2/\pi^2 R_L}{E_m{}^2/2 \sqrt{2} R_L} = \frac{2 \sqrt{2}}{\pi^2} = 0.287$$

$$(9\text{–}5)$$

The meaning of this ratio may best be explained by the use of a numerical example. If a 1-kva transformer is used in a half-wave rectifier circuit with resistive load, the irregular nonsinusoidal waveforms which occur limit the available d-c power to 287 watts. Since the ratio of rectification is 0.406, the input power from the line is 287/0.406 or 706 watts. In practice the figure of 287 watts would be too high since we have assumed that the diode does not absorb power in plate dissipation. The transformer utilization ratio is the power factor of the secondary winding of the transformer.

There is a direct current in the diode and in the load. This same direct current must flow in the transformer secondary winding. This direct current may saturate the secondary winding. A condition of saturation materially reduces the transformer output by reducing the amplitude of the secondary voltage wave. In order to prevent an adverse effect caused by saturation, the transformer core size must be increased. This effectively means that the transformer utilization factor of 0.287 must be reduced still further in practice.

In conclusion, we may state that the single-phase rectifiers have four material disadvantages:

1. A very high ripple.
2. A low ratio of rectification (efficiency).
3. A low transformer utilization factor.
4. Definite possibility of d-c saturation of the transformer secondary.

The circuit has the advantage of being the simplest possible rectifier arrangement. It is used only for such applications where the advantage of the simple circuit arrangement outweighs the disadvantages. Also it is commonly used where the load current requirements are very low.

### Section 9–2    The Full-Wave Rectifier

In a full-wave rectifier circuit (Fig. 9–3a) the transformer secondary coil has a center tap, $b$, which is the common return point of the rectifier circuit. The secondary voltage is considered to be measured from $b$ to $c$ and from $b$ to $a$ and not from $c$ to $a$. To avoid confusion, the voltage

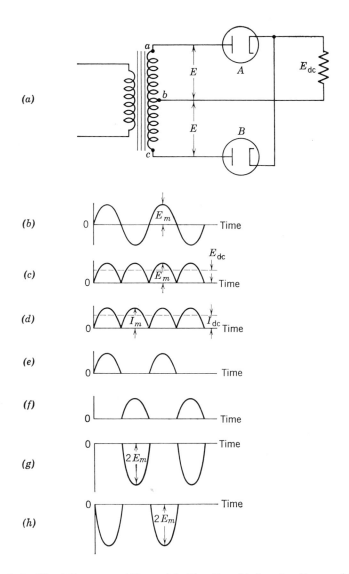

**Figure 9-3** The full-wave rectifier. (*a*) Circuit. (*b*) Input voltage. (*c*) Load voltage. (*d*) Load current. (*e*) Diode *A* current. (*f*) Diode *B* current. (*g*) Diode *A* voltage. (*h*) Diode *B* voltage.

of a secondary winding intended for use in this circuit is specified as, for example, 350–0–350 volts. This means that from $b$ to $a$ we have 350 volts rms, and from $b$ to $c$ the voltage reading is also 350 volts rms. Between $c$ and $a$ the voltage is 700 volts rms.

When $a$ is positive, tube $A$ passes current and $c$ is negative, making the plate of tube $B$ negative with respect to the cathode. When $c$ is positive, there is current in tube $B$ and the plate of tube $A$ is negative, preventing current in tube $A$. In this manner tube $A$ handles the positive half of the a-c cycle and tube $B$ handles the negative half of the a-c cycle. Current then flows through the load with each half of the a-c cycle. This full-wave action contrasts with the half-wave rectifier in which a pulse of load current flows only once per a-c cycle. The waveforms in the load are shown in Figs. 9–3$c$ and $d$. Each tube by itself carries only half-wave current (Figs. 9–3$e$ and $f$). The envelope of the load-current and load-voltage waveforms repeats twice for each full a-c cycle of the supply voltage. The ripple frequency is then twice the line frequency.

If we consider the instant when $a$ is at positive $E_m$, $b$ is at negative $E_m$ with respect to the common circuit return $b$. Tube $A$ rectifies, and, if it is ideal without tube drop, the load voltage is positive $E_m$. The cathode of tube $A$, the cathode of tube $B$, and the high side of the load resistance form a common junction point for the circuit. Now the cathode of tube $B$ is at $+E_m$ volts, and the plate of tube $B$ is at $-E_m$ volts. This means that the *peak inverse-voltage* stress on tube $B$ is twice the peak of the incoming alternating supply voltage $E$, and is twice the peak of the load voltage. If a diode has a peak inverse-voltage rating of 600 volts, the maximum load voltage that can be obtained from a full-wave rectifier circuit using this diode is 300 volts direct current. The waveforms showing this inverse voltage are Figs. 9–3$g$ and $h$.

Since both halves of the a-c wave are now rectified, many of the values obtained for the half-wave rectifier are changed by a factor of two.

$$E_{\text{dc}} = \frac{2}{\pi} E_m = \frac{2\sqrt{2}\,E}{\pi} = 0.636E_m = 0.90E \qquad (9\text{–}6)$$

and $\quad I_{\text{dc}} = \frac{2}{\pi} I_m = \frac{2}{\pi}\frac{E_m}{R_L} = \frac{2\sqrt{2}\,E}{\pi R_L} = \frac{E_{\text{dc}}}{R_L} = 0.636I_m = \frac{0.90E}{R_L}$

Using the method developed in the previous section, since the rms load voltage is $E_m/\sqrt{2}$ and the direct load voltage is $2E_m/\pi$, the rms value for the a-c ripple $E_R$ is

$$\left(\frac{E_m}{\sqrt{2}}\right)^2 = \left(\frac{2E_m}{\pi}\right)^2 + E_R{}^2$$

$$E_R{}^2 = \frac{E_m{}^2}{2} - \frac{4E_m{}^2}{\pi^2} = \left(\frac{1}{2} - \frac{4}{\pi^2}\right)E_m{}^2$$

$$E_R = \sqrt{\frac{1}{2} - \frac{4}{\pi^2}}\, E_m = 0.307E_m = 0.434E \qquad (9\text{-}7)$$

The ripple factor is obtained by dividing $E_R$ by $E_{dc}$:

$$\text{Ripple factor} = \frac{E_R}{E_{dc}} = \frac{0.307E_m}{0.636E_m} = 0.482 \qquad (9\text{-}8)$$

The a-c load power is

$$\frac{E_m}{\sqrt{2}}\frac{E_m}{\sqrt{2}\,R_L} = \frac{E_m{}^2}{2R_L}$$

The d-c load power is

$$\frac{2E_m}{\pi} \times \frac{2E_m}{\pi R_L} = \frac{4}{\pi^2}\frac{E_m{}^2}{R_L}$$

Taking the ratio of these, we have

$$\text{Ratio of rectification} = \frac{4E_m{}^2/\pi^2 R_L}{E_m{}^2/2R_L} = \frac{8}{\pi^2} = 0.812 \qquad (9\text{-}9)$$

The calculation of the transformer utilization factor for a full-wave rectifier must be done quite carefully to avoid pitfalls. In the secondary winding, we have *two* circuits, each of half-wave rectification. Each half of the winding has within itself a direct current flow. Then, the transformer utilization factor is merely twice that of the half-wave rectifier:

$$\text{Transformer utilization factor for secondary} = 2 \times 0.287$$
$$= 0.574 \quad (9\text{-}10a)$$

When we consider the winding as a whole, we are, in effect, considering the primary of the transformer. From Eq. 9-6, we have

$$E_{dc} = \frac{2\sqrt{2}}{\pi}E \quad \text{and} \quad I_{dc} = \frac{2\sqrt{2}}{\pi}I$$

Then

$$E = \frac{\pi}{2\sqrt{2}} E_{dc} \quad \text{and} \quad I = \frac{\pi}{2\sqrt{2}} I_{dc}$$

Multiplying these together, we have

$$EI = \frac{\pi^2}{8} E_{dc} I_{dc}$$

Then

Transformer utilization factor for primary $= \dfrac{E_{dc} I_{dc}}{EI}$

$$= \frac{8}{\pi^2} = 0.812 \quad (9\text{–}10b)$$

In practice, the average value of these two figures is usually taken:

Average transformer utilization factor $= \dfrac{0.574 + 0.812}{2}$

$$= 0.693 \quad (9\text{–}10c)$$

Using this average transformer utilization factor of 0.693, a transformer that has a rating of 1 kva can deliver 693 watts direct current to a resistive load in a full-wave rectifier circuit. As the ratio of rectification is 0.812, the required primary demand is 693/0.812 or 854 volt-amperes. Again it must be remembered that these numerical examples do not consider the power losses of the diodes or the effects of an actual transformer. Since each half of the secondary a-c cycle is used in the full-wave rectifier, the net effect of the d-c flux in the secondary cancels so that there can be no problem of a d-c saturation.

### Section 9–3    The Full-Wave Bridge

The full-wave rectifier circuit requires a center tap on the source of the alternating voltage which is to be rectified. In many applications, the advantages of the higher output and efficiency of the full-wave circuit are required, but only a two-terminal source of voltage without a center tap is available. The full-wave bridge rectifier circuit (Fig. 9–4) is used to care for this problem.

From the circuit of the bridge rectifier, it is seen that the cathodes of the diodes are at three different potential levels, $a$, $b$, and $c$. When vacuum tubes are used in a bridge, three separate filament supplies are required since most vacuum-tube rectifiers are filament-type tubes. To avoid this expense of multiple windings, metallic rectifiers are gen-

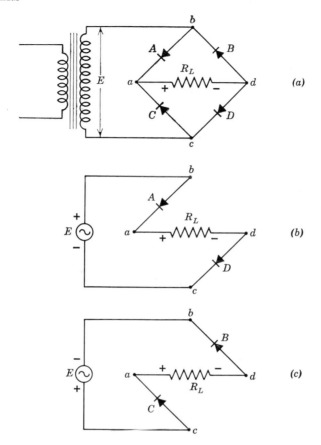

**Figure 9–4**  The bridge rectifier.  (a) Circuit.   (b) Current path when b is positive.   (c) Current path when c is positive.

erally used as the diodes in the full-wave bridge.   When b is positive and c is negative, the path of current flow is shown in Fig. 9–4b. Diodes B and C are connected in reverse to this polarity and "block." When c is positive and b is negative (Fig. 9–4c), diodes A and D block the current flow which is now through diodes B and C.   Thus, a half-cycle of load current and of load voltage occurs for each half-cycle of line voltage.   When diode A passes current, the full load voltage $E_m$ is across diode B as an inverse voltage.   The full load-voltage is also across diode C since diode D is passing current.   In a full-wave bridge rectifier, then, the peak inverse voltage is the peak of the incoming line voltage.

The direct load voltage and load current are, as in the full-wave circuit:

$$E_{dc} = \frac{2}{\pi} E_m = \frac{2\sqrt{2}}{\pi} E = 0.636 E_m = 0.90E \qquad (9\text{--}11)$$

$$I_{dc} = \frac{2}{\pi} I_m = \frac{2}{\pi}\frac{E_m}{R_L} = \frac{2\sqrt{2} E}{\pi R_L} = \frac{E_{dc}}{R_L} = 0.636 I_m = 0.90I$$

Since these equations are the same as Eq. 9–8, the values for the ripple and for the ripple factor must be the same as in Eq. 9–7 and Eq. 9–8:

$$E_R = 0.307 E_m = 0.434E \qquad (9\text{--}12)$$

$$\text{Ripple factor} = 0.482 \qquad (9\text{--}13)$$

Also, the ratio of rectification must be the same as in Eq. 9–9:

$$\text{Ratio of rectification} = 0.812 \qquad (9\text{--}14)$$

In this circuit, the transformer secondary current and voltage are purely alternating without any consideration for a d-c flow in the secondary winding. This means that the transformer utilization factor is the same as the ratio of rectification for the full-wave bridge:

$$\text{Transformer utilization factor} = 0.812 \qquad (9\text{--}15)$$

Now, with a bridge rectifier, a 1-kva transformer can deliver 812 watts of d-c power to a load. The bridge rectifier is the best circuit from the viewpoint of over-all performance, but it does have the great disadvantage of requiring four diodes instead of one or two. Also, the full secondary of the transformer (or source) is utilized instead of one-half the secondary voltage as in the full-wave circuit. When the cost of the transformer is the main consideration in a rectifier assembly, invariably the bridge is used. This is particularly true for large rectifiers which have a low-voltage and a high-current rating. There is an additional power loss in the bridge because two rectifiers carry current at all times.

### Section 9–4   Comparison of the Three Basic Rectifier Circuits

A comparison among the three rectifier circuits must be made very judiciously lest very serious errors in the reasoning enter and false assumptions be made. As an example, consider the full-wave rectifier circuit shown in Fig. 9–5. Assume that the transformer is ideal and is rated at 1 kva. There is a knife switch $S$ in one of the plate leads.

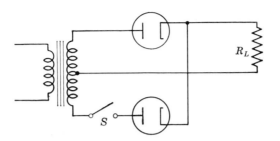

**Figure 9-5** A combined half-wave and full-wave rectifier.

When the switch is opened, it is true that the load current and the load voltage decrease by one half, but the available loading on the transformer changes. If the power in the load is 693 watts in the full-wave position of the switch, it is 173.25 watts when the switch is opened. Although the transformer utilization factor for a half-wave

TABLE I. COMPARISON OF RECTIFIER CIRCUITS WITH RESISTIVE LOAD

Rectifier Circuit

|  | Half Wave | Full Wave | Bridge |
|---|---|---|---|
| Line voltage ($E_m = \sqrt{2}\,E$) | $E$ | $E*$ | $E$ |
| Number of diodes | 1 | 2 | 4 |
| Peak inverse voltage | $E_m$ | $2E_m$ | $E_m$ |
| Direct output voltage | $\dfrac{E_m}{\pi} = 0.318E_m$ | $\dfrac{2E_m}{\pi} = 0.636E_m$ | $\dfrac{2E_m}{\pi} = 0.636E_m$ |
| Ripple factor | 1.21 | 0.482 | 0.482 |
| Ratio of rectification | 0.406 | 0.812 | 0.812 |
| Transformer utilization factor | 0.287 | 0.693† | 0.812 |
| D-c power available from a 1-kva transformer, watts | 287 | 693 | 812 |
| Ripple frequency | $f$ | $2f$ | $2f$ |

\* One-half secondary voltage.
† Average of primary and secondary.

rectifier is 0.287, it is only 0.1435 when only one-half the secondary winding is used. This means that the transformer is fully loaded when delivering only 143.5 watts with the switch opened.

One of the more important considerations in a comparison is the problem of the d-c saturation in the half-wave rectifier. The lower ripple factors of the full-wave types are important in applications along with their more efficient transformer utilization factors. The relationships and factors are summarized in Table I.

### Section 9–5   The Capacitor Filter

A single capacitor filter used with a half-wave rectifier circuit is shown in Fig. 9–6. During the positive half of the supply cycle, the capacitor is charged in the time interval between $a$ and $b$. When the applied a-c wave falls below the value of the direct voltage on

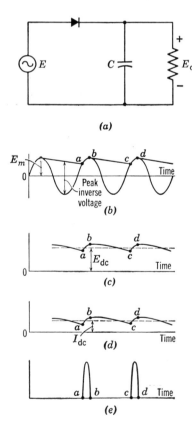

*(a)*

*(b)*

*(c)*

*(d)*

*(e)*

Figure 9–6   Half-wave rectifier with capacitor filter. (*a*) Circuit. (*b*) Action of the capacitor. (*c*) Load voltage. (*d*) Load current. (*e*) Diode current.

the capacitor, point $b$, the charging current from the diode ceases, and the load current continues to flow by the discharging action of the filter capacitor in the interval from $b$ to $c$. At point $c$, the increasing supply voltage again exceeds the voltage on the capacitor and the filter capacitor recharges. The load-voltage waveform (Fig. 9–6$c$) is also the capacitor-voltage waveform. The load current (Fig. 9–6$d$) has the same shape as the load-voltage waveform since the load is resistive. Diode current can only occur during capacitor recharging time, between $a$ and $b$ and between $c$ and $d$. Thus, the diode current is in the form of short pulses (Fig. 9–6$e$). The peak inverse voltage is shown in Fig. 9–6$b$. When a filter capacitor is used, the peak inverse voltage can be as high as twice the peak of the alternating line voltage.

The area under the load-current curve (Fig. 9–6$d$) must equal the area under the diode-current curve (Fig. 9–6$e$), since the total charge delivered to the capacitor is delivered to the load as load current in the form of discharge. This statement has a slight error since the diode, when it is recharging the capacitor, also at the same time supplies current into the load. However, the discussion of the operation of many rectifier circuits is greatly simplied by separating the two concepts, and by assuming that the sole function of the diode or diodes is to recharge the filter capacitors and that the sole function of the filter capacitors is to supply load current by discharge. The diode current takes the form of very sharp, short-duration pulses. If the load current is fixed and if the size of the capacitor is increased, the diode-current pulses become very narrow with a very high amplitude. A vacuum tube has an upper limit of current which is determined by the total emission of the cathode. It is necessary to limit the peak current to a safe value in a metallic rectifier by placing a resistance between the diode and the line-voltage source. As a general rule, capacitor filters are never used with gas tubes as the large peak currents of the capacitor recharge can cause a destructive multiple ionization in the gas. The narrow and sharp diode pulses make the transformer utilization factors still lower than those values obtained with a pure resistive loading.

When the value of the capacitor is high and the load current is very small, the drop in voltage from $b$ to $c$ is negligible. Then the load voltage is the peak of the line voltage, and the ripple approaches zero. As the load-current demand increases, several things happen. The rate of discharge of the capacitor increases. The recharge action starts at $e$ (Fig. 9–7) instead of at $c$. Also, the capacitor discharge starts later then $d$, at $f$. The average value of the envelope, the direct load voltage, is now lower and the amount of variation of the envelope,

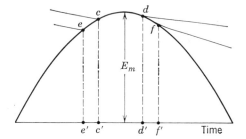

**Figure 9–7**   Voltage waveform under different loads.

the ripple voltage, is greater.   The angle or width of diode-current flow increases from $c'd'$ to $e'f'$ in order to handle the extra load current. As we pointed out in the previous paragraph, as long as we are within the peak current limitations of the diode, we can bring the envelope back to points $c$ and $d$ by adding sufficient capacitance to the filter.

These same considerations apply to the full-wave rectifier using a capacitor filter.   The waveforms are similar and have two pulses of charging current per cycle which result in a slightly higher direct load voltage with less ripple.

If we consider a circuit in which the tube drop is not neglected, we must modify Fig. 9–7 and include the voltage drop caused by the circuit resistance (Fig. 9–8).   When the capacitor is recharging, the difference between the supply voltage and the load or capacitor voltage is the forward plate voltage $e_b$ of the diode.   The product of $e_b \times i_b$ represents the plate dissipation of the diode.

Calculations for a single-capacitor filter are quite complex and beyond the needs of this textbook.   In most cases, tube manual data, for example Fig. 9–9, give a sufficient range of capacitor curves to serve most requirements.   The direct output voltage decreases with an increase in load.   Also the per cent ripple increases sharply with an increase in load.   Simple capacitor filters are used primarily where the

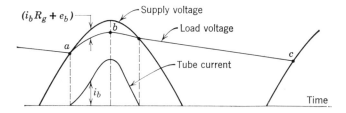

**Figure 9–8**   Voltage waveforms considering rectifier and source resistance.

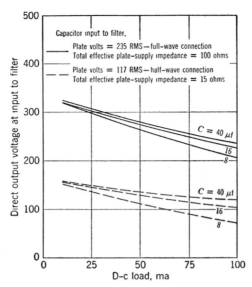

**Figure 9–9** Load characteristics of a typical vacuum tube rectifier with capacitor filter. (*Courtesy RCA*)

load-current requirements are small. They provide a low-cost and lightweight solution for a filtering problem.

### Section 9–6  The Choke Filter

A full-wave rectifier using a *choke* as part of the filter network is shown in Fig. 9–10. The actual filter, the $LC$ combination, is termed either an $L$ *filter* or a *choke-input filter*. The action of the choke is to store up energy in the magnetic field and to release it to the load evenly. Thus the choke increases its energy storage during the time of the peaks of the alternating current and releases it when the rectifier output falls below the load voltage.

When the choke is too small or when the load current is very small, the choke does not deliver current over the full cycle. There are times in the cycle, *ab* and *cd* (Fig. 9–10), when the choke current is zero. At these times, the overall-filter acts as if it were a simple capacitor filter. The load voltage falls from $A$ to $B$ (Fig. 9–11) with an increase of current from 0 to $B'$. At $B$ a critical value is reached. Either sufficient inductance is in the filter or the load current has increased so that the critical value for the inductance is reached. At this critical value, the distances *ab* and *cd* (Fig. 9–10a) are just zero. Now

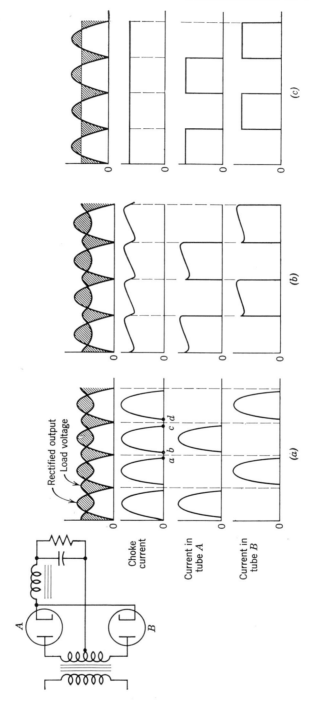

**Figure 9–10**  Waveforms for the choke filter.  (*a*) Small inductance.  (*b*) Normal inductance.  (*c*) Infinite inductance.

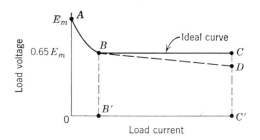

**Figure 9–11**   Ideal load curve for a choke filter.

current is flowing at all times in the choke.  This flow of current in the coil prevents the capacitor from discharging, and the load voltage is maintained at a constant value, from $B$ to $C$ for the ideal rectifier circuit.  The voltage at $B$ is ideally $0.65E_m$.  The waveforms for this condition are shown in Fig. 9–10$b$.  In an actual circuit, the d-c resistance of the choke and the tube drop causes the voltage to fall from $B$ to $D$.

A choke that is specifically designed to have a low inductance for the load current at $C'$ (Fig. 9–11) and a high inductance for low currents is called a *swinging choke*.  A properly designed swinging choke will move point $B$ quite close to the voltage axis.

*Voltage regulation* is a measure of the change of load voltage with load current and is defined as

$$\% \text{ voltage regulation} = \frac{\text{no load} - \text{full load}}{\text{full load}} \times 100 \quad (9\text{--}16)$$

A bleeder resistor is a resistor that is connected in parallel with the load.  A bleeder has a twofold purpose in a rectifier circuit.  It serves to discharge the capacitors when the power supply is turned off so that no dangerous residual charge is left on the filter capacitors.  Also the no-load voltage is not point $A$ but point $B$ on Fig. 9–11.  In the ideal choke-input rectifier circuit, we can see that the regulation with a bleeder is zero between $B$ and $C$ whereas it is $(E_m - 0.63E_m)/0.63E_m$ or $58.7\%$ without the bleeder.

Involved derivations show that the necessary value of the inductance at point $C$ (and $B$) is

$$L = \frac{R_L}{1000}$$

$$(9\text{--}17)$$

and $$\% \text{ ripple} = \frac{100}{LC}$$

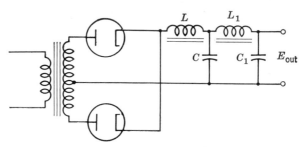

**Figure 9–12**   Full-wave rectifier with complex filter.

where $L$ is in henrys and $C$ is in microfarads.   Between points $A$ and $B$, the choke does not have sufficient inductance to satisfy Eq. 9–17.

An improvement in this value of ripple can be made by using two L sections in the filter (Fig. 9–12).   The considerations for the operation and for the minimum value of inductance remain the same as for the single $LC$ filter.   If the circuit is ideal, and if $L_1$ has no d-c resistance, the output voltage will not be changed by the addition of the second L section, but the ripple will be reduced:

$$\% \text{ ripple } = \frac{650}{LL_1(C + C_1)^2} \qquad (9\text{–}18)$$

Since the tube currents are limited by the input choke, it is quite safe to use gas-tube rectifiers with this filter.   In fact, the only circuits in which a gas tube may be used are those circuits that have either a resistive load or a choke-input filter.   The use of a gas tube as compared to a vacuum tube decreases the plate dissipation loss and brings the actual curve of load voltage closer to the ideal.

### Section 9–7   The $\pi$ Filter

A $\pi$ filter is an L filter that has a single capacitor connected across the input to the filter (Fig. 9–13a).   The capacitor filter has an output characteristic that is higher than the L filter (Fig. 9–13b).   On the other hand, the regulation of the $\pi$ filter is poorer than that of the L filter.   Because of the additional filtering effect of the input capacitor, the per cent ripple is lower than the ripple content of the L-filter output.   A double $\pi$-filter circuit (Fig. 9–14) gives a still further reduction in ripple, but the direct voltage drop of the second choke causes the voltage regulation to become still poorer.

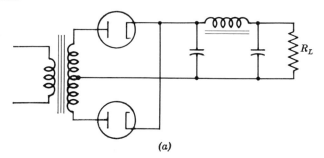

*(a)*

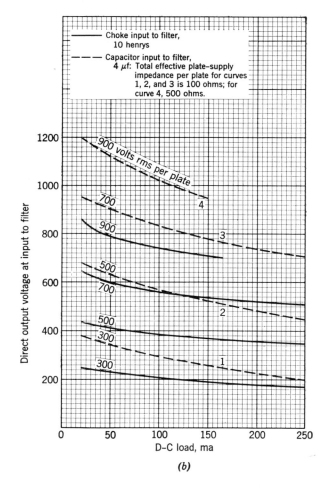

*(b)*

**Figure 9–13** Circuit and load curves for the $\pi$ filter using 5R4-GY. *(a)* Circuit. *(b)* Load curves. *(Courtesy RCA)*

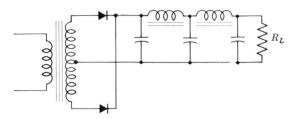

**Figure 9–14**    Full-wave rectifier using a double-$\pi$ filter.

The question of which filter should be used for a particular application is resolved by considering a number of factors. The size, the weight, and the cost of the filter components must be balanced against the electrical requirements of the filtering problem, the load current, the regulation, and the permissible ripple. The final filter design is a compromise between these factors.

### Section 9–8    Voltage Doublers

A *full-wave voltage doubler* is obtained by replacing two diodes in the full-wave bridge rectifier with capacitors (Fig. 9–15a). Usually the circuit is laid out in the form of Fig. 9–15b. Diode $A$ charges $C_A$ when $m$ is positive and $n$ is negative. When $n$ is positive and $m$ is negative, diode $B$ charges $C_B$. The two capacitors, $C_A$ and $C_B$, are in series; so the voltage across them is twice the voltage on each, or is *doubled*. The load resistor $R_L$ is across the capacitor combination. The load current through $R_L$ comes from the discharge of the capacitors. The waveforms are shown in Fig. 9–15d. The output load voltage is the total spread between the top of the envelope and the bottom of the envelope. When the load current is very small, the load voltage is twice the peak of the line $2E_m$. There are two impulses of charging current into the capacitors per cycle; therefore the ripple frequency is twice the frequency of the line. The action of the two diodes in the full-wave rectifier charges the whole filter twice each cycle, whereas the charging action of this circuit charges each capacitor once per cycle, but at different times. It is in this sense a full-wave rectifier and not a half-wave rectifier. The ripple in this circuit is greater and the regulation is poorer than in the equivalent full-wave rectifier. The peak inverse-voltage ratings of the diodes are twice the peak of the line voltage $2E_m$. Since this circuit is often used on an a-c line without either an isolating transformer or a step-up or step-down transformer, it is important to note that there is no common connection between the line and the load. When the expense of a line transformer is justified, it is preferable to use the superior circuit of the conventional full-wave rectifier. Typical load curves for the circuit are shown in Fig. 9–15c.

The *half-wave voltage doubler* or the *cascade voltage-doubler* circuit is shown in Fig. 9–16a. When $n$ is positive and $m$ is negative, $C_A$ charges through diode $A$ to $E_m$, the peak of the line voltage. This action is shown in the waveform of Fig. 9–16c. When the cycle reverses, $n$ is negative and $m$ is positive. Now, the line voltage $e$ and the voltage

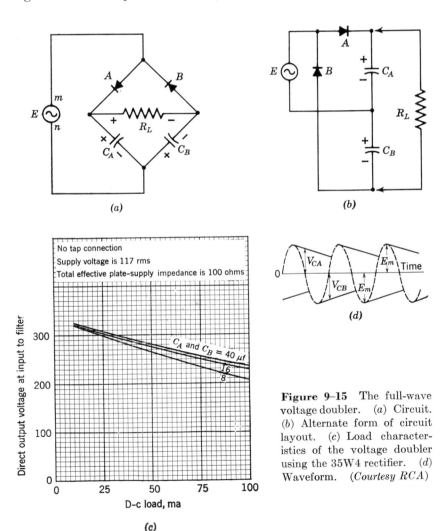

(a)

(b)

(d)

No tap connection
Supply voltage is 117 rms
Total effective plate-supply impedance is 100 ohms

$C_A$ and $C_B$ = 40 µf
16
8

Direct output voltage at input to filter

300

200

100

0

0    25    50    75    100

D-c load, ma

(c)

**Figure 9–15** The full-wave voltage doubler. (*a*) Circuit. (*b*) Alternate form of circuit layout. (*c*) Load characteristics of the voltage doubler using the 35W4 rectifier. (*d*) Waveform. (*Courtesy RCA*)

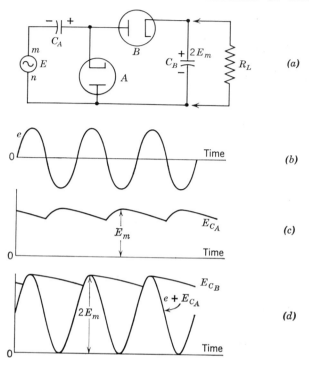

**Figure 9–16** The half-wave voltage doubler. (*a*) Circuit. (*b*) Input voltage. (*c*) Waveform across $C_A$. (*d*) Waveform across $C_B$.

across $C_A$ are in series aiding. The maximum value this condition can have is $2E_m$, and $C_B$ charges to $2E_m$ through diode $B$ (Fig. 9–16*d*). The load is connected across $C_B$. The load receives only one charging pulse per cycle. The ripple frequency is the line frequency giving a basis for the use of the term "half wave." The regulation of this circuit is very poor, and the ripple is very high, even with medium values of load current. The peak inverse voltage on diode $A$ is $2E_m$, and the peak inverse voltage on diode $B$ is $2E_m$ also. This circuit does have a common connection between the line and the load. Its use is restricted to very high-voltage supplies where the load-current demands are very low such as television kinescope supplies and portable Geiger counters.

### Section 9-9   Mechanical Rectifiers

A vibrator (Fig. 9–17) is a mechanical device that "interrupts" a direct current converting it to alternating current in a manner similar

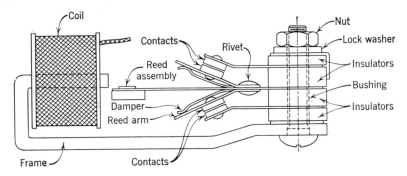

**Figure 9–17** Mechanical construction of a vibrator. (*Courtesy P. R. Mallory & Co.*)

to the action of a buzzer or doorbell.   The armature on the end of the reed has a specific mechanical period of vibration which determines the frequency of operation.   When the switch is closed (Fig. 9–18), the armature is pulled from $b$ (Fig. 9–19) toward the coil, and the contact $y$ is made.   Current flows through the lower half of the transformer winding.   When the contact $y$ is made, the energizing coil is short-circuited, and the inertia of the armature carries the reed to $b$ and then back through $a$ toward $c$.   During this travel, contact $y$ opens and contact $x$ closes.   Now current flows through the upper half

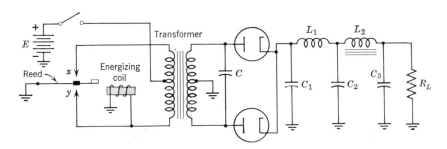

**Figure 9–18**   The simple or nonsynchronous vibrator circuit.

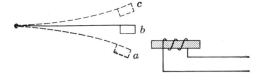

**Figure 9–19**   Action of the vibrating armature.

of the transformer primary, producing a flux which is opposite in direction to the flux caused by the current when contact $y$ was closed. Also the energizing coil again has a current flow, and now it will pull the armature back from $c$ toward $b$, causing the sequence to repeat. The waveform of the voltage impressed on the primary is shown in Fig. 9–20. Ideally the short times between the two successive halves of the cycle should be zero. The limitation is the mechanical design of the spring contacts. The peak-to-peak value of the a-c square wave applied to the primary of the transformer is $2E$ volts.

A very high-quality version of this vibrator has wide applications in the field of instrumentation and is called a *chopper*. A chopper has an energizing coil which is not operated from $E$ but from a separate power source. The chopper converts a signal $E$ to an alternating voltage which may be amplified for measurement or for use in a servo control system.

A square-wave voltage impressed on a transformer develops very short-duration peaks of very high voltage in the secondary. A capacitor $C$ is placed across the secondary winding to absorb the energies of these peaks which might otherwise break down the insulation of the circuit. The capacitor that is used for this purpose is called a *buffer*. The short-duration pulses are energies which occur at very high-frequency multiples of the basic frequency of the vibrator and often fall into the classification of radio frequencies. The first filter section, $C_1$ and $L_1$, is designed to remove these high frequencies, while the second section filters out the ordinary power-supply ripple.

The usual frequency of operation of a vibrator is 115, 400, or 2400 cycles, although choppers are available at many other frequencies. The vibrator has the disadvantage of being dependent on a mechanical action of its parts. The chief reason for failure of vibrators in service is due to the pitting and destruction of the contacts at $x$ and $y$.

When the vibrator is made with a second set of contacts (Fig. 9–21), the second set of contacts is in exact mechanical synchronism with the first set. One set delivers power into the primary of the step-up

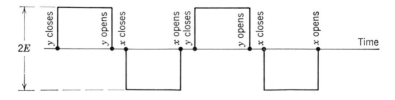

**Figure 9–20**   The transformer primary-voltage waveform.

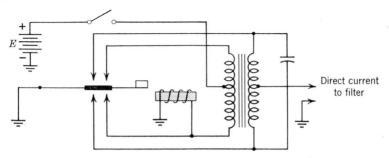

**Figure 9-21**   The synchronous vibrator circuit.

transformer, and the second set takes the power from the secondary of the transformer. The reed serves as its own mechanical rectifying device since the reed changes from one set of contacts to the other set just as the polarity of the secondary reverses. This arrangement is known as a *synchronous vibrator* power supply. The synchronous vibrator is both more expensive and less rigid mechanically than the nonsynchronous vibrator with the same contact current rating. The synchronous rectifier is actually constructed with two reeds, one for the primary and one for the secondary with a common weighted armature. In some models the two reeds with their contacts are insulated from each other.

### Section 9-10   Thyratron Rectifiers

A thyratron, when used as a rectifier, may be controlled with either a direct or an alternating voltage on the grid. A test circuit which shows the action of a d-c grid control is given in Fig. 9-22. An alternating voltage $E$ is impressed on the plate of the thyratron. The load

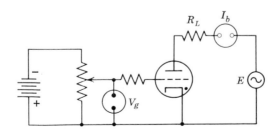

**Figure 9-22**   Circuit for d-c control of a thyratron.

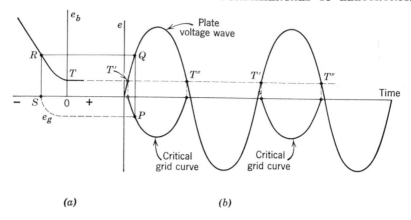

*(a)*                                                    *(b)*

**Figure 9-23**  D-c control waveforms.  *(a)* Control characteristic.  *(b)* Development of the critical grid curve.

resistor $R_L$ is in series with the plate and the a-c line.  The grid voltage can be varied by adjusting the potentiometer.  The firing-control characteristic obtained from the thyratron data sheet is shown in Fig. 9-23a.  The impressed alternating line voltage is plotted in Fig. 9-23b.  Let us consider any point $Q$ on the positive half of the cycle.  The plate voltage at point $Q$ corresponds to $R$ on the firing characteristic.  The grid voltage for point $R$ is $S$.  Now, at that instant of time at which the plate voltage is $Q$, we plot this firing-control grid voltage $S$ as point $P$.  If different $Q$'s are taken, the corresponding $P$'s plot into a locus which is called the critical grid curve.  It should be noted carefully that the firing-control characteristic is invariant and is not dependent on the circuit, whereas the critical grid line is very

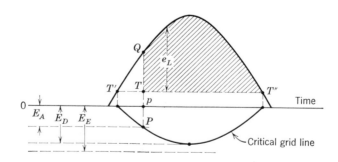

**Figure 9-24**  Details of the critical grid line.

definitely determined by the amplitude of the alternating voltage source in the plate circuit.

One positive cycle of the alternating line voltage is redrawn in Fig. 9–24 for greater detail. If the grid bias is set to $-E_A$ volts, it intersects the critical grid line at point $P$ where the plate supply voltage is $Q$. Up to the time $p$, the direct grid voltage is more negative than or below the critical grid line. As long as the grid is more negative than the critical grid line, the thyratron will not be fired. At the instant of intersection of the bias line and the critical grid line, which is $P$ at time $p$, the tube fires. The plate voltage falls from $Q$ to $T$. The voltage $T$ is the tube drop under conduction. Once the tube is fired, the grid cannot regain control, and the plate voltage remains at this level until $T''$ is reached in the cycle. At this point, the line voltage $e$ falls below the tube drop, and the thyratron deionizes. If the grid voltage remains at $E_A$, the thyratron will fire at point $Q$ on each succeeding cycle. If the grid is made less negative, the firing point advances earlier in the cycle. If the grid is made more negative, the firing point occurs later in the cycle. If the grid is made more negative than $E_D$, for instance $E_E$, there will be no point of intersection, and the thyratron cannot conduct at all.

When the thyratron fires, the difference between the tube drop, $TT''$, and the source voltage $e$ is shown as the shaded area in Fig. 9–24. The instantaneous voltage difference between the tube drop, $TT''$, and the applied voltage $e$ is $e_L$, the instantaneous load voltage across $R_L$. By Ohm's law, $i_L = e_L/R_L$. Therefore, the load current and voltage are proportional and have the same waveform. The complete waveforms for this analysis are shown in Fig. 9–25.

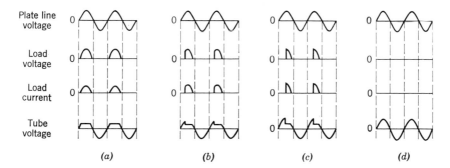

**Figure 9–25** Waveforms at different d-c control settings. (a) Zero bias. (b) Bias at $E_A$. (c) Bias at $E_D$. (d) Bias at $E_E$.

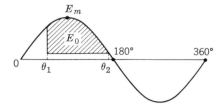

**Figure 9–26**  Details of the plate-voltage waveform.

In Fig. 9–26, let the firing point for the thyratron be at $\theta_1$ degrees and the extinction point be at $\theta_2$ degrees. Also, let the tube drop after conduction be designated as $E_o$ volts and the peak of the line voltage as $E_m$ volts. By methods of calculus, the direct load current or plate current is

$$I_{dc} = \frac{E_m(\cos \theta_1 - \cos \theta_2)}{2\pi R_L} - \frac{E_0}{R_L}\left(\frac{\theta_2 - \theta_1}{360}\right) \tag{9-19}$$

and $$E_{dc} = I_{dc}R_L$$

In using this equation, it should be noted that $\theta_2$ is an angle which is greater than 90° and less than 180°. Cosines of angles between 90° and 180° are negative numbers. Thus, in Eq. 9–19, the term $(\cos \theta_1 - \cos \theta_2)$ is usually numerically larger than one.

If the magnitude of the applied a-c wave is large, $\theta_2$ may be taken as 180° and $E_0$, the tube drop, may be neglected. Then, this equation simplifies to

$$I_{dc} = \frac{E_m[1 + \cos \theta_1]}{2\pi R_L} \tag{9-20}$$

When $\theta_1$ is zero, this formula simplifies to $I_{dc} = E_m/\pi R_L$ which is the value of load current for a half-wave rectifier.

In a vacuum-tube or metallic-rectifier circuit, the load current is determined by the load resistance, assuming that the diodes have no effect. With d-c control on the thyratron, the current can be adjusted by the grid voltage from a maximum value of a full half-cycle condition continuously and smoothly to one-half this maximum value. Also, zero load current may be obtained.

This control is shown graphically on Fig. 9–27. The particular points discussed for Fig. 9–24 are also located on this graph for a comparison.

The other important circuit arrangement for grid control of a thyratron is shown in Fig. 9–28a. A line alternating voltage is applied to the plate circuit through a resistance and a separate alternating voltage

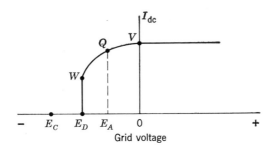

**Figure 9–27**   The d-c control characteristic.

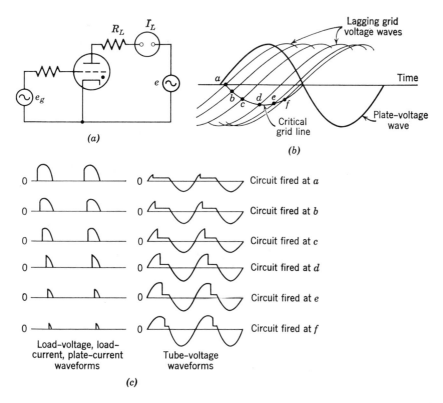

**Figure 9–28**   A-c control of a thyratron.   (*a*) Circuit.   (*b*) Plate   and   grid
waveforms for different lagging angles.   (*c*) Waveforms for a-c control.

(a)                                    (b)

**Figure 9–29**   The effect of a leading grid voltage.   (a) Grid-lead angle 90°. (b) Grid-lead angle almost 180°.

is connected between the grid and cathode.   In this circuit, the exact magnitude of the grid voltage is not of major importance, and, for convenience, we shall assume that $e$ and $e_g$ have the same peak values. However, the *phase* of the grid voltage with respect to the plate-circuit voltage is controlled by some form of a *phase shift circuit*.

The plate-circuit waveform with its critical grid line is shown in Fig. 9–28b, along with several different lagging grid voltages.   The different grid voltages intersect the critical grid line at different points (a, b, c, d, e, and f), and each causes the thyratron to fire at a different time in the cycle.   The greater the angle of the lag of the grid voltage, the later in the cycle the thyratron fires.   When the grid voltage lags by an angle of about 160° to 170°, f, the tube fires for only a few degrees before it goes out because of the falling plate-circuit voltage.   The waveforms for these different lagging grid voltages are shown in Fig. 9–28c.   In this circuit we can obtain *full* control over the load current from zero to maximum.   Equations 9–19 and 9–20 are both valid for this circuit.

Figure 9–29a shows the conditions that exist for a leading grid voltage.   The grid is already more positive than the critical grid line when the plate goes positive.   The tube fires over the full half-cycle, and the angle of lead has no effect or control over the load current. At a very large angle of lead, of the order of 175° (Fig. 9–29b), the grid voltage "misses" and falls below the critical grid line completely. At that sufficiently high angle of lead, the load current abruptly becomes zero.   The full control for leading and lagging grid voltages is shown graphically in Fig. 9–30.

We have confined this discussion of the two methods of grid control to half-wave rectifiers.   Both circuits are completely adaptable to full-wave applications, and they are very often so used.   We will not develop them in this textbook as the exact circuit for the phase-shifted grid voltage so often is an integral part of another complex circuit. These grid-controlled thyratron rectifiers have infinite application in

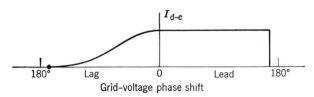

180°     Lag     0     Lead     180°

Grid-voltage phase shift

**Figure 9–30** The a-c control characteristic.

many widely diverse branches of electronics. Some examples are phototube relays, electronic motor control, timing circuits, theater light dimmers, printing equipment, automatic packaging machinery, and welding controls.

The method used to obtain a phase shift for the grid voltage depends entirely upon the application of the controlled rectifier circuit. The most commonly used arrangement is a simple $LR$ or $CR$ series circuit for the purpose. If a voltage $V_{AC}$ from a centertapped transformer is applied to a network of $R$ and $L$ (Fig. 9–31), the current $I$ lags $V_{AC}$ by an angle $\theta$. The $IR$ drop is in phase with $I$, and the current lags the $IX_L$ drop by 90°. These phasors are sketched in the phasor diagram. $B$ is the midpoint of $V_{AC}$ since it is the center tap on the transformer. Angle $ADC$ is the right angle of a right triangle whose hypotenuse is $AC$. If either $L$ or $R$ is varied, the lengths of the legs of the right triangle change, but the hypotenuse is fixed. By a theorem in plane geometry, the locus of the point $D$ must follow a semicircle. The voltage $V_{BD}$ represents the voltage from the center tap to the junction of the resistor and the inductance. In the phasor diagram, $DC$ and $BD$ are radii of the semicircle making triangle $BCD$ isosceles. Then,

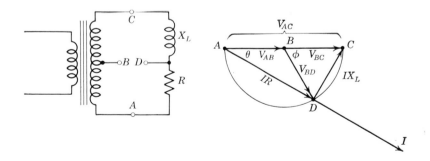

**Figure 9–31** $LR$ network producing a lagging phase angle.

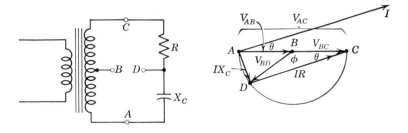

**Figure 9-32**   $CR$ network producing a lagging phase angle.

angle $BCD$ equals angle $BDC$.   But, since triangle $ACD$ is right triangle,

$$\theta + \angle ACD = 90$$

then $$\angle BCD = 90 - \theta$$

since $$\angle BCD = \angle BDC$$

and since $$\angle BCD + \angle BDC + \phi = 180$$

then $$(90 - \theta) + (90 - \theta) + \phi = 180$$

or $$\phi = 2\theta \quad \text{where} \quad \tan \theta = X_L/R \qquad (9\text{-}21a)$$

If $V_{BC}$ (or another voltage in phase with $V_{BC}$) is used as the plate supply, and if $V_{BD}$ is used to control the grid, a variation in either $L$ or $R$ can produce a full range of lagging phase-shift control over the required 180°.   The grid voltage $V_{BD}$ is a radius of the semicircle, and will not change its magnitude as the phase angle is varied.   When $R$ equals $X_L$, point $D$ is the midpoint between $A$ and $C$, and the phase angle is 90°.   If $R$ is the variable element in the phase-shift circuit, an increase in $R$ moves point $D$ from $A$ toward $C$, decreasing the phase angle.   If $L$ is variable, an increase in $L$ moves point $D$ toward $A$, increasing the phase angle.

If $L$ and $R$ are interchanged, the phase angle is no longer lagging, but leading.   A leading grid voltage will not allow a control over the thyratron load current.   The development of the phasor diagram to show this leading phase-shift angle is left to the reader as an exercise.

The lagging phase-shift angle may also be obtained from a $CR$ circuit (Fig. 9-32).   The current in the $CR$ circuit leads the impressed voltage $V_{AC}$ by $\theta$ degrees.   The current leads the $IX_C$ voltage phasor by 90° and is in phase with (parallel to) the $IR$ voltage phasor.   By the same logic as in the $LR$ circuit, the locus of point $D$ traces out a semicircle.

$V_{BD}$ lags $V_{BC}$ by the angle $\phi$.   $\phi$ can vary from zero to 180° by changing either $R$ or $C$.   Since $\angle ACD$ is $\theta$, the angle by which $V_{BD}$ lags
$V_{BC}$ is

$$\phi = 180 - 2\theta$$

where $$\tan \theta = \frac{X_C}{R} \tag{9–21b}$$

When the value of the resistor is increased, point $D$ moves toward $A$,
and the phase-shift angle $\phi$ increases.   If the capacitance is increased,
$X_C$ decreases, and point $D$ again moves toward $A$.   When $R$ equals
$X_C$, point $D$ is at the midpoint on the semicircle, and the phase shift
is 90°.

## Section 9–11   Shunt Rectifiers

The shunt rectifier is a form of the half-wave rectifier used in several
diverse applications in electronics and instrumentation.   A half-wave
rectifier with a pure capacitive load is shown in Fig. 9–33.   The
capacitor charges to the peak value of the line voltage and maintains
this fixed d-c polarity (Fig. 9–33c).   The voltage waveform across the
diode is shown in Fig. 9–33d.   The sum of the voltage across the capacitor and the voltage across the diode must be the sine-wave input
voltage.

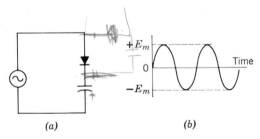

(a)                                    (b)

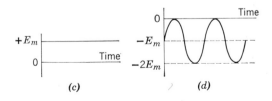

(c)                                    (d)

**Figure 9–33**   The basic half-wave rectifier.   (a) Circuit.   (b) Supply voltage.
(c) Capacitor voltage.   (d) Inverse voltage across the diode.

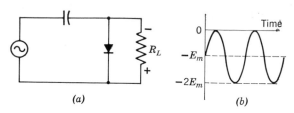

*(a)* *(b)*

**Figure 9-34** The basic shunt rectifier. (a) Circuit. (b) Output voltage waveform.

In the shunt rectifier (Fig. 9–34), the conventional positions of the capacitor and the diode rectifier are reversed. The load $R_L$ is now placed in parallel with the diode. The peak voltage across $R_L$ is twice the peak of the line voltage, and its average value is the peak voltage of the line. The resistance $R_L$ partially discharges the capacitor between peaks of the line voltage. When $R_L$ is very large, the discharging action is slight. A current pulse is required from the source to recharge the capacitor back to the peak value. This pulse can be converted to an rms value of current, and, when this value of current is divided into the source rms voltage, the effective value of the impedance of the circuit is obtained.

This circuit (Fig. 9–34a) can be used as a *clamp*. A clamping circuit accepts a pure a-c waveform and converts it into a unidirectional waveform. When the incoming a-c wave is a train of pulses (Fig. 9–35a), the output waveform is negative at all times (Fig. 9–35b). When the diode element is reversed, the polarity of the output waveform is reversed (Fig. 9–35c). Very often, this basic circuit is referred to in the literature as a clamp and not as a shunt rectifier.

In Fig. 9–36 an $RC$ filter is added to the basic shunt-rectifier circuit. The filter $R_2C_2$ establishes a pure direct voltage across $R_L$ which is equal to twice the peak of the source voltage. This circuit is often used in the probes of vacuum-tube voltmeters which are designed to

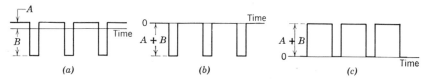

*(a)* *(b)* *(c)*

**Figure 9-35** Waveforms of a clamp. (a) Input. (b) Output for circuit of Fig. 9–34a. (c) Output with diode reversed.

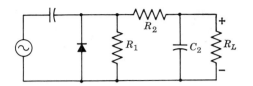

**Figure 9-36**  Shunt rectifier with output filter.

measure audio- and radio-frequency voltages without placing a severe shunting load impedance on the circuit where the measurement is taken.

The resistor $R_2$ in the circuit can be replaced by a filter choke for use as a source of d-c power.   This version is used as a means of obtaining a low direct voltage for bias supplies which operate with low-current requirements.   Also the circuit is used to provide high-voltage low-current d-c sources.   When the resistor $R_2$ in the filter is replaced by a second diode, the voltage-doubler circuit of Fig. 9-16 results.

. . . . **Suggested References for Further Study**

1. J. Millman, *Vacuum-Tube and Semiconductor Electronics*, Chapters 14 and 19, McGraw-Hill Book Co., New York, 1958.
2. F. E. Terman, *Radio Engineer's Handbook*, Section 8, McGraw-Hill Book Co., New York, 1943.
3. F. Langford-Smith *Radiotron Designer's Handbook*, 4th ed., Chapters 30 through 33, RCA, Harrison, N. J., 1953.
4. S. P. Jackson, *Selection and Application of Metallic Rectifiers*, McGraw-Hill Book Co., New York, 1957.
5. J. D. Ryder, *Engineering Electronics*, Chapter 14, McGraw-Hill Book Co., New York, 1957.
6. T. L. Martin Jr., *Electronic Circuits*, Chapter 14, Prentice-Hall, Inc., Englewood Cliffs, N. J., 1955.
7. S. Seely, *Electron-Tube Circuits.*  Chapter 7, McGraw-Hill Book Co., New York, 1950.   (Clamps)

. . . . **QUESTIONS**

1. Define or explain each of the following terms: (a) peak inverse voltage, (b) ripple factor, (c) ratio of rectification, (d) transformer utilization factor, (e) d-c saturation, (f) voltage regulation, (g) reed, (h) buffer, (i) chopper, (j) critical grid curve.

2. If a d'Arsonval meter movement is used to measure the voltage across a rectifier load, what does it indicate? If an iron-vane voltmeter is used? If an output voltmeter is used?

3. What is the effect on a half-wave rectifier if the diode opens? Short-circuits?

4. Can the numerical value of the ripple factor exceed unity? Explain.

5. What are the advantages and disadvantages of half-wave rectification?

6. Why is the ripple factor for a full-wave rectifier less than half the value for a half-wave rectifier (both with resistive loads)?

7. What are the advantages of a full-wave rectifier?

8. What is the effect on a full-wave rectifier if a diode opens? Short-circuits?

9. What are the advantages and disadvantages of a full-wave bridge?

10. What is the effect on a full-wave bridge if one diode opens? Short-circuits?

11. What is the peak inverse voltage on a diode when a capacitor filter is used?

12. Why is diode current limited to sharp pulses when a capacitor filter is used?

13. In Fig. 9–9, if the curves are extended to the $Y$ axis, what is the load voltage for zero load current?

14. What is the significance of a negative voltage regulation?

15. What is meant by a critical value of inductance in a filter?

16. What is the effect of the d-c resistance of chokes in a power supply?

17. Give advantages and disadvantages of using gas tubes as rectifiers.

18. What is the effect on a full-wave voltage doubler if one diode opens? Short-circuits? If the other opens? Short-circuits?

19. Answer question 18 for the half-wave voltage doubler.

20. Compare the two voltage-doubler circuits.

21. What is the effect of contact pitting in a vibrator?

22. What is the a-c waveform produced by a vibrator, and why is a buffer needed?

23. Give advantages and disadvantages of a synchronous vibrator.

24. What is the range of d-c grid control in a thyratron rectifier?

25. What is the range of a-c grid control in a thyratron rectifier?

26. What is a circle diagram?

27. Why is a leading grid voltage undesirable in a thyratron rectifier?

28. Explain the action of a clamp.

29. Why is a shunt-rectifier circuit used in metering circuits?

30. Name several applications of a shunt rectifier.

# . . . . PROBLEMS

1. A half-wave rectifier circuit is connected to terminals $A$ and $C$ in the diagram. Determine the direct output voltage and current, the per cent ripple, the a-c input power, and the required volt-ampere rating of the transformer.

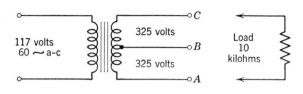

**Prob. 9–1**

2. Solve problem 1 for a full-wave rectifier circuit.

3. Solve problem 1 for a full-wave bridge rectifier connected between $A$ and $C$.

4. A choke-input filter is required with the rectifier circuit of problem 2. The allowed ripple is 2%. What size components are used in the filter section? What is the full-load output voltage, assuming that the choke has a resistance of 265 ohms? When a second L section is added, using the same component values, what are the new ripple and the new load voltage?

In the following two problems, assume that the control characteristic of the thyratron (Fig. 9–23a) is linear between $E_b = 300$ volts, $E_g = -30$ volts and $E_b = 20$ volts, $E_g = 0$.

5. In Fig. 9–22, the alternating plate supply voltage is 117 volts rms, and $R_L$ is 2000 ohms. Obtain sufficient data to plot the d-c control characteristic shown in Fig. 9–27.

6. The thyratron shown in Fig. 9–28a has a 1500-ohm resistor as the plate load. The plate supply is 230 volts rms. The grid voltage is obtained from the phase-shift circuit shown in Fig. 9–32 in which $V_{AC}$ is also 230 volts rms. Obtain sufficient data to plot the a-c control characteristic shown in Fig. 9–30.

# The vacuum-tube
# amplifier

• • • • • • • • • • • • • • • • • • • • CHAPTER 10

The most useful function of the vacuum tube is its ability to amplify when properly connected in a circuit. The basic waveforms (Section 10–1) and the equivalent circuits (Section 10–2) lead to the detailed load-line analysis (Section 10–4). Inherent distortion (Section 10–5) and other factors that limit the performance of amplifiers (Section 10–7) must be considered. Also included in the chapter are discussions of bias supplies (Section 10–3) and of the application of pentodes and beam-power tubes to amplifier circuits (Section 10–6).

### Section 10–1   The Basic Circuit

In Section 3–5, we considered the basic principles of a simple triode amplifier in order to relate the theory to a specific application. A signal voltage $e_g$ in series with the grid causes the plate current to vary in accordance with the grid variations. A load resistor $R_L$ is placed

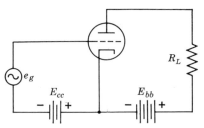

**Figure 10–1**   The basic amplifier circuit.

228

in series with the plate (Fig. 10–1). A plate supply voltage $E_{bb}$ is used to provide the positive plate voltage. A grid bias supply $E_{cc}$ keeps the grid negative with respect to the cathode at all times. These direct voltages establish a particular plate current which is called the direct *operating plate current*, $I_b$. $I_b$ produces a direct voltage drop $I_b R_L$ in the load resistor. The *operating plate voltage* $E_b$ is less than $E_{bb}$ by the amount of the direct load-voltage drop. This relation may be represented as

$$E_{bb} = E_b + I_b R_L$$

The positive lead of $E_{bb}$ is called "*B* plus" or "*B*+," and the negative lead is called "*B* minus or "*B*−."

If a signal voltage $e_g$ is placed in series with the grid, the total instantaneous grid voltage instantaneously varies with the signal and is the sum of $e_g$ and $E_{cc}$. When the signal is positive, the total grid voltage is less negative than $E_{cc}$ alone. The plate current instantaneously increases. The voltage drop in the load resistance increases, causing the instantaneous plate voltage to drop. When the grid signal becomes negative, the plate current decreases and the plate voltage rises. Since an increase in grid signal produces a decrease in plate voltage, and since a decrease in grid signal produces an increase in plate voltage, we form a very important conclusion in vacuum-tube theory:

*A tube used as a conventional amplifier develops a 180° phase shift between the input and output voltage.*

Figure 10–2 shows the relation between the grid and plate voltages and currents in an amplifier. Lower-case letters are reserved for instantaneous values. Capitals with a single or double subscript $b$ or $c$ (e.g., $I_b$ and $E_{cc}$) designate voltages and currents that can be measured directly with d-c meters. Capitals with a single subscript $g$ or $p$ (e.g., $E_g$, $E_p$, and $I_p$) represent the rms or effective values of the alternating current which the circuit is amplifying. The terms $e_b$, $i_b$, and $e_c$ describe *total* instantaneous values which include the operating point *plus* the signal; $e_g$, $e_p$, and $i_p$ denote instantaneous values of the a-c signal alone. The mathematical relations between these symbols are shown in Fig. 10–2 with the waveforms they describe.

A very important concept in the study of electronics may be visualized in Fig. 10–2. The zero voltage or "ground" is taken as the reference point. $E_{bb}$ is a straight line, and it is drawn parallel to the zero voltage reference time axis. The voltage between $E_{bb}$ and "ground"

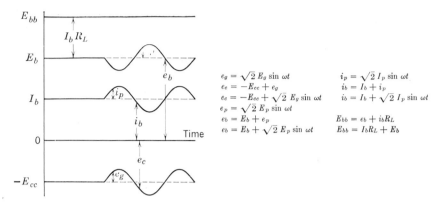

**Figure 10–2** Waveforms and relations in an amplifier for a sine-wave signal.

is purely direct. No alternating current is involved. This means that *the a-c potential of the supply voltage $E_{bb}$ is zero.* $E_{bb}$ is usually the voltage developed by one of the power supplies using capacitor, L, or $\pi$ filters described in Chapter 9. In the power supply relatively large values of capacitance are used to filter or bypass the a-c ripple present in the $B+$ supply. This capacitance causes the $B+$ lead to be at a-c ground potential. In this and in succeeding chapters, we assume that the power supplies are ideal; that is, they have zero a-c impedance. In Section 17–8, we will discuss the problem that exists when this is not the case.

The *voltage gain* or *voltage amplification* $A_e$ of an amplifier is defined as the ratio of the output voltage to the input signal:

$$A_e = \frac{E_p}{E_g} = \frac{e_p}{e_g} \tag{10–1}$$

In this textbook we define the voltage gain as a number, the magnitude of which must be greater than or equal to zero. As an example, if the input signal is 4 volts and the output voltage is 64 volts, the voltage gain $A_e$ is 64/4 or 16.

### Section 10–2   Equivalent Circuits

An understanding of the equivalent circuit of a vacuum tube is the basis for a quantitative approach to the study of amplifiers. An equivalent circuit for an amplifier does not include any of the d-c operating potentials or currents.   The vacuum tube is a device that absorbs d-c power and converts part into useful a-c output.

By Thévenin's theorem (Section 7–9) any circuit may be represented by an open-circuited emf in series with the internal impedance.   For a vacuum tube, this emf is the amplifying action of the tube itself.   The tube accepts a signal $e_g$, multiplies the signal by the inherent amplification factor $\mu$, and presents this resultant voltage $\mu e_g$ to the plate circuit. The internal impedance of the plate circuit is the a-c plate resistance $r_p$.   The inclusion of the load resistance $R_L$ in series completes the equivalent circuit (Fig. 10–3).   In the equivalent circuit, which does not show d-c potentials or currents, we indicate $e_p$ as the only voltage across $R_L$.   In the actual circuit, $e_p$ is measured between plate and cathode.

A vacuum tube is theoretically a four-terminal network (Section 7–10).   However, we have specified that the grid is negative at all times and does not have any direct grid current.   If we also specify that there is no alternating grid current which might be produced from the reactances of the interelectrode capacitances, it is valid to use this simple equivalent circuit.   The assumption that there is no grid current is valid at low frequencies.   The modifications necessitated by the consideration of the interelectrode capacitances will be discussed later in the development of the theory of the vacuum-tube cascaded amplifier (Section 13–4).

From this simple circuit we note that

$$-\mu e_g = i_p(r_p + R_L)$$

or

$$i_p = \frac{-\mu e_g}{r_p + R_L}$$

since

$$e_p = i_p R_L$$

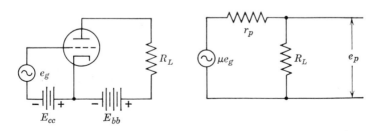

**Figure 10–3**   The actual and the equivalent circuits.

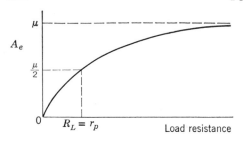

**Figure 10–4** Gain variation with load resistance.

By substitution

$$e_p = \frac{-\mu e_g R_L}{r_p + R_L}$$

as the voltage gain is defined by

$$A_e = \frac{e_p}{e_g}$$

Then
$$A_e = \frac{-\mu R_L}{r_p + R_L} \qquad (10\text{--}2a)$$

This equation may be made more general by replacing $R_L$ with $Z_L$,

$$A_e = \frac{-\mu Z_L}{r_p + Z_L} \qquad (10\text{--}2b)$$

When both the numerator and denominator of Eq. 10–2a are divided by $R_L$, the equation becomes

$$A_e = -\frac{\mu}{1 + r_p/R_L} \qquad (10\text{--}2c)$$

When $\mu$ and $r_p$ are fixed, as $R_L$ becomes very large, the term $(1 + r_p/R_L)$ approaches unity. This shows that *the voltage gain of an amplifier cannot exceed $\mu$.* When $R_L$ equals $r_p$, the gain is $\frac{1}{2}\mu$. The gain of an amplifier in which the only variable is $R_L$ is plotted in Fig. 10–4.

The results shown in Fig. 10–4 are predicated on a fixed $\mu$ and a fixed $r_p$. We established in Section 3–4 (Fig. 3–12) that $r_p$ varies inversely with $I_b$. To keep $I_b$ constant with an increasing $R_L$ requires an ever-increasing value of $E_{bb}$. Obviously, there is a practical limitation to this increase in $E_{bb}$. The actual gain obtained in an amplifier circuit is a compromise between these two considerations.

A second form of the equivalent circuit may be obtained from the first equivalent circuit.  If we substitute

$$\mu = r_p g_m \tag{3-1d}$$

in

$$e_p = \frac{-\mu e_g R_L}{r_p + R_L}$$

we obtain

$$e_p = \frac{-r_p g_m e_g R_L}{r_p + R_L}$$

which may be arranged in the form

$$e_p = -(g_m e_g)\left(\frac{r_p R_L}{r_p + R_L}\right)$$

The units of $(g_m e_g)$ are mhos $\times$ volts, or volts/ohms, or amperes. Thus $(g_m e_g)$ represents a current.  The expression $r_p R_L/(r_p + R_L)$ is the parallel combination of the two resistances.  $e_p$ results from the $IR$ drop of this current, $g_m e_g$, flowing through the parallel resistance combination.  Using these relations, we can represent an alternate form of the equivalent circuit in Fig. 10–5.

This new equivalent circuit can be obtained from Fig. 10–3 directly by application of Norton's theorem.  By Norton's theorem the short-circuit current is $\mu e_g/r_p$ or $g_m e_g$, and the shunt impedance is $r_p$. The load resistance $R_L$ is then placed in parallel with $r_p$.

The gain may be expressed as

$$A_e = -g_m \frac{r_p R_L}{r_p + R_L} \tag{10-3a}$$

If the value of plate resistance $r_p$ is at least ten times the load resistance, $r_p$ may be neglected:

$$A_e = -g_m R_L \quad \text{when} \quad r_p \geq 10R_L \tag{10-3b}$$

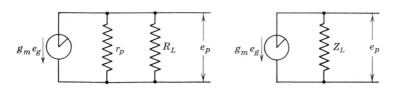

**Figure 10–5**  The constant current equivalent circuit.

If $R_L$ is replaced by $Z_L$, we have

$$A_e = -g_m Z_L \quad \text{when} \quad r_p \geq 10 Z_L \qquad (10\text{--}3c)$$

Thus far we have developed two equivalent circuits. Either version may be used for the same amplifier since they are equivalent to each other. It must be remembered that an equivalent circuit is not an actual circuit but is only a mathematical means of analysis. We find, however, that the first method, the so-called constant-voltage equivalent circuit, is best suited for analyzing triodes where low values of $r_p$ are found as compared to the magnitude of $R_L$. The second method, the constant-current equivalent circuit, is more useful where the values of $r_p$ are very high compared to $R_L$ and often may be neglected for many tetrode and pentode circuits.

### Section 10–3    Cathode Bias and Screen Voltage

Up to this point in the discussion, we have used two d-c power sources, $E_{bb}$ and $E_{cc}$, to supply operating potentials to the amplifier. Occasionally, it is advisable to provide a power supply which develops several positive and negative voltages by using a multitapped bleeder and divider resistor placed across the output of the power supply. Usually, the power supply is kept as simple as possible, and a different means of providing the bias voltage and other electrode voltages becomes necessary.

In the circuit of Fig. 10–6 we wish to derive both screen and cathode voltages from a common supply $E_{bb}$. The combined screen and plate currents flow through $R_K$ to ground. This current develops a direct voltage drop across $R_K$ with the polarity shown. The grid d-c potential with respect to ground is zero. The d-c potential of the cathode with respect to ground is positive. Therefore, the grid is

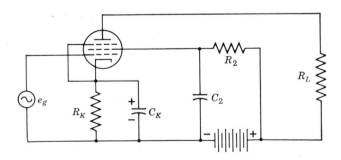

**Figure 10–6**   A pentode amplifier with a single direct voltage supply.

d-c negative with respect to the cathode by the amount of the cathode-resistance voltage drop. This drop across $R_K$ serves the same purpose as the bias battery $E_{cc}$. The capacitor $C_K$ serves as a filter to insure a pure direct voltage across $R_K$.

In the screen circuit, $R_2$ serves as the voltage dropping resistor to reduce $E_{bb}$ to the proper operating screen voltage $E_{c2}$. $C_2$ serves as the filter capacitor. The $L$ filter configuration of $R_2$ and $C_2$ gives rise to the nomenclature *screen decoupling filter*. By a rule of thumb, the value of the bypass capacitor is determined by making the reactance of the capacitor at the lowest frequency to be amplified no greater than one-tenth the value of the resistor it bypasses.

To show the method of calculation, let us assume that for a particular tube the operating values of current and voltage are as follows:

$$E_{bb} = 300 \text{ volts}, \qquad I_b = 3 \text{ ma}$$

$$E_{c2} = 100 \text{ volts}, \qquad I_{c2} = 2 \text{ ma}$$

$$E_{cc} = -4 \text{ volts}, \qquad I_K = I_b + I_{c2} = 5 \text{ ma}$$

Then

$$R_K = \frac{E_{cc}}{I_b + I_{c2}} = \frac{4}{0.005} = 800 \text{ ohms}$$

and

$$R_2 = \frac{E_{bb} - E_{c2}}{I_{c2}} = \frac{300 - 100}{0.002} = 100,000 \text{ ohms}$$

For operation down to 30 cycles,

$$X_{CK} = 0.1 R_K$$

$$\frac{1}{2\pi f C_K} = 0.1 R_K$$

$$\frac{1}{2\pi 30 C_K} = 80$$

$$C_K = 66.5 \ \mu\text{f}$$

$$X_{C2} = 0.1 R_2$$

$$\frac{1}{2\pi f C_2} = 0.1 R_2$$

$$\frac{1}{2\pi 30 C_2} = 10,000$$

$$C_2 = 0.053 \ \mu\text{f}$$

### Section 10-4   Load Lines

A load line, often called the *static load line*, is a plot of the circuit operation with a signal on a tube characteristic for a specific bias voltage, for a specific plate supply voltage and for a specific load resistance. The basic load line is obtained from the equation:

$$e_b + i_b R_L = E_{bb}$$

A plot of this equation on a plate characteristic must be a straight line since it is a linear first-degree equation.

If the end points of a straight line are determined, the line may be constructed. In the equation, if $i_b$ is zero, $e_b$ equals $E_{bb}$. If $e_b$ is zero, $i_b$ is $E_{bb}/R_L$. Thus, the end points of the load line (Fig. 10-7) are $E_{bb}$ and $E_{bb}/R_L$. The load line has a slope of $-1/R_L$. The operating point which is determined by the value of $E_{cc}$ is to be the midpoint of the linear range of the grid intercepts on this load line. In Fig. 10-7, the operating point for $E_{cc}$ is $-5$ volts. This operating point determines $I_b$ and $E_b$. On this diagram, the range of linear operation is between 0 volts on the grid and $-10$ volts on the grid. These limit points determine $E_{max}$, $E_{min}$, $I_{max}$, and $I_{min}$, as shown on the diagram.

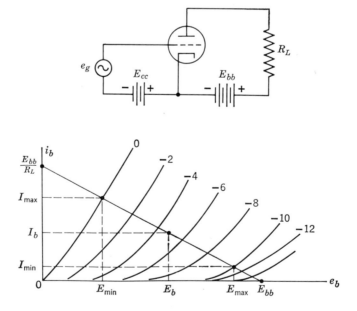

**Figure 10-7**   The Amplifier and the load line.

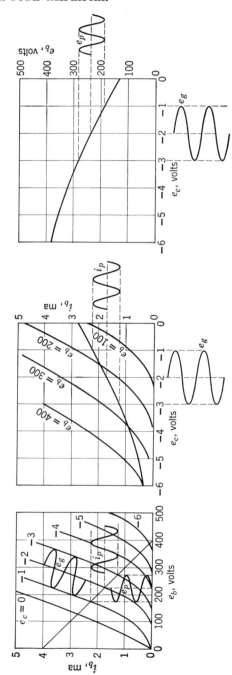

**Figure 10-8**  Dynamic load lines for a 6SL7 with 100-kilohms plate load.

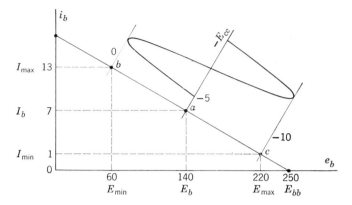

**Figure 10–9**   The dynamic load line.

If these limits are exceeded, the grid would be positive on one end of the load line and would go into the nonlinear region at the other end.

In Section 3–2, three types of the triode curves were discussed, the plate characteristic $e_b$, $i_b$, the transfer characteristic $e_c$, $i_b$, and the constant plate current family $e_b$, $e_c$.   The load line is necessarily linear only on the plate characteristic.   In Fig. 10–8, the load line is transferred from the plate characteristic to the other two characteristics as a point-by-point development.   The load lines plotted on these other two characteristics, although nonlinear, are more useful at times because they show directly the relation among the input signal, the output current, and the output voltage.

Thus far we have learned to draw a load line on a plate characteristic, to obtain the operating point bias, and to establish the limits of acceptable grid swing.   For a further analysis of the properties of the load line, refer to Fig. 10–9.   The operating point is at $a$, and the maximum grid swing is from $b$ to $c$.   The distance from $b$ to $c$ represents the *peak to peak* of the a-c values.   If we divide these by two, we obtained *peak* values, and, dividing again by $\sqrt{2}$ or 1.414, we obtain the rms or effective values.   Thus the maximum signal conditions are as follows:

$$E_g = \frac{2E_{cc}}{2\sqrt{2}} = 0.707 E_{cc} \qquad (10\text{–}4)$$

$$E_p = \frac{E_{\max} - E_{\min}}{2\sqrt{2}} \qquad (10\text{–}5a)$$

$$I_p = \frac{I_{\max} - I_{\min}}{2\sqrt{2}} \qquad (10\text{–}5b)$$

The power supply delivers to the circuit $E_{bb}I_b$ watts. $E_bI_b$ watts is the power input to the tube and ($E_{bb}I_b - E_bI_b$) watts are dissipated in the load resistor in the form of heat. The plate circuit of the tube absorbs $E_bI_b$ watts and converts part of this power into useful power output $P_o$.

$$P_o = I_p E_p = \frac{I_{\max} - I_{\min}}{2\sqrt{2}} \frac{E_{\max} - E_{\min}}{2\sqrt{2}}$$

$$P_o = \frac{(I_{\max} - I_{\min})(E_{\max} - E_{\min})}{8} \qquad (10\text{--}6)$$

The plate-circuit efficiency is the measure of effectiveness of conversion of the input power into useful a-c output power:

$$\eta_{\text{pl}} = \frac{P_o}{E_b I_b} \qquad (10\text{--}7)$$

The over-all efficiency of the circuit is

$$\eta_{\text{ov}} = \frac{P_o}{E_{bb} I_b} \qquad (10\text{--}8)$$

The voltage gain of the circuit is the peak-to-peak alternating plate-voltage swing divided by the peak-to-peak grid-voltage swing:

$$A_e = \frac{E_{\max} - E_{\min}}{2 E_{cc}} \qquad (10\text{--}9)$$

The total input power may be represented by the area of the rectangle *0–7–10–11* in Fig. 10–10. The area *0–7–9–12* represents the plate input power $E_b I_b$. The rectangle *2–4–1–5* represents ($E_{\max} - E_{\min}$)($I_{\max} - I_{\min}$). The net output power is then one eighth of this

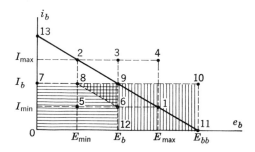

**Figure 10–10**  Representation of powers on the plate characteristic.

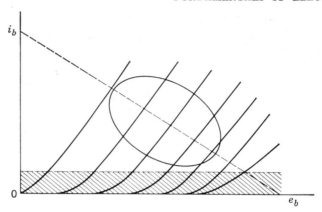

**Figure 10–11**   Inductive load line.

area or triangle *6–8–9*.   If the amplifier is ideal, we would be able to make use of the entire load line for grid swing.   Point 2 would approach point 13, point 1 would approach point 11, point 8 would approach point 7, point 6 would approach point 12, and the operating point would be at the midpoint of the load line.   Under these circumstances, the area of *0–7–9–12* would be one-half the area of *0–7–10–11*. The area of triangle *6–8–9* would be one-half the area of *0–7–9–12*. From this ideal set of conditions, the circuit has a maximum theoretical plate efficiency of 50% and a maximum theoretical over-all efficiency of 25%.   Typical actual values encountered in practice are of the order of up to 30% and 18% respectively.

Load lines may be drawn for inductive loads also, but the technique is beyond the scope of this book.   In Fig. 10–11 the region of curvature is cross-hatched and the inductive load line is drawn in the linear region.

### Section 10–5   Distortion

Ideally an amplifier accepts a grid signal and reproduces the signal in the plate circuit without changing its shape or form.   An amplifier can be free of distortion only if all the intercepts are exactly equal in Fig. 10–8.   Practically, a distortion-free amplifier is an impossibility. Thus, it is necessary to discuss distortion with a view to obtaining both qualitative and quantitative evaluations of the problem.   Qualitatively, the distortion occurs in three forms: amplitude, frequency, and phase.

*Amplitude distortion* is defined as the result of different amplifier gains at differential signal levels. If a 2-volt signal produces 40 volts output, an 8-volt signal without distortion is amplified to 160 volts. If the plate supply is only 90 volts, an output of 160 volts would not be possible. Nonlinearity of the dynamic load line, overloading, and cutoff, all contribute to amplitude distortion.

*Frequency distortion* results from different gains at different frequencies. To be free from frequency distortion, the amplifier must be *flat* over the necessary frequency range. As an example, lack of bass in an amplifier is a frequency distortion.

*Phase distortion* must be explained before it is defined. If a signal consists of a fundamental and a third harmonic (Fig. 10–12), in order for the plate wave to have the same shape, both the fundamental and the third harmonic must be zero at the same time. If the fundamental has a phase shift of 7° with respect to itself, the third harmonic which is three times the fundamental frequency must have a phase shift of 3 × 7 or 21°. Disregarding the natural 180° inversion of the signal in an amplifier stage, *no phase distortion occurs* if

1. The phase shift is zero, or
2. The phase shift is proportional to frequency.

In audio work, little attention is paid to phase-shift distortion. In video amplifiers and in pulse amplifiers, a serious phase-shift distortion could change a square pulse into a triangular pulse. Fortunately, when the frequency response is satisfactory for passing all necessary harmonics without frequency distortion, the phase-shift distortion is almost negligible.

It should be noted that amplitude distortion is developed by the nonlinearity of the circuit components and by the nonlinearity of the

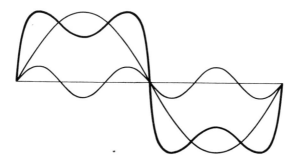

**Figure 10–12**   Wave consisting of fundamental and third harmonic.

vacuum tube itself.   Frequency distortion and phase distortion arise
primarily from the variation of the impedances of the reactive elements
in the circuit (inductance and capacitance).   This distortion is present
under circumstances where the amplitude distortion is negligible.   As
an example, an amplifier that is designed to deliver 35 watts has a very
small amplitude distortion when the output is only one watt, but it
still has limitations on the low- and on the high-frequency response.

A distortion that is often considered as independent of the amplitude
distortion discussed above is *intermodulation distortion*.   Let us assume
that an amplifier is distortionless when it is amplifying either a 200-
cycle signal or a 4000-cycle signal.   When both signals are simultaneously present in the input, any interaction between them is called
intermodulation distortion.   This distortion is important when the
complex waveforms of speech and music are considered.

For a quantitative analysis of amplitude distortion, we use the
equation for the triode:

$$i_b = K(e_b + \mu e_g)^{3/2} \tag{3-2}$$

This is expanded by the binomial theorem

$$(x + y)^{3/2} = x^{3/2} + \tfrac{3}{2}x^{1/2}y + \frac{\tfrac{3}{2} \cdot \tfrac{1}{2}}{1 \cdot 2}x^{-1/2}y^2 + \frac{\tfrac{3}{2} \cdot \tfrac{1}{2} \cdot (-\tfrac{1}{2})}{1 \cdot 2 \cdot 3}x^{-3/2}y^3 + \cdots$$

as

$$i_b = Ke_b^{3/2} + K\tfrac{3}{2}e_b^{1/2}\mu e_g + K\frac{\tfrac{3}{2} \cdot \tfrac{1}{2}}{1 \cdot 2}e_b^{-1/2}\mu^2 e_g^2$$

$$+ K\frac{\tfrac{3}{2} \cdot \tfrac{1}{2}(-\tfrac{1}{2})}{1 \cdot 2 \cdot 3}e_b^{-3/2}\mu^3 e_g^3 + \cdots$$

Taking $e_b$ as a constant and $e_g$ as the variable, we obtain, by replacing
the products of a number of constants by a single constant:

$$i_b = a_0 + a_1 e_g + a_2 e_g^2 + a_3 e_g^3 + a_4 e_g^4 + \cdots$$

This form is the well-known power series of mathematics.   Without
taking the trouble to derive the expression, a mathematician would
state immediately that, since an amplifier is not an exact linear device,
the plate current can be represented by a power series in terms of the
grid signal.   In this expression $a_0$ represents $I_b$, and, accordingly, we
may write

$$i_b = I_b + a_1 e_g + a_2 e_g^2 + a_3 e_g^3 + a_4 e_g^4 + \cdots$$

If we let $e_g = E \sin \omega t$, we have

$$i_b = I_b + a_1 E \sin \omega t + a_2 E^2 \sin^2 \omega t + a_3 E^3 \sin^3 \omega t$$
$$+ a_4 E^4 \sin^4 \omega t + \cdots$$

From trigonometric tables of identities, we find

$$\sin^2 x = \tfrac{1}{2} - \tfrac{1}{2} \cos 2x$$

$$\sin^3 x = (\tfrac{1}{2} - \tfrac{1}{2} \cos 2x) \sin x$$

$$= \tfrac{1}{2} \sin x - \tfrac{1}{2} \cos 2x \sin x$$

$$= \tfrac{1}{2} \sin x - \tfrac{1}{4} \sin 3x + \tfrac{1}{4} \sin x$$

$$= \tfrac{3}{4} \sin x - \tfrac{1}{4} \sin 3x$$

$$\sin^4 x = (\tfrac{1}{2} - \tfrac{1}{2} \cos 2x)^2$$

$$= \tfrac{1}{4} - \tfrac{1}{2} \cos 2x + \tfrac{1}{4} \cos^2 2x$$

$$= \tfrac{1}{4} - \tfrac{1}{2} \cos 2x + \tfrac{1}{8} + \tfrac{1}{8} \cos 4x$$

$$= \tfrac{3}{8} - \tfrac{1}{2} \cos 2x + \tfrac{1}{8} \cos 4x$$

Then

$$i_b = I_b + \left(\frac{a_2 E^2}{2} + \frac{3a_4 E^4}{8} + \cdots\right) + \left(a_1 E + \frac{3a_3 E^3}{4} + \cdots\right) \sin \omega t$$

$$- \left(\frac{a_2 E^2}{2} + \frac{a_4 E^4}{2} + \cdots\right) \cos 2\omega t - \left(\frac{a_3 E^3}{4} + \cdots\right) \sin 3\omega t$$

$$+ \left(\frac{a_4 E^4}{8} + \cdots\right) \cos 4\omega t + \cdots$$

which may be simplified as

$$i_b = I_b + A_0 + A_1 \sin \omega t + A_2 \sin 2\omega t + A_3 \sin 3\omega t$$
$$+ A_4 \sin 4\omega t + A_5 \sin 5\omega t + \cdots$$

This derivation proves that an amplifier not only amplifies a signal but also introduces harmonics which are unwanted multiples of the grid signal frequency. $A_1$ is the amplitude of the fundamental in the output, $A_2$ is the amplitude of the second harmonic, $A_3$ is the amplitude of the third harmonic, $A_4$ is the amplitude of the fourth harmonic, and $A_5$ is the amplitude of the fifth harmonic. Fortunately, the magnitude of the harmonic amplitudes decreases rapidly to the point where we are ordinarily concerned only up to the fifth and usually only up to the second and third.

The per cent of the second harmonic is $(A_2/A_1) \times 100$; of the third, $(A_3/A_1) \times 100$; of the fourth, $(A_4/A_1) \times 100$; and of the fifth, $(A_5/A_1) \times 100$. Figure 10–13 shows the relation of the total harmonic content to the load resistance for a class-A amplifier operated at

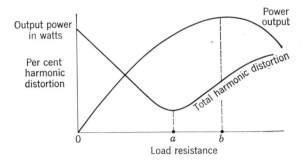

**Figure 10–13** Output characteristics of a tetrode or pentode power tube at full signal.

maximum grid-signal drive. It is found that the maximum power output and the minimum distortion do not occur at the same value of load resistance. Usually a vacuum tube is operated at the point of minimum distortion and not at the point of maximum power output.

When the grid signal of an amplifier is increased from zero to maximum and the results plotted, we obtain the curve of Fig. 10–14. Amplitude distortion causes a decrease in output voltage at $a$. This loss of output voltage causes the output power to fall at $b$. The presence of the various harmonics accounts for the $A_0$ term in

$$i_b = I_b + A_0 + A_1 \sin \omega t + A_2 \sin 2\omega t + A_3 \sin 3\omega t + \cdots$$

As the signal voltage increases, the magnitude of the $A_0$ term increases. This actually produces first a decrease and then a rise in the total

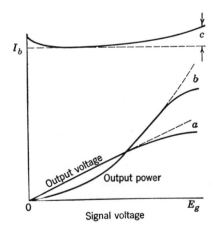

**Figure 10–14** Output characteristics of a power tube with a varying signal.

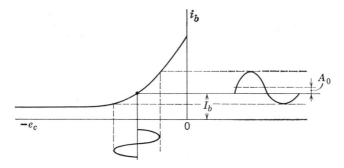

**Figure 10–15**   Distortion produced by the dynamic-transfer load line.

current as the signal increases.   The $A_0$ term is often referred to as
"the rectification of the grid signal in the plate circuit."   This
terminology may be clarified by referring to Fig. 10–15.   Here a grid
signal is applied to a nonlinear dynamic-transfer load line.   The output current is severely distorted from a sine wave.   The average of
the output wave is not $I_b$ but is the dotted line which is higher than
$I_b$ by the amount $A_0$.

A quantitative approach which has been developed for predetermining the harmonic distortion makes use of the following formulas:

Increase in $I_b$
(rectified component)
$$A_0 = \frac{\frac{1}{2}(I_{\max} + I_{\min}) + I_2 + I_3 - 3I_b}{4}$$
$$(10\text{–}10a)$$

Rms value of
fundamental
$$A_1 = \frac{\sqrt{2}\,(I_2 - I_3) + I_{\max} - I_{\min}}{4\sqrt{2}}$$
$$(10\text{–}10b)$$

Rms value of
second harmonic
$$A_2 = \frac{I_{\max} + I_{\min} - 2I_b}{4\sqrt{2}} \qquad (10\text{–}10c)$$

Rms value of
third harmonic
$$A_3 = \frac{I_{\max} - I_{\min} - 2\sqrt{2}\,A_1}{2\sqrt{2}} \qquad (10\text{–}10d)$$

Rms value of
fourth harmonic
$$A_4 = \frac{2A_0 - I_2 - I_3 + 2I_b}{2\sqrt{2}} \qquad (10\text{–}10e)$$

The location of the values of the symbols used is shown in Fig. 10–16.

To illustrate this method of harmonic-distortion analysis, a load
line for 3000 ohms and a supply voltage of 600 volts is drawn on the

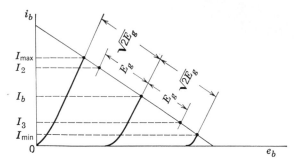

**Figure 10–16** Graphical procedure for harmonic determination.

triode-connected plate characteristic of the 6L6 (Fig. 10–17). The operating point is at $E_{cc} = -45$ volts. The grid swing is then $\pm 45$ volts. $I_2$ is located where the grid swing is 0.707 of the maximum value and is $(-45 + 31.8)$ or $-13.2$ volts. $I_3$ is located at $(-45 - 31.8)$ or $-76.8$ volts. A tabulation of values taken from the graph gives:

$$I_{max} = 132 \text{ ma}, \qquad I_{min} = 4 \text{ ma}$$

$$I_2 = 107 \text{ ma}, \qquad I_3 = 10 \text{ ma}$$

$$I_b = 49 \text{ ma}$$

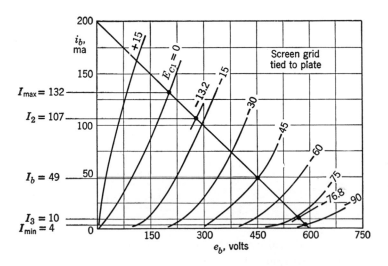

**Figure 10–17** Calculation of distortion for a 6L6 triode-connected amplifier.

Putting these values in the equations and evaluating, we have the following:

$$A_0 = \frac{\frac{1}{2}(I_{max} + I_{min}) + I_2 + I_3 - 3I_b}{4}$$

$$= \frac{\frac{1}{2}(132 + 4) + 107 + 10 - 3 \times 49}{4} = 9.5 \text{ ma}$$

$$A_1 = \frac{\sqrt{2}(I_2 - I_3) + I_{max} - I_{min}}{4\sqrt{2}}$$

$$= \frac{\sqrt{2}(107 - 10) + 132 - 4}{4\sqrt{2}} = \frac{65.4}{\sqrt{2}} = 46.9 \text{ ma}$$

$$A_2 = \frac{I_{max} + I_{min} - 2I_b}{4\sqrt{2}} = \frac{132 + 4 - 2 \times 49}{4\sqrt{2}} = 6.7 \text{ ma}$$

$$A_3 = \frac{I_{max} - I_{min} - 2\sqrt{2}A_1}{2\sqrt{2}} = \frac{132 - 4 - 2\sqrt{2}\,46.9}{2\sqrt{2}} = 1.0 \text{ ma}$$

$$A_4 = \frac{2A_0 - I_2 - I_3 + 2I_b}{2\sqrt{2}} = \frac{2 \times 9.5 - 107 - 10 + 2 \times 49}{2\sqrt{2}} = 0$$

$$P_{out} = A_1{}^2 R_L = 0.0469^2 \times 3000 = 6.56 \text{ watts}$$

$$\% \text{ 2nd harmonic} = \frac{A_2}{A_1} \times 100 = \frac{6.7}{49.6} \times 100 = 14.3\%$$

$$\% \text{ 3rd harmonic} = \frac{A_3}{A_1} \times 100 = \frac{1.0}{46.9} \times 100 = 2.1\%$$

$$\% \text{ 4th harmonic} = \frac{A_4}{A_1} \times 100 = 0$$

$$\text{Total harmonic distortion} = \sqrt{(\% \text{ 2nd})^2 + (\% \text{ 3rd})^2 + (\% \text{ 4th})^2}$$

$$= \sqrt{(14.3)^2 + (2.1)^2}$$

$$= 14.4\%$$

## Section 10-6   Pentode and Beam-Power-Tube Considerations

In Fig. 10–18, the plate characteristics of a triode and a beam-power tube are superimposed. The useful operating range of a pentode or a beam power tube is greater than the operating range of a triode.

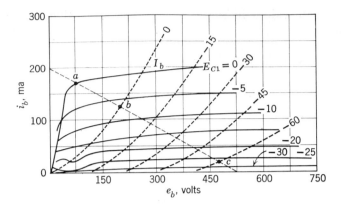

$e_b$, volts

**Figure 10–18**  Superimposed beam-power and triode-plate characteristics for the 6L6.  Solid lines—beam-power connection.  Dotted lines—triode connection. Beam-power load-line operation $ac$.  Triode load-line operation $bc$.

Consequently, it is expected that a pentode or a beam-power tube will deliver a greater power and show a higher over-all efficiency than the corresponding triode power amplifier.   On the other hand, it is evident that the triode grid line divides the load line into nearly equal segments as compared to the pentode or beam power tube.   Accordingly, the triode operates at a lower inherent harmonic distortion.

### Section 10–7   Limitations of Amplifiers

Gain in an amplifier is not unlimited.   The largest output voltage obtainable from an amplifier is determined by the operating point and the plate supply voltage.   As the grid signal is increased, we note that the grid is driven positive or into cutoff or both.

An amplifier cannot respond to all frequencies.   There must be a lower limit and an upper limit which are dependent on its design. The topic of frequency limitations is developed at length in Chapters 12 and 13.

Random motions of electrons within a vacuum tube cause a noise voltage to be developed across the load.   If the signal is so small that the amplified output is masked by the internally developed noise, it is lost.   This inherent noise is produced from several sources.   *Shot noise* is caused by random emission of electrons from the cathode. *Thermal noise* is developed by random electron flow in the grid circuit. *Partition noise* is produced in the screen-plate region of tetrodes and pentodes caused by random variations in the division of screen and plate currents.

*Microphonics* are variations in plate current caused by mechanical vibrations within the tube. Tapping a microphonic tube causes a "ping" in the audio output of an amplifier. Special low-microphonic tubes are available. A tube that is possibly sensitive to microphonics is often shock-mounted on rubber or Neoprene.

Hum in an amplifier often limits its performance. A poorly filtered full-wave rectifier power supply introduces hum at twice line frequency. A half-wave supply introduces hum at line frequency. Stray fields from unshielded transformers, a-c supply lines, etc. can introduce line-frequency hum. Heater–cathode leakage introduces line-frequency hum. In certain high-fidelity amplifier systems, the power-supply components are well designed to minimize hum, and the power-supply chassis is separated from the amplifier chassis to keep stray field pickup at a minimum. Also sensitive tubes may be operated with direct current on the heaters to eliminate the problem of hum caused by heater–cathode leakage.

## . . . . Suggested References for Further Study

1. F. Langford-Smith, *Radiotron Designer's Handbook*, 4th ed., Chapter 12, RCA, Harrison, N. J., 1953.
2. J. D. Ryder, *Engineering Electronics*, Chapter 4, McGraw-Hill Book Co., New York, 1957.

## . . . . QUESTIONS

1. Define or explain each of the following terms: (a) equivalent circuit, (b) screen decoupling filter, (c) dynamic load line, (d) inductive load line, (e) amplitude distortion, (f) frequency distortion, (g) phase distortion, (h) intermodulation distortion, (i) microphonics, (j) heater–cathode leakage.

2. Explain what each of the following symbols indicates in a vacuum-tube amplifier circuit: $e_g$, $E_g$, $I_b$, $e_b$, $E_{bb}$, $i_p$, $e_c$, $I_p$, $E_{cc}$, $E_p$, $i_b$, $E_b$.

3. What is meant by voltage gain?

4. What are the units of $\mu e_g$ and $g_m e_g$?

5. What are the gain equations for the two basic equivalent circuits?

6. How is the value of $C_K$ determined?

7. What is the purpose of a screen decoupling filter?

8. How is the slope of the load line related to the load resistance?

9. What limits the maximum allowable grid input voltage to an amplifier?

10. How is plate efficiency related to the magnitude of the input signal?

11. What is the maximum theoretical efficiency of an amplifier with resistive load?

12. What is a power series?

13. How does a power series treat the presence of harmonics in an output signal?

14. How is total harmonic distortion obtained if the values for the individual harmonics are given?

15. Does the maximum power output occur at the point of minimum distortion?

16. Why does a beam-power tube give a higher efficiency than a triode?

17. What are the advantages of a beam-power tube?

18. List and explain the factors that limit the performance of an amplifier.


## . . . . PROBLEMS

1. An amplifier has a 15,000-ohm load. The amplifier tube has a $g_m$ of 1800 micromhos and a plate resistance of 40,000 ohms. Determine the voltage gain of the circuit.

2. Solve problem 1 for a plate load-resistance value of 5,000 ohms.

3. Solve problem 1 for a plate load-resistance value of 25,000 ohms.

4. Solve problem 1 for a plate load-resistance value of 70,000 ohms.

5. Solve problem 1 for a plate load that consists of a 140-mh coil in series with a 2000-ohm resistance. Calculate the gain at 1000 cycles and at 10 kc.

6. Solve problem 5 when the plate load is a 0.01-$\mu$f capacitor in parallel with a 16,000-ohm resistance.

7. Using the plate characteristic for the 6AS5 given in the tube manual, determine (a) the cathode bias resistance, (b) the output power, (c) the plate efficiency, (d) the voltage gain, (e) the maximum peak-to-peak output voltage, when the supply voltage is 300 volts and the plate load resistance is 3000 ohms.

8. Using the plate characteristic for the 6AQ5 given in the tube manual, determine (a) the cathode bias resistance, (b) the plate dissipation, (c) the output power, (d) the voltage gain, (e) the maximum allowable grid swing, (f) the d-c power dissipated in the load resistance when the plate supply voltage is 500 volts and the plate load is 5000 ohms.

9. Determine the values of $\mu$, $r_p$, and $g_m$ at the operating point used in problem 7.

10. Determine the values of $\mu$, $r_p$, and $g_m$ at the operating point used in problem 8.

11. Determine the harmonic content of the output signal in problem 7.

12. Determine the harmonic content of the output signal in problem 8.

13. Plot the dynamic-transfer characteristic for the load line in problem 7.

14. Plot the dynamic-transfer characteristic for the load line in problem 8.

# The transistor amplifier

The procedure for the analysis of the basic transistor amplifiers follows a definite sequence:

1. Establishment of a load line on the transistor characteristic.
2. Analysis of the information on the load line.
3. Development of an equivalent circuit.
4. Finding the equations for voltage gain, current gain, power gain, input resistance, and output resistance.
5. Determination of the maximum possible gain under matched conditions.
6. Analytic solution of the example used for the load line.

The three circuits, the grounded- or common-base amplifier (Section 11–1), the grounded- or common-emitter amplifier (Section 11–2), and the grounded- or common-collector amplifier (Section 11–3) are considered, each in this manner. At the end of the chapter is a table summarizing these results as a reference. An examination of biasing methods (Section 11–4) completes the chapter. The frontispiece illustrates the use of standard symbols.

### Section 11–1  The Grounded-Base Amplifier

The discussion in Section 3–7 served to show in a qualitative manner the action of a grounded-base transistor amplifier. At that point, it was sufficient to develop the concept of transistor gain and to show the inphase relation of the output and input voltages. Now we must extend the analysis to the load line and to the equivalent circuits as with the vacuum tube.

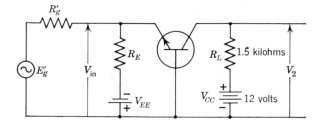

**Figure 11-1**  Circuit for a grounded-base amplifier using a junction transistor.

The circuit of Fig. 11-1 uses an *NPN* transistor in a grounded-base amplifier circuit.  The load line for the 1500-ohm load resistance is plotted on the characteristic curves (Fig. 11-2) in the same manner as the load line for a vacuum tube.  One end of the load line is the supply voltage $V_{CC}$, and the other end is the current $V_{CC}/R_L$ through the load resistance when the collector is short-circuited to the base.  The load line must be linear since it satisfies

$$v_C + i_C R_L = V_{CC}$$

which is a first-degree linear equation.

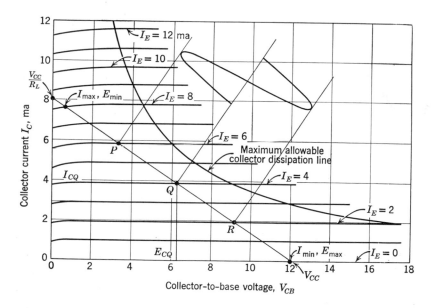

**Figure 11-2**  Load line for the circuit of Fig. 11-1.

The operating point is located at the midpoint of the linear intercepts on the load line. For this example, the operating current bias is 4 ma. A small a-c signal is shown on Fig. 11–2. This signal variation between the points $P$ and $R$ on the load line causes changes in the collector circuit which may be tabulated as follows:

| For the Emitter | For the Collector | |
|---|---|---|
| $I_{EP} = 6$ ma | $V_{CP} = 3.25$ volts, | $I_{CP} = 5.85$ ma |
| $I_{EQ} = 4$ ma | $V_{CQ} = 6.25$ volts, | $I_{CQ} = 3.90$ ma |
| $I_{ER} = 2$ ma | $V_{CR} = 9.10$ volts, | $I_{CR} = 1.95$ ma |

The calculations based on the load line are made in the same manner as for the vacuum-tube circuit:

The alternating emitter current is

$$I_e = \frac{I_{EP} - I_{ER}}{2\sqrt{2}} = \frac{6 - 2}{2\sqrt{2}} = 1.41 \text{ ma} \quad \text{(rms)}$$

The alternating load current is

$$I_c = \frac{I_{CP} - I_{CR}}{2\sqrt{2}} = \frac{3.90}{2\sqrt{2}} = 1.38 \text{ ma} \quad \text{(rms)}$$

The alternating load voltage is

$$V_c = \frac{V_{CR} - V_{CP}}{2\sqrt{2}} = \frac{9.10 - 3.25}{2\sqrt{2}} = 2.07 \text{ volts} \quad \text{(rms)}$$

The circuit current gain is

$$A_{ib} = \frac{I_{CP} - I_{CR}}{I_{EP} - I_{ER}} = \frac{5.85 - 1.95}{6 - 2} = 0.975$$

The harmonic content of the output can be obtained in the same manner as for the vacuum tube (Section 10-5).

When the signal is increased, the limiting values without serious overloading or clipping are represented by minimum and maximum values as was done for the vacuum tube. Tabulating these results for this transistor circuit, we find the following:

| For the Emitter | For the Collector | |
|---|---|---|
| $I_{EQ} = 4$ ma | $I_{CQ} = 3.90$ ma, | $V_{CQ} = 6.25$ volts |
| $I_{E,\max} = 8$ ma | $I_{C,\max} = 7.60$ ma, | $V_{C,\max} = 12.00$ volts |
| $I_{E,\min} = 0$ | $I_{C,\min} = 0,$ | $V_{C,\min} = 0.54$ volts |

Proceeding in the same manner as with the vacuum-tube circuit:
The alternating output current is

$$I_2 = I_c = \frac{I_{C,\max} - I_{C,\min}}{2\sqrt{2}} = \frac{7.60 - 0}{2\sqrt{2}} = 2.69 \text{ ma} \quad \text{(rms)}$$

The alternating output voltage is

$$V_2 = V_c = \frac{V_{C,\max} - V_{C,\min}}{2\sqrt{2}} = \frac{12 - 0.54}{2\sqrt{2}} = 4.05 \text{ volts} \quad \text{(rms)}$$

The alternating input current is

$$I_e = \frac{I_{E,\max} - I_{E,\min}}{2\sqrt{2}} = \frac{8 - 0}{2\sqrt{2}} = 2.83 \text{ ma} \quad \text{(rms)}$$

The a-c power output is

$$P_o = \frac{(V_{C,\max} - V_{C,\min})(I_{C,\max} - I_{C,\min})}{8}$$

$$= \frac{(12.00 - 0.54)(7.60 - 0)}{8} = 10.9 \text{ mw}$$

The total circuit input power is

$$V_{CC} \times I_{CQ} = 12.00 \times 3.90 = 46.8 \text{ mw}$$

The total collector input is

$$V_{CQ} \times I_{CQ} = 6.25 \times 3.90 = 24.4 \text{ mw}$$

The efficiency of the circuit is

$$\frac{10.9}{46.8} 100 = 23.3\%$$

The efficiency of the collector is

$$\frac{10.9}{24.4} 100 = 44.7\%$$

It is immediately apparent that these efficiencies are very close to the maximum theoretical values of 25% and 50%. These high values correspond to values of up to 18% and 30% which are typical for a vacuum-tube circuit.

If the values of $I_E$ and $I_C$ for points along the load line are plotted, we obtain a curve, (Fig. 11–3) which corresponds to the load line for a

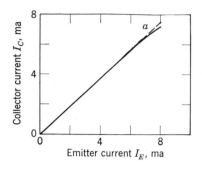

**Figure 11–3**  Dynamic load line for the circuit of Fig. 11–1.

vacuum tube shown on the transfer characteristic. The curve deviates from a straight line only at high-current values. If the operating point is kept as near the origin as possible, the distortion decreases, but the power output is reduced. Also there is less drain on the supply batteries.

This particular transistor-amplifier circuit requires an operating bias of 4 ma in the emitter. In the discussion in Chapter 3, we showed that the actual forward emitter-to-base voltage $V_{EB}$ which is required to develop this bias current is very low, usually of the order of a small fraction of a volt. If the emitter bias voltage $V_{EE}$ is at least 1.5 volts, a very close approximation to the value of the emitter resistor $R_E$ required may be made by dividing $V_{EE}$ by $I_E$. As the value of $V_{EE}$ increases, the accuracy of this method increases. In the circuit of Fig. 11–1, a bias current of 4 ma is needed. If $V_{EE}$ is 3 volts, $R_E$ is 3 volts/4 ma, or 750 ohms. If $V_{EE}$ is 6 volts, $R_E$ is 6 volts/4 ma, or 1500 ohms. If $V_{EE}$ is 12 volts, $R_E$ is 3000 ohms. The bias resistor $R_E$ is then a function of the bias voltage used. In a vacuum-tube circuit, the cathode resistor is not subject to the possibility of many combinations but is only the one value that is determined by the currents at the operating point.

The complexity of transistor analysis is brought about by the fact that the input is not infinite impedance as a vacuum tube, but is finite and must be included in the analysis. From the load line for the small-signal condition, the effective value of the alternating emitter current $I_e$ is 1.41 ma. Figure 11–4 shows in detail the input side of the amplifier circuit omitting $V_{EE}$, which, if it is properly bypassed, does not contribute to the a-c signals. When there is an alternating current in the emitter, there is also a shunting alternating current through $R_E$. The current from the signal source must be $I_e + I_{RE}$ or $I_{in}$. $I_{in}$ and $V_{in}$ could be calculated if the input characteristic ($I_{EB} - V_{EB}$)

of the transistor were given. However, the curves for the input are completely dependent both on the load impedance and on the collector operating point. In the development of the equivalent circuit later in this section, we will show that this dependency must exist. In order to be useful, the transistor input characteristics would have to be available for a very large number of combinations of output circuit conditions.

It has been found that it is not necessary to provide these curves since there is a different approach that may be used. The actual output voltage, current, and power conditions may be determined by a graphical analysis of the load line. The gain of the circuit is found from the equivalent circuit. If the output values of voltage, current, and power are divided by the gains determined from the equivalent circuit, the actual input voltage, current, and power are found. In the vacuum-tube circuit, we can determine gain either by the graphical approach or by the equivalent circuit. In transistors, both the graphical method and the equivalent circuit must be combined in the analysis.

TABLE I. HYBRID PARAMETER SUMMARY

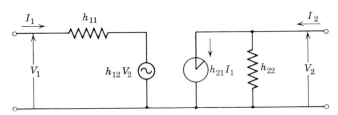

**Figure 7–32b** Equivalent circuit for a four-terminal network.

$$V_1 = h_{11}I_1 + h_{12}V_2 \qquad (7\text{–}12) \qquad h_{12} = \frac{V_1}{V_2} \quad (I_1 = 0) \qquad (7\text{–}15)$$

$$I_2 = h_{21}I_1 + h_{22}V_2 \qquad (7\text{–}13) \qquad h_{21} = \frac{I_2}{I_1} \quad (E_2 = 0) \qquad (7\text{–}16)$$

$$h_{11} = \frac{V_1}{I_1} = Z_1 \quad (V_2 = 0) \qquad (7\text{–}14) \qquad h_{22} = \frac{I_2}{V_2} = \frac{1}{Z_2} \quad (I_1 = 0) \qquad (7\text{–}17)$$

When $I_1 = 0$, the input is open-circuited and, when $V_2 = 0$, the output is short-circuited.

$h_{11}$ is called the input resistance with the output short-circuited.

$h_{12}$ is called the reverse-voltage ratio (or feedback-voltage ratio) with the input open-circuited.

$h_{21}$ is called the forward-current ratio with the output short-circuited.

$h_{22}$ is called the output conductance (or admittance) with the input open-circuited.

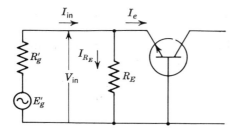

**Figure 11–4**   Input circuit for the grounded-base amplifier.

In Section 7–10, we developed an equivalent circuit for a four-terminal network. It is repeated here together with the associated equations for convenience using standard notation in Table I. These $h$ factors may be measured directly by test circuits and bridges and are listed for the transistor by the manufacturer just as values of $\mu$, $r_p$, and $g_m$ are tabulated for the vacuum tube.

By agreement with established standards for transistor nomenclature, the direction of $I_2$ is taken toward the transistor and not from the transistor. When $\alpha$ was defined as $I_2/I_1$, the two currents were in the same direction. Thus, $h_{21}$ is $-\alpha$. Also $V_2$ is $(-I_2 R_L)$, and $P_o$, the output power, which is the product of $V_2$ and $I_2$ is a negative number. As long as it is understood that by a negative power we mean that the power is delivered *to* the load and not taken *from* the load in the transistor circuit and that a negative $V_2$ indicates that the load is a sink (a resistance) and not a source (an emf), no confusion should result. All the equations for the transistor equivalent circuits are completely consistent with each other.

Figure 7–32*b* may be readily modified for the transistor circuit of Fig. 11–1. In this new circuit (Fig. 11–5) $E_g$ and $R_g$ are taken as the

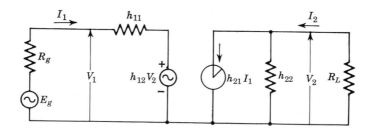

**Figure 11–5**   Equivalent circuit showing the source and the load for the grounded-base amplifier.

values for an equivalent circuit of $E'_g$, $R'_g$, and $R_E$ in Fig. 11–1 and in Fig. 11–4. A load resistance $R_L$ is placed across the output. The network equations do not change, and the objective of the analysis is to solve the two equations in such a manner as to develop equations for the various gains and impedances.

$$h_{11}I_1 + h_{12}V_2 = V_1 \qquad (7\text{–}12)$$

$$h_{21}I_1 + h_{22}V_2 = I_2 \qquad (7\text{–}13)$$

By Ohm's law, the relation across the load is

$$V_2 = -I_2R_L$$

Then, Eq. 7–12 and Eq. 7–13 become

$$h_{11}I_1 - h_{12}R_LI_2 = V_1 \qquad (A)$$

$$h_{21}I_1 - h_{22}R_LI_2 = I_2 \qquad (B)$$

or $\qquad\qquad h_{21}I_1 - (1 + h_{22}R_L)I_2 = 0 \qquad (B)$

If we use the relation $I_2 = -V_2/R_L$ and substitute in Eq. 7–13, we have

$$h_{21}I_1 + h_{22}V_2 = -\frac{V_2}{R_L} \qquad (C)$$

or $\qquad\qquad h_{21}I_1 + \left(h_{22} + \frac{1}{R_L}\right)V_2 = 0 \qquad (C)$

In order to simplify the algebra and to reduce the length of the resulting equations, we define $\Delta^h$ as

$$\Delta^h = h_{11}h_{22} - h_{12}h_{21} \qquad (11\text{–}1)$$

If we take Eq. $B$ and solve for the ratio of $I_2/I_1$, we obtain the *circuit current gain* which is

$$A_i = \frac{I_2}{I_1} = \frac{h_{21}}{1 + h_{22}R_L} \qquad (11\text{–}2)$$

If we take Eq. 7–12 and Eq. $C$ and solve the pair to eliminate $I_1$, the result involves $V_1$ and $V_2$ which may be expressed as a ratio $V_2/V_1$. This ratio is the *circuit voltage gain*

$$A_e = \frac{V_2}{V_1} = -\frac{h_{21}R_L}{\Delta^h R_L + h_{11}} \qquad (11\text{–}3)$$

The product of $A_i$ and $A_e$ gives the *power gain of the circuit*

$$A_p = - \frac{h^2{}_{21}R_L}{(1 + h_{22}R_L)(\Delta^h R_L + h_{11})} \tag{11-4}$$

As we pointed out, the minus sign merely shows that power is delivered to the load and not by the load.

If we take Eq. $A$ and divide by $I_1$, we have

$$h_{11} - h_{12}R_L \frac{I_2}{I_1} = \frac{V_1}{I_1}$$

$I_2/I_1$ can be replaced by the expression for current gain (Eq. 11–2), and $V_1/I_1$ is the *circuit input resistance* $r_{in}$, which simplifies to

$$r_{in} = \frac{R_L\Delta^h + h_{11}}{1 + h_{22}R_L} \tag{11-5}$$

From this equation, it is apparent that the input resistance to a transistor-amplifier circuit is very definitely a function of the output resistance and cannot be neglected.

If the generator is turned off in Fig. 11–4, the input voltage $V_1$ must be zero. The input-voltage loop equation is then

$$(R_g + h_{11})I_1 + h_{12}V_2 = 0$$

or $$I_1 = - \frac{h_{12}}{R_g + h_{11}} V_2$$

If this is substituted in Eq. 7–13, the ratio of $V_2/I_2$ is the *output circuit resistance*, $r_{out}$:

$$r_{out} = \frac{R_g + h_{11}}{h_{22}R_g + \Delta^h} \tag{11-6}$$

From this equation, we see that $r_{out}$ depends on the signal source impedance $R_g$. Thus the action of a transistor is more complex than that of the vacuum tube since the dual consideration exists where the input impedance depends on the load impedance and the output impedance depends on the source impedance. It also means that an input matching is exact only for one value of load and that output matching will not be maintained if the generator impedance changes. Also, exact matching requires that both the input and the output circuits must be *dually matched*.

In Fig. 11–5, the circuit input voltage is the generator voltage less its internal impedance drop

$$V_1 = E_g - I_1 R_g$$

If we substitute this relation for $V_1$ in Eq. 7–12 and solve this equation with Eq. $C$ for $V_2$ by eliminating $I_1$, we have

$$V_2 = - \frac{R_L h_{21} E_g}{h_{22} R_g R_L + R_g + \Delta^h R_L + h_{11}}$$

The load power is $V_2{}^2/R_L$ or

$$P_L = \frac{V_2{}^2}{R_L} = \frac{R_L h^2{}_{21} E_g{}^2}{(h_{22} R_g R_L + R_g + \Delta^h R_L + h_{11})^2}$$

In a generator which is connected to a matched load (the load resistance equals the generator resistance), the current is $E_g/2R_g$. The power in the load by $I^2 R$ is $E_g{}^2/4R_g$. Now, if we divide $P_L$ by $E_g{}^2/4R_g$, we have the gain which is called the *transducer gain* or the *operating gain:*

$$A_{\text{tr}} = \frac{4 R_g R_L h^2{}_{21}}{(h_{22} R_g R_L + R_g + \Delta^h R_L + h_{11})^2} \qquad (11\text{–}7)$$

If we substitute in this equation the value of load resistance which matches the output resistance of the transistor, we substitute Eq. 11–6 in Eq. 11–7. This gain is the ratio of the *available power of the transistor output* to the *available generator power* and is called the *available power gain:*

$$A_{\text{av}} = \frac{R_g h^2{}_{21}}{(R_g + h_{11})(\Delta^h + h_{22} R_g)} \qquad (11\text{–}8)$$

When the circuit is matched,

$$r_{\text{in}} = R_g \quad \text{and} \quad r_{\text{out}} = R_L$$

Substituting in Eq. 11–5 and in Eq. 11–6,

$$R_g = \frac{R_L \Delta^h + h_{11}}{1 + h_{22} R_L}$$

$$R_L = \frac{R_g + h_{11}}{h_{22} R_g + \Delta^h}$$

If each of these equations is cleared of fractions and then the two results are subtracted, we find

$$R_g = \Delta^h R_L$$

Putting this back in the equations for $r_{in}$ and $r_{out}$, we find

$$R_g = \left(\frac{\Delta^h h_{11}}{h_{22}}\right)^{\frac{1}{2}} \tag{11-9}$$

and

$$R_L = \left(\frac{h_{11}}{\Delta^h h_{22}}\right)^{\frac{1}{2}} \tag{11-10}$$

These expressions for $R_L$ and $R_g$ are those values of input and output resistances which properly match the load and the generator to the transistor. If we substitute these values in the expression for the transducer gain (Eq. 11-7), we find the gain under properly matched circuit conditions. This gain is called the *maximum available gain:*

$$\text{MAG} = \frac{h^2{}_{21}}{(\sqrt{h_{11}h_{22}} + \sqrt{\Delta^h})^2} \tag{11-11}$$

The transistor has, for the circuit operating conditions of Fig. 11-1, the following $h$-parameter values given in the technical data sheet:

$$h_{11} = 48.6 \text{ ohms}$$
$$h_{21} = -0.982$$
$$h_{12} = 3.58 \times 10^{-4}$$
$$h_{22} = 2.5 \times 10^{-7} \text{ mho}$$

In order to continue the analysis which was started in the examination of the properties of the load line, calculations based on Eq. 11-1 through Eq. 11-11 are made with a discussion of the significance of the results:

For Eq. 11-1,

$$\Delta^h = h_{11}h_{22} - h_{12}h_{21}$$
$$= 48.6(2.5 \times 10^{-7}) + 0.982(3.58 \times 10^{-4})$$
$$= 36.42 \times 10^{-5}$$

The value used for the load resistance $R_L$ was 1500 ohms. Assume a source resistance $R_g$ of 200 ohms. This value of 200 ohms for Fig.

11–1 includes both the generator resistance and the shunting effect of $R_E$.

For Eq. 11–2,

$$A_i = \frac{h_{21}}{1 + h_{22}R_L}$$

$$= \frac{-0.982}{1 + (2.5 \times 10^{-7})1500}$$

$$= -0.982$$

For Eq. 11–3,

$$A_e = \frac{-h_{21}R_L}{\Delta^h R_L + h_{11}}$$

$$= \frac{0.982 \times 1500}{(36.42 \times 10^{-5})1500 + 48.6}$$

$$= 30$$

The positive sign of $A_e$ indicates that this circuit arrangment has no phase shift between the input and the output voltages.  Since the product of $A_i$ and $A_e$ is the power gain

$$A_p = -0.982 \times 30$$

$$= -29.46 = 14.65 \text{ db}$$

From Eq. 11–5, $\quad r_{\text{in}} = \dfrac{R_L \Delta^h + h_{11}}{1 + h_{22}R_L}$

$$= \frac{(36.42 \times 10^{-5})(1.5 \times 10^3) + 48.6}{1 + (2.5 \times 10^{-7})(1.5 \times 10^3)}$$

$$= 49.15 \text{ ohms}$$

From Eq. 11–6, $\quad r_{\text{out}} = \dfrac{R_g + h_{11}}{h_{22}R_g + \Delta^h}$

$$= \frac{200 + 48.6}{(2.5 \times 10^{-7})200 + 36.42 \times 10^{-5}}$$

$$= 600 \text{ kilohms}$$

In order to have a perfect impedance match, the source resistance and the load resistance would have to be changed to

$$R_g = \left(\frac{\Delta^h h_{11}}{h_{22}}\right)^{\frac{1}{2}} \tag{11-9}$$

$$= \left[\frac{(36.42 \times 10^{-5})48.6}{2.5 \times 10^{-7}}\right]^{\frac{1}{2}}$$

$$= 266 \text{ ohms}$$

$$R_L = \left(\frac{h_{11}}{\Delta^h h_{22}}\right)^{\frac{1}{2}} \tag{11-10}$$

$$= \left[\frac{48.6}{(36.42 \times 10^{-5})(2.5 \times 10^{-7})}\right]^{\frac{1}{2}}$$

$$= 730 \text{ kilohms}$$

Using these values of $R_g$ and $R_L$, we find by substituting in Eq. 11-2 and in Eq. 11-3 that

$$A_e = 2280$$

and $$A_i = -0.83$$

Instead of substituting in Eq. 11-11, we may find the maximum available gain by multiplying together these values of $A_e$ and $A_i$ since they have been evaluated by using the dually matched values of $R_g$ and $R_L$.

$$\text{MAG} = 2280(-0.83)$$

$$= -1892 = 32.77 \text{ db}$$

It appears that there is a very large discrepancy between the voltage gain of 30 and the power gain of 29.46, from the results of the graphical analysis, and a voltage gain of 2280 and a maximum available gain of 1892, under the optimum matched conditions. The conditions of matching provide a *maximum power gain*. For a power amplifier, we are seeking a *large power output* and not a large power gain. If $V_{CC}$ is fixed, and the load resistance is increased from 1500 ohms to higher values, the numerical values of $I_{max}$ and $I_C$ must decrease. This means that the a-c power output decreases but the power gain for this transistor increases. Accordingly, as for vacuum tubes, two types of transistor units are available. One class is intended for use as a small-signal amplifier (a voltage amplifier or a current amplifier), and the other class is intended for use as a large-signal power amplifier. Since we have found that a high value of load resistance is required for matching this transistor, it is evident that it is intended primarily as a small-signal amplifier rather than as a power amplifier.

From the results of the graphical analysis, the alternating output voltage is 4.05 volts, and the output power is 10.9 mw. Since the voltage gain is 30, the input signal $V_1$ required is 4.05/30 or 0.135 volts. Likewise, the a-c power input to the emitter is 10.9/29.4 or 0.370 mw or 370 $\mu$w. The current-gain equation (Eq. 11–4) and the maximum available gain equation (Eq. 11–11) do *not* include either the a-c power loss in the generator or the a-c power loss in the bias resistor $R_E$. The gain figures consider as the input power $V_1 \times I_1$ only. Therefore, it is important not to forget to include the losses in the input coupling circuit as a supplementary calculation if necessary (Section 13–5).

In the preceding discussion, we used the symbols $h_{11}$, $h_{22}$, $h_{12}$ and $h_{21}$ as the values for the hybrid parameters for the grounded base circuit. According to joint AIEE–IRE Standards, these symbols are not strictly correct. These $h$ values using double-subscript notation apply to an equivalent circuit for a four-terminal network and not for a common-base transistor amplifier. A special set of $h$-parameter symbols is recommended for the grounded-base circuit

$$h_{ib} \quad \text{for} \quad h_{11}$$

$$h_{rb} \quad \text{for} \quad h_{12}$$

$$h_{fb} \quad \text{for} \quad h_{21}$$

$$h_{ob} \quad \text{for} \quad h_{22}$$

The $i$ refers to the *i*nput (resistance); the $r$ refers to *r*everse (voltage ratio); the $f$ refers to *f*orward (current ratio); the $o$ refers to *o*utput (conductance); and the $b$ refers to the grounded-*b*ase circuit. It is recognized that, because of the nature of the development of the equations from the four-terminal network, there will be a tendency for the carry-over of $h_{11}$, $h_{22}$, $h_{12}$, and $h_{21}$ into grounded-base nomenclature. Thus, it is understood that, if a numerical value is listed for $h_{22}$, for example, it means and refers to $h_{ob}$ only. This set may be called either $h$ parameters or $h^b$ parameters.

Tables II and III at the end of this chapter contain all the equations and the numerical results obtained for the example as a convenient reference for comparing this and the next two transistor circuits.

### Section 11–2  The Grounded-Emitter Amplifier

When the emitter is the common point between the input and the output circuits instead of the base, the resulting circuit is called the

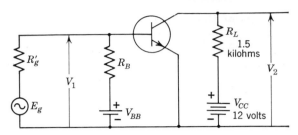

**Figure 11–6**   Circuit for a grounded-emitter amplifier.

grounded-emitter or common-emitter amplifier (Fig. 11–6).   This
circuit was discussed in Section 3–7 to the extent of showing a resulting
gain along with a 180° phase shift between the input and output
voltages.   A material advantage of this circuit is that a single battery
may be used as the supply for both $V_{EE}$ and $V_{CC}$ since the two electrodes have the same polarity.

The graphical analysis of this circuit (Fig. 11–7) is done in the same
manner as in Section 11–1.   The operating point $P$ is located at the
center of the linear intercepts.   It is evident from this load line that

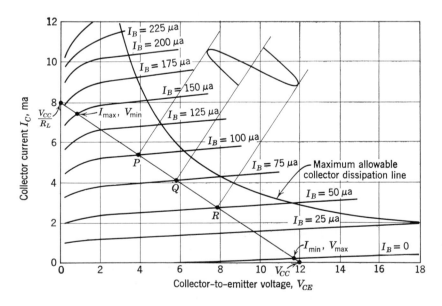

**Figure 11–7**   Load line for the circuit of Fig. 11–6.

the changes in the collector voltage and collector current are about the same order as in the common-base circuit, but the signal changes are increments of microamperes instead of milliamperes. This means that we obtain the same outputs with very much less power in the signal. For a small signal which has a low distortion, the swing is between $P$ and $R$. The current gain is

$$A_{ie} = \frac{I_{CP} - I_{CR}}{I_{BP} - I_{BR}} = \frac{5.44 - 2.76}{100 - 50} = \frac{2.68 \text{ ma}}{50 \text{ } \mu\text{a}} = 53.6$$

The base bias current $I_{BQ}$ for this operating point is 75 $\mu$a. The base bias resistance $R_B$ is determined by

$$R_B = \frac{V_{BB}}{I_{BQ}}$$

Again, in this circuit, the actual generator current is determined by the parallel combination of the bias resistance $R_B$ and the input resistance of the transistor circuit.

The values for the points on the load line for the condition of a maximum signal are as follows:

For the Base

$I_{B,\max} = 150$ $\mu$a

$I_{BQ} = 75$ $\mu$a

$I_{B,\min} = 0$

For the Collector

$V_{C,\max} = 11.7$ volts,  $I_{C,\max} = 7.4$ ma

$V_{CQ} = 5.85$ volts,  $I_{CQ} = 4.10$ ma

$V_{C,\min} = 0.80$ volts,  $I_{C,\min} = 0.2$ ma

The output signal is

$$\frac{V_{C,\max} - V_{C,\min}}{2\sqrt{2}} = \frac{11.7 - 0.8}{2\sqrt{2}} = 3.85 \text{ volts}$$

The output power is

$$P_o = \frac{(V_{\max} - V_{\min})(I_{\max} - I_{\min})}{8}$$

$$= \frac{(11.7 - 0.8)(7.4 - 0.2)}{8} = 9.81 \text{ mw}$$

The total collector circuit input power is

$$V_{CC} \times I_{CQ} = 12 \times 4.10 = 49.20 \text{ mw}$$

The total collector input power is

$$V_{CQ} \times I_{CQ} = 5.85 \times 4.10 = 23.99 \text{ mw}$$

The over-all efficiency is

$$\frac{9.81}{49.20} \, 100 = 20.0\%$$

The collector efficiency is

$$\frac{9.81}{23.99} \, 100 = 40.9\%$$

These efficiencies are still close to the theoretical values, but not quite as high as in the grounded-base circuit. The dynamic-transfer characteristic (Fig. 11–8) shows that the linearity of the circuit falls off sooner than the curve for the grounded-base circuit. However, the increased power gain obtained because the current gain is considerably greater than unity more than offsets the lowered efficiency and increased nonlinearity. In stages where the signals are very small, the grounded-emitter amplifier is almost universally used to take advantage of this greater signal gain. On the other hand, grounded-base amplifiers are usually found in the large-signal power-amplifier stages.

It is possible to develop a set of equations similar to Eq. 11–1 through Eq. 11–11 for the grounded-emitter circuit. If this were done, there would be eleven more equations for this circuit and then eleven more equations for the circuit in the next section, the grounded-

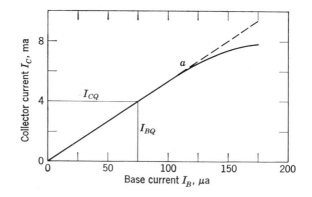

**Figure 11–8**   Dynamic load line for the circuit of Fig. 11–6.

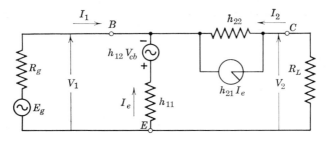

**Figure 11-9**   Rearranged equivalent circuit for the grounded-emitter amplifier.

collector circuit.   On the other hand, if it is possible to convert the equivalent circuit for the grounded-emitter amplifier to a new equivalent circuit which is in the same form as the equivalent circuit for the grounded-base amplifier, then, all the equations that have been developed for the grounded-base amplifier will automatically be valid for the grounded-emitter amplifier.   Now the method of attack is to determine a set of $h^e$ parameters for the grounded-emitter circuit which are the $h_{11}$, the $h_{22}$, the $h_{12}$, and $h_{21}$ values used in Eq. 11-1 through Eq. 11-11.   Manufacturer's data for a transistor, by joint AIEE-IRE recommendations, is given for $h^b$ parameters.   Therefore, what is sought in the development of the grounded-emitter equivalent circuit is a set of equations that will convert $h^b$ parameters to $h^e$ parameters for use in Eq. 11-1 through Eq. 11-11.

The equivalent circuit of Fig. 11-9 is obtained by changing the ground connection and the input signal connection of Fig. 11-5. But the equations developed for impedance and gain are only valid for an equivalent circuit in the form of Fig. 11-10.   From the discussion on the concept of the "black box" (Section 7-10), as long as $I_1$, $V_1$,

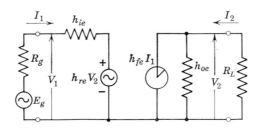

**Figure 11-10**   Equivalent circuit for the grounded-emitter amplifier using $h^e$ parameters.

$I_2$, and $V_2$ do not change, it does not matter whether the internal circuit of the transistor is that of Fig. 11–9 or that of Fig. 11–10. Since they are the same as far as the external input and output circuits are concerned, the objective is to express the components of one in terms of the other. We define the $h^e$ parameters for Fig. 11–10 in the same manner as we did for the $h^b$ parameters:

$$h_{ie} = \frac{V_1}{I_1} \quad \text{where} \quad V_2 \text{ is zero}$$

$$h_{fe} = \frac{I_2}{I_1} \quad \text{where} \quad V_2 \text{ is zero}$$

$$h_{re} = \frac{V_1}{V_2} \quad \text{where} \quad I_1 \text{ is zero}$$

$$h_{oe} = \frac{I_2}{V_2} \quad \text{where} \quad I_1 \text{ is zero}$$

When the load is short-circuited, $V_2$ is zero and $h_{ie}$ and $h_{fe}$ can be obtained from Fig. 11–9. The loop equation for Fig. 11–9 with $V_2$ zero is

$$V_1 = - I_e h_{11} - h_{12} V_{cb}$$

and, if we call $I_3$ the current through $h_{22}$,

$$V_1 = \frac{I_3}{h_{22}} = \frac{h_{21} I_e - I_2}{h_{22}}$$

From Fig. 11–9,

$$I_1 + I_2 = -I_e$$

and, when $R_L$ is short-circuited,

$$V_1 = - V_{cb}$$

When these two substitutions are made, the equations can be solved for $V_1/I_1$ and for $I_2/I_1$:

$$\frac{V_1}{I_1} = h_{ie} = \frac{h_{11}}{\Delta^h + h_{21} - h_{12} + 1}$$

and

$$\frac{I_2}{I_1} = h_{fe} = - \frac{\Delta^h + h_{21}}{\Delta^h + h_{21} - h_{12} + 1}$$

We find that, when actual circuit measurements are made,

$$(1 + h_{21}) \gg (\Delta^h - h_{12})$$

and

$$h_{21} \gg \Delta^h$$

Making these simplifications, we have

$$h_{ie} = \frac{h_{11}}{1 + h_{21}} \tag{11-12}$$

and

$$h_{fe} = \frac{-h_{21}}{1 + h_{21}} \tag{11-13}$$

From the definition of $\beta$ made in Section 3–8 (Eq. 3–4),

$$h_{fe} = -\beta$$

When the generator $E_g$ is removed from the circuit of Fig. 11–9, the input current $I_1$ is zero. The voltage equations are

$$V_2 = \frac{I_2 - h_{21}I_e}{h_{22}} - h_{12}V_{cb} - h_{11}I_e$$

and

$$V_1 = -h_{12}V_{cb} - h_{11}I_e$$

In these, may be substituted

$$I_e = -I_2$$

and

$$V_{cb} = \frac{I_2 - h_{21}I_e}{h_{22}}$$

When the resulting equations are solved for $V_1/V_2$ and $I_2/V_2$, we find

$$\frac{V_1}{V_2} = h_{re} = \frac{\Delta^h - h_{12}}{\Delta^h + 1 + h_{21} - h_{12}}$$

and

$$\frac{I_2}{V_2} = h_{oe} = \frac{h_{22}}{\Delta^h + 1 + h_{21} - h_{12}}$$

Again, using the numerical simplifications which show that

$$(1 + h_{21}) \gg (\Delta^h - h_{12})$$

we have

$$h_{re} = \frac{\Delta^h - h_{12}}{1 + h_{21}} \tag{11-14}$$

and

$$h_{oe} = \frac{h_{22}}{1 + h_{21}} \tag{11-15}$$

At this point, we will evaluate the same set of calculations for the circuit of Fig. 11–6 that we made for the grounded-base circuit. In Section 11–1, we used for the transistor these $h^b$ parameters:

$$h_{11} = h_{ib} = 48.6 \text{ ohms}$$

$$h_{12} = h_{rb} = 3.58 \times 10^{-4}$$

$$h_{21} = h_{fb} = -0.982$$

$$h_{22} = h_{ob} = 2.5 \times 10^{-7} \text{ mho}$$

In order to determine the $h^e$ parameters, we substitute these values in Eq. 11–12 through Eq. 11–15:

$$\Delta^h = h_{11}h_{22} - h_{12}h_{21}$$

$$= 48.6(2.5 \times 10^{-7}) + 0.982(3.58 \times 10^{-4})$$

$$= 3.64 \times 10^{-4}$$

From Eq. 11–12,

$$h_{ie} = \frac{h_{11}}{1 + h_{21}}$$

$$= \frac{48.6}{1 - 0.982}$$

$$= 2720 \text{ ohms}$$

From Eq. 11–13,

$$h_{fe} = \frac{-h_{21}}{1 + h_{21}}$$

$$= \frac{0.982}{1 - 0.982}$$

$$= 55$$

From Eq. 11–14,

$$h_{re} = \frac{\Delta^h - h_{12}}{1 + h_{21}}$$

$$= \frac{3.64 \times 10^{-4} - 3.58 \times 10^{-4}}{1 - 0.982}$$

$$= 3.23 \times 10^{-4}$$

From Eq. 11–15,

$$h_{oe} = \frac{h_{22}}{1 + h_{21}}$$

$$= \frac{2.5 \times 10^{-7}}{1 - 0.982}$$

$$= 14 \times 10^{-6} \text{ mho}$$

In the actual circuit, we used the value of 1500 ohms for the load resistance $R_L$, and assumed the value of the source resistance in parallel with the bias resistance $R_E$ to be 200 ohms. When these values are put in Eq. 11–1 through Eq. 11–6, using $h_{ie}$ for $h_{11}$, $h_{re}$ for $h_{12}$, $h_{fe}$ for $h_{21}$, and $h_{oe}$ for $h_{22}$, we find

$$\Delta^h = 758.5 \times 10^{-4} = 0.07585$$

$$A_e = -29.15$$

$$A_i = 53$$

$$A_p = 1541 = 31.88 \text{ db}$$

$$r_{\text{in}} = 2730 \text{ ohms}$$

$$r_{\text{out}} = 37.1 \text{ kilohms}$$

The negative sign for $A_e$ indicates there is a 180° phase shift between the input and output voltages. The graphical result of 53.6 for $A_i$ is very close to the value of 53 from the equivalent circuit. We note a severe mismatch between the load and the transistor output, but again we found from the graphical method a power output that has a low distortion at high level rather than a maximum power-gain condition. The results of the graphical analysis gave an output power of 10.38 mw at 3.85 volts. Using the voltage-gain value of 29.15 and the power-gain value of 1541, an input signal level of 132 mv and 6.75 μw is required. This compares to the 135 mv and the 370 μw required for the input to the grounded-base circuit.

When the circuit is properly matched, we find from Eqs. 11–9, 11–10, and 11–11 that

$$R_g = 3830 \text{ ohms}$$

$$R_L = 50{,}600 \text{ ohms}$$

$$\text{MAG} = 13{,}700 = 41.87 \text{ db}$$

When these values of $R_g$ and $R_L$ are substituted in Eq. 11–2 and in Eq. 11–3, we have

$$A_i = 32.2$$

and

$$A_e = -425$$

Under ideal conditions, the gain figures for the grounded-base circuit were

$$A_i = -0.83$$

$$A_e = 2280$$

and

$$\text{MAG} = 1893$$

The equations and results developed in this section are summarized in Tables II and III for convenient reference at the end of this chapter.

### Section 11–3   The Grounded-Collector Amplifier

In the grounded- or common-collector amplifier (Fig. 11–11) the collector is grounded with respect to the a-c signal since, as we have often stated, the impedance of a battery supply is zero.   It is possible to rearrange the circuit so that the collector is at ground potential for both the alternating and the direct voltages (Fig. 11–14d).   For a qualitative analysis of the circuit, assume that $V_{BE}$ is 0.1 volt.   In order to maintain this 0.1 volt, the total voltage from base to ground must at all times be greater than the total voltage from the emitter to ground.   When $I_E$ is 2 ma, $V_{out}$ is 3 volts and $V_{in}$ is 3.1 volts.   When $I_E$ is 4 ma, $V_{out}$ is 6 volts and $V_{in}$ is 6.1 volts.   In this circuit using the transistor, $V_{in}$ and $V_{out}$ are both positive with respect to ground. An increase of $V_{in}$ produces an increase in $V_{out}$.   Thus, in the com-

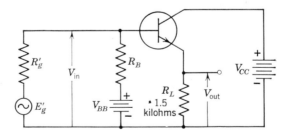

**Figure 11–11**   Circuit for a grounded-collector amplifier.

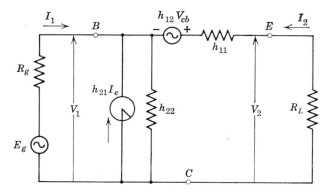

**Figure 11-12** Rearranged equivalent circuit for the grounded-collector amplifier.

mon-collector amplifier, the output voltage is *in phase with* the input voltage.

It is evident from the numerical values used that this circuit, in contrast to the grounded-base and grounded-emitter amplifiers, requires large voltage signals for operation which are of the same order as the output signal. In fact, as will be shown later, the voltage gain of the circuit is less than one. Actually the grounded-collector circuit is a special case of the application of feedback (Chapter 17). It is similar to the cathode follower which will be considered in that chapter. The determination of the bias point will also be examined in that chapter. For instance, if the operating emitter current in Fig. 11-11 is $I_E$, the operating bias current $I_B$ is

$$I_B = \frac{V_{BB} - I_B R_L}{R_B}$$

if the forward bias voltage $V_{EB}$ is neglected. The output voltage and power are of the same order as in the other two circuits.

The common-collector circuit is discussed in this chapter because it is one of the three basic transistor arrangements, and it is analyzed by means of the equations developed in Section 11-1 when the $h^c$ parameters are known. The $h^c$ parameters are evaluated in terms of the $h$ ($h^b$) parameters in the same manner as was done for the grounded-emitter circuit. The equivalent circuit of Fig. 11-5 is rearranged as a grounded-collector circuit (Fig. 11-12). The equivalent circuit which must be used, if the equations of Section 11-1 are to be valid, is

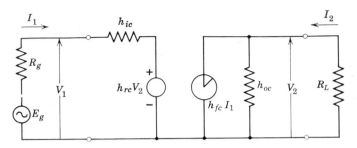

**Figure 11–13**  Equivalent circuit for the grounded-collector amplifier using $h^c$ parameters.

shown in Fig. 11–13.  The $h^c$ parameters are defined as follows:

$$h_{ic} = \frac{V_1}{I_1} \quad \text{and} \quad h_{fc} = \frac{I_2}{I_1} \quad \text{when } V_2 \text{ is zero}$$

and
$$h_{rc} = \frac{V_1}{V_2} \quad \text{and} \quad h_{oc} = \frac{I_2}{V_2} \quad \text{when } I_1 \text{ is zero}$$

When the load resistance $R_L$ is short-circuited, $V_2$ is zero.  The resulting equations from Fig. 11–12 are as follows:

$$V_1 = \frac{I_1 + h_{21}I_e + I_2}{h_{22}}$$

and
$$V_1 = -h_{12}V_{cb} - h_{11}I_1$$

Into these equations may be substituted the relations:

$$I_e = I_2 \quad \text{and} \quad V_{cb} = -V_1$$

When the two equations are solved for $V_1/I_1$ and $I_2/I_1$, we find

$$\frac{V_1}{I_1} = h_{ic} = \frac{h_{11}}{\Delta^h - h_{12} + 1 + h_{21}}$$

and
$$\frac{I_2}{I_1} = h_{fc} = -\frac{1 - h_{12}}{\Delta^h - h_{12} + 1 + h_{21}}$$

Since an examination of typical numerical values shows that

$$(1 + h_{21}) \gg (\Delta^h - h_{12})$$

the equations for the parameters reduce to

$$h_{ic} = \frac{h_{11}}{1 + h_{21}} \qquad (11\text{--}16)$$

and

$$h_{fc} = -\frac{1}{1 + h_{21}} \qquad (11\text{--}17)$$

When the generator is removed, $I_1$ is zero and then $h_{rc}$ and $h_{oc}$ may be evaluated by solving the open-circuit equations:

$$V_1 = \frac{h_{21}I_e + I_2}{h_{22}}$$

and

$$V_2 = I_2 h_{11} + h_{12}V_{cb} + V_1$$

Since

$$I_e = I_2 \quad \text{and} \quad V_{cb} = -V_1$$

The solutions for $V_1/V_2$ and for $I_2/V_2$ are

$$\frac{V_1}{V_2} = h_{rc} = \frac{h_{21} + 1}{\Delta^h - h_{12} + h_{21} + 1}$$

$$\frac{I_2}{V_2} = h_{oc} = \frac{h_{22}}{\Delta^h - h_{12} + h_{21} + 1}$$

Using the simplification

$$(1 + h_{21}) \gg (\Delta^h - h_{12})$$

we find

$$h_{rc} = \frac{h_{21} + 1}{h_{21} + 1} = 1 \qquad (11\text{--}18)$$

and

$$h_{oc} = \frac{h_{22}}{1 + h_{21}} \qquad (11\text{--}19)$$

The $h^c$ parameters for the transistor in the example are evaluated, as were the $h^e$ parameters, from the given $h$ $(h^b)$ parameters:

$$h_{11} = h_{ib} = 48.6 \text{ ohms}$$

$$h_{12} = h_{rb} = 3.58 \times 10^{-4}$$

$$h_{21} = h_{fb} = -0.982$$

$$h_{22} = h_{ob} = 2.5 \times 10^{-7} \text{ mho}$$

Substituting these values in Eq. 11–16 through Eq. 11–19, we find

$$h_{ic} = \frac{h_{11}}{1 + h_{21}}$$

$$= \frac{48.6}{1 - 0.982}$$

$$= 2720 \text{ ohms}$$

$$h_{rc} = 1$$

$$h_{fc} = -\frac{1}{1 + h_{21}}$$

$$= -\frac{1}{1 - 0.982}$$

$$- -56$$

$$h_{oc} = \frac{h_{22}}{1 + h_{21}}$$

$$= \frac{2.5 \times 10^{-7}}{1 - 0.982}$$

$$= 14 \times 10^{-6} \text{ mho}$$

In the actual circuit of Fig. 11–11, $R_L$ is 1500 ohms and $R_g$ is assumed to be 200 ohms.   Equations 11–1 through 11–6 are evaluated to obtain

$$\Delta^h = 56.04$$

$$A_i = -54$$

$$A_e = 0.968$$

$$A_p = -52.4 = 17.20 \text{ db}$$

$$r_{\text{in}} = 83.5 \text{ kilohms}$$

$$r_{\text{out}} = 52.1 \text{ ohms}$$

These results show some of the interesting and useful properties of this circuit.   The voltage gain which is less than one is a positive number which indicates the inphase relation between the input and the output voltages.   Even though the voltage gain is less than one, the power gain is large, since there is a current gain of the same order as in the common-emitter amplifier.   The input resistance of the circuit is very high, and the output resistance is very low.   This feature of the circuit, which is also shared by the vacuum-tube cathode follower, makes the circuit very useful in many applications that would be very difficult to handle with the other two circuits.

When optimum conditions are evaluated by Eqs. 11–9, 11–10, and 11–11, we find

$$R_g = 104 \text{ kilohms}$$

$$R_L = 1865 \text{ ohms}$$

$$A_i = -54.54$$

$$A_e = 0.964$$

$$\text{MAG} = -52.45 = 17.21 \text{ db}$$

In the grounded-base and grounded-emitter amplifiers, the results for dually matched conditions were greatly different from the results obtained from the operation of the amplifier with a source resistance of 200 ohms and a load resistance of 1500 ohms. In the common-collector circuit, there is a very slight difference in the results. Thus, the operation of the grounded-collector amplifier becomes substantially independent of the external circuit components and is one of its most useful properties.

Again, the results of this section are tabulated for reference at the end of the chapter in Tables II and III.

## Section 11–4 Bias Circuits

The simple biasing methods for the three transistor circuit configurations are shown in Fig. 11–14. For the common-base amplifier (Fig. 11–14$a$), the Kirchhoff's law equation for the input circuit is

$$V_{EE} - R_E I_E - V_{EB} = 0$$

Then

$$R_E = \frac{V_{EE} - V_{EB}}{I_E}$$

and, if $V_{EB}$ is neglected,

$$R_E = \frac{V_{EE}}{I_E} \tag{11–20a}$$

Similarly, for the grounded-emitter circuit (Fig. 11–14$b$), the voltage equation is

$$V_{BB} - R_B I_B - V_{EB} = 0$$

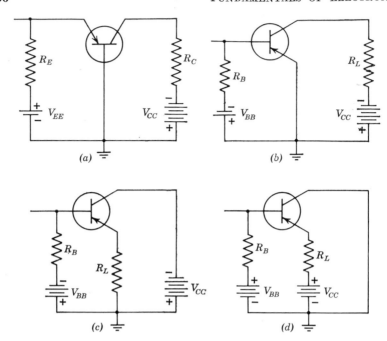

**Figure 11–14** Simple biasing methods. (*a*) Grounded-base circuit. (*b*) Grounded-emitter circuit. (*c*) Grounded-collector circuit. (*d*) Alternative form of the grounded-collector circuit.

and

$$R_B = \frac{V_{BB} - V_{EB}}{I_B}$$

and, if $V_{EB}$ is neglected,

$$R_B = \frac{V_{BB}}{I_B} \tag{11-20b}$$

In the first grounded-collector circuit (Fig. 11–14*c*), the voltage equation is

$$V_{BB} - I_B R_B - V_{EB} - (I_C + I_B)R_L = 0$$

Then

$$R_B = \frac{V_{BB} - V_{EB} - I_C R_L}{I_B} - R_L$$

and, if $V_{EB}$ is neglected,

$$R_B = \frac{V_{BB} - I_C R_L}{I_B} - R_L \tag{11-20c}$$

In the alternate grounded-collector circuit (Fig. 11–14$d$), the voltage equation is

$$V_{BB} - V_{CC} + (I_C - I_B)R_L + V_{EB} + I_B R_B = 0$$

Then

$$R_B = \frac{V_{BB} + V_{EB} - V_{CC} + I_C R_L}{I_B} - R_L$$

and, if $V_{EB}$ is neglected,

$$R_B = \frac{V_{BB} - V_{CC} + I_C R_L}{I_B} - R_L \tag{11-20d}$$

In employing these bias equations, the values should be used without regard as to whether the circuit is for a *PNP* or an *NPN* transistor. All substitutions are made by taking all values of currents and voltages as positive numbers in these equations. Accordingly, $(V_{BB} - V_{EB})$ is a smaller number than $V_{BB}$, and $(V_{BB} + V_{EB})$ is a larger number than $V_{BB}$.

In order to use a single battery for the grounded-emitter amplifier circuit, the arrangement of Fig. 11–15 is often employed, in which $R_1$ and $C_1$ serve as a decoupling filter in the same manner as a screen decoupling filter. Calculation of the bias resistance by means of Eq. 11–20$b$ yields a value of resistance equal to $(R_B + R_1)$. The circuit permits a possible impedance match by allowing a range

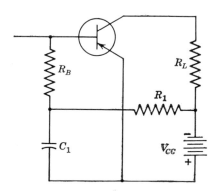

**Figure 11–15** Bias circuit using a single battery and a decoupling filter.

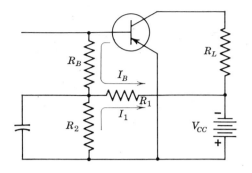

**Figure 11–16** Bias circuit using a voltage divider.

of values for $R_B$ up to the value calculated from Eq. 11–20$b$ as a maximum.

Another arrangement for the grounded-emitter circuit is the combination bleeder and voltage divider of Fig. 11–16. Since there are two loops, two equations result:

$$I_1 R_2 + (I_B + I_1) R_1 = V_{CC}$$

and     $$I_B R_B + V_{BE} + (I_B + I_1) R_1 = V_{CC}$$

Solving for $R_B$ and simplifying, we have

$$R_B = \frac{R_2}{R_1 + R_2} \left( \frac{V_{CC}}{I_B} - R_1 \right) - \frac{V_{BE}}{I_B}$$

If the term $V_{BE}/I_B$ is neglected, the equation simplifies to

$$R_B = \frac{R_2}{R_1 + R_2} \left( \frac{V_{CC}}{I_B} - R_1 \right) \qquad (11\text{–}20e)$$

For use in testing and measuring, it should be noted that, from the junction of $R_1$ and $R_2$ to ground, the voltage is

$$I_1 R_2 = V_{BE} + I_B R_B$$

A very serious problem in transistor circuits is created by the relative instability of the characteristics (Fig. 11–17). Two main sources of difficulty give rise to this problem. Often the transistors vary to some extent from unit to unit in production, although newer manufacturing techniques are reducing this variation. The other cause of the problem is that, as the ambient temperature rises, the current through the collector increases. The change in the characteristic curves is indicated on the collector characteristic by the set of dotted lines. This means that the operating point $Q$ shifts to $Q'$, and the

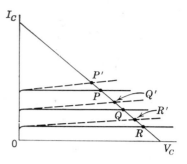

**Figure 11-17** Load-line instability.

limits of signal variation shift from $P$ and $R$ to $P'$ and $R'$. It is desired to maintain the signal variation limits and the operating point at $P$, $Q$, and $R$. If the operation is shifted to $P'$, $Q'$, and $R'$, the distortion level may change, and it is possible that the operation may shift into either the cutoff or the saturation region and produce severe clipping.

The most generally used method of solving this problem in the common-emitter amplifier is to use a *stabilizing* circuit, $R_3$ and $C_1$, in the emitter lead (Fig. 11-18). The voltage equations for the network are

$$R_2(I_1 + I_B) + I_1 R_1 = V_{CC}$$

and $$R_2(I_1 + I_B) + I_B R_B - V_{EB} = R_3(I_C - I_B)$$

$I_1$ is eliminated from the equations, and the result is solved for $R_B$ to yield

$$R_B = \frac{R_2}{R_1 + R_2} \frac{V_{CC}}{I_B} + \frac{R_1 R_2}{R_1 + R_2} - \frac{V_{EB}}{I_B} - R_3 \left( \frac{I_C}{I_B} - 1 \right) \quad (11\text{-}21)$$

**Figure 11-18** Bias circuit with emitter stabilizing network.

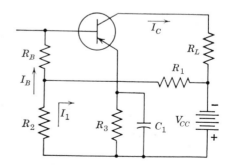

The method of using a thermistor for stabilization purposes is discussed in Section 15–5.

There is another source of distortion in transistor circuits which is not a characteristic of vacuum-tube amplifiers. The input resistance is not constant with variations in input signal (Figs. 3–21 and 3–24). The input resistance variation in a common-emitter amplifier is greater than the variation in a grounded-base amplifier and, correspondingly,

TABLE II. TABULATION OF RESULTS FOR THE TRANSISTOR USING
$R_g = 200$ OHMS AND $R_L = 1500$ OHMS

|  | Grounded Base | Grounded Emitter | Grounded Collector |
|---|---|---|---|
| $h_{11}$ ohms | 48.6 | 2720 | 2720 |
| $h_{12}$ | $3.58 \times 10^{-4}$ | $3.23 \times 10^{-4}$ | 1 |
| $h_{21}$ | $-0.982$ | 55 | $-56$ |
| $h_{22}$ mhos | $2.5 \times 10^{-7}$ | $14 \times 10^{-6}$ | $14 \times 10^{-6}$ |
| $\Delta^h$ | $36.42 \times 10^{-5}$ | $0.07585$ | 56.04 |
| $r_{in}$ | 49.15 | 2730 | 83.5K |
| $r_{out}$ | 600K | 37.1K | 52.1 |
| $A_e$ | 30 | $-29.15$ | 0.968 |
| $A_i$ | $-0.982$ | 53 | $-54$ |
| $A_p$ | $-29.46 = 14.65$ db | $-1541 = 31.88$ db | $-52.4 = 17.2$ db |
| | Results when the circuits are dually matched | | |
| $R_L$ | 730K | 50.6K | 1865 |
| $R_g$ | 266 | 3830 | 104K |
| $A_e$ | 2280 | $-425$ | 0.964 |
| $A_i$ | $-0.83$ | 32.2 | $-54.54$ |
| MAG | $-1893 = 32.77$ db | $13700 = 41.87$ db | $-52.45 = 17.21$ db |

TABLE III. SUMMARY OF EQUATIONS

|  | Grounded Base | Grounded Emitter | Grounded Collector |
|---|---|---|---|
| Input resistance | $h_{11} = h_{ib}$ | $h_{ie} = \dfrac{h_{11}}{1 + h_{21}}$ | $h_{ic} = \dfrac{h_{11}}{1 + h_{21}}$ |
| Reverse voltage ratio | $h_{12} = h_{rb}$ | $h_{re} = \dfrac{\Delta^h - h_{12}}{1 + h_{21}}$ | $h_{rc} = 1$ |
| Forward current ratio | $h_{21} = h_{fb}$ | $h_{fe} = \dfrac{-h_{21}}{1 + h_{21}}$ | $h_{fc} = -\dfrac{1}{1 + h_{21}}$ |
| Output conductance | $h_{22} = h_{ob}$ | $h_{oe} = \dfrac{h_{22}}{1 + h_{21}}$ | $h_{oc} = \dfrac{h_{22}}{1 + h_{21}}$ |

TABLE III. SUMMARY OF EQUATIONS—*(continued)*

$\Delta^h = h_{11}h_{22} - h_{12}h_{21}$

Input resistance:

$$r_{\text{in}} = \frac{R_L\Delta^h + h_{11}}{1 + h_{22}R_L}$$

Output resistance:

$$r_{\text{out}} = \frac{R_g + h_{11}}{h_{22}R_g + \Delta^h}$$

Circuit voltage gain:

$$A_e = \frac{-h_{21}R_L}{\Delta^h R_L + h_{11}}$$

Circuit current gain:

$$A_i = \frac{h_{21}}{1 + h_{22}R_L}$$

Circuit power gain:

$$A_p = \frac{-h^2_{21}R_L}{(\Delta^h R_L + h_{11})(h_{22}R_L + 1)}$$

For perfect matching:

$$R_L = \sqrt{\frac{h_{11}}{\Delta^h h_{22}}}$$

$$R_g = \sqrt{\frac{\Delta^h h_{11}}{h_{22}}}$$

Transducer gain:

$$A_{\text{tr}} = \frac{4R_g R_L h^2_{21}}{(\Delta^h R_L + h_{22}R_g R_L + R_g + h_{11})^2}$$

Available gain:

$$A_{\text{av}} = \frac{R_g h^2_{21}}{[R_g + h_{11}][\Delta^h + h_{22}R_g]}$$

Maximum available gain:

$$\text{MAG} = \frac{h^2_{21}}{(\sqrt{h_{11}h_{22}} + \sqrt{\Delta^h})^2}$$

From algebraic manipulation of the conversion equations, we find

$$h_{ib} = \frac{h_{ie}}{1 + h_{fe}} \qquad h_{fb} = -\frac{h_{fe}}{1 + h_{fe}}$$

$$h_{rb} = \frac{\Delta^{he} - h_{re}}{1 + h_{fe}} \qquad h_{ob} = \frac{h_{oe}}{1 + h_{fe}}$$

and $\quad h_{ic} = h_{ie} \qquad h_{rc} = 1 \qquad h_{fc} = -(1 + h_{fe}) \qquad h_{oc} = h_{oe}$

produces a greater distortion. With large input currents the input resistance is low, and with small input currents the input resistance is high. The over-all effect on a signal is to clip one half of the cycle and to peak the other half, creating an increased amount of even-harmonic distortion.

## . . . . Suggested References for Further Study

1. D. DeWitt and A. L. Rossoff, *Transistor Electronics*, Chapters 4 and 5, McGraw-Hill Book Co., New York, 1957

2 L. P. Hunter, editor, *Handbook of Semiconductor Electronics*, McGraw-Hill Book Co., New York, 1956.

3. R. B. Hurley, *Junction Transistor Electronics*, Chapter 3, John Wiley & Sons, New York, 1958.

4. R. F. Shea, editor, *Transistor Circuit Engineering*, Chapter 3, John Wiley & Sons, New York, 1957.

## . . . . QUESTIONS

1. Explain each of the following symbols:

$$
\begin{array}{cccccccc}
V_{EE} & v_c & I_C & V_C & V_B & v_E & I_c & V_{BB} \\
V_E & P_o & v_C & I_E & I_e & Z_o & V_e & v_B \\
V_b & Z_i & p_C & v_e & r_{in} & I_B & V_{CC} & v_C \\
I_b & V_{EEB} & z_{out} & z_{in} & V_{CCB} & r_{out} & p_o & v_b
\end{array}
$$

2. Explain each of the following symbols:

$$
\begin{array}{cccc}
h_{fc} & h_{22} & h_{rc} & h_{rb} \\
h_{re} & h_{ic} & h_{oc} & h_{ib} \\
h_{ob} & h_{fe} & h_{11} & h_{12} \\
h_{ie} & h_{21} & h_{fb} & h_{ro}
\end{array}
$$

3. What are the end points of the load line in the grounded-base amplifier? In the grounded-emitter amplifier?

4. What is the order of current gain of the common-base amplifier?

5. What is the phase relation between the input and the output voltages in a grounded-base amplifier? In a grounded-collector amplifier?

6. What is the theoretical efficiency of a transistor amplifier with a resistive load? How do the actual efficiencies compare with those of a vacuum-tube amplifier?

7. What is a sink, and what is a source?

8. What is the principle behind the concept of a dually matched circuit?

9. Define transducer gain, operating gain, available gain, and maximum available gain?

10. Can the actual output power be obtained from an equivalent circuit? Explain.

11. How is the load line established for a grounded-emitter circuit?

12. Why does the equation for $A_e$ for a grounded-emitter circuit have a minus sign?

13. Compare the voltage and current gains for the three basic circuit arrangements.

14. What is the order of input and output resistances for the three basic circuit arrangements?

15. Discuss the advantages and disadvantages of the grounded-collector amplifier.

16. What determines the operating point for a transistor amplifier?

17. Show how the operating point for a transistor amplifier tends to be unstable.

, . . . . **PROBLEMS**

If transistor characteristic curves are available, problems 1, 2, 7, and 8 requiring graphical solution can be rearranged to suit the available data. The problems given here are based on the curves shown in Fig. 11–2 and Fig. 11–7.

1. A common-base amplifier has a collector supply voltage of $-16$ volts, and the collector load is 2000 ohms. Determine the current gain, the output power, the collector efficiency, and the over all circuit efficiency.

2. Solve problem 1 for a collector supply voltage of $-10$ volts and an 850-ohm load resistance.

3. The hybrid parameter values for a particular transistor are:

$$h_{ie} = 4800 \text{ ohms}, \qquad h_{re} = 9.1 \times 10^{-4}$$

$$h_{fe} = 45, \qquad h_{oe} = 12.4 \text{ micromhos}$$

The external input resistance is 300 ohms, and the load resistance is 60,000 ohms. Calculate $A_e$, $A_i$, $A_p$, $r_{in}$, and $r_{out}$ for the common-base connection.

4. Determine the values of $R_g$ and $R_L$ required for perfect matching in problem 3, and determine $A_e$, $A_i$, and $A_p$ for this condition.

5. The hybrid parameter values for a particular transistor are:

$$h_{ie} = 1667 \text{ ohms}, \qquad h_{re} = 4.95 \times 10^{-4}$$

$$h_{fe} = 44, \qquad h_{oe} = 22.8 \text{ micromhos}$$

The external input resistance is 80 ohms and the load resistance is 130,000 ohms. Calculate $A_e$, $A_i$, $A_p$, $r_{in}$, and $r_{out}$ for the common-base connection.

6. Determine the values of $R_g$ and $R_L$ required for perfect matching in problem 5, and determine $A_e$, $A_i$, and $A_p$ for this condition.

7. A common-emitter amplifier has a collector supply voltage of $-16$ volts, and the collector load is 2000 ohms. Determine the current gain, the output power, the collector efficiency, and the over-all collector circuit efficiency.

8. Solve problem 7 for a collector supply voltage of $-10$ volts and a 1000-ohm load resistance.

9. The hybrid parameter values for a particular transistor are:

$$h_{ie} = 2880 \text{ ohms}, \qquad h_{re} = 5.5 \times 10^{-4}$$

$$h_{fe} = 55, \qquad h_{oe} = 16.3 \text{ micromhos}$$

The external input resistance is 1200 ohms, and the load resistance is 10,000 ohms. Calculate $A_e$, $A_i$, $A_p$, $r_{in}$, and $r_{out}$ for the common-emitter connection.

10. Determine the values of $R_g$ and $R_L$ required for perfect matching in problem 9, and determine $A_e$, $A_i$, and $A_p$ for this condition.

11. The hybrid parameter values for a particular transistor are:

$$h_{ie} = 6040 \text{ ohms}, \qquad h_{re} = 17.2 \times 10^{-4}$$

$$h_{fe} = 32, \qquad h_{oe} = 11.1 \text{ micromhos}$$

The external input resistance is 800 ohms, and the load resistance is 12,000 ohms. Calculate $A_e$, $A_i$, $A_p$, $r_{in}$, and $r_{out}$ for the common-emitter connection.

12. Determine the values of $R_g$ and $R_L$ required for perfect matching in problem 11, and determine $A_e$, $A_i$, and $A_p$ for this condition.

13. In a common-collector amplifier, the external input resistance is 1800 ohms, and the load resistance is 30,000 ohms. The hybrid parameter values for this transistor are:

$$h_{ie} = 3200 \text{ ohms}, \qquad h_{re} = 6.2 \times 10^{-4}$$

$$h_{fe} = 48, \qquad h_{oe} = 18 \text{ micromhos}$$

Determine the values for $A_e$, $A_i$, $A_p$, $r_{in}$ and $r_{out}$.

14. Determine the dually matched resistances and gains for the common-collector amplifier of problem 13.

15. For the amplifier given in problem 7, obtain values for the bias network shown in Fig. 11–15.

16. For the amplifier given in problem 7, obtain values for the bias network shown in Fig. 11–16.

17. For the amplifier given in problem 8, obtain values for the bias network shown in Fig. 11–15.

18. For the amplifier given in problem 8, obtain values for the bias network shown in Fig. 11–16.

# Transformers and transformer-coupled amplifiers

• • • • • • • • • • • • • • • • • • • • • CHAPTER 12

The transformer is one of the basic components of an electronic circuit. An understanding of the theory of operation (Section 12–1) leads to the development of the equivalent circuit (Section 12–3). Transformers are used as impedance-changing devices (Section 12–2) to match one value of impedance to another. An analysis of the operation of the transformer together with the equivalent circuit involves the factors that determine the frequency response (Section 12–4). A discussion of applications and the load-line calculations for both the vacuum-tube circuit (Section 12–5) and the transistor circuit (Section 12–6) completes the chapter.

### Section 12–1  Theory of the Transformer

Figure 12–1 shows a simple transformer consisting of a primary winding of $N_1$ turns and a secondary winding of $N_2$ turns on a magnetic core. When an alternating line voltage $V_1$ is applied to the transformer winding, an exciting current $I_0$ flows. $I_0$ creates an exciting flux $\phi_{11}$. Part of this flux, $\phi_{12}$, passes completely through the core linking the secondary winding of $N_2$ turns. This linking a-c flux induces a voltage $E_2$ in the secondary winding. We may show (refer to any standard textbook on transformers and a-c machines) that, for a given core and winding arrangement, the voltage per turn is a con-

**289**

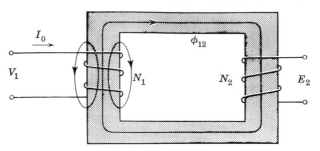

**Figure 12-1** The elementary transformer.

stant, providing that there is no magnetic saturation. For example, if the applied voltage is 120 volts and $N_1$ is 240 turns, this figure is 0.5 volt per turn. If $N_2$ is 30 turns, the secondary voltage $E_2$ is 15 volts. If $N_2$ is 800 turns, $E_2$ is 400 volts.

Ideally all the primary flux should link the secondary or $\phi_{12}$ should be equal to $\phi_{11}$. Practically, $\phi_{12}$ must be less than $\phi_{11}$ because there are air gaps and fringing effects in the magnetic path. The ratio of $\phi_{12}/\phi_{11}$ is defined as the coefficient of coupling $k$. The flux of the primary which does not link the secondary is $(\phi_{11} - \phi_{12})$ or $\phi_{11}(1 - k)$. The inductance this flux produces in the primary is

$$\frac{N_1(\phi_{11} - \phi_{12})}{I_1 10^8} = \frac{N_1\phi_{11}(1 - k)}{I_1 10^8} = L_1(1 - k)$$

This inductance is called the *primary leakage inductance*. By the same process of reasoning, the *secondary leakage inductance* is

$$\frac{N_2(\phi_{22} - \phi_{21})}{I_2 10^8} = \frac{N_2\phi_{22}(1 - k)}{I_2 10^8} = L_2(1 - k)$$

When a load is placed across the secondary terminals, the voltage $E_2$ produces a current $I_2$ in the load. This secondary current develops a flux in the secondary winding which opposes the primary flux. The net flux in the core is the primary flux less the secondary flux. However, the transformer is an inherent constant potential device, and, for a fixed supply voltage, the core flux is constant. If a constant net value of flux is required in the core, when there is an opposing flux caused by the secondary current, there must be an increase in the primary flux to oppose the secondary flux. This increase in primary flux is produced by a rise in the primary current. In this manner, the application of a load on a transformer secondary winding causes a rise in input current while maintaining constant-voltage values throughout the transformer.

### Section 12–2    Impedance Ratios

Impedance ratios are determined by considering the ideal transformer of Fig. 12–2. If a transformer is ideal, the energy transfer is complete and the efficiency is 100%. We may analyze the unit by considering that the primary volt-amperes (or kva) equals the secondary volt-amperes (or kva) or that the value of the primary power in watts (or kw) numerically equals the secondary power in watts (or kw). The *turns ratio* $\alpha$ of a transformer is defined as the ratio of the secondary turns to the primary turns:

$$\alpha = \frac{N_2}{N_1} \qquad (12\text{–}1)$$

If $\alpha$ exceeds unity, the transformer is step-up in voltage; if $\alpha$ is less than unity, the transformer is step-down. Since the voltage per turn of the ideal transformer is a constant, the voltage ratio must be the same as the turns ratio:

$$\alpha = \frac{E_2}{E_1} \qquad (12\text{–}2a)$$

By applying the principle of conservation of energy that the primary volt-amperes equal the secondary volt-amperes, the current ratio is inverse to the voltage ratio:

$$\alpha = \frac{I_1}{I_2} \qquad (12\text{–}2b)$$

Then $\qquad\qquad \alpha E_1 = E_2 \quad \text{and} \quad I_1 = \alpha I_2$

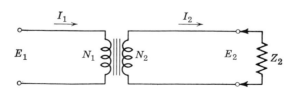

**Figure 12–2**   Currents and voltages in a transformer under load.

Dividing one by the other,

$$\frac{\alpha E_1}{I_1} = \frac{E_2}{\alpha I_2}$$

But $E_1/I_1$ is $Z_1$, and $E_2/I_2$ is $Z_2$.  Then

$$\alpha Z_1 = \frac{Z_2}{\alpha}$$

$$\alpha^2 Z_1 = Z_2$$

Finally $\qquad\qquad \dfrac{Z_2}{Z_1} = \alpha^2 \quad\text{or}\quad \alpha = \left(\dfrac{Z_2}{Z_1}\right)^{\frac{1}{2}}$ $\qquad$ (12–3)

We may put this relation into words:

1. The impedance ratio is the square of the turns ratio, or,
2. The turns ratio is the square root of the impedance ratio.

Very often, a transformer is referred to as an impedance-matching device or an impedance-changing device.  As an example, if power is obtained from a 10,000-ohm source and must be delivered to a 16-ohm load, the required transformer would be step-down with a turns ratio of

$$\alpha = \left(\frac{16}{10,000}\right)^{\frac{1}{2}} = \left(\frac{1}{625}\right)^{\frac{1}{2}} = \frac{1}{25}$$

Transformers are usually constructed with multiple windings on the secondary.  The calculation of impedances is based on the relation

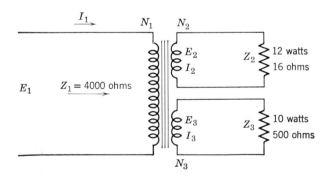

**Figure 12–3**  Example of a transformer with multiple loads.

that the total power of the secondary loads is equal to the primary input power. For example, assume that a transformer (Fig. 12–3) operates from a 4000-ohm source and delivers 12 watts into a 16-ohm load and 10 watts into a 500-ohm load. The turns ratios are required. Since power is $I^2R$, for the loads we have

$$P_2 = I_2{}^2R_2, \qquad\qquad P_3 = I_3{}^2R_3$$

$$12 = I_2{}^2 \times 16, \qquad\qquad 10 = I_3{}^2 \times 500$$

$$I_2 = 0.866 \text{ ampere}, \qquad I_3 = 0.141 \text{ ampere}$$

and $\qquad E_2 = 13.88 \text{ volts}, \qquad E_3 = 70.7 \text{ volts}$

For the primary, by reflection, we have

$$P_1 = P_2 + P_3$$

$$= 12 + 10 = 22 \text{ watts}$$

Then, since $\qquad P_1 = I_1{}^2R_1$

$$22 = I_1{}^2 \times 4000$$

$$I_1 = 0.0741 \text{ ampere}$$

and $\qquad E_1 = 296 \text{ volts}$

The turns ratio is directly determined by the ratios of the voltages:

$$N_1 : N_2 : N_3 = 296 : 13.88 : 70.7 \quad \text{or}$$

$$= 1 : 0.0458 : 0.239 \quad \text{or}$$

$$= 21.4 : 1 : 5.10 \quad \text{or}$$

$$= 4.18 : 0.196 : 1$$

## Section 12–3    The Equivalent Circuit

The equivalent circuit of a transformer (Fig. 12–4) like the equivalent circuit of the vacuum tube and the transistor is a fictitious approach, but it is very useful in terms of circuit performance and analysis. For purposes of simplification, we consider a transformer that has a single primary winding and a single secondary winding. We showed in Section 12–1 that the primary current consisted of two parts: the flux-producing part $I_0$, plus the component $I'_2$, which is the reflected value of the load current. This suggests a parallel-circuit

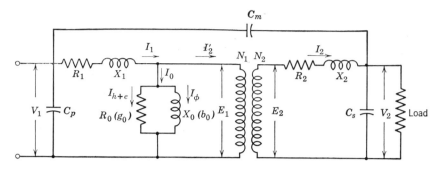

**Figure 12-4**    Equivalent circuit of a transformer.

arrangement wherein $I_1$ divides into two branches, one for $I_0$ and the other for $I'_2$.

The exciting current $I_0$ may be broken into two components.   There is an inphase or resistive component which produces the heat energy of the hysteresis and eddy-current loss of the core material.   The inductive or wattless component produces the operating flux.   The exciting current is represented by $I_0$, the resistive component by $I_{h+e}$, and the flux-producing component by $I_\phi$.   The a-c resistance of the windings is denoted by $R_1$ in the primary and $R_2$ in the secondary. As the coefficient of coupling of a transformer is, in practice, less than unity, $X_1$ represents the primary leakage reactance and $X_2$ is the secondary leakage reactance.   The step-up or step-down action of the transformer is represented by an ideal transformer having $N_1$ turns in the primary and $N_2$ turns in the secondary winding.

Capacitance effects within the transformer are separated into three parts.   The winding capacitance, the lead capacitance, and the capacitance between turns in the primary are together denoted by $C_p$.   $C_s$ represents the sum of these three capacitances in the secondary.   The mutual capacitance between the primary and the secondary windings is $C_m$.

From Eq. 12-2a, the ratio of $E_2/E_1$ is the turns ratio $\alpha$.   A direct measurement of voltage to obtain the turns ratio gives $\alpha$ as $V_2/V_1$, whereas $E_2/E_1$ is the true value of the turns ratio.   If $I_2$ is reduced toward zero, the error in the measurement diminishes considerably. For practical purposes, a turns-ratio measurement is made by two voltmeter readings, $V_1$ and $V_2$, taken under no-load conditions with a reduced primary voltage which prevents any saturation in the transformer core.   Certain specialized measurements require that $V_1$ and $V_2$ be corrected to give the true turns ratio, $E_2/E_1$.

## Section 12-4    Frequency Response

Reference to the equivalent circuit of the transformer (Fig. 12-4) assists in analyzing the distortion created by the use of a transformer. In an ideal transformer, $C_p$, $C_m$, and $C_s$ shrink to zero as do $R_1$, $R_2$, $X_1$, and $X_2$. $R_0$ and $X_0$ become infinite in order to reduce $I_0$ to zero.

$C_m$ permits an energy transfer from the primary to the secondary winding. In a transformer, energy should be transferred only by means of the changing magnetic field and not by capacitance effects. In Section 4-1, we discussed the function of a capacitance shield. In a transformer, the capacitance shield consists of a single turn of copper sheeting placed between the primary and the secondary windings. The ends of the sheet overlap, but they must be insulated to prevent the shield from acting like a short-circuited turn. This copper sheet is mechanically bonded to the frame of the transformer which also serve as the ground point since the transformer is both electrically and mechanically fastened to the chassis.

$R_1$ and $R_2$ may be reduced by using a larger wire size. For a given number of turns, an increase in wire size necessitates a larger available window area. This increases the amount of steel used in the transformer.

$X_1$ and $X_2$ depend directly on the value of the coefficient of coupling between the primary and the secondary windings. An increase in $k$ may be obtained by any one or all of several ways. The physical layout of the primary- and secondary-coil windings may be improved to secure a greater mutual flux. A lower operating flux density tends to force fewer lines of the flux out of the magnetic path. A lower flux density is obtained by using a larger core cross section. Increasing core area increases the cost and the weight and lengthens the turns of the copper wire. The use of special steels may increase $k$ by operating at lower values of magnetomotive force. Careful core construction can reduce air gaps and flux fringing. Toroidal cores without air gaps are used in transformers in which the leakage reactance must be kept to an absolute minimum.

The exciting current $I_0$ offers a shunt path to the primary current. An increase in the number of turns in the primary reduces $I_\phi$. Improved steels permit the required value of operating flux to be obtained with a lower value of magnetomotive force, thus decreasing $I_\phi$. The method used in stacking and interleaving the laminations plays an important part in reducing air gaps in the core. $R_{h+e}$ represents the equivalent of the iron losses: eddy currents and hysteresis. Eddy currents are reduced by laminating the core and insulating the

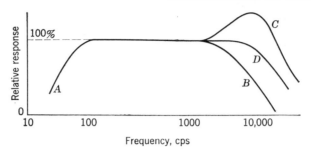

**Figure 12-5**   Frequency response of a transformer.

laminations from each other.   If the laminations become very thin, the total thickness of the varnish or scale insulation takes up too great a percentage of the core cross-sectional area.   Hysteresis losses are reduced by using a better-grade steel.   Both the eddy-current and the hysteresis losses may be reduced by operating at a lower flux density.

The input and output capacitances, $C_p$ and $C_s$, are produced by capacitance between turns and leads.   A reduction of these capacitances calls for special winding methods along with larger transformer window areas.

Good transformer design is predicated on a careful balance among the various factors discussed.   Some transformers are designed for the least cost, whereas in others the designer seeks the ideal without regard to cost as, for example, transformers used for pulse amplifiers and for extreme high-fidelity amplifiers.

The shunting action of $X_0$ at low frequencies causes the decrease in output at $A$ in Fig. 12-5.   The shunt capacitances $C_p$ and $C_s$ cause the frequency response to fall off at the high frequencies, at $B$ in Fig. 12-5.   The transformer secondary voltage is developed *within* the secondary winding and not *across* the secondary winding.   Thus, if the $Q$ of the secondary winding is sufficiently high, there may be a pronounced effect of a series resonance in the secondary circuit which produces a *rise* in the response characteristics at high frequencies, at $C$ in Fig. 12-5.   Usually, transformers are designed to reduce this effect to give the extended flat response of $D$ in Fig. 12-5.

### Section 12-5   Vacuum-Tube Circuits and Load Lines

The circuit of Fig. 12-6 uses two transformers, each showing slightly different considerations.   $T1$ is an input transformer in which the main function is to provide a stepped-up signal voltage to the grid of $V2$. If the operation of $V2$ is class A without grid current, $V2$ will not draw power from $T1$. $T2$ is a power-transferring device. The principal purpose of this transformer is to reflect the low load impedance back into the primary as a high impedance. Thus, a high-impedance source $V2$ works into a low-impedance load such as a loudspeaker by using the transformer as an impedance-changing device.

The input transformer, since it is not loaded, may tend to show the high-$Q$ characteristic of $C$ in Fig. 12–5. The impedance that this transformer presents to $V1$ at middle-range audio frequencies (400 to 1000 cycles) is very high. Ideally, this impedance is infinite. As we recall from Fig. 10–4, if the external load impedance in the plate circuit of an amplifier stage is infinite, the stage voltage gain approaches the value of the amplification factor $\mu$. In addition, the transformer itself develops a voltage gain equal to its turns ratio $\alpha$. If we consider both factors, at middle frequencies, the voltage gain of a transformer-amplifier stage is given by

$$A_e = \mu\alpha \qquad (12\text{–}4)$$

The gain falls off at high and low frequencies for the reasons outlined in the previous section. In addition to these considerations, there is a direct current $I_{BQ}$ in the primary winding. This direct current complicates the analysis as it could produce a saturation within the core even for small signals. A saturation clips the flux during that part of the a-c cycle when the a-c flux is additive to the d-c flux, thereby causing a severe distortion in the developed transformer secondary voltage.

Usually the low value of the secondary load impedance on $T2$ reduces the $Q$ to such a low value that any resonant rise effect can be

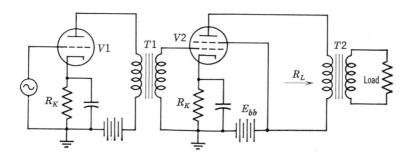

**Figure 12–6**   Amplifier using transformers.

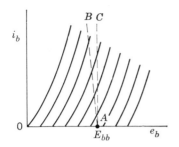

**Figure 12–7**    Determination of the operating point.

ignored in the power-output transformers. The turns ratio of the transformer is determined by the desired value of the reflected impedance and by the actual value of the load impedance.

When the d-c resistance of the primary of $T2$ is taken into consideration, a load line $AB$ is drawn on the characteristic curves for the tube (Fig. 12–7) in the same manner as the load lines in Chapter 10. Usually this d-c resistance is neglected, and the load line for this value of zero d-c resistance is the vertical load line $AC$. The operating point must lie on the d-c load line. For the load line $AC$, we note that the operating plate voltage $E_b$ is identical with the supply voltage $E_{bb}$. The operating point is then determined by the value of the total cathode current and the bias resistance $R_K$ of the amplifier (Fig. 12–6). Through the operating point, an a-c load line equal to the value of the reflected resistance $R_L$ is drawn.

Figure 12–8 shows the method of drawing the load line on a set of plate characteristics. Assume, for example, that the operating point is located

$$E_{bb} = E_b = 300 \text{ volts}$$

$$E_{cc} = -8 \text{ volts}$$

and $$I_b = 20 \text{ ma}$$

Also, assume a value of 25,000 ohms for the reflected load resistance. The load line must pass through the operating point. The reflected load impedance determines the slope of the load line. A simple method is to assume a small convenient current change and, by Ohm's law, determine the corresponding voltage change. For 25,000 ohms, an assumed current change of 4 ma gives a voltage change of 0.004 × 25,000 or 100 volts. On Fig. 12–8, if we shift 100 volts to the left along path $p$ and up 4 ma along path $q$, we locate point $x$. Likewise a shift of 100 volts along path $n$ and down 4 ma along path $m$ locates point $y$. Points $o$, $x$, and $y$ must lie on a straight line. The line, that is drawn through points $o$, $x$, and $y$ and extended beyond $x$ and $y$ is the load line. The maximum class-A drive is limited to a maximum positive grid swing which goes to zero volts and a maximum negative swing to $-2E_{cc}$ volts. If the bias $E_{cc}$ is $-8$ volts, the limits of the instantaneous grid swing are zero and $-16$ volts. These values establish $I_{max}$, $I_{min}$, $E_{min}$, and $E_{max}$.

The calculations for output current, output voltage, output power, and the distortion are identical with the methods outlined in Chapter 10. From Fig. 12–8, we note that $E_{bb}$ is the same as $E_b$. This means that no d-c power is lost in the transformer primary. The d-c power supplied to the circuit and the d-c power supplied to the tube are the same. We conclude then that, for transformer coupling, the plate efficiency and the over-all efficiency are identical and have maximum theoretical values of 50%. The universal use of transformers in power amplifiers is customary because of this increased efficiency. In certain special load applications, such as a d-c motor winding, the output transformer cannot be used and the inherent lower over-all efficiency is tolerated.

The no-signal plate dissipation in a class-A power amplifier is the product of $E_b$ and $I_b$. If the maximum rating of the plate dissipation is exceeded, the plate becomes too hot and may turn red or yellow, or even melt. For a typical plate characteristic, the value of the rated maximum plate dissipation is plotted as the dotted curve $ABC$ in Fig. 12–9. The operating point of the tube must be on or below this curve. An infinite number of operating points can be selected, and through each of them an infinite number of load lines drawn. There is one particular operating point and one particular load line that produces a maximum power output without damage to the tube.

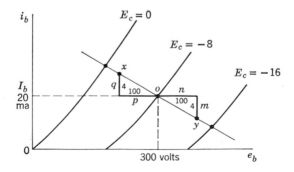

**Figure 12–8**   Load line for a transformer-coupled amplifier.

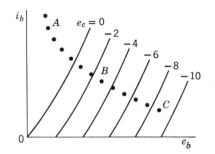

**Figure 12-9** Maximum allowable plate dissipation line.

Also there is one particular operating point and load line that produces the greatest power output with the least distortion. When there is an input signal, some of the d-c plate input energy is converted into a-c power output, and the plate dissipation goes down. In certain special applications, when a signal always exists, it is possible to move the operating point above the dotted line in Fig. 12–9. However, it should be noted that, if the signal is lost, the tube is automatically overloaded. These calculations are of a design nature and as such are beyond the scope of the presentation of this book.

### Section 12-6  Transistor Circuits

A typical two-stage transistor amplifier using transformers is shown in Fig. 12-10. Each of the grounded-emitter amplifiers has an emitter stabilization circuit, $R_2C_2$ and $R_4C_4$. The operating bias is obtained from $V_{CC}$ by means of the base bias resistors, $R_1$ and $R_3$, which are bypassed by $C_1$ and $C_3$. The load lines are obtained for transistors on the collector characteristics in the identical manner as for the vacuum tube. The operating point $V_C$ is the supply voltage $V_{CC}$ if the d-c resistance of the primary winding of the transformer is neglected. In transistor circuits, also, the theoretical maximum collector efficiency is 50%. In practice, efficiencies close to this figure can be obtained.

In the individual stages of a vacuum-tube amplifier, the considerations that determine the plate load are normally independent of the other stages. In transistor circuitry, this is not the case at all, making gain computations more complex. $R_L$ reflects back through $T3$ as $R_a$ ohms. The input resistance $R_b$ of transistor $V2$ is determined by the $h^e$ parameters and $R_a$. Now, with $R_a$ and $R_b$ known, the gain of $V2$ may be determined. $R_b$ reflects through transformer $T2$ as $R_c$ which is the load on transistor $V_1$. Again, by using the $h^e$ parameters and the value for $R_c$, $R_d$ may be evaluated. Then the gain of the

stage using $V1$ may be found.    It is not possible in this circuit to start
from the input and work toward the output.    The sequence must be to
begin at the load and, by calculating each stage in turn, to proceed
toward the signal source.

When ideal transformers are considered, the power gain of the
transformers themselves is unity or zero decibels.    Then the total gain
is the product of the power gains of the individual stages.    When
decibels are used, the total gain is the sum of the decibel gains of the
individual stages.    It is very difficult to try to interpret the over-all
voltage or current gains in terms of the voltage or current gains of
the individual stages because of the different transformer turns ratios.
Let us assume that the circuit has a power gain of 1000 and that the
power in the load resistance is one watt.    Then the power input to
transformer $T1$ must be 1 mw.    If $R_e$ is 10 ohms, by using $P = E^2/R$,
the input voltage is 0.1 volt.    When $R_e$ is 100,000 ohms, the input
voltage is 10 volts.    Thus, the over-all voltage and current gains
depend on the turns ratios of the transformers, assuming that the
source is matched for all values.    The power gain is, however, fixed.
Thus, it should be apparent that it is much easier to talk of power gains
in transistor circuits instead of in terms of current and voltage gains.

It is important to note that it is a simple problem to obtain a gain
equal to the maximum available gain from each of the stages.    The
only requisite is that the turns ratios of the transformers be correct.

In the multistage amplifier of Fig. 12–11, the bias for each stage is
taken off a different point on a voltage-divider circuit.    Also each
point in the voltage divider is carefully bypassed to ground.    Although

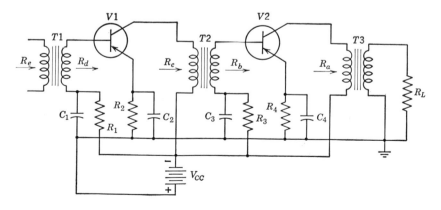

**Figure 12–10**    Transformer-coupled amplifier using transistors.

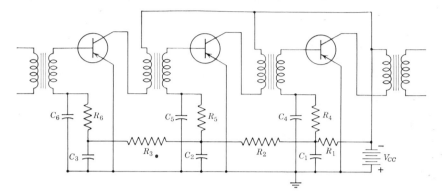

**Figure 12-11** Multistage transformer-coupled amplifier.

many resistors and capacitors are used in this circuit, this method of bias decoupling may be necessary to prevent interaction between the different collector and base circuits in a critical application.

#### . . . . Suggested References for Further Study

1. MIT Electrical Engineering Staff, *Magnetic Circuits and Transformers*, John Wiley & Sons, New York, 1943.
2. R. F. Shea, editor, *Principles of Transistor Circuits*, Chapter 7, John Wiley & Sons, New York, 1953.
3. J. D. Ryder, *Engineering Electronics*, Chapter 4, McGraw-Hill Book Co., New York, 1957.
4. F. Langford-Smith, *Radiotron Designer's Handbook*, 4th ed., Chapter 12, RCA, Harrison, N. J., 1953.

#### . . . . QUESTIONS

1. Define or explain each of the following terms: (*a*) exciting flux, (*b*) leakage reactance, (*c*) hysteresis, (*d*) eddy current, (*e*) volt-ampere, (*f*) mutual capacitance, (*g*) impedance ratio, (*h*) lamination, (*i*) reflected value, (*j*) midband gain.

2. Explain why a load on the secondary winding of a transformer produces an increase in the primary current.

3. Referring to Fig. 12–4, tell what factors of transformer construction influence $R_1$, $R_2$, $X_1$, $X_2$, $C_p$, $C_m$, $C_s$, $R_0$, and $X_0$.

4. Why are transformers laminated?

5. Why is the turns ratio not exactly the voltage ratio, $V_2/V_1$?

6. How does the turns ratio compare to the impedance ratio?

7. Explain the method of establishing the a-c load line for a transformer-coupled amplifier.

8. Compare the over-all efficiency of a transformer-coupled amplifier with a resistive load to the plate efficiency.

9. Why does the response of a transformer-coupled amplifier fall at low frequencies?

10. Why does the response of a transformer-coupled amplifier fall at high frequencies?

11. Why, and under what conditions, does the transformer response peak at high frequencies?

12. How is the gain calculated for a three-stage transistor amplifier using transformers?

## . . . . PROBLEMS

1. A transformer has 1200 turns on the primary and 40 turns on the secondary winding. A 12-ohm load is connected across the secondary. How much current does the transformer take when the primary is connected to a 220-volt line? What is the impedance ratio?

2. A transformer is designed to transfer 10 watts from a 6500-ohm circuit to a 16-ohm circuit. What turns ratio is required? What is the primary current, and what is the secondary voltage?

3. A transformer is designed to supply power from an 8500-ohm source to multiple loads that must be fed by individual windings. The load requirements are: (a) 4 watts at 6 ohms, (b) 2 watts at 8 ohms, (c) 10 watts at 16 ohms, (d) 3 watts at 500 ohms. Determine the turns ratio required for the transformer.

4. If the transformer secondary in problem 3 has a tapped secondary winding with a common return for the loads, specify the turns and the taps in the secondary winding.

5. Using the tube manual, draw a load line for a 6L6 which is transformer-coupled to a load. The load reflects 3000 ohms into the transformer primary. The tube is operated at a 15-volt bias, and the plate supply voltage is 300 volts. Assume that the signal has a peak-to-peak value of 30 volts. Determine the power output, the plate efficiency, the plate dissipation, and the value of the cathode resistor necessary for self-bias.

6. Determine the harmonic content in the output of problem 5.

7. Solve problem 5 when the tube is operated at a supply voltage of 250 volts with a bias of $-10$ volts. The peak-to-peak input signal is now 20 volts.

8. Determine the harmonic content in the output of problem 7.

9. The transformer-coupled circuit shown in Fig. 12-10 has the following values:

$$R_L = 16 \text{ ohms} \quad \text{and} \quad \text{Load power} = 20 \text{ mw}$$

The hybrid parameters for $V2$ are:

$$h_{ib} = 29 \text{ ohms}, \qquad h_{rb} = 4 \times 10^{-4}$$

$$h_{fb} = -0.991, \qquad h_{ob} = 0.5 \text{ micromhos}$$

The hybrid parameters for $V1$ are:

$$h_{ib} = 32 \text{ ohms}, \qquad h_{rb} = 3 \times 10^{-4}$$

$$h_{fb} = -0.950, \qquad h_{ob} = 1.0 \text{ micromho}$$

The internal resistance of the device that drives $T1$ is 55 ohms. Determine the turns ratio required for $T1$, $T2$, and $T3$. What is the over-all gain, and how much power is required from the source to obtain full output power? What are the input and the output voltages?

# Resistance–capacitance–coupled amplifiers

• • • • • • • • • • • • • • • • • • • CHAPTER 13

The operation and the equivalent circuit of an amplifier using the resistance–capacitance coupling is discussed (Section 13–1). For predetermining the frequency response, certain simplifications are made in the equivalent circuit to obtain the relations between the mid-frequency gain, the low-frequency gain, and the high-frequency gain (Section 13–2). The midband gain of the amplifier may also be determined graphically by the use of load lines (Section 13–3). The input impedance or admittance of a tube has a very definite bearing on the high-frequency response (Section 13–4). $RC$-coupled amplifiers using transistors may be handled in a similar fashion (Section 13–5). Volume, tone, and equalizing circuits are generally associated with these amplifiers (Section 13–6).

### Section 13–1  General Considerations of the $RC$-Coupled Amplifier

In most applications a single vacuum-tube amplifier does not have sufficient voltage gain. Therefore, two or more stages are necessary. For example, if a microphone delivers 30 mv into the grid of a stage which has a gain of 40, the output voltage is 30 × 40 or 1200 mv. This voltage is insufficient to drive a power amplifier, and a second stage with a gain of 15 raises the signal level to 1.2 × 15 or 18 volts. The combined voltage gain of the two stages is 40 × 15 or 600.

In order that an amplifier stage can drive a following stage, the signal must be fed into the grid of the second tube as a pure a-c signal with the

305

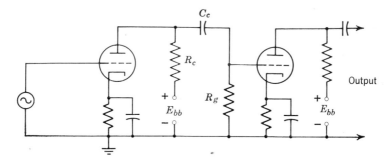

**Figure 13–1** Resistance–capacitance-coupled amplifier.

direct plate voltage blocked out. A transformer-coupled stage, such as Fig. 12–6, performs this function, but a cheaper alternative method is in general use (Fig. 13–1).

The coupling resistor $R_c$ is required in series with the plate which functions as the conventional plate load resistance. The blocking or coupling capacitor $C_c$, keeps the direct voltage on the plate from being applied to the next grid. If this is not done, the grid bias on the next stage is positive. The grid leak resistor $R_g$ is necessary to give a d-c return path from the grid to the cathode. An open grid resistor or lack of a grid resistor creates the unstable condition of a *floating grid*. When the d-c return path to ground from the grid does not exist, stray electrons accumulate on the grid, giving it a negative d-c charge. This charge on the floating grid produces a changing bias to give erratic operation of the amplifier and can often cause a cutoff condition in that stage. Shunt capacitance from three sources exists. The plate-to-cathode capacitance $C_{pk}$ of the first tube, the total shunting effect of the circuit wiring $C_w$, and the input capacitance $C_{in}$ of the next tube tend to bypass energy to ground.

At middle-range audio frequencies, approximately 300 to 3000 cycles, the reactance of the coupling capacitor $X_{Cc}$ is very small with respect to $R_g$, and the reactances of $C_{pk}$, $C_w$, and $C_{in}$ are high compared to $R_c$ and $R_g$. Thus, at middle-range frequencies, the effects of the various capacitances may be neglected. As the frequency decreases, at low frequencies, $X_{Cc}$ becomes large, and $C_c$ and $R_g$ act as a voltage divider, allowing less and less signal on the grid of the second tube for a fixed signal level from the first tube. At low frequencies, the effect of the shunting capacitances is completely negligible. At high audio frequencies, above 3000 cycles, the reactance of $C_c$ is very small with

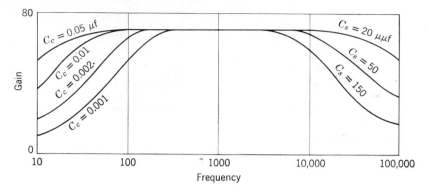

**Figure 13–2** Effect of variable $C_c$ and $C_s$ on amplifier response.

respect to $R_g$ and is neglected. Now $C_{pk}$, $C_w$, and $C_{in}$ are in parallel and may be grouped into the single shunting capacitance $C_s$. The low reactance of $C_s$ lowers the total load impedance and thus decreases the stage gain and the output voltage. For a typical amplifier, the effects of a variation of $C_c$ and $C_s$ on the frequency response are shown in Fig. 13–2.

An exact equivalent circuit of the $RC$-coupled amplifier is shown in Fig. 13–3.

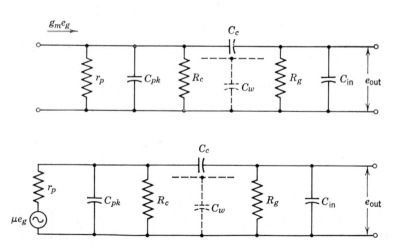

**Figure 13–3** Constant-current and constant-voltage equivalent circuits.

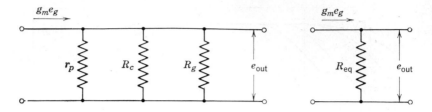

**Figure 13-4** Equivalent circuit at middle frequencies.

### Section 13-2 Gain Calculations

At middle-range audio frequencies, which are approximately from 300 to 3000 cycles, all capacitance effects are neglected, and the equivalent circuit simplifies to the circuit given in Fig. 13-4. The resistances $r_p$, $R_c$ and $R_g$ are in parallel and may be replaced by $R_{eq}$ ($R$ *equivalent*). $R_{eq}$ may be calculated from

$$\frac{1}{R_{eq}} = \frac{1}{r_p} + \frac{1}{R_c} + \frac{1}{R_g} \tag{13-1}$$

The output voltage as determined by Ohm's law is

$$e_{out} = (g_m e_g) R_{eq}$$

Dividing both sides by $e_g$:

$$\frac{e_{out}}{e_g} = g_m R_{eq}$$

but $e_{out}/e_g$ is the voltage amplification

$$A_{e,MF} = g_m R_{eq} \tag{13-2}$$

At low frequencies, the effect of the coupling capacitor $C_c$ reduces the output voltage as the frequency decreases. That part of the circuit to the left of $mn$ in Fig. 13-5 which includes $\mu e_g$, $r_p$, and $R_c$ is replaced by Thévenin's theorem to give a network that consists of $E$ volts in series with $B$ ohms. $E$ is the open-circuit voltage across $mn$, and $B$ is the back impedance measured across $mn$ when $\mu e_g$ is zero. The current through the loop of the equivalent circuit to the left of $mn$ is

$$\frac{\mu e_g}{r_p + R_c}$$

$E$ is this current times $R_c$ or

$$E = \frac{\mu e_g}{r_p + R_c} R_c = \mu e_g \frac{R_c}{r_p + R_c}$$

The back impedance $B$ is merely $R_c$ in parallel with $r_p$:

$$B = \frac{r_p R_c}{r_p + R_c}$$

Now we have a series circuit in which $E$ is applied to the series combination of $B$, $C_c$, and $R_g$. The current in this circuit is

$$i = \frac{E}{B + R_g - jX_{C_c}}$$

$$i = \frac{\mu e_g \dfrac{R_c}{r_p + R_c}}{\dfrac{r_p R_c}{r_p + R_c} + R_g - jX_{C_c}}$$

$$= \frac{g_m e_g \dfrac{r_p R_c}{r_p + R_c}}{\dfrac{r_p R_c}{r_p + R_c} + R_g - jX_{C_c}}$$

But $$e_{\text{out}} = iR_g$$

Divide the numerator and the denominator by

$$\frac{r_p R_c}{r_p + R_c} + R_g \quad \text{which equals} \quad \frac{r_p R_c + R_g R_c + R_g r_p}{r_p + R_c}$$

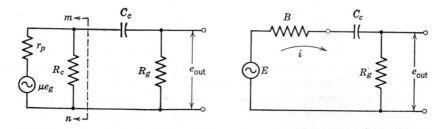

**Figure 13-5** Equivalent circuit at low frequencies.

and in this substitution let us define a new resistance $R$ as

$$R = \frac{r_p R_c}{r_p + R_c} + R_g \qquad (13\text{-}3)$$

We find

$$e_{\text{out}} = \frac{g_m e_g \left(\dfrac{r_p R_c R_g}{r_p + R_c}\right)\left(\dfrac{r_p + R_c}{r_p R_c + R_g r_p + R_c R_g}\right)}{1 - j(X_{Cc}/R)}.$$

But from Eq. 13–1 we note that

$$\frac{1}{R_{\text{eq}}} = \frac{1}{r_p} + \frac{1}{R_c} + \frac{1}{R_g} = \frac{r_p R_c + R_g r_p + R_c R_g}{r_p R_c R_g}$$

Replacing this in the last equation, we have

$$e_{\text{out}} = \frac{g_m e_g R_{\text{eq}}}{1 - j(X_{Cc}/R)}$$

Then the gain at the low frequencies is

$$A_{e,\text{LF}} = \frac{e_{\text{out}}}{e_g} = \frac{g_m R_{\text{eq}}}{1 - j(X_{Cc}/R)} = \frac{A_{e,\text{MF}}}{1 - j(X_{Cc}/R)}$$

$$k_{\text{LF}} = \frac{A_{e,\text{LF}}}{A_{e,\text{MF}}} = \frac{1}{1 - j(X_{Cc}/R)} \qquad (13\text{-}4a)$$

Normally, we are interested only in the magnitude of the gain and not in the phase angle enabling this formula to be reduced to

$$k_{\text{LF}} = \frac{A_{e,\text{LF}}}{A_{e,\text{MF}}} = \frac{1}{\sqrt{1 + (X_{Cc}/R)^2}} \qquad (13\text{-}4b)$$

This relation gives the ratio of gain at a particular low frequency to the gain at midband. Midband gain is normally taken as the gain at 400 or 1000 cycles. It is not difficult to remember the equation for finding $R$. In both the equivalent circuit and the actual circuit, $C_c$ separates $R_g$ from $r_p$ and $R_c$. Now $R$ is this separated resistance $R_g$, plus the parallel combination of the other two, $r_p$ and $R_c$.

At high frequencies, $C_s$ acts as a shunt, reducing the output impedance as the frequency increases. If we replace the section to the left of $pq$ in Fig. 13–6 by Thévenin's theorem, the no-load terminal voltage across $pq$ is the output voltage at mid-frequencies, and the back

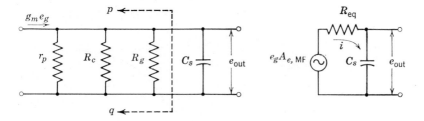

**Figure 13-6** Equivalent circuit at high frequencies.

impedance is $r_p$, $R_c$, and $R_g$ in parallel which is $R_{eq}$. In the new circuit, the loop current $i$ is

$$i = \frac{e_g A_{e,\mathrm{MF}}}{R_{eq} - jX_{C_s}}$$

The output voltage is

$$e_{out} = i(-jX_{C_s})$$

Substituting $\quad e_{out} = \dfrac{e_g A_{e,\mathrm{MF}}(-jX_{C_s})}{R_{eq} - jX_{C_s}} = \dfrac{e_g A_{e,\mathrm{MF}}}{1 + j(R_{eq}/X_{C_s})}$

Then $\qquad A_{e,\mathrm{HF}} = \dfrac{e_{out}}{e_g} = \dfrac{A_{e,\mathrm{MF}}}{1 + j(R_{eq}/X_{C_s})}$

And $\qquad k_{\mathrm{HF}} = \dfrac{A_{e\,\mathrm{HF}}}{A_{e,\mathrm{MF}}} = \dfrac{1}{1 + j(R_{eq}/X_{C_s})}$ $\qquad$ (13–5a)

When the phase angle is disregarded, this equation becomes

$$k_{\mathrm{HF}} = \frac{1}{\sqrt{1 + (R_{eq}/X_{C_s})^2}} \qquad (13\text{–}5b)$$

If $R$ and $C_c$ are known, $k_{\mathrm{LF}}$ can be calculated for any specified low frequency. If $R_{eq}$ and $C_s$ are known, $k_{\mathrm{HF}}$ can be determined for any specified high frequency. If $X_{C_c}/R$ and $R_{eq}/X_{C_s}$ are taken as a ratio, $k_{\mathrm{LF}}$ and $k_{\mathrm{HF}}$ may be plotted as a universal curve valid for any $RC$-coupled amplifier (Fig. 13–7). At one particular frequency $f_1$, $R$ equals $X_{C_c}$:

$$R = X_{C_c} = \frac{1}{2\pi f_1 C_c}$$

or $\qquad\qquad\qquad\qquad f_1 = \dfrac{1}{2\pi C_c R}$ $\qquad\qquad$ (13–6)

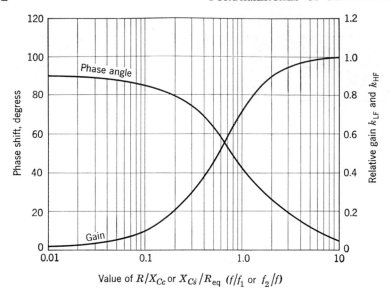

**Figure 13–7**  Universal amplification curve.  Angles are lead for low frequencies and lag for high frequencies in addition to normal 180° shift.

At another frequency $f_2$, $R_{\text{eq}}$ equals $X_{Cs}$:

$$R_{\text{eq}} = X_{Cs} = \frac{1}{2\pi f_2 C_s}$$

or

$$f_2 = \frac{1}{2\pi C_s R_{\text{eq}}} \tag{13–7}$$

The *bandwidth* is defined as $f_2 - f_1$.  At $f_1$

$$k_{\text{LF}} = \frac{1}{\sqrt{1+1}} = \frac{1}{\sqrt{2}} = 0.707$$

and at $f_2$

$$k_{\text{HF}} = \frac{1}{\sqrt{1+1}} = \frac{1}{\sqrt{2}} = 0.707$$

As both $k_{\text{LF}}$ and $k_{\text{HF}}$ are voltage ratios, 0.707 is equivalent to $-3$ db, which is the half-power point.  The bandwidth is that range of frequencies between the half-power points or that frequency range wherein the loss in gain does not exceed 3 db.

When Eq. 13–6 is substituted in Eq. 13–4b and when Eq. 13–7 is substituted in Eq. 13–5b, the resulting equations are

$$k_{LF} = \frac{1}{\sqrt{1 + (f_1/f)^2}} \qquad (13\text{-}8)$$

$$k_{HF} = \frac{1}{\sqrt{1 + (f/f_2)^2}} \qquad (13\text{-}9)$$

The universal curve (Fig. 13–7) may also be used directly. When the universal curve is used, the first step is to determine the −3-db $f_1$ and $f_2$, and then the gain at any frequency may be quickly determined.

**Section 13–3    Load Lines**

The load-line method is an alternative method of calculation of midband gain by using the plate characteristics. The equivalent-circuit method cannot establish the proper d-c cathode bias. The graphical method does give this information. In Fig. 13-8, assume that $E_{bb}$ is 400 volts, $R_c$ is 100,000 ohms, and $R_g$ is 100,000 ohms. The load line for $R_c$ is drawn on Fig. 13-9 as $AB$ in the usual manner. The parallel combination of $R_c$ and $R_g$ is 50,000 ohms. The actual a-c operating load line has a slope of 50,000 ohms and must have its operating point located on the line $AB$. Assume a current of 2 ma in the 50,000 ohms. By Ohm's law, it causes a voltage drop of 100 volts. The line $DC$ drawn between 2 ma and 100 volts has the required slope of 50,000 ohms. All lines parallel to $DC$ must have a slope of 50,000 ohms. Therefore, the desired load line must be parallel to $DC$ and cross $AB$ at the operating point. The desired load line must fall between $E$ and $F$. If the load line were $E$, all positive swings of the

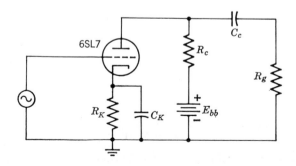

**Figure 13-8**   Circuit diagram for graphical analysis.

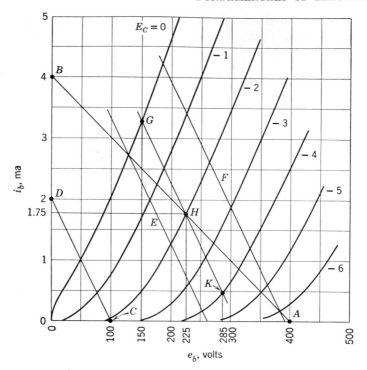

**Figure 13–9**  Graphical load-line analysis.

signal would draw grid current.   If the load line were $F$, all negative swings of the signal would cut off the tube.   By trial and error, line $GHK$ seems most appropriate.   This load line allows a peak-to-peak swing of 4 volts on the grid.   The corresponding peak-to-peak output voltage is $(285 - 150)$ volts.   The mid-frequency gain of the stage is

$$A_e = \frac{285 - 150}{4} = \frac{135}{4} = 33.8$$

From the intersection which is the operating point, we find that $E_b$ is 225 volts, $E_{cc}$ is $-2$ volts, and $I_b$ equals 1.75 ma.   The value of the cathode resistor is

$$R_K = \frac{-E_{cc}}{I_b} = \frac{2}{1.75 \times 10^{-3}} = 1430 \text{ ohms}$$

The values for $r_p$, $\mu$, and $g_m$ may be obtained at the operating point by the usual methods discussed in Section 3–4.

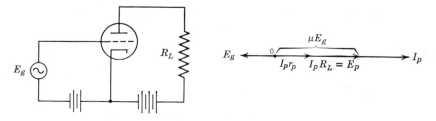

**Figure 13–10**   Simple amplifier with resistive load and phasor diagram.

## Section 13–4   Input Loading

In Chapter 10, we considered the topic of amplification based on the premise that, in a class-A amplifier, the grid does not absorb energy from the signal source.   The presence of the interelectrode capacitances, $C_{gk}$ and $C_{gp}$, actually causes alternating currents to flow in the grid circuit when there is an a-c signal, even though the grid is negative at all times with respect to the cathode.   The purpose of this section is to develop the quantitative relations that exist for a-c flow.

In the simple amplifier of Fig. 13–10, a signal $E_g$ is fed to the grid. Using the voltage form of the equivalent circuit, the action of the triode as an amplifier multiplies the signal by $\mu$ and places it across the series combination of $r_p$ and $R_L$ with a phase shift of 180°.   $I_p r_p$ plus $I_p R_L$ must equal $\mu E_g$, as shown in the phasor diagram.   $I_p$ is in phase with $E_p$ and leads $E_g$ by 180°.

In Fig. 13–11, in which the plate load is inductive, the grid signal $E_g$ is again amplified to $\mu E_g$ with a 180° phase shift.   In this case, because of the inductive load, $I_p$ lags $\mu E_g$.   The $I_p r_p$ and the $I_p R_L$ voltage drops are in phase with the current $I_p$.   The $I_p X_L$ voltage drop leads $I_p$ by 90°.   The angle that the load voltage $I_p Z_L$ makes with $I_p$ is $\phi$, the phase angle of the load.   If the input $E_g$ and the output $I_p Z_L$

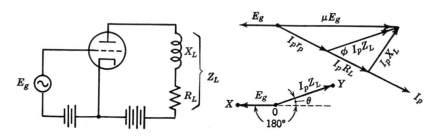

**Figure 13–11**   Simple amplifier with inductive load and phasor diagram.

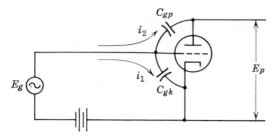

**Figure 13–12**   Input currents in a vacuum-tube amplifier.

voltage phasors are redrawn, it is evident that $I_p Z_L$ leads $E_g$ by $(180 + \theta)$ degrees.

Figure 13–12 shows the input circuit to an amplifier in which the applied signal $E_g$ causes a current flow. One current flows through the grid-to-cathode capacitance $C_{gk}$, and the other current flows through the grid-to-plate capacitance $C_{gp}$.

$$I_g = i_1 + i_2 = E_1 Y_1 + E_2 Y_2$$

where $E_1$ is the voltage across $C_{gk}$ and $E_2$ is the voltage across $C_{gp}$.

$$I_g = E_1(j\omega C_{gk}) + E_2(j\omega C_{gp})$$

$E_1$ is obviously $E_g$. $E_2$ is the voltage difference between $X$ and $Y$ in the phasor diagram of Fig. 13–11:

$$E_2 = E_g - I_p Z_L \big/ \underline{180 + \theta}$$

$$E_2 = E_g - E_p \big/ \underline{180 + \theta}$$

Substituting we have

$$I_g = j\omega C_{gk} E_g + j\omega C_{gp}(E_g - E_p \big/ \underline{180 + \theta})$$

$$= j\omega C_{gk} E_g + j\omega C_{gp} E_g - j\omega C_{gp} E_p \big/ \underline{180 + \theta}$$

Divide through by $E_g$, and replace $E_p/E_g$ by $A_e$:

$$I_g/E_g = j\omega C_{gk} + j\omega C_{gp} - j\omega C_{gp} A_e \big/ \underline{180 + \theta}$$

But $+j1$ represents $\underline{/90}$ and $-j1$ represents $\underline{/-90}$:

$$I_g/E_g = \omega C_{gk} \big/ \underline{90} + \omega C_{gp} \big/ \underline{90} + \omega C_{gp} A_e \big/ \underline{90 + \theta}$$

$$= -\omega C_{gp} A_e \sin \theta + \omega C_{gk} \big/ \underline{90} + \omega C_{gp} \big/ \underline{90} + \omega C_{gp} A_e \cos \theta \big/ \underline{90}$$

$$= -\omega C_{gp} A_e \sin \theta + \omega \big/ \underline{90}[C_{gk} + C_{gp}(1 + A_e \cos \theta)]$$

$$= -\omega C_{gp} A_e \sin \theta + j\omega[C_{gk} + C_{gp}(1 + A_e \cos \theta)]$$

which is in the form

$$\frac{I_g}{E'_g} = G + jB = \frac{1}{R_{\text{in}}} + j\omega C_{\text{in}}$$

Then
$$C_{\text{in}} = C_{gk} + C_{gp}(1 + A_e \cos \theta) \qquad (3\text{--}10a)$$

and
$$R_{\text{in}} = \frac{1/\omega C_{gp}}{-A_e \sin \theta} \qquad (3\text{--}10b)$$

When the plate load is resistive, which is effectively the case in RC-coupled amplifiers at normal frequencies, the input resistance is infinite since $\sin \theta$ is zero, and the input capacitance since $\cos \theta$ is unity becomes

$$C_{\text{in}} = C_{gk} + C_{gp}(1 + A_e) \qquad (13\text{--}11)$$

This relation is known as the *Miller effect*.

A tube manual gives the following data on two typical low-frequency amplifier tubes:

| 6SL7 Triode | 6SJ7 Pentode |
|---|---|
| $C_{gp} = 2.8 \ \mu\mu f$ | $C_{gp} = 0.005 \ \mu\mu f$ |
| $C_{gk} = 3.0 \ \mu\mu f$ | $C_{gk} = 6.0 \ \mu\mu f$ |
| $C_{pk} = 3.8 \ \mu\mu f$ | $C_{pk} = 7.0 \ \mu\mu f$ |

If each of these tubes is used in an amplifier stage with a gain of 30, the input capacitances of the two stages are as follows:

For the triode:

$$C_{\text{in}} = 3.0 + 2.8(30 + 1) = 3.0 + 86.8 = 89.8 \ \mu\mu f$$

For the pentode:

$$C_{\text{in}} = 6.0 + 0.005(30 + 1) = 6.0 + 0.155 = 6.2 \ \mu\mu f$$

Assume that the output capacitance of the previous stage plus the wiring capacitance amounts to 20 $\mu\mu f$. In a circuit using the triode, $C_s$ is 20 + 89.8 or 109.8 $\mu\mu f$. If a pentode is used in the same circuit, $C_s$ is reduced to 20 + 6.2 or 26.2 $\mu\mu f$. The high effective shunting capacitance of the triode materially reduces the high-frequency response of the circuit. Therefore, when several stages are cascaded, it is imperative that at least one pentode stage be used in order to maintain a suitable frequency response. In high-frequency amplifiers, pentodes are normally used to the exclusion of triodes.

When the plate load on an amplifier is inductive (Fig. 13–11), the phase angle $\theta$ is leading or positive. Then, by Eq. 13–10b, the input resistance to the circuit is negative. When the load on the amplifier is capacitive, the phase angle $\theta$ is lagging or negative. Numerically, $\sin \theta$ for negative angles is negative, making the input resistance a positive number. By conventional designation, a negative resistance delivers power from the negative resistance to the source, whereas a positive resistance absorbs power. In other words, a negative resistance acts as a generator. There is a very important application of this negative-resistance concept which provides the class of oscillators known as negative-resistance oscillators. These circuits are considered in detail in Chapter 19.

### Section 13–5   The Transistor $RC$-Coupled Amplifier

The problem of the cascaded transistor amplifier (Fig. 13–13) is more complex than the analysis of the vacuum-tube circuit since there is an input impedance consideration at all frequencies. In the vacuum-tube circuit, it is necessary to consider the input loading of the Miller effect at high frequencies only.

In Chapter 11, the method of mid-frequency gain calculation is outlined. First the gain of $V3$ is determined. This gain, by Eq. 11–4, is a function of the hybrid parameters and the load resistor $R_6$. The input resistance $r_{\text{in}3}$ to the stage, from Eq. 11–5, is also a function of the hybrid parameters and the load resistor $R_6$. The load resistance for $V2$, neglecting capacitance effects at mid-frequencies, is the resultant of $R_4$, $R_5$, and $r_{\text{in}\,3}$, all in parallel. If this resulting load resistance is called $R'_{L2}$, then

$$R'_{L2} = \frac{R_4 R_5 r_{\text{in}\,3}}{R_4 R_5 + R_4 r_{\text{in}\,3} + R_5 r_{\text{in}\,3}}$$

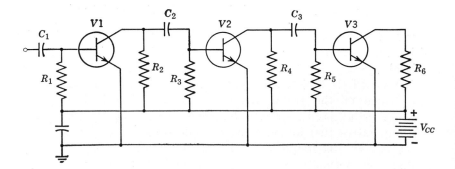

**Figure 13–13**   Three-stage $RC$-coupled amplifier.

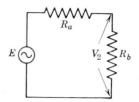

**Figure 13–14**   Equivalent circuit of the coupling
network at middle frequencies.

The gain and the input resistance, $r_{\text{in } 2}$, may be determined for $V2$ by
using the value of $R'_{L2}$ as the load resistance for Eq. 11–4 and Eq.
11–5.   The load resistance $R'_{L1}$ for $V1$ is the parallel combination of
$R_2$, $R_3$, and $r_{\text{in } 2}$.   Now the gain and the input resistance of $V1$ may
be calculated.   The total gain of the three-stage amplifier is the product of the three stage gains.   If the gain is expressed in decibels, the
total gain is the sum of the three stage gains.

   An a-c load line can be drawn for a transistor provided $R'_L$ is known.
The load resistor $R_L$ establishes the d-c load line.   The a-c load line
for $R'_L$ is drawn in exactly the same manner as for the vacuum tube
(Fig. 13–9).   The proper operating bias can be determined by the
selection of the a-c load line which permits the maximum useful
positive and negative swing.

   The cause of a loss in gain at low frequencies is the increased reactance of the coupling capacitors, $C_1$, $C_2$, and $C_3$, which cause a voltage-
dividing action in the same manner as in the vacuum-tube circuit.
If we consider the transistor and its load resistance alone at the mid-
frequencies, we may make an equivalent circuit using Thévenin's
theorem (Fig. 13–14), consisting of a voltage $E$ in series with a resistance $R_a$.   $R_a$ is the parallel combination of the output resistance of
the transistor and its load:

$$R_a = \frac{r_{\text{out}} R_L}{r_{\text{out}} + R_L}$$

The load for this series circuit is $R_b$ which is the parallel combination of
the bias resistor $R_B$ (or $R_E$ in the grounded-base circuit) in parallel
with the input resistance of the next stage $r_{\text{in}}$:

$$R_b = \frac{R_x r_{\text{in}}}{r_{\text{in}} + R_x}$$

where $R_x$ is either $R_B$ or $R_E$, depending on the circuit arrangement,
$E$ must be such a value that it produces the actual output voltage.

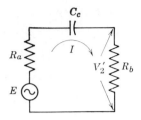

**Figure 13–15**   Equivalent circuit of the coupling network at low frequencies.

$V_2$ across $R_b$ at mid-frequencies.   The current through $R_b$ is

$$I = \frac{V_2}{R_b}$$

Then the voltage $E$ is

$$E = I(R_a + R_b) = \frac{V_2}{R_b}(R_a + R_b)$$

or

$$V_2 = \frac{R_b}{R_a + R_b} E$$

In order to have a simple and usable solution for determining the low-frequency response, we must assume that, as the frequency decreases, the only variation in the circuit is the changing reactance of the coupling capacitor $X_{Cc}$.   The values of $r_{\text{in}}$ and $r_{\text{out}}$ are assumed to remain fixed.   The equivalent circuit is now the equivalent circuit of Fig. 13–14 with the coupling capacitor added (Fig. 13–15).   The loop current through this new circuit is

$$I = \frac{E}{(R_a + R_b) - jX_{Cc}}$$

The output voltage is now $V'_2$:

$$V'_2 = IR_b = \frac{ER_b}{(R_a + R_b) - jX_{Cc}}$$

The ratio of the output voltage at a low frequency to the output voltage at the middle frequencies is

$$\frac{V'_2}{V_2} = \frac{\dfrac{ER_b}{(R_a + R_b) - jX_{Cc}}}{ER_b/(R_a + R_b)}$$

$$= \frac{R_a + R_b}{R_a + R_b - jX_{Cc}}$$

Dividing top and bottom by $(R_a + R_b)$,

$$\frac{V'_2}{V_2} = \frac{1}{1 - j\dfrac{X_{Cc}}{R_a + R_b}}$$

If we define $R$ as

$$R = R_a + R_b = \frac{r_{out}R_L}{r_{out} + R_L} + \frac{R_x r_{in}}{R_x + r_{in}} \qquad (13\text{--}12)$$

where $R_x$ is either $R_B$ or $R_E$, depending on the circuit arrangement, then

$$\frac{V'_2}{V_2} = \frac{1}{1 - j(X_{Cc}/R)}$$

In rectangular form, the equation becomes

$$\frac{V'_2}{V_2} = \frac{1}{[1 + (X_{Cc}/R)^2]^{1/2}} \qquad (13\text{--}13a)$$

The resistance $R$ as defined in Eq. 13–12 has the same sense as the $R$ of Eq. 13–3 used for the low-frequency calculations in the vacuum-tube amplifier. It is the sum of the two sets of resistances which are separated by the coupling capacitor. In the vacuum-tube circuit, the tube input resistance is infinite, and we consider only $R_g$. In the transistor circuit, we must put the bias resistor in parallel with the transistor input resistance. Equation 13–13a has the same form as Eq. 13–4b. However, there is a major difference. Equation 13–4b is for the over-all stage gain of the amplifier, whereas Eq. 13–13a is for the coupling circuit *alone* and *not* for the over-all transistor stage gain.

The input power for the mid-frequency is $V_2^2/R_{in}$, and at a low frequency it is $V'_2{}^2/R_{in}$. Then the power ratio for the coupling circuit is

$$\frac{V'_2{}^2/R_{in}}{V_2^2/R_{in}} = \left(\frac{V'_2}{V_2}\right)^2$$

In decibels, this expression becomes

$$10 \log \left(\frac{V'_2}{V_2}\right)^2 = 20 \log \frac{V'_2}{V_2} = 20 \log \frac{1}{[1 + (X_{Cc}/R)^2]^{1/2}}$$

Expressing this as a loss

Coupling network loss in db $= -10 \log \left[ 1 + \left(\dfrac{X_{Cc}}{R}\right)^2 \right] \qquad (13\text{--}13b)$

To show the use of these equations, let us assume that the mid-frequency gains of the three stages of an amplifier are $+16$ db, $+14$db, and $+18$ db, respectively. Then, the total mid-frequency gain is $+48$ db. Now, let us assume that, from Eq. 13–13, the input coupling-network losses at 100 cycles are $-4$ db, $-8$ db, and $-7$ db, respectively. The total coupling network loss is $-19$ db. Then, the over-all circuit gain at 100 cycles is $+48 - 19$ or $+29$ db.

We can evaluate Eq. 13–13 as $-3$ db when the ratio $X_{Cc}/R$ is unity. This is the same low-frequency half-power point $f_1$ that was used in Eq. 13–6. Now, however, we used the value of $R$ which is found for the transistor circuit by Eq. 13–12. Then Eq. 13–13$b$ becomes

$$\text{Coupling network loss in db} = -10 \log \left[1 + (f_1/f)^2\right] \quad (13\text{–}14a)$$

In this form, the universal amplifier curve (Fig. 13–7) may also be used for the transistor-circuit calculation. The ordinate scale of Fig. 13–7 is given as a ratio of a voltage which numerically is between zero and unity. This scale can be converted to a decibel loss by using

$$\text{Db loss} = 20 \log 1/k_{\text{LF}} \quad (13\text{–}14b)$$

The analysis of the high-frequency response of the coupling circuit is similar to the analysis of the vacuum-tube circuit. In the case of the transistor, the equivalent resistance $R_{\text{eq}}$, is the parallel combination of *four* resistances instead of three:

$$\frac{1}{R_{\text{eq}}} = \frac{1}{r_{\text{out}}} + \frac{1}{R_L} + \frac{1}{R_x} + \frac{1}{r_{\text{in}}} \quad (13\text{–}15)$$

where $R_x$ is either $R_B$ or $R_E$, depending on the circuit arrangement.

The total shunt capacitance $C_s$ is the combination of the wiring capacitance $C_w$, plus the output capacitance $C_{\text{out}}$, of the transistor which delivers power to the network for which the loss is being calculated.

$$C_s = C_w + C_{\text{out}}$$

The output capacitance of the transistor which is usually given in the manufacturer's data sheet for the transistor is the output capacitance $C_{CB}$ between the collector and the base for the grounded-base circuit. When the grounded-emitter connection is used, a result is found that is very similar to the Miller effect. The output capacitance $C_{CE}$

for the grounded-emitter circuit is given by

$$C_{CE} = \frac{C_{CB}}{1 + h_{21}} \qquad (13\text{-}16)$$

where $h_{21}$ is the value for the grounded-base connection, $h_{fb}$.

The ratio of the voltage at high frequency in the coupling network to the voltage at mid-frequencies may be expressed as

$$\frac{V'_2}{V_2} = \frac{1}{[1 + (R_{eq}/X_{Cs})^2]^{1/2}}$$

In decibels, the ratio becomes

$$\text{Coupling network loss in db} = -10 \log \left[1 + \left(\frac{R_{eq}}{X_{Cs}}\right)^2\right] \qquad (13\text{-}17)$$

From this form of the equation, it is seen that, when $R_{eq}$ equals $X_{Cs}$, the coupling loss is $-3$ db. When this frequency $f_2$ is calculated from Eq. 13–7, it can be used to convert Eq. 13–17 to the form

$$\text{Coupling network loss in db} = -20 \log 1/k_{HF}$$

$$= -10 \log \left[1 + \left(\frac{f}{f_2}\right)^2\right] \qquad (13\text{-}18)$$

and the universal amplifier curve (Fig. 13–7) may be used. These coupling-circuit losses must be subtracted from the mid-frequency gains in the same manner as the low-frequency coupling losses.

There is still an additional high-frequency loss that must be analyzed. In the manufacturer's data, *alpha-frequency cutoff*, $f_{\alpha o}$ or $f_{CE}$, is given for the common-base connection. Sometimes, the *beta-frequency cutoff*, $f_{\beta o}$ or $f_{CB}$, is given for the common-emitter connection. Some manufacturers call both $f_{CE}$ and $f_{CB}$ *alpha-frequency cutoff*, which is quite confusing unless particular attention is paid to the subscripts. The frequency cutoff is that high frequency at which $h_{21}$ falls 3 db or decreases to 70.7 % of the value at mid-frequencies. We have analyzed the loss for the coupling circuit itself which involves primarily the output capacitance of the preceding transistor. Now, this new value $h'_{21}$ is the loss of gain due to high-frequency effects within the transistor itself. It has been found that $h'_{21}$ is related to $h_{21}$ by

$$h'_{21} = \frac{h_{21}}{[1 + (f/f_x)^2]^{1/2}} \qquad (13\text{-}19a)$$

when $f_x$ is $f_{\alpha o}$, $h'_{21}$ and $h_{21}$ are values for the common-base connection, and when $f_x$ is $f_{\beta o}$, $h'_{21}$ and $h_{21}$ are values for the common emitter connection.

This equation may be expressed in decibels as

Transistor decrease in gain at high frequencies in db

$$= -10 \log \left[ 1 + \left( \frac{f}{f_{\alpha o}} \right)^2 \right] \quad (13\text{--}19b)$$

for the common-base connection, and

Transistor decrease in gain at high frequencies in db

$$= -10 \log \left[ 1 + \left( \frac{f}{f_{\beta o}} \right)^2 \right] \quad (13\text{--}19c)$$

for the common-emitter connection.

The universal amplifier curve (Fig. 13–7) may be used for this correction factor if the loss is taken as $-10 \log 1/k$. Also

$$f_{\alpha o} = \frac{f_{\beta o}}{1 + h_{21}} \quad (13\text{--}19d)$$

where $h_{21}$ is the value for the grounded-base connection.

For instance, the transistor used in the example in Chapter 11 has an $f_{\alpha o}$ equal to 700 kc. $h_{21}$ equals $-0.982$. Then

$$f_{\beta o} = f_{\alpha o}(1 + h_{21})$$
$$= 700,000(1 - 0.982)$$
$$= 12,600 \text{ or } 12.6 \text{ kc.}$$

We see that the transistor connection used radically affects the frequency response. This lowered frequency response of the grounded-emitter circuit creates a serious problem in its use as a high-frequency amplifier. The methods that enable transistors to be used at high frequencies are studied in Chapter 22.

In conclusion, it is important to remember that, whereas at low frequencies one correction is made to account for the effect of the coupling capacitor, at high frequencies there are two correction factors, one for the network because of the shunt capacitance and the other which is the inherent characteristic of the transistor's poor response at the high frequencies.

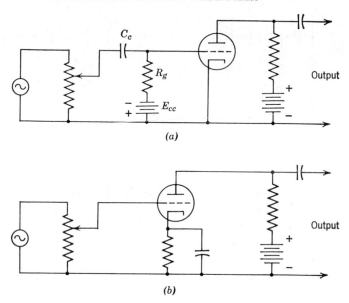

Figure 13-16   Simple volume-control circuits.   (*a*) Circuit with fixed bias.
(*b*) Circuit with cathode bias.

## Section 13-6   Volume and Tone Controls

A vacuum-tube amplifier is usually equipped with a manually operated potentiometer which serves as a voltage divider to control the signal level at the grid of one of the stages (Fig. 13-16).

Conventional wiring practice requires that a clockwise rotation produces an increase in level output for volume controls. Since the level of hearing is logarithmic (Chapter 8), the resistance taper of the audio control cannot be linear but must be logarithmic, in order to have the desired perceptible and smooth increase in listening level with a uniform clockwise rotation of the control shaft. Many applications of amplifier circuits do require linear tapers on the level controls.

Volume controls are available in which the level is not continuously variable but is switched in equal decibel steps. These are called *attenuators*. Fixed-resistance networks which reduce the level are called *pads* and are usually inserted in or removed from the circuit by special switches called *keys*. Both attenuators and pads are designed in various network configurations: *L pads, T pads, H pads, lattices*, etc.

In transistor circuits using level controls, the control must be placed

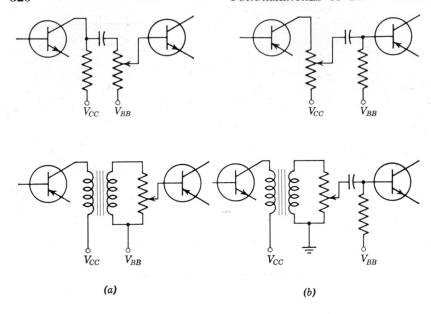

(a)                                                   (b)

**Figure 13–17**  Volume-control placement in transistor circuits.  (a) Incorrect level control circuits.  (b) Correct level control circuits.

in the circuit in such a position that it does not change the operating bias values when the setting is changed.  Figure 13–17a shows incorrect methods of control connections.  In both examples, a change in the variable arm of the potentiometer changes the bias.  In Fig. 13–17b, the bias does not depend on the setting of the level control.

In the circuit of the three-position tone control (Fig. 13–18), when $C$ is switched to position 1, most of the high frequencies are bypassed to ground.  When $C$ is switched to position 2, some of the high fre-

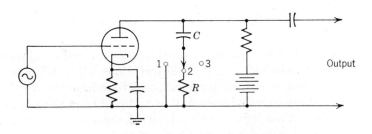

**Figure 13–18**  Three-position tone control.

quencies are bypassed to ground. In position 3, there is no bypassing of the signal frequency. The switch positions may be labeled:

No. 1 Bass
No. 2 Normal
No. 3 Treble

The circuit of Fig. 13–19 uses a volume control which has a tap $T$, from which point a capacitor is placed to ground. When the volume control is set at a high level, the effect of the capacitor is negligible on the high-frequency response. As the level is reduced, the bypassing action of the capacitor at high frequencies becomes greater. The resulting curves are an attempt to approximate the equal-loudness contours shown in Fig. 8–3.

If equal-loudness contours are duplicated in an amplifier, theoretically there is no need for a tone control. There are available a number of circuits and commercial units which appear under the designation of *loudness controls* to serve this purpose. Some arrangements, such as the circuit of Fig. 13–19, compensate only for the low-

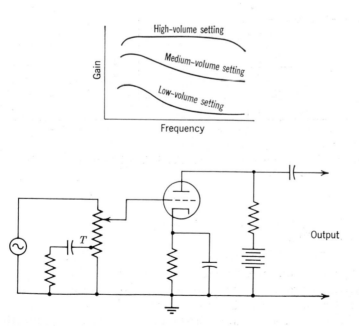

**Figure 13–19** Method of tapping a volume control for tone compensation.

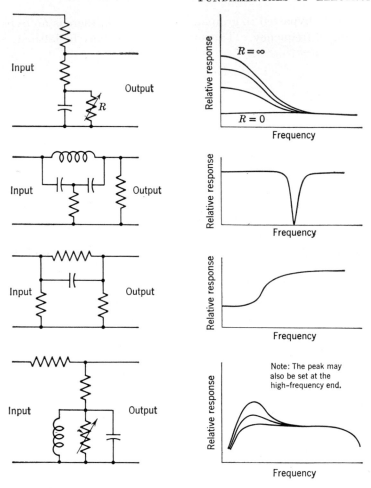

**Figure 13–20**  Typical passive networks designed to provide special frequency responses.

and middle-frequency ranges whereas other more complex circuits approach the loudness contours at all frequencies and at all levels.

Very often audio circuits become quite complex in order to allow for separate bass and treble controls. Other circuits provide special response characteristics to *equalize* or compensate for the special frequency-response characteristics of transducers, records, speakers, etc. A few of the infinite variety of circuit arrangements that are used to obtain special frequency responses are shown in Fig. 13–20.

. . . . **Suggested References for Further Study**

1. F. Langford-Smith, *Radiotron Designer's Handbook*, 4th ed., Chapters 12, 13, 15, and 16, RCA, Harrison, N. J., 1953.
2. R. F. Shea, editor, *Transistor Circuit Engineering*, Chapter 4, John Wiley & Sons, 1957.
3. L. P. Hunter, *Handbook of Semiconductor Electronics*, McGraw-Hill Book Co., New York, 1956.
4. F. E. Terman, *Radio Engineer's Handbook*, McGraw-Hill Book Co., New York, 1943.

. . . . **QUESTIONS**

1. Define or explain each of the following terms: (a) floating grid, (b) Thévenin's theorem, (c) bandwidth, (d) universal curve, (e) negative resistance, (f) alpha-frequency cutoff, (g) beta-frequency cutoff, (h) attenuator, (i) loudness control, (j) level control.

2. Why are the individual voltage gains of two stages multiplied and not added?

3. Why does the gain fall off at low frequencies for a vacuum-tube amplifier? For a transistor amplifier?

4. Why does the gain fall off at high frequencies for a vacuum-tube amplifier? For a transistor amplifier?

5. What information does a load-line analysis give that cannot be obtained from the equivalent-circuit analysis?

6. What information does an equivalent-circuit analysis give that cannot be obtained from the load-line analysis?

7. Why is input loading a problem, and what are its effects?

8. State carefully the Miller effect.

9. How do the determination of $R$ and $R_{eq}$ differ in vacuum-tube and in transistor-circuit analysis?

10. In transistor-circuit analysis $C_{CE}$ and $C_{CB}$ differ. Why?

11. In transistor-circuit analysis, how does $h_{21}$ vary with frequency?

12. Why is it preferable to use decibels in transistor low-frequency and high-frequency analysis?

13. Point out the need for equalization circuits.

14. Why are tone controls necessary?

15. Explain why the circuits of Fig. 13–20 yield the response curves shown.

## . . . . PROBLEMS

1. Show the phasor diagram for an amplifier when the load is capacitive. Refer to Fig. 13–11.

TABLE A

| Circuit | $\mu$ | $r_p$, meg-ohms | $g_m$, micro-mhos | $R_c$, meg-ohms | $C_c$, $\mu f$ | $R_g$, meg-ohms | $C_s$, $\mu\mu f$ |
|---------|-------|-----------------|-------------------|-----------------|----------------|-----------------|-------------------|
| A | 65 |       | 1200 | 0.047 | 0.05  | 0.130 | 65 |
| B |    | 0.070 | 4000 | 0.100 | 0.001 | 0.750 | 70 |
| C | 30 |       | 2600 | 0.330 | 0.02  | 0.240 | 43 |
| D |    | 2.00  | 1900 | 0.270 | 0.005 | 0.240 | 34 |

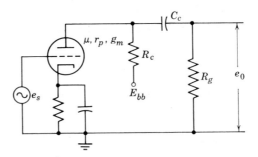

Prob. 13–2

2. Determine the midband gain for the circuit using each set of values given in Table A.

3. Determine the gain at 20 cycles for each circuit shown in the table.

4. Determine the gain at 75 kc for each circuit shown in the table.

5. Using Eq. 13–6 and Eq. 13–7, determine the half-power frequencies for each circuit shown in the table.

6. A 12AT7 amplifier stage is operated from a supply of 400 volts. $R_c$ is 10,000 ohms, and $R_g$ is 10,000 ohms. Determine the cathode resistor required for bias, the voltage gain, and the maximum peak-to-peak output voltage.

7. A 6SL7 amplifier stage is operated from a supply of 350 volts. $R_c$ is 100,000 ohms, and $R_g$ is 150,000 ohms. Determine the cathode resistor required for bias, the voltage gain, and the maximum peak-to-peak output voltage.

8. A 6CN7 amplifier stage is operated from a supply of 300 volts. $R_c$ is 150,000 ohms, and $R_g$ is 200,000 ohms. Determine the cathode resistor required for bias, the voltage gain, and the maximum peak-to-peak output voltage.

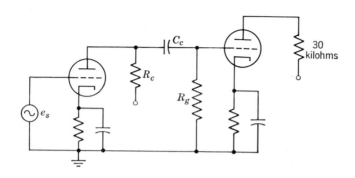

**Prob. 13–9**

9. The two amplifier tubes in the circuit are identical. Each has a grid-to-plate interelectrode capacitance of 4.5 $\mu\mu$f. Using the circuit values given in the table for problem 2, determine the high-frequency half-power points for each set of circuit values.

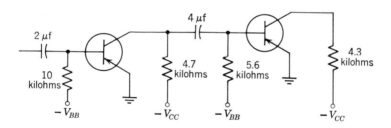

**Prob. 13–10**

10. For the circuit diagram shown, the transistors have the following hybrid parameter values:

$h_{ie} = 1600$ ohms,        $h_{re} = 4 \times 10^{-4}$

$h_{fe} = 40$,                       $h_{oe} = 25$ micromhos

$C_{CB} = 40$ $\mu\mu$f,              Wiring capacitance $= 10$ $\mu\mu$f

Alpha-cutoff frequency $= 650$ kc

Determine the stage gain at midband, at 10 cycles, and at 20 kc.

11. Solve problem 10 if the transistors each have the following values:

$$h_{ie} = 2700 \text{ ohms}, \qquad h_{re} = 5 \times 10^{-4}$$

$$h_{fe} = 50, \qquad h_{oe} = 15 \text{ micromhos}$$

$$C_{CB} = 20 \ \mu\mu\text{f}, \qquad \text{Wiring capacitance} = 10 \ \mu\mu\text{f}$$

Alpha-cutoff frequency = 700 kc.

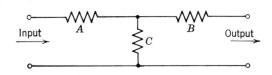

**Prob. 13–12**

12. A T pad, designed to be inserted into a 500-ohm line without disturbing the impedance match, is to provide a 4-db attenuation. Determine the resistance values of the arms $A$, $B$, and $C$.

13. Solve problem 12 for an attenuation of 9 db.

14. Solve problem 12 for an attenuation of 20 db.

# Special amplifiers

• • • • • • • • • • • • • • • • • • • • • • CHAPTER $14$

There are a number of special amplifiers whose characteristics do not readily and conveniently fall into one of the categories of the previous chapters.  From the group of special amplifier circuits, we consider in this chapter the vacuum-tube d-c amplifier (Section 14–1), the transistor complementary symmetry circuit (Section 14–2), the grounded-grid amplifier (Section 14–3), and diode clipping circuit (Section 14–4).

### Section 14–1  The Vacuum-Tube Direct-Coupled Amplifier

It is possible to have a grid connected directly to the plate of the preceding stage if the proper relationships between electrode voltages are maintained.  Figure 14–1 shows the circuit of a three-stage direct-coupled amplifier known as the *Loftin–White* amplifier.  In this circuit we are using to illustrate the principles, each grid is 10 volts less positive than the corresponding cathode, providing each tube with a 10-volt negative bias.  The plate voltage is the difference of potential between the cathode and the plate and is 50 volts.

The voltage relations for this three-stage amplifier are shown in Fig. 14–2.  In order to secure the proper operating voltage sources, it is necessary to use a voltage-dividing network across the power supply.  Each successive stage requires higher direct voltages than the last stage.  This complex supply network is one of the disadvantages of the circuit.  If there is a change in the power-supply voltage, the change reflects into the amplifier as an unwanted signal.  If the input signals are very small, the regulation of the power supply

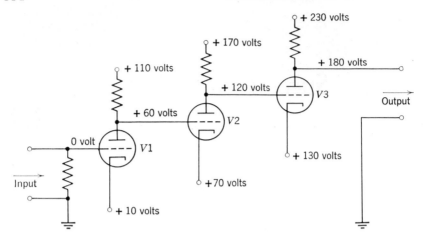

**Figure 14-1**   D-c amplifier.

must be very small in order to prevent the variations in the power supply from masking out the signal itself.

There are a number of circuits that can be used for d-c amplification without the disadvantage of a changing power-supply voltage which is characteristic of the first circuit. A prototype of these stabilized circuits is shown in Fig. 14-3. This circuit can be cascaded into as many stages as necessary to develop the required amplification. The design of the amplifier requires that the components, $R_1$, $R_2$, and $R_3$,

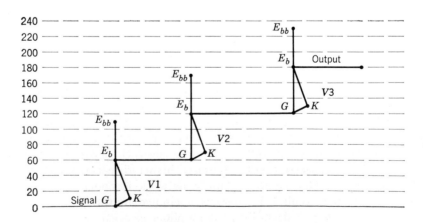

**Figure 14-2**   Voltage relations in a d-c amplifier.

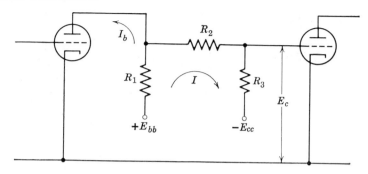

**Figure 14–3**  D-c amplifier using positive and negative supply voltages.

be set to establish a suitable negative bias on the second stage.  When $R_p$ is defined as the d-c resistance of the first amplifier as $E_b/I_b$ (Eq. 2–2a), Kirchhoff's voltage equations may be written for the circuit:

$$E_{bb} = I_b R_1 + I R_1 + I_b R_p$$

and $$E_{bb} + E_{cc} = I_b R_1 + I R_1 + I R_2 + I R_3$$

In the grid circuit of the second stage,

$$I R_3 = E_c + E_{cc}$$

or $$I = \frac{E_c + E_{cc}}{R_3}$$

Substituting this expression for $I$ and $E_b/R_p$ for $I_b$, the equations become

$$E_{bb} = E_b \frac{R_1}{R_p} + (E_c + E_{cc}) \frac{R_1}{R_3} + E_b$$

and $$E_{bb} + E_{cc} = E_b \frac{R_1}{R_p} + (E_c + E_{cc}) \frac{R_1 + R_2 + R_3}{R_3}$$

From these equations, suitable circuit component values can be established.

In Fig. 14–4, the signal is fed into $V1$ which operates as a conventional d-c amplifier stage.  The output of $V1$ is directly coupled to the grid of $V2$.  The cathode resistor of $V2$ is common to the cathode of $V3$.  The grid voltage of $V3$ is set at the same no-signal voltage as the grid of $V2$ by the dividing network of $R_4$ and $R_5$.  The

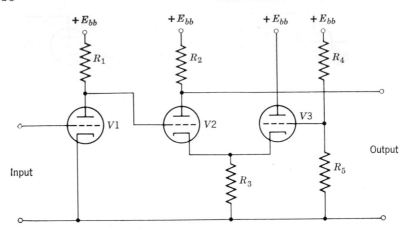

**Figure 14–4**    Two-stage cathode-coupled amplifier.

circuit of $V2$ and $V3$ is essentially a cathode-follower arrangement (Section 17–6), producing a negative feedback which stabilizes the operation of $V2$.   The output from the plate of $V2$ can be used to drive a stage which duplicates $V2$ and $V3$ to give a total of three stages of d-c amplification.

These last two circuits are typical of a number of circuit arrangements that have been developed to fulfill the need where a d-c amplifier cannot be avoided.

In many applications where a d-c amplifier could be used, the signal is converted by a chopper into an a-c signal which can be amplified by a conventional amplifier.   The output of the a-c amplifier can be rectified if necessary to provide a direct output voltage which is proportional to the original signal.

### Section 14–2   Complementary Symmetry

The concept of *complementary symmetry* is unique in its application to transistors.   Complementary symmetry is a means of obtaining the equivalent of a Loftin–White amplifier without the necessity of a complex battery supply system; the supply in complementary symmetry is a simple, single battery.   The circuit (Fig. 14–5) requires two transistors.   In this example, $V1$ is a *PNP* transistor and $V2$ is an *NPN* transistor.   In order to understand the circuit operation, the d-c operating potentials are given on the diagram.   Since the base voltage on $V1$ is $-3.2$ volts and the emitter voltage is $-3$ volts, the emitter is 0.2 volt positive with respect to the base which is the correct polarity for the $PNP$ transistor. The collector, at $-10$ volts, is directly coupled to the base of $V2$. The emitter voltage of $V2$ is $-10.2$ volts, making the emitter of $V2$, an $NPN$ unit, negative with respect to the base. The collector-voltage of $V2$ is $-4.8$ volts, making the collector less negative or positive with respect to the emitter. The voltage distribution of this circuit is sketched in Fig. 14–6, showing the relative voltages of the electrodes of the transistors. By adjusting the values of the resistors, the output d-c potential could be made the same as the input d-c potential.

A positive input signal $E_{in}$ reduces the emitter to base voltage on $V1$. This reduction occurs because this positive signal is applied to the negative base instead of the positive emitter. This reduction of emitter-to-base voltage causes the collector current in $V1$ to decrease. A decreased collector current lowers the voltage drop across the collector load resistance. A decreased load-voltage drop causes the collector voltage of $V1$ to become more negative. Since the base of $V2$ is directly coupled to the collector of $V1$, the base of $V2$ becomes more negative. Now the signal on $V2$ is smaller, and this reduced signal decreases the collector current in $V2$. The load-voltage drop across the output resistor becomes smaller, making the output (the collector voltage of $V2$) less negative. A voltage that becomes less negative shows a change in the positive direction. In this manner, a positive signal on the input of $V1$ produces a positive output signal

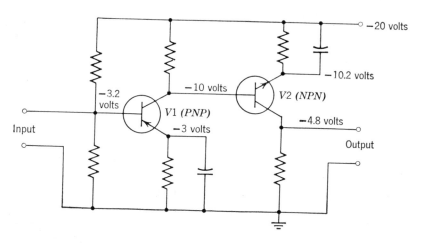

**Figure 14–5** Circuit showing complementary symmetry.

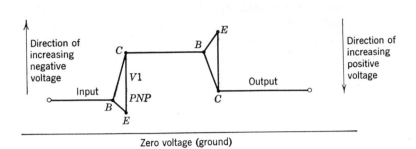

**Figure 14–6**   Operating voltage levels in complementary symmetry.

from $V2$.   This information is evident since the circuit consists of two
grounded-emitter amplifier stages, each of which produce a phase
shift of 180°, and which, when taken together, shift the signal 360° or
back in phase.   One of the major disadvantages of the Loftin–White
circuit is that a change in supply voltage creates a false signal.   The
use of alternate $NPN$ and $PNP$ stages reduces this difficulty since the
change produced in one stage is counteracted by the change produced
in the next stage.

It is possible to select the transistors so that the collector current of
the first stage is the base current of the second stage (Fig. 14–7).
In order to do this, the first stage must be a smaller unit than the
second stage.   In this circuit, when the input signal is positive, there

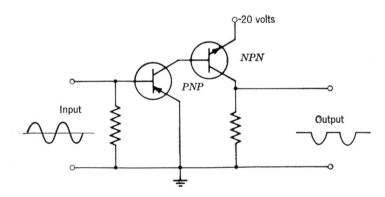

**Figure 14–7**   Transistor clipper circuit.

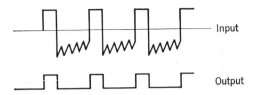

**Figure 14–8**    A clipped waveform.

is a reverse voltage on the *PNP* transistor.   There can be no collector current in a transistor unless the transistor is forward-biased
in the base-emitter circuit.   Thus, the first transistor is cut off.
Since the base current of the second stage must be zero, it is also cut
off, and the output is zero.   When the signal is negative, the *PNP*
transistor is biased in the forward direction, and current flows in the
collector.   This current, in turn, produces a collector current in the
second stage.   In this manner, we show that an output signal exists
only when the signal is negative.   If the input signal is a sine wave,
the output is a half sine wave.   The term *class-B amplifier* describes
this circuit condition.   In a class-B amplifier, output current flows
through just 180° of the full cycle.   Class-B operation may be established in a vacuum-tube circuit only if the tube is biased to cutoff by a
special bias supply.   In transistor circuits, class-B operation is obtained
very simply: a zero bias (no bias) automatically produces class-B
operation.

The circuit of Fig. 14–8 is very useful as a clipper.   It allows only
the positive or negative side of a wave to pass, depending on whether
the first transistor is a *PNP* or an *NPN* type.   As an example, the
complex input signal of Fig. 14–8 can be changed to an output signal
which consists only of short pulses.

## Section 14–3    The Grounded-Grid Amplifier

In the study of transistors, three circuit connections for a transistor
were considered: the common-base amplifier, the common-emitter
amplifier, and the common-collector amplifier.   There are three
vacuum-tube circuits that are analogous to these three transistor
forms.   The conventional vacuum-tube amplifier may be thought of
as equivalent to the grounded-emitter amplifier.   The cathode follower (Section 17–6) is equivalent to the grounded-collector amplifier.
The grounded-grid amplifier is very similar to the grounded-base
amplifier.   We studied the three transistor circuits collectively as a

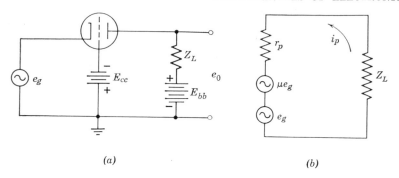

*(a)*                                                    *(b)*

**Figure 14–9**  The grounded-grid amplifier.  (*a*) Actual circuit.  (*b*) Equivalent circuit.

unit topic since all three forms are commonly used.  This is not true of the vacuum-tube amplifiers.  The grounded-grid amplifier, because of its special characteristics, is encountered only in very high-frequency circuits.  A grounded grid serves to act as a shield between the input and the output circuits, and this shielding action reduces the interelectrode capacitance between the input and the output circuits. In the study of the vacuum tube, we found that the approach used to reduce this input to output mutual capacitance was the development of the multigrid tubes, and, accordingly, our study at that time went in that direction.  The pentode amplifier cannot be used at high frequencies where the *transit time* of travel of an electron from the cathode to the plate becomes an appreciable part of the a-c cycle. A special triode designed for use as a grounded-grid amplifier has a very close spacing between the cathode and the plate and can be used at frequencies at which the pentode is unsatisfactory.

The circuit and the equivalent circuit for the grounded-grid amplifier are shown in Fig. 14–9.  When the incoming signal is positive on the cathode, the total bias on the tube increases negatively.  The plate current decreases, and, since the $IZ_L$ drop decreases, the plate voltage increases.  Thus, a positive input signal produces a positive output voltage, and the amplifier does not develop a phase inversion.  Then, in the equivalent circuit, the signal voltage $e_g$ and $\mu e_g$ are additive. The plate current is

$$i_p = \frac{\mu e_g + e_g}{r_p + Z_L} = \frac{e_g(\mu + 1)}{r_p + Z_L}$$

The output voltage is

$$e_o = i_p Z_L = \frac{e_g Z_L(\mu + 1)}{r_p + Z_L}$$

The voltage gain is

$$A_e = \frac{e_o}{e_g} = \frac{(\mu + 1)Z_L}{r_p + Z_L} \tag{14-1}$$

The input impedance is

$$Z_{\text{in}} = \frac{e_g}{i_p} = \frac{r_p + Z_L}{\mu + 1} \tag{14-2}$$

The grounded-grid amplifier has a higher gain than the conventional amplifier. On the other hand, even though the operation of the tube is in class A, the load on the driving voltage is finite and is relatively a low impedance. This means that there is a power-transfer consideration in the input circuit as in the case of the transistor, and this matching problem cannot be ignored in determining the over-all gain.

**Section 14–4   Diode Clipping Circuits**

The action of a transistor in clipping a wave was described in the section covering the introduction to complementary symmetry. Diodes can also serve useful application in clipping circuits.

The simple single-phase rectifier (Fig. 14–10) can be considered a clipping circuit. One half of the a-c waveform appears across the load resistance, and the other half is the inverse voltage on the diode. The connection of the diode determines which half of the input is the output voltage across the load.

Two biased diodes (Fig. 14–11) allow that part of the waveform which is less than the bias to appear as the voltage across the load.

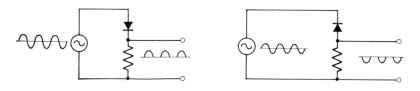

**Figure 14–10**   The diode clipper.

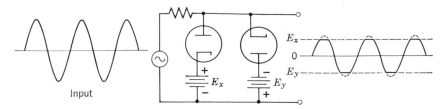

**Figure 14–11**   The diode limiter.

When the incoming waveform exceeds the bias voltages, the diodes effectively short-circuit the signal.   The circuit can be used to "square off" a waveform.   If the output waveform is amplified and fed into a second diode-limiting circuit, the resulting waveform has very square fronts.

Zener diodes (Section 5–5) are often used in the clipping circuit (Fig. 14–12).   The back impedance of a Zener diode is very high before the breakdown potential is reached, and the forward resistance is very low at all voltages.   Connecting two Zener diodes back-to-back places a very high impedance across the output, but, when the Zener potential is reached, the resistance of the diode combination is very low, and the diode current flowing through $R$ produces an $IR$ drop which absorbs any source voltage that is in excess of the Zener potential.   The resistor $R$ limits the diode current to values that do not exceed the safe dissipation limits of the Zener diode.   The Zener diodes are available in voltage rating from about 2 volts to 300 volts, allowing output square waves to be formed with peak-to-peak voltages from 4 to 600 volts.

A pentode (or triode) can be used to act as a limiting circuit.   This circuit is described in Section 24–4 since its major application is to frequency modulation.

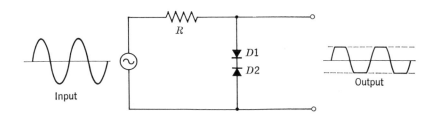

**Figure 14–12**   Clipping circuit using Zener diodes.

## . . . . Suggested References for Further Study

1. F. Langford-Smith, *Radiotron Designer's Handbook*, 4th ed., Chapter 12, RCA, Harrison, N. J., 1953.
2. J. D. Ryder, *Engineering Electronics*, Chapter 8, McGraw-Hill Book Co., New York, 1957.
3. R. B. Hurley, *Junction Transistor Electronics*, Chapter 10, John Wiley & Sons, New York, 1958.
4. E. J. Angelo, *Electronic Circuits*, Chapter 11, McGraw-Hill Book Co., New York, 1958.

## . . . . QUESTIONS

1. Define or explain each of the following terms: (*a*) direct-coupled, (*b*) regulation, (*c*) cathode-coupled, (*d*) complementary symmetry, (*e*) chopper, (*f*) class B, (*g*) transit time, (*h*) clipper, (*i*) limiter, (*j*) Zener diode.

2. What is the low-frequency response of a d-c amplifier?

3. What are the disadvantages of a Loftin–White amplifier?

4. Explain how the d-c amplifier of Fig. 14–3 overcomes the disadvantages of the Loftin–White amplifier.

5. Explain why complementary symmetry can be obtained by transistors and not by vacuum tubes.

6. Explain the operation of the circuit shown in Fig. 14–5.

7. Explain the operation of the circuit shown in Fig. 14–5 if $V1$ is an *NPN* transistor.

8. Explain the operation of the circuit of Fig. 14–7 if the *PNP* transistor is replaced by an *NPN* unit and the *NPN* is replaced by a *PNP* transistor.

9. How is class-B operation obtained in a transistor circuit and in a vacuum-tube circuit?

10. When is a grounded-grid amplifier used?

11. Does the grounded-grid amplifier give phase inversion?

12. How does the gain of a grounded-grid amplifier compare with the gain of a conventional amplifier?

13. What determines the input impedance to a grounded-grid amplifier stage?

14. What is the effect of reversing the diode in a diode clipper?

15. Why is a resistor placed in series with the input of a diode clipper?

16. Why is a resistor placed in series with the input of a diode limiter?

17. What are the advantages in using Zener diodes in a limiter?

# Push–pull and
# phase inversion

• • • • • • • • • • • • • • • • • • • • • • • CHAPTER 15

Push–pull amplifiers are widely used for applications possessing requirements that a single tube cannot meet or cannot conveniently meet. The discussion in this chapter gives the basic class-A circuit (Section 15–1), analyzes the circuit (Sections 15–2 and 15–3), and compares this push–pull circuit with the previously studied single-ended amplifiers (Section 15–4). Class-A transistor push–pull circuits are considered (Section 15–5). Section 15–6 treats the necessary auxiliary circuitry which is used in conjunction with push–pull amplifiers. Class-AB and class-B amplifiers (Section 15–7) are presented both for vacuum tubes and for transistors. The use of complementary symmetry in push–pull (Section 15–8) is restricted to transistor circuits.

### Section 15–1   The Basic Circuit

The signal voltage is the primary voltage of the input transformer $T1$ in Fig. 15–1. The secondary winding of the input transformer is grounded at the center tap. When the center tap on the winding is made the reference point (in this case, ground), the voltage from the center tap to the top of the winding is 180° out of phase with the voltage from the center tap to the bottom of the winding. By use of a center tap, the number of turns in the top half of the winding equals the number of turns in the bottom half of the winding, and $e_{g1}$ is exactly equal in magnitude to $e_{g2}$. Thus, if we consider the grid voltage of

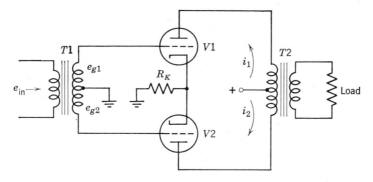

**Figure 15-1** The basic push-pull circuit.

$V1$ to be instantaneously $+4$ volts, the grid voltage of $V2$ must be $-4$ volts at that instant. Accordingly, when $e_{g1}$ is positive, $i_1$ increases, and, as $e_{g2}$ is equal to $e_{g1}$ but negative, $i_2$ decreases. If we assume that the circuit is ideally linear, the rise of $i_1$ equals the decrease of $i_2$. Correspondingly, $e_{p1}$ and $e_{p2}$ are out of phase with each other. Since the action of the tube as an amplifier introduces a 180° phase shift, $e_{p1}$ is in phase with $e_{g2}$ and is out of phase with $e_{g1}$ and $e_{p2}$. Since $i_1$ increases as $i_2$ decreases, and since $i_1$ decreases as $i_2$ increases, the sum of $i_1$ and $i_2$ is a constant and does not vary with the signal. The $IR$ drop of $(i_1 + i_2)$ flowing through $R_K$ develops the cathode bias voltage. A bypass capacitor across the cathode resistor is not necessary because this voltage drop is a pure direct voltage.

Let us assume on the diagram that the flux in the primary of $T2$ caused by $i_1$ acts upward and that the flux caused by $i_2$ acts downward. Without a signal, $i_1$ and $i_2$ are equal, and the two fluxes produced are equal and cancel, with the result that the net flux in the transformer is zero. With a signal, $i_1$ and $i_2$ differ. Then $(i_1 - i_2)$ produces the net primary flux which develops the load voltage and the load power in the secondary winding of $T2$.

Some push-pull amplifiers have a potentiometer connected in series with the cathodes of $V1$ and $V2$. This circuit arrangement is termed a *balance control*. The balance control is adjusted to equalize the no-load direct currents in $V1$ and in $V2$. This procedure compensates for the actual differences that are found in the characteristics of the two tubes used. In addition, we often find that $V1$ and $V2$ are special tubes which have been closely matched to give a better balance.

In checking the operation of a push-pull circuit with a test signal, $e_{g1}$ should equal $e_{g2}$, using either an oscilloscope or an a-c meter. This test should be made with $V1$ and $V2$ in place and with $V1$ and $V2$ removed from their sockets. The observed alternating plate voltages on $V1$ and $V2$ should also be equal.

## Section 15–2    Quantitative Analysis of Harmonics

In Section 10-5, the expression for the plate current in a vacuum tube was shown to be represented by the power series

$$i_b = a_0 + a_1 e_g + a_2 e_g^2 + a_3 e_g^3 + a_4 e_g^4 + \cdots$$

The current of each tube in the push–pull amplifier may be expressed by this power series with the same coefficients since the circuit and the tubes are matched. As the grid voltages are 180° out of phase, we may replace $e_g$ in the power series by

$$e_{g1} = E \sin \omega t$$

and                         $$e_{g2} = - E \sin \omega t$$

Then

$$i_{b1} = a_0 + a_1 E \sin \omega t + a_2 E^2 \sin^2 \omega t + a_3 E^3 \sin^3 \omega t$$
$$+ a_4 E^4 \sin^4 \omega t + \cdots$$

and

$$i_{b2} = a_0 - a_1 E \sin \omega t + a_2 E^2 \sin^2 \omega t - a_3 E^3 \sin^3 \omega t$$
$$+ a_4 E^4 \sin \omega t - \cdots$$

By subtracting these two power series, we have the expression for the push–pull output:

$$i_{b1} - i_{b2} = 2a_1 E \sin \omega t + 2a_3 E^3 \sin^3 \omega t + \cdots$$

The discussion of the power series for the vacuum tube in Section 10–5 showed that the direct current is the $a_0$ term; the fundamental is the $a_1$ term; the second harmonic is the $a_2$ term; the third harmonic is the $a_3$ term; and the fourth harmonic is the $a_4$ term. The expression for the output of a push–pull amplifier ($i_1 - i_2$) does not contain an $a_0$ term, an $a_2$ term, or an $a_4$ term. The expression contains only the $a_1$ and $a_3$ terms. Several conclusions can be drawn from this. The absence of the $a_0$ term confirms mathematically that there is no d-c flux in the transformer primary winding which could cause saturation. Also, there is no second harmonic or fourth harmonic (or any even harmonic) in the output of the push–pull amplifier. This feature of reduced harmonic distortion is the main advantage of the push–pull amplifier.

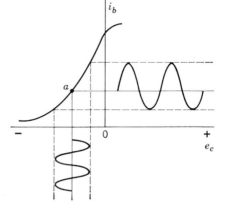

**Figure 15–2** Single tube dynamic-transfer characteristic.

The coefficient of the fundamental term in the power series for each tube is $a_1E$. In the combined push–pull output, the coefficient is $2a_1E$. Thus, the power from a push–pull circuit is twice that of a single tube. In a single tube, the ratio of the third harmonic to the fundamental, which is the third-harmonic distortion, is $a_3E^3/a_1E$. In push–pull, this ratio has the same value, $2a_3E^3/2a_1E$. This shows that the percentage of odd harmonics is neither increased nor decreased by using push–pull.

### Section 15–3   Qualitative Analysis of Harmonics

In Section 7–8, we showed that, if a wave has true symmetry, it contains the fundamental and odd harmonics only. Now we show that this symmetry must exist in the push–pull circuit. Figure 15–2

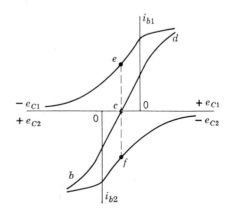

**Figure 15–3** Push–pull dynamic-transfer characteristic.

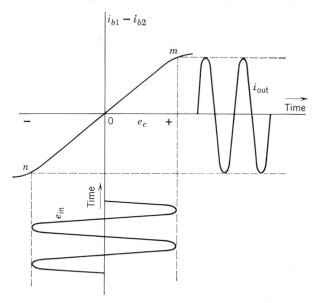

**Figure 15–4**   Resultant push–pull dynamic-transfer characteristic.

illustrates the typical dynamic-transfer characteristic which is obtained
from a single-tube amplifier stage.   The grid-signal and the plate-
current waveforms are shown for the operating point at $a$.   The
asymmetry in the output current wave is evident.   Thus, the output
wave consists of the fundamental with both odd and even
harmonics.

A push–pull characteristic is the *composite* or resultant of the difference $(i_{b1} - i_{b2})$, of the two individual tubes.   One tube characteristic
is reversed to care for the 180° push–pull phase relationship and is so
placed that the grid-voltage value of the operating point of one tube
coincides with the grid-voltage value of the operating point of the
second tube.   This is shown in Fig. 15–3 wherein point $e$ is the
operating point of one tube and point $f$ is the operating point of the
other.   If one curve is subtracted point by point from the other, we
obtain the resultant composite curve $bcd$.   This resultant is redrawn
as the composite transfer curve in Fig. 15–4 in which $(i_{b1} - i_{b2})$ is the
ordinate and the grid signal is the abscissa.   If the individual tubes
are identical, the curvature at $m$ *must* be identical with the curvature
at $n$ but reversed in sign.   This curvature produces a symmetrical
output waveform which cannot have any even harmonics.

## Section 15–4   Comparison between Push–Pull and Single-Ended Operation

As we recall from Section 10–5, for a fixed signal input and for a fixed supply voltage, the output power and the distortion vary with the effective load resistance, as shown in Fig. 15–5. The single-ended tube is normally operated at point $a$ in order to obtain the benefits of minimum distortion. However, push–pull operation permits a shift in the location of the operating point from the point of minimum distortion $a$ to the point of maximum power output $b$. This can be illustrated by using the numerical values on the graph. When two single-ended tubes are used in parallel and operated at point $a$, the output power is 2 × 5 or 10 watts at 9% distortion. By using the load resistance which produces maximum power output, a push–pull connection, by operating at point $b$ instead of at point $a$, eliminates the second and fourth harmonics and delivers 2 × 6 or 12 watts at only 4% harmonic distortion.

Let us assume that the turns ratio of an output transformer (Fig. 15–6) is one to one from each half of the primary to the secondary winding. Then, each tube has $R_L$ as a load resistance. The full primary-to-secondary turns ratio is two to one. Since the impedance varies as the square of the turns ratio, the plate-to-plate impedance is $4R_L$. The alternating current in the top tube is $i_{p1}$, and in the bottom tube $i_{p2}$. $i_{p2}$ is equal in magnitude to $i_{p1}$, but it is 180° out of phase. Actually $i_{p2}$ flows through the primary winding in a direction opposite

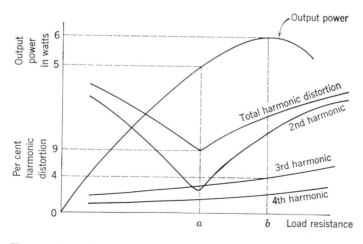

**Figure 15–5**   Output characteristic of a power pentode or tetrode.

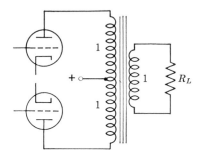

**Figure 15–6**    Output transformer loading.

to $i_{p1}$. The effective current in the primary winding may be considered to be $i_{p1}$. Then, the total alternating plate-to-plate voltage drop is $i_{p1}(4R_L)$. The alternating voltage across one tube is one-half this or $2i_{p1}R_L$. In a single tube this load-voltage drop is $i_{p1}R_L$. Thus, it appears in the push–pull circuit that the value of alternating plate current is doubled. Actually, this means that there is an effective reduction by one half in the internal plate resistance of the tubes when used in push–pull as compared to the single-ended operation.

The factors influencing frequency response of output transformers detailed in Section 12–4 apply also to the output transformers used in push–pull circuits. The problem of d-c saturation in the primary winding, however, does not exist for the push–pull connection.

Advantages of the use of class-A push–pull operation include the following:

1. A marked reduction of developed harmonic distortion is obtained. The rigid specification for low distortion in high-fidelity amplifiers requires the use of a push–pull power amplifier.

2. Since the no-signal flux in the core is zero, the transformer cannot become saturated because of too high a value of operating plate current. A smaller transformer could be used.

3. The cost of a cathode bypass capacitor is saved.

4. Hum in the power supply does not affect the operation of the push-pull circuit. The hum is simultaneously present in each plate current, and the difference in the plate currents $(i_{b1} - i_{b2})$, cancels out the effect of the hum voltage. A less well-filtered power supply may be used for push–pull circuits.

5. An increased output power is obtained by having a reduced internal impedance in the plates of the tubes.

6. Two small tubes may be less costly than one large tube to meet a specific power requirement.

7. At full grid-signal drive, the over-all operating efficiency is increased since the operating point has been shifted from the point of minimum distortion to the point of maximum power output.

Disadvantages of push–pull operation include:

1. A complex driving circuit is needed to produce the balanced voltage 180° out of phase.

2. Transformers with center taps are required.

3. Two tubes, two sockets, and the associated wiring may be more expensive than a single large tube.

## Section 15–5   Transistor Power Amplifier

The transistor class-A push–pull amplifier (Fig. 15–7) is very similar to the vacuum-tube circuit. Essentially the differences possible in transistor circuit arrangements lie in the method of the bias that is used. In the circuit of Fig. 15–7a, the proper operating bias on the transistors is obtained by means of an emitter resistor $R_E$ for each transistor. In order to prevent the bias currents from being short-circuited, blocking capacitors $C$ are required. The bias can also be obtained from a voltage-dividing network (Fig. 15–7b) which is simultaneously applied to both bases. In the circuit of Fig. 15–7c, the bias circuit is modified to provide a temperature compensation. If the ambient temperature rises, the collector characteristics shift (Fig. 11–17) in the direction of an increased collector current. In order to keep the operating point in the center of the load line, the bias current must decrease when the curves rise. The resistor $R_3$ is a *thermistor* which is used for the compensation. As the ambient increases, the resistance of the thermistor decreases, causing more current to be shunted to ground and less bias current to enter into the transistor. Proper design of this circuit keeps the operating point at the center of the load line at different temperatures. As we explained in Section 1–6, an increase in temperature increases the number of electron-hole pairs. More electrons are available to flow under the influence of an applied potential. As far as the external circuit is concerned, it is acting with a lowered d-c resistance. This property is deliberately sought in the design of the thermistor. The thermistor, thus, has the property of having a decreasing resistance with an increase in temperature.

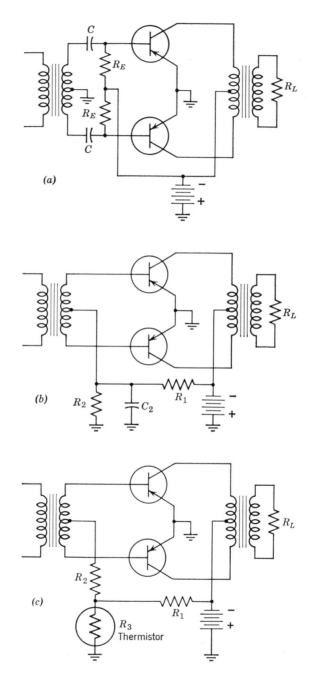

**Figure 15–7** Typical transistor push–pull circuits. (*a*) Circuit using bias resistors. (*b*) Bias obtained from voltage divider. (*c*) Temperature-compensated bias.

## Section 15-6    Phase Inverters

A circuit arrangement to produce balanced voltages which are 180° out of phase for the grids of the push–pull stage is termed a *phase inverter*. Many circuit variations have been developed for this purpose. We will consider some of the fundamental designs that are in common use.

The circuit of Fig. 15–8 provides a simple and effective means of obtaining the balanced driving voltages. The balance in this circuit is determined by the exactness of the location of the center tap. The simplicity of the circuit is often outweighed by the expense of the driver transformer, especially if it is to be used for high-fidelity equipment. When there exists a grid-current requirement in the push–pull stage (Section 15–8), the use of the driver transformer cannot be avoided without producing a very large distortion which is caused by the $IZ$ drop in the grid-driving circuit and a shift in the operating point.

In the cascade phase inverter (Fig. 15–9) two identical amplifier stages are used. In order to understand the operation of this circuit, assume that the value of the signal $e_{in}$ is one volt, and that the stage gain of $V1$ is 15. The voltage from the grid to ground of $V3$ is then 15 volts, and it is also 180° out of phase with $e_{in}$. The grid circuit of $V3$ is divided so that

$$\frac{R_6}{R_5 + R_6} = \frac{1}{A_e}$$

In this example, 1/15 of the grid voltage (15 volts) is developed across $R_6$. This one volt across $R_6$ is directly coupled into the grid of $V2$.

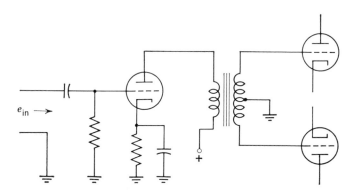

**Figure 15–8**    Transformer phase inverter.

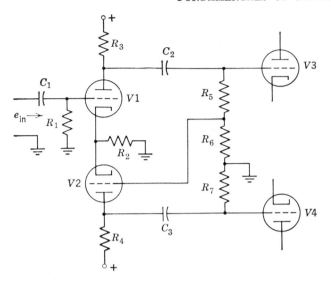

**Figure 15–9**   Cascade phase inverter.

The grid voltage of $V2$ is equal to, but out of phase with, the grid voltage of $V1$ which is $e_{in}$.   The circuit of $V2$ provides the same gain, 15, as $V1$ and delivers 15 volts to the grid of $V4$.   This 15-volt signal on $V4$ is 180° out of phase with the 15 volts at the grid of $V3$.   This circuit provides voltage gain while securing the proper out-of-phase relation.   Exact balance is obtained by using low tolerance or matched

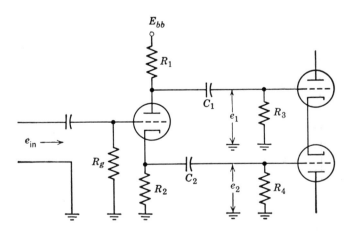

**Figure 15–10**   Cathode-resistor method of phase inversion.

components and tubes.   An adjustment of $R_6$ can provide a critical balance if necessary.

The cathode-resistor method of phase inversion (Fig. 15–10) provides exact balance if $R_1$ and $R_2$, $C_1$ and $C_2$, and $R_3$ and $R_4$ are matched or precision components.   The balance in this circuit does not depend on the tube characteristics or on a divider network.   This very simple circuit provides balance as long as $i_p R_1$ equals $i_p R_2$.

A positive signal increases the plate-current flow.   An increase in plate current produces an increased $i_p R_2$ drop from cathode to ground, making $e_2$ in phase with $e_{in}$.   The plate voltage $e_1$ is 180° out of phase with $e_{in}$, giving the 180° phase difference between $e_1$ and $e_2$ that is required for driving the push–pull output stage.

The disadvantage of this circuit is that the voltage gain cannot equal or exceed unity.   Also, under circumstances where $E_{bb}$ is large and the phase inverter tube has a high mu, it may be necessary to return $R_g$ not to ground, but to the proper point on the cathode resistor.   Unless this is done, the tube will cut off the negative half-cycle of the signal.

In self-balancing circuits, such as Fig. 15–11, the various corresponding components of the two triode amplifiers must be matched.   A positive input signal causes the plate current of $V1$ to rise.   This action tends to develop a larger bias across the cathode resistor $R_K$. This larger bias, by decreasing the plate current of the other tube $V2$,

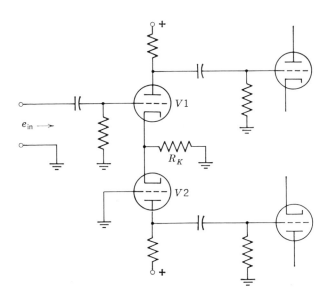

**Figure 15–11**   Self-balanced phase inverter.

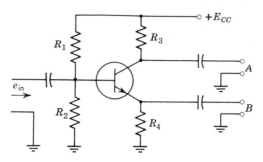

**Figure 15–12**    Transistor phase inverter.

acts as if it were a negative signal on the grid of $V2$.    A negative input signal, by reducing the plate current of $V1$, decreases the bias and causes the plate current of $V2$ to increase.

The usual form of the phase inverter in transistor circuits is a transformer-coupled circuit which provides phase inversion by means of a center tap of the secondary winding.    A transistor version (Fig. 15–12) of the cathode-resistor inversion method is used.    The network of $R_1$ and $R_2$ establishes the bias operating point.    When $R_3$ equals $R_4$, the two outputs, $A$ and $B$, are not exactly equal since the collector current must be less than the emitter current.    It is not possible to obtain a combination of $R_3$ and $R_4$ that will make output $A$ equal to output $B$.    A small unbalance is a characteristic of this circuit.

### Section 15–7    Class-AB and Class-B Amplifiers

The term *class* describes the operation of an amplifier by specifying the conditions of plate- and grid-current flow for an a-c cycle of the signal (Fig. 15–13).    In a *class-A* amplifier, plate current is continuous throughout the full cycle of the a-c signal.    It is understood that there is no grid current at all in a class-A amplifier.    In a circuit in which there is a grid current, it is necessary to specify the operation as *class* $A_2$.    A class-A amplifier is biased for optimum results halfway between cutoff and grid current.    In a *class-AB* amplifier, the plate current flows for more than half the a-c cycle but less than a full a-c cycle. It is necessary to term circuit operation where there is no grid current as *class* $AB_1$ and where there is grid current as *class* $AB_2$.    In a *class-B* amplifier, grid current is usual, and it is assumed.    It would be unusual to have class-B operation without grid current.    Under these circumstances, we find that the subscript 2 is omitted in writing class B.

In *class B*, plate current flows for half the cycle only.    The bias must be set at cutoff to accomplish this.    In a push–pull amplifier, one tube handles the positive half of the signal cycle while the other tube handles the other half because one tube carries current when the other is cut off.    In *class-C* operation, plate current flows for less than half the cycle, and the bias must be below cutoff.    Chapter 16 is devoted to a study of the class-C amplifier.

Without signals, there are definite values of operating plate currents for the class-A and class-AB amplifiers.    Without signals, the operating plate currents of class-B and class-C amplifiers are zero.    Con-

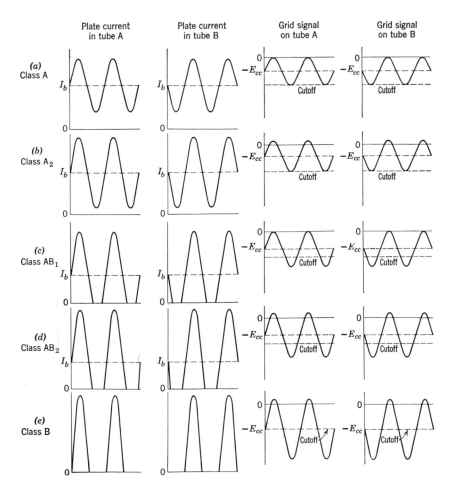

**Figure 15–13**    Class-A, class-AB, and class-B operation.

sequently, the bias of the class-A and the class-AB circuits can be
obtained by use of a self-biasing cathode resistor, whereas a separate
fixed-bias source must be used for the class-B and class-C circuits.
Generally, a fixed bias is also used in the class-AB$_2$ amplifier to provide
a greater output. A comparison of these classes of operation can be
made from a tabulation (Table I) of the tube manual ratings for the
6L6 beam-power tubes in push–pull.

TABLE I

| Class | Bias | Output Power |
|-------|------|--------------|
| A$_1$ | Fixed | 18.5 |
|  | Cathode resistor | 17.5 |
| AB$_1$ | Fixed | 26.5 |
|  | Cathode resistor | 24.5 |
| AB$_2$ | Fixed | 47.0 |

The waveforms for one signal cycle of a class-B amplifier are shown
in Fig. 15–14. The direct current in each tube is, by Eq. 9–1:

$$I'_{dc} = \frac{I_m}{\pi}$$

Then, for two tubes, the direct current is

$$I_{dc} = \frac{2I_m}{\pi}$$

and the power-supply demand is

$$P_{in} = E_{bb} \times I_{dc} = \frac{2I_m E_{bb}}{\pi}$$

The a-c power in the load is

$$P_{out} = \frac{E_m}{\sqrt{2}} \times \frac{I_m}{\sqrt{2}} = \frac{E_m I_m}{2}$$

The plate dissipation is

$$P_{diss} = P_{in} - P_{out} = 2I_m \left( \frac{E_{bb}}{\pi} - \frac{E_m}{4} \right)$$

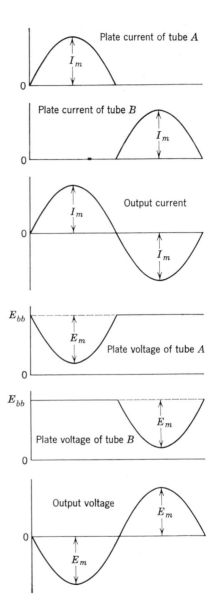

**Figure 15–14** Waveforms of a class-B amplifier.

If we consider a circuit in which the power is supplied to a load by an output transformer, there is no d-c power lost in the load, and the plate efficiency is

$$\eta_{pl} = \frac{E_m I_m/2}{2 I_m E_{bb}/\pi} = \frac{\pi}{4} \frac{E_m}{E_{bb}}$$

When the operation of the circuit is ideal, the plate voltage of the tube is zero at the instant of the peak of the alternating plate voltage or $E_m$ equals $E_{bb}$. Then, *the maximum theoretical efficiency of a class-B amplifier is $\pi/4$ or 78.5%*. This figure of 78.5% compares to the 50% value obtained for the class-A amplifier. The efficiencies of the class-$AB_1$ and the class-$AB_2$ amplifiers are intermediate values dependent on the bias conditions.

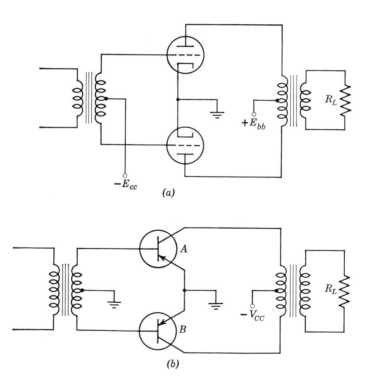

(a)

(b)

**Figure 15–15** Class-B amplifier. (*a*) Vacuum‑tube circuit. (*b*) Transistor circuit.

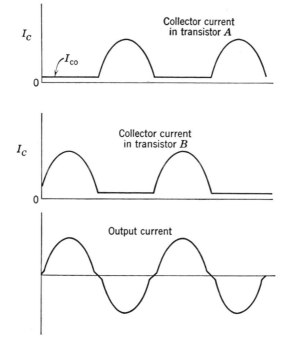

**Figure 15–16**   Cross-over distortion.

Class-AB and particularly class-B amplifiers create problems of power-supply regulation. In class B, with a maximum signal, the drain on the power supply is a maximum. When the signal is zero, the power supply is at no-load conditions. In order to keep the harmonic content of the output low, the voltage regulation of the power supply must be kept as low as possible by providing large line transformers, large chokes, and large filter capacitors.

The vacuum tube circuit of Fig. 15–1 and the transistor circuits of Fig. 15–7 can be operated in class $AB_1$ or class $AB_2$ merely by proper choice of the biasing components and the signal level. Typical class-B amplifier circuits are shown in Fig. 15–15. The fixed bias $E_{cc}$ of the vacuum-tube circuit must be set exactly at cutoff to insure a 180° current flow in each tube. Class B is very simply obtained in transistor circuits. When the bias is zero, one half of the signal cycle is a forward bias causing collector current while the other half of the signal cycle is a reverse bias preventing collector current.

The presence of collector cutoff current (Fig. 3–19) which is a collector current due to minority current carriers at zero bias, creates a problem in transistor class-B circuits that does not occur in vacuum-tube circuits. The individual collector currents of the two transistors (Fig. 15–16) are never quite zero during the full cycles of the signal. The difference of the two collector currents which is the output shows a slight irregularity or deviation from a sinusoidal waveform as the wave crosses the zero or time axis. This irregularity is called *cross-over distortion*. This distortion is an inherent characteristic of the class-B transistor circuit, and it can be avoided only by keeping the operating point slightly off class B and into class AB.

### Section 15–8   Complementary Symmetry in Push–Pull

The principles of complementary symmetry described in Section 14–2 may be applied to the push–pull amplifier (Fig. 15–17). This circuit uses neither an input nor an output transformer. The current through the load is the sum of the two collector currents, $I_{C1}$ and $I_{C2}$. Since one of the transistors is a $PNP$ unit and the other an $NPN$ unit, one current is positive and the other negative, so that the load current is $(I_{C1} - I_{C2})$ which is a true push–pull concept. When the signal is positive, the emitter-to-base voltage on the $PNP$ transistor is

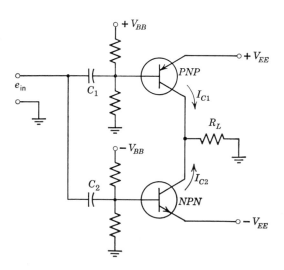

**Figure 15–17**   Push-pull using complementary symmetry.

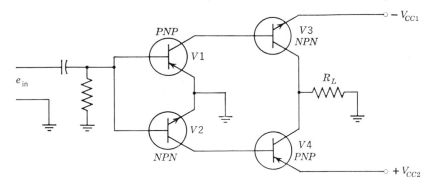

**Figure 15–18**   Class-B amplifier using complementary symmetry.

reduced while the emitter-to-base voltage on the $NPN$ transistor increases. This positive signal increases the collector current in the $NPN$ unit and decreases the collector current in the $PNP$ unit. Correspondingly, a negative signal increases the output current in the $PNP$ transistor and decreases the output current in the $NPN$ transistor.

The blocking capacitors, $C_1$ and $C_2$, must be used to isolate the two biases. The $PNP$ and the $NPN$ transistors must be identical but with opposite polarity in all ratings to secure a balance.

Another circuit arrangement using complementary symmetry in conjunction with class-B amplifiers is shown in Fig. 15–18. When there is no signal at the input, both driver transistors, $V1$ and $V2$, are cut off since the bias voltages on them are zero. Also, there is no bias current on the output transistors, $V3$ and $V4$, and their collector currents are zero. In this manner, without a signal, there is no drain on the supply batteries, $V_{CC1}$ and $V_{CC2}$. When the signal is positive, there is a bias current and a collector current in $V2$ but not in $V1$. The collector current in $V2$ is the base current for $V4$, allowing $V4$ to supply energy into the load resistance $R_L$. When the signal is negative, there are currents in $V1$ and $V3$, but not in $V2$ and $V4$.

Again, in this circuit, matched characteristics are necessary for both the driver transistors, $V1$ and $V2$, and the output transistors, $V3$ and $V4$. The relation of ratings between the driver transistors and the output transistors must be such that the magnitude of the collector currents of $V1$ and $V2$ is of the order of the base currents of $V3$ and $V4$.

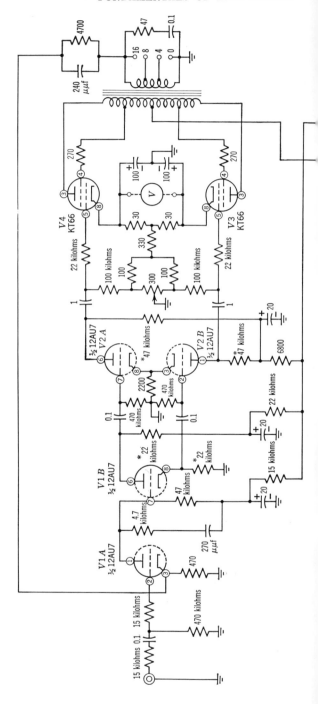

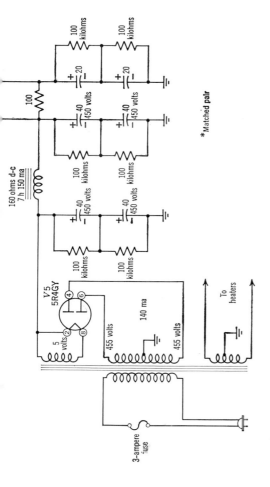

**Figure 15-19** Commercial high-fidelity amplifier. (*Courtesy Heath Co.*)

**. . . . Suggested References for Further Study**

1. F. Langford-Smith, *Radiotron Designer's Handbook*, 4th ed., Chapters 12 and 13, RCA, Harrison, N. J., 1953.
2. L. P. Hunter, editor, *Handbook of Semiconductors*, McGraw-Hill Book Co., New York, 1956.

**. . . . QUESTIONS**

1. Define or explain each of the following terms: (*a*) balance control, (*b*) composite, (*c*) thermistor, (*d*) cascade, (*e*) class $A_2$, (*f*) class $AB_1$, (*g*) class $AB_2$, (*h*) class B, (*i*) class C, (*j*) crossover distortion.

2. Describe the process in checking the operation of a push–pull amplifier.

3. What does a d-c core saturation do to an a-c waveform in a transformer?

4. What is the effect of a push–pull connection on even harmonics? On odd harmonics?

5. How is a composite load line developed?

6. Give five advantages for push–pull operation.

7. Give three disadvantages for push–pull operation.

8. Describe four vacuum-tube phase-inverter circuits.

9. Explain the operation of the circuit shown in Fig. 15–12.

10. What are the maximum theoretical efficiencies of a class-A and a class-B amplifier?

11. Explain, step by step, the operation of the complementary symmetry circuit shown in Fig. 15–17.

12. Explain, step by step, the operation of the complementary symmetry circuit shown in Fig. 15–18.

The following questions all refer to the circuit shown in Fig. 15–19:

13. What is the use of the capacitor in series with the input jack? The 15,000 ohm resistor?

14. Explain the action of the 4700-ohm resistor in the plate circuit of $V1A$.

15. Trace out the phase-inverter circuit.

16. What is the purpose of the 22,000-ohm resistors in series with the grids of $V3$ and $V4$?

17. What is the purpose of the 47-ohm resistor across the secondary of the output transformer?

18. Why is a choke used in one section of the main power-supply filter and a resistor in the other?

19. Why are the capacitors in the main filter connected in series, and what is the use of the resistors in parallel with them?

## . . . . PROBLEM

1. A dual triode which has the characteristics of the 6AV6 is used for the cascade phase inverter shown in Fig. 15–9. The supply voltage is 300 volts. $R_3$ and $R_4$ are each 100,000 ohms. $R_7$ and $(R_5 + R_6)$ are each 100,000 ohms. Determine the gain and the values of $R_2$, $R_5$, and $R_6$.

# Class-C amplifiers

♦ ♦ ♦ ♦ ♦ ♦ ♦ ♦ ♦ ♦ ♦ ♦ ♦ ♦ ♦ ♦ ♦ ♦ ♦ ♦ ♦ ♦ ♦ CHAPTER 16

In a class-C amplifier the bias is so adjusted that plate current flows for less than one half the a-c cycle. A fixed-bias source is generally associated with class-C amplifiers, but very often in low-power applications the grid-leak method provides the operating bias (Section 16–1). The plate loads in class-C amplifiers are tuned circuits (Section 16–2). A load line may be established for this amplifier (Section 16–3), and from this load line an analysis can be made of the plate circuit (Section 16–4) and of the grid circuit (Section 16–5). The adjustment and the method of tuning of a class-C amplifier require special considerations (Section 16–6). A class-C amplifier may also be used as a harmonic generator and amplifier (Section 16–7). When triodes are used as class-C amplifiers, it is necessary to follow the procedure of neutralization (Section 16–8).

The purpose of this chapter is to present a careful analysis of how the class-C amplifier functions and of the meaning of the various problems encountered in its adjustment. It is not the intent of this chapter to develop a design procedure.

### Section 16–1   Grid-Leak Bias

A grid-leak bias is a means of developing a negative direct bias voltage between the grid and the cathode of a tube by rectifying the incoming signal for the purpose. The applications of grid-leak bias go beyond the class-C vacuum-tube amplifier, and, when these applications are discussed, reference will be made back to this section.

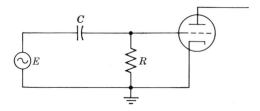

**Figure 16-1** Grid-leak bias.

A grid-leak bias can be recognized in a circuit (Fig. 16-1) as it differs from an ordinary cathode bias circuit in two respects:

1. The cathode is usually connected directly to the common return, the ground, and

2. A grid-leak resistor $R$ and a grid-leak capacitor $C$ are placed between the signal source $E$ and the grid of the tube.

An additional restriction on the circuit is that there must be a d-c path through the source $E$. We assume for the purpose of this discussion that the d-c resistance of the source is zero. A typical source of voltage that has a negligible d-c resistance is the secondary winding of a transformer.

When the a-c polarity of the signal is such that the grid is positive and the ground is negative (Fig. 16-2), there is a current flow in the grid. The current flow is limited by the grid resistor $R$, and a direct voltage is developed across this grid resistor with the polarity shown on the circuit diagram. Since the d-c resistance of the source is zero, the grid-leak capacitor $C$ is effectively in parallel with the grid-leak resistor $R$, as far as the d-c circuit is concerned. The grid-leak capacitor $C$ charges up to the peak value of the source voltage $E$.

The capacitor discharges through the grid-leak resistor when the applied signal is less than the peak value. The source $E$ supplies

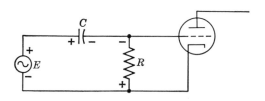

**Figure 16-2** Operation of grid-leak bias.

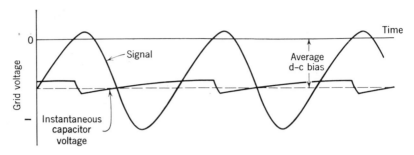

Figure 16–3   Grid-leak bias wave forms.

just enough energy to recharge the capacitor each cycle.   The action of this circuit is similar to the action of the capacitor filter in a rectifier circuit (Section 9–5).   If $R$ is large, if $C$ is small, and if the time constant $RC$ is long with respect to the time of one cycle, $1/f$, the energy absorbed by the grid-leak circuit is small.   The negative direct voltage at the grid almost equals the magnitude of the peak of the signal. If the signal changes in level, the bias changes proportionally.   Because of this, a grid-leak bias is very often termed an "automatic bias." The waveforms illustrating this discussion are shown in Fig. 16–3.

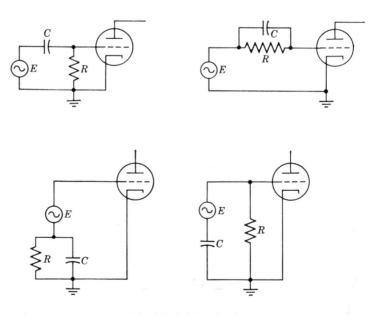

Figure 16–4   Grid-leak bias circuit arrangements.

Since the d-c resistance of the source $E$ is negligible when compared to the grid-leak resistance, it is possible to rearrange the circuit of Fig. 16–1 as long as the grid-leak resistor and the grid-leak capacitor are effectively in parallel in the d-c circuit. Several different circuit arrangements are shown in Fig. 16–4.

## Section 16–2   The Tank Circuit

If a charged capacitor is connected to the coil by closing a switch (Fig. 16–5), energy is transferred to the coil and then back to the capacitor in an oscillatory motion. The sinusoidal voltage across the capacitor will gradually diminish to zero with time. The rate of decay of this transient oscillation is termed the *damping* or the *damping factor* of the circuit and is caused by the effective resistance of the tank circuit which produces an $I^2R$ heat loss. When the $Q$ of the circuit is at least five, the frequency of the oscillation is determined by:

$$f_0 = \frac{1}{2\pi \sqrt{LC}}$$

If a pulse of energy can be fed into this oscillating system once each cycle to replace the energy lost over the cycle, the *flywheel effect* of the tank circuit carries the action through the complete cycle to the next pulse. It is possible to feed in energy every second, third, or fourth cycle. Practically, an extreme limit is about a pulse of energy every tenth cycle. By using this principle, a one-megacycle source of energy could keep a 5-megacycle tank in oscillation. This action is called *frequency multiplication*.

When the tank is connected into the plate circuit of an amplifier stage, the plate voltage is also oscillatory. Energy need be fed into

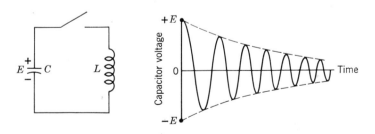

**Figure 16–5**   The tank circuit and damped wave.

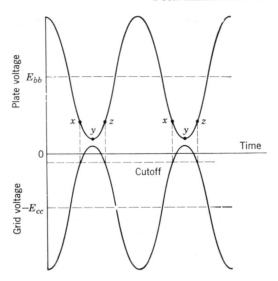

**Figure 16–6**   Waveforms of class-C grid and plate voltages.

the tank only between points $x$ and $z$ of Fig. 16–6.   To provide this energy, a grid signal which is biased at $-E_{cc}$ is kept below cutoff at all times except for the interval $xz$.   During the time $xz$, plate current flows.   If this time $xz$ is expressed in degrees of the full cycle, then $xz$ represents the *angle of plate-current flow*.   If the bias $-E_{cc}$ is increased, and if the peak value of the a-c grid signal is increased, the time interval $xz$ decreases.   When the total energy content of each charging pulse is constant and when the charging time interval $xz$ decreases, the rate of charge must increase.   This charging rate is the plate current.

In Fig. 16–6, the distance between $y$ and the time axis, between $x$ and the time axis, and between $z$ and the time axis are particular values of $e_b$ during the time of plate-current flow.   The instantaneous product of $e_b$ and $i_b$ is the plate dissipation.   If the tube were ideal and without losses, the plate dissipation would necessarily have to be zero. Under this ideal condition, point $y$ would lie on the time axis, and the angle of plate current flow would have to be zero.   This pulse of plate current which has zero width would be infinite in amplitude.   Thus it is theoretically possible to obtain a figure of 100% for the plate efficiency of the class-C amplifier.   Practically, the tube drop at $y$ must be finite and not zero, and the amplitude of the plate current is limited by the saturation value for the tube.   Class-C amplifiers using vacuum tubes have typical efficiencies in the plate of the order of 70 to 80%.  By use of transistors, the efficiency can be raised to values well over 90%.

## Section 16–3   Class-C Load Line

When there is a fixed bias on the class-C amplifier, the plate voltage may be expressed when there is a signal as

$$e_b = E_{bb} - E_{pm} \cos \omega t$$

and the grid voltage by

$$e_c = -E_{cc} + E_{gm} \cos \omega t$$

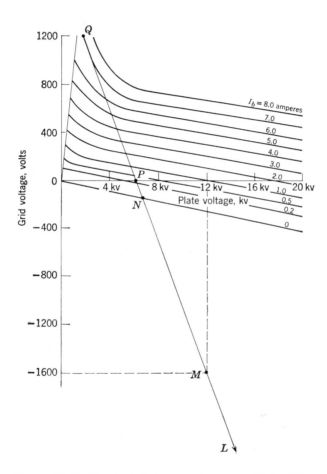

**Figure 16–7**   Constant plate-current curves with load line.

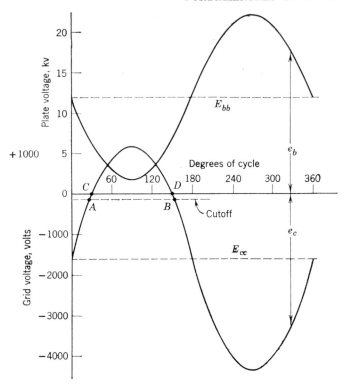

**Figure 16–8**   Grid and plate waves in a class-C amplifier.

If we solve each of these for cos $\omega t$ and equate the results, we have

$$\cos \omega t = \frac{e_c + E_{cc}}{E_{gm}} = \frac{E_{bb} - e_b}{E_{pm}}$$

If $E_{cc}$, $E_{bb}$, $E_{gm}$, and $E_{pm}$ are fixed quantities, then

$$\frac{e_c + E_{cc}}{E_{gm}} = \frac{E_{bb} - e_b}{E_{pm}}$$

will plot as a straight line on the constant-current tube characteristic ($e_b$, $e_c$ curves, Fig. 16–7).

For our example (Fig. 16–7) the following values are assigned to the class-C amplifier:

Plate-supply voltage, $E_{bb}$ 12,000 volts
Grid-bias supply, $E_{cc}$ $-1{,}600$ volts
Grid-signal drive, $\sqrt{2}\,E_g$ 2,800 volts peak
 or $E_g$ 1,980 volts rms
Plate voltage, $\sqrt{2}\,E_p$ 10,300 volts peak
 or $E_p$ 7,280 volts rms

These given values establish the operating point $M$ and one extreme point $Q$ on the load line. The other end of the load line is in the direction toward $L$ at a distance so that $ML$ equals $MQ$. We do not need to show this end of the load line because the tube is cut off and the flywheel effect of the tank circuit is maintaining the oscillation during this cutoff time. Below $N$ on the load line, there is no plate current and the tube is cut off. Above $P$ on the load line, the grid is positive and grid current flows.

The grid-voltage and the plate-voltage signals are taken from this load line for a sinusoidal signal and are plotted in Fig. 16–8. Plate current flows between $A$ and $B$ for a total of 64° out of the full cycle of 360°. There is a grid-current flow between $C$ and $D$ which is 58° of the full cycle. During the rest of the cycle, the tube is cut off.

## Section 16–4 Plate-Circuit Analysis

From the load line of Fig. 16–7 sufficient data are taken in the region of plate-current flow (Table I) to develop a detailed graph.

TABLE I

| $i_b$ | $e_b$ | $e_p$ | $\sin\theta$ | $\theta$ | $\theta$ | $e_b i_b$ |
|---|---|---|---|---|---|---|
| 0 | 6600 | 5,400 | 0.524 | 31.5 | 148.5 | 0 |
| 0.2 | 6050 | 5,950 | 0.577 | 35.4 | 144.6 | 1,210 |
| 0.5 | 5950 | 6,050 | 0.587 | 36.0 | 144.0 | 2,975 |
| 1 | 5600 | 6,400 | 0.621 | 38.5 | 141.5 | 5,600 |
| 2 | 5200 | 6,800 | 0.660 | 41.3 | 138.7 | 10,400 |
| 3 | 4850 | 7,150 | 0.700 | 44.5 | 135.5 | 14,550 |
| 4 | 4500 | 7,500 | 0.728 | 46.6 | 133.4 | 18,000 |
| 5 | 4050 | 7,950 | 0.771 | 50.5 | 129.5 | 20,250 |
| 6 | 3600 | 8,400 | 0.815 | 54.5 | 125.5 | 21,600 |
| 7 | 2400 | 9,600 | 0.931 | 68.5 | 111.5 | 16,800 |
| 7 | 1700 | 10,300 | 1.000 | 90 | 90 | 11,900 |

Steps of current are taken at even intervals. The corresponding values of instantaneous plate voltage $e_b$ are read from the load line, and the values of $e_p$ are determined by substituting in

$$e_p = E_{bb} - e_b = 12,000 - e_b$$

The ratio of the value of $e_p$ at any point to its peak value, 10,300 volts, gives the value of the sine of the angle. The product of $e_b$ and $i_b$ gives the instantaneous plate dissipation. This detailed region is plotted in Fig. 16–9.

The area under the curve of the plate current is determined by counting squares. Dividing this area by the *full length* of 360° gives the average value of the plate current $I_b$. From the data used in this example $I_b$ is 1.7 amperes. Using the same procedure for the curve of the plate dissipation $p$ we find

$$P_{pl} = 4.68 \text{ kw}$$

The total input power from the plate power supply is

$$P_{in} = E_{bb}I_b = 12,000 \times 1.7$$
$$= 20,400 \text{ watts}$$
$$= 20.4 \text{ kw}$$

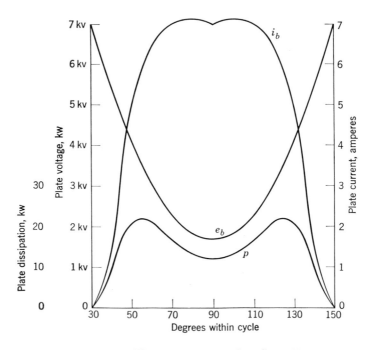

**Figure 16–9** Plate analysis of a class-C amplifier.

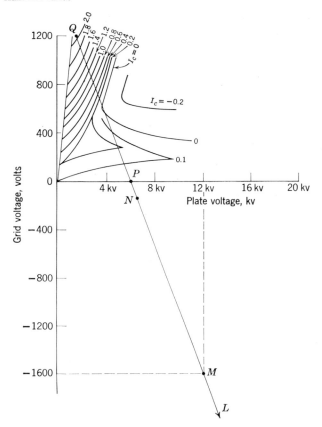

**Figure 16–10** Constant grid-current curves with load line.

The a-c power output developed in the plate tank is

$$P_{\text{out}} = P_{\text{in}} - P_{\text{pl}}$$

$$= 20.40 - 4.68 = 15.72 \text{ kw}$$

Since the rms load voltage was given as 7280 volts, the rms plate current is

$$I_p = \frac{P_{\text{out}}}{E_p} = \frac{15,720}{7280} = 2.16 \text{ amperes}$$

The a-c load impedance of the tank circuit is

$$Z_L = \frac{E_p}{I_p} = \frac{7280}{2.16} = 3370 \text{ ohms}$$

The plate efficiency is

$$\eta_{pl} = \frac{P_{out}}{P_{in}} = \frac{15.72}{20.40} = 0.771 = 77.1\%$$

## Section 16–5   Grid-Circuit Analysis

The constant-current characteristic shows not only lines of constant plate currents but also lines of the constant values of the grid current. For this tube and for the set of operating conditions given in Section 16–3, the load line is shown on the grid family in Fig. 16–10. For even increments of grid current, corresponding values of grid voltage are taken from this load line. The values of the grid signal $e_g$ are found from

$$e_g = -E_{cc} + e_c = -1600 + e_c$$

Using the peak value of grid signal of 2800 volts, the value of the sine of the angle is $e_g/2800$. The product of $e_c$ and $i_c$ gives the instantaneous grid dissipation, Table II.

TABLE II

| $i_c$ | $e_c$ | $e_g$ | $\sin \theta$ | $\theta$ | $\theta$ | $e_c i_c$ |
|---|---|---|---|---|---|---|
| 0 | 0 | 1600 | 0.571 | 34.9 | 145.1 | 0 |
| 0.1 | +120 | 1720 | 0.615 | 38.0 | 143.0 | 12 |
| 0.2 | +290 | 1890 | 0.675 | 42.5 | 137.5 | 58 |
| 0.1 | +420 | 2040 | 0.729 | 46.6 | 133.3 | 42 |
| 0 | +560 | 2160 | 0.771 | 50.5 | 129.5 | 0 |
| 0 | +620 | 2220 | 0.793 | 51.4 | 127.6 | 0 |
| 0.4 | +680 | 2280 | 0.815 | 54.5 | 125.5 | 272 |
| 0.6 | +760 | 2360 | 0.844 | 57.5 | 122.5 | 456 |
| 0.8 | +820 | 2420 | 0.865 | 60.0 | 120.0 | 656 |
| 1.0 | +860 | 2460 | 0.879 | 61.5 | 118.5 | 860 |
| 1.2 | +920 | 2520 | 0.900 | 64.0 | 116.0 | 1100 |
| 1.4 | +960 | 2560 | 0.915 | 66.1 | 113.9 | 1340 |
| 1.6 | +1040 | 2640 | 0.944 | 70.8 | 109.2 | 1660 |
| 1.8 | +1110 | 2710 | 0.967 | 75.0 | 105.0 | 2000 |
| 2.0 | +1180 | 2780 | 0.988 | 81.0 | 99.0 | 2360 |
| 2.1 | +1200 | 2800 | 1.000 | 90 | 90 | 2520 |

This information is plotted to a time scale in Fig. 16–11. The areas of the grid-current curve and the grid-dissipation curve are determined by the method of counting squares; by dividing these

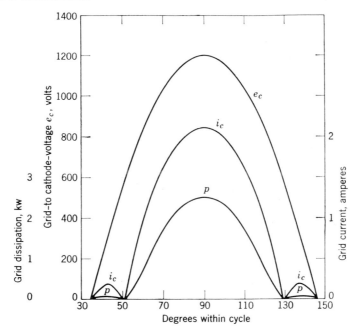

**Figure 16-11** Grid analysis of a class-C amplifier.

areas by the length of the full 360° cycle, we obtain

Average grid current, $I_c$     0.312 ampere

Average grid dissipation, $P_g$     321 watts

This grid current is opposed to the direction of normal current direction through the bias battery and thus represents a charging effect on the bias battery. In other words, power is delivered to the bias battery and not taken from the bias battery. This energy amounts to

$$E_{cc}I_c = 1600 \times 0.312 = 495 \text{ watts}$$

These two grid powers represent a total of 321 + 495 or 816 watts. The output power of the driving or preceding stage must therefore be 816 watts plus the heating loss in its own tank circuit. The alternating grid current in the tube is

$$I_g = \frac{P_g}{E_g} = \frac{816}{1980} = 0.412 \text{ ampere}$$

The a-c grid impedance of the tube is

$$Z_g = \frac{E_g}{I_g} = \frac{1980}{0.412} = 4800 \text{ ohms}$$

The power gain of this class-C amplifier is

$$A_p = \frac{P_{out}}{P_g} = \frac{15,720}{816} = 19.2 \text{ or } +12.8 \text{ db}$$

### Section 16–6   Summary and Adjustment

The class-C amplifier, because of the short duration of the plate-current flow, is not suited for audio applications without producing extreme distortion.   It is used for radio-frequency applications where a fixed-signal level is available and a fixed output level is required. Reference to Figs. 16–7, 16–8, and 16–10 shows that a small change in the location of point $Q$ which is the end of the load line can radically affect the over-all results.   Among other factors, the limitations that must be closely observed in a tube used as a class-C amplifier are the peak plate current, the peak grid current, the maximum allowable plate dissipation, and the maximum allowable grid dissipation. This assumes that the voltages used for the plate supply and for the grid supply are suitable values which do not exceed the ratings of the tube.   The variables which are normally available for the purposes of tuning and adjustment are:

1. The plate-tank tuning capacitance,
2. The grid-tank tuning capacitance,
3. A variable grid drive, and
4. A variable-output load coupling.

Two meters are needed for adjusting the class-C amplifier of Fig. 16–12.   Both meters are d-c movements.   One meter reads the plate current, and the other reads the grid current.   When the plate tank is properly tuned, its losses are at a minimum, and the direct plate-current meter indicates a minimum value.   When the grid tank is properly tuned, it delivers the largest signal to the grid, and the direct grid-current meter reads a maximum value.   When these two adjustments are made, if it is seen that the tube does not deliver sufficient power, the grid drive is increased.   If an increase in grid drive to the point of maximum allowable grid dissipation fails to produce the rated

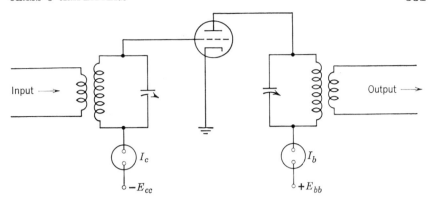

**Figure 16–12**   Class-C amplifier tuning.

or desired output power, the next step is to increase the output coupling into the load. It is quite possible that optimum conditions may be obtained only by making an adjustment in the fixed value of the grid bias $-E_{cc}$. At each step in the adjustment of the class-C amplifier, the grid tank and the plate tank must be carefully retuned to maintain resonance.

### Section 16–7   Harmonic Operation

If the plate tank is set to a multiple of the frequency of the grid drive, the class-C amplifier is termed a *harmonic generator* or a *frequency multiplier*. Figure 16–13 shows the plate wave of a frequency doubler superimposed on the curves for a straight single-frequency class-C amplifier. In both cases, the duration of the plate-current flow $AB$ and of the grid current flow $CD$ are the same. However, the corresponding value of the second-harmonic plate voltage, curve $y$, during current flow is much higher than for the plate-voltage wave at fundamental frequency operation, curve $x$. This also produces much larger values of instantaneous plate currents and grid currents. Correspondingly, the curves for the grid dissipation and for the plate dissipation are much higher than the curves for the dissipation at the operation at the fundamental frequency. In order to keep the plate circuit and the grid circuit at or below the rated dissipation values, it is necessary to reduce materially the value of the grid drive. Thus, in frequency-multiplying operations, the a-c power output of the tube is lowered considerably. In commercial practice, in order to obtain the greatest over-all efficiency, frequency multiplying is done at

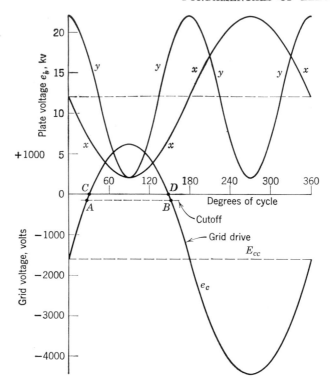

**Figure 16–13**    Harmonic operation of a class-C amplifier.

low-power levels, and the high-power stages are reserved for amplification at one frequency.

### Section 16–8    Neutralizing Circuits

In Section 13–4, we developed the Miller effect in detail. In a class-C amplifier, the normal tuning procedure allows the plate load to swing from inductive to capacitive to resistive values freely. We cannot permit the reaction produced by the Miller effect of a changing load impedance to affect adversely the tuning procedure. The process of making the amplifier independent of the Miller effect is termed *neutralization*. The use of tetrodes and pentodes avoids the necessity of neutralization in many cases. However, neutralization is necessary when triodes are used as a conventional radio-frequency amplifier.

Energy is fed back from the plate to the grid within the tube through

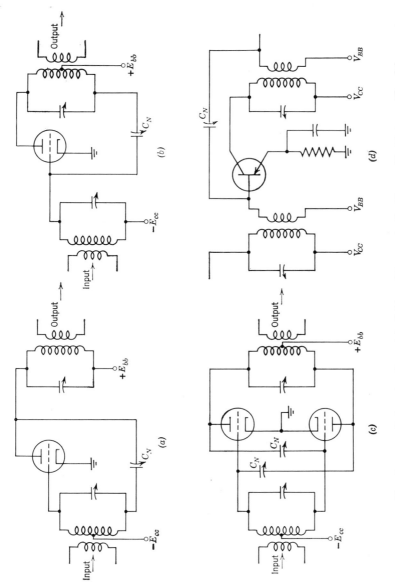

**Figure 16-14** Simple neutralizing circuits. (a) Grid or Rice neutralization. (b) Plate or Hazeltine neutralization. (c) Push–pull or cross neutralization. (d) Neutralized transistor circuit.

the grid-to-plate capacitance. In a neutralizing circuit, energy is fed from the plate back into the grid through a circuit parallel to the grid-to-plate capacitance. The energy which is fed back through this external circuit is 180° out of phase to produce a net value of zero by cancelation. The 180° phase difference is obtained by tapping either the grid coil, (Fig. 16–14a) or the plate coil (Fig. 16–14b). When the tap on the coil is exactly at the center, the value of the neutralizing capacitance $C_N$ equals the value of the grid-to-plate capacitance. In a push–pull circuit (Fig. 16–14c), the neutralization is effectively a combination of the two basic methods. In the transistor circuit (Fig. 16–14d), the required 180° phase shift in voltage is obtained by using the voltage from the secondary of the transformer in the collector.

The first step in the procedure to neutralize an amplifier circuit is to remove the plate-supply voltage and the screen-supply voltage if the circuit uses a tetrode. The grid-driving voltage is left on, and the filament supply is left on. When the neutralization is correctly established by a proper setting of the neutralizing capacitor $C_N$, there should be no effect on the reading of the direct grid current meter when the plate tank tuning is varied. If this procedure is not sufficiently sensitive for a critical adjustment, a different approach is used. There should be no energy transferred into the plate-tank circuit. A neon lamp, a wave meter, a grid dip meter, or even a radio receiver may be used to detect energy in the plate tank. The grid tank is adjusted to resonance by setting its tuning for a maximum energy in the plate-tank circuit. The plate tank is adjusted to set this energy at a maximum. Now the neutralizing capacitor $C_N$ is adjusted to reduce this energy to zero. It may be necessary to run through this cycle of the three steps of tuning several times to bring this energy exactly to zero.

When the sufficient degree of neutralization is obtained, the plate (and screen) direct supply voltages are turned back on. It is very important not to disturb any of the tuning adjustments, particularly the setting of $C_N$, while other class-C adjustments are made.

Usually there is no need to neutralize a circuit using a tetrode. Also, there is no need to neutralize a stage in which frequency multiplication takes place because the energies in the two tank circuits are at different frequencies and normally do not interfere with each other.

**. . . . Suggested References for Further Study**

1. L. B. Arguimbau, *Vacuum-Tube Circuits and Transistors*, Chapter 11, John Wiley & Sons, New York, 1956.

2. S. Seely, *Electron-Tube Circuits*, Chapter 11, McGraw-Hill Book Co., New York, 1950.

. . . . QUESTIONS

1. Define or explain each of the following terms: (a) automatic bias, (b) damping factor, (c) flywheel effect, (d) frequency multiplication, (e) grid dip meter, (f) driving power, (g) grid dissipation, (h) harmonic operation, (i) wave meter, (j) angle of plate-current flow.

2. Compare grid-leak bias with shunt rectification.

3. What different circuit arrangements can be used for grid-leak bias?

4. What is the principle of frequency multiplication?

5. How does the grid drive affect the angle of plate-current flow?

6. How is plate dissipation obtained in the plate analysis?

7. How is average current obtained in the plate analysis?

8. How is power output obtained in the plate analysis?

9. Why is the product of $E_{cc}I_c$ considered a driving power and not a power *from* a battery.

10. Carefully explain the adjustments of the grid and plate tanks for optimum operation.

11. Why is harmonic operation necessary?

12. Why is operation as a frequency multiplier less efficient than straight single-frequency operation?

13. What is the theoretical maximum class-C efficiency? What are typical values?

14. Name three methods of neutralization.

15. Why is neutralization required?

16. Why is neutralization not required with a tetrode amplifier?

17. Why is neutralization not required in a frequency multiplier?

18. Describe the circuit adjustments necessary to complete the process of neutralization.

19. Describe the process which combines tuning *and* neutralizing.

. . . . PROBLEMS

1. A class-C amplifier operates under the following conditions: $E_{bb} = 13$ kv, $E_{cc} = -1500$ volts, $E_{p,\max} = 11,800$ volts, $E_{g,\max} = 1900$ volts. Using the curves shown in Fig. 16–7 and Fig. 16–10, determine the grid dissipation, the plate dissipation, the output power, the load impedance, and the power gain.

2. Solve problem 1 for the following conditions: $E_{bb} = 8$ kv, $E_{cc} = -1200$ volts, $E_{p,\max} = 7000$ volts, and $E_{g,\max} = 2000$ volts.

3. Redraw the triode-connected plate characteristic for the 6L6 to form constant-current curves. Use a supply voltage of 250 volts and a fixed bias of $-80$ volts. Select a point equivalent to $a$ in Fig. 16–7 and determine if, for these conditions, the safe plate dissipation is exceeded. Draw the circuit that corresponds to these conditions and label all currents and voltages. Neglect the grid-driving power.

# Feedback

$\bullet \quad \bullet \quad \bullet \quad \bullet \quad \bullet \quad \bullet \quad \bullet \quad \bullet \quad \bullet \quad \bullet \quad \bullet \quad \bullet \quad \bullet \quad \bullet \quad \bullet \quad \bullet \quad \bullet \quad \bullet$ CHAPTER **17**

The basic principles of feedback lead to the development of a general formula (Section 17–1). Both positive feedback (Section 17–2) and negative feedback (Section 17–3) are considered along with the advantages and disadvantages of the feedback circuit. Typical basic negative-feedback circuits are discussed (Section 17–4). The importance of negative current feedback warrants specific consideration (Section 17–5) along with the cathode-follower circuit (Section 17–6). Feedback in transistor circuits is discussed (Section 17–7). To prevent an undesired interaction between different circuits within the same piece of equipment, decoupling circuits (Section 17–8) are required. A special application of negative feedback is the electronic voltage regulator used in power supplies (Section 17–9).

## Section 17–1 The Fundamental Feedback Equation

For an ordinary amplifier (Fig. 17–1) the voltage gain is the output voltage divided by the input signal voltage. In this conventional amplifier, the signal $E_s$ is amplified by the factor of $A_e$ to the value $E_o$ of output voltage. If a feedback loop is added to this amplifier (Fig. 17–2), a fractional part $\beta$ of the output voltage is fed back into the input. The total input signal is the original signal plus the feedback voltage. The amplifier amplifies this total signal by the same

**Figure 17–1** Block diagram of amplifier without feedback.

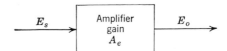

387

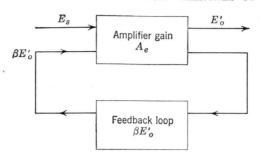

**Figure 17–2**   Block diagram of amplifier with feedback.

factor $A_e$ as in Fig. 17–1, producing the output voltage $E'_o$.   We note that the signal $E_s$ is the same in each case, but that the output voltages $E_o$ and $E'_o$ are different.   The term $\beta$ is the *feedback*, and it is used as a decimal value in the equations, but, in a discussion, $\beta$ is considered to be a percentage.   For instance, 15% feedback is 0.15 when used in calculations.

The voltage fed from the output back into the input is $\beta E'_o$.   The total input voltage to the amplifier is $E_s + \beta E'_o$.   Since the input voltage times the gain is the output voltage, we may write

$$(E_s + \beta E'_o)A_e = E'_o$$

Expanding gives

$$E_s A_e + \beta A_e E'_o = E'_o$$

Rearranging, we have

$$E_s A_e = E'_o - \beta A_e E'_o = E'_o(1 - \beta A_e)$$

Then

$$\frac{A_e}{1 - \beta A_e} = \frac{E'_o}{E_s}$$

But $E'_o/E_s$ is the net gain of the circuit with feedback.   Calling this gain $A'_e$, we have

$$A'_e = \frac{A_e}{1 - \beta A_e} \tag{17–1}$$

where $A_e$ is the amplifier gain without feedback, $\beta$ is the feedback, and $A'_e$ is the amplifier gain with feedback.   The term $\beta A_e$ is defined as the *feedback factor*.

### Section 17–2   Positive Feedback

In the analysis of the block diagram, we used $(E_s + \beta E'_o)$ as the total input voltage.   Purposely, no reference was made to the algebraic sign of $\beta$. If $\beta$ is taken as a positive number, the feedback voltage is in phase with and adds to the incoming signal. This circuit condition is termed *positive feedback*.

An understanding of positive feedback may be obtained from a simple numerical example. Let us assume that an amplifier has a gain of 10 without feedback and substitute various values, Table I, of positive feedback into the general equation:

$$A'_e = \frac{A_e}{1 - \beta A_e} = \frac{10}{1 - 10\beta}$$

TABLE I

| $\beta$ | $\beta A_e$ | $1 - \beta A_e$ | $A'_e$ |
|---------|-------------|-----------------|--------|
| 0 | 0 | 1 | 10 |
| 2% | 0.20 | 0.80 | 12.5 |
| 4% | 0.40 | 0.60 | 16.7 |
| 6% | 0.60 | 0.40 | 25.0 |
| 8% | 0.80 | 0.20 | 50.0 |
| 9% | 0.90 | 0.10 | 100.0 |
| 9.9% | 0.99 | 0.01 | 1000 |
| 9.99% | 0.999 | 0.001 | 10,000 |
| 9.999% | 0.9999 | 0.0001 | 100,000 |
| 10% | 1.00 | 0 | $\infty$ |

The immediate conclusion that can be drawn from the results of this table is that positive feedback increases the gain of an amplifier. For this reason, positive feedback is often called *regenerative* feedback. We will show in the next section of this chapter that positive feedback increases the distortion content of the output of an amplifier. Thus, the advantage of an increased gain must be carefully weighed against the disadvantage of an increased distortion level. As a result, we do not find positive feedback used to any great extent in amplifier design. In one application in which the feedback circuit is frequency-selective, a positive feedback is used as either a bass or a treble boost.

As the feedback factor $\beta A_e$ approaches unity, we note from the table that the gain becomes infinite. Mathematically the equation shows that the gain is infinite, but electrically this does not happen. What does happen is that the circuit *oscillates*. Since the gain is infinite, the oscillator supplies its own signal for self-sustained operation. We now can state the very important and necessary conditions that must exist if a circuit is to oscillate:

1. The feedback must be positive, and
2. The feedback factor must be +1.

Alternatively, these conditions may be expressed in this form:

> In order to have an oscillator, the feedback must be positive and must be strong enough to sustain the oscillation.

H. Nyquist, in his famous paper, "Regeneration Theory," (*Bell System Technical Journal*, January 1932), originated and extended this theory at length. Both $A_e$ and $\beta$ are complex numbers having magnitude and phase angle. Then, the feedback factor $\beta A_e$ has both magnitude and phase angle. Nyquist's conditions for oscillation require that $\beta A_e$ contain the point $(1 + j0)$. Thus, it is possible for an amplifier circuit to be stable at one frequency and to oscillate at another. These principles form the basic theory for the operation of the feedback oscillators discussed in Chapter 18. A direct application of positive feedback is the regenerative receiver (Section 24–2).

### Section 17–3   Negative Feedback

With negative feedback, the voltage $\beta E'_o$ which is fed from the output back to the input is 180° out of phase with the input. The algebraic sign of $\beta$ for negative feedback is minus when used in the feedback equations. To illustrate negative feedback, we consider the effect of negative feedback on the amplifier which was used to illustrate positive feedback in Section 17–2. The amplifier without feedback has a gain of 10, and, substituting the minus sign for $\beta$ in the feedback equation, we have

$$A'_e = \frac{A_e}{1 - \beta A_e} = \frac{10}{1 + 10\beta}$$

TABLE II

| $\beta$ | $\beta A_e$ | $1 - \beta A_e$ | $A'_e$ |
|---------|-------------|-----------------|--------|
| 0       | 0           | 1               | 10     |
| $-1\%$  | $-0.10$     | 1.10            | 9.09   |
| $-2\%$  | $-0.20$     | 1.20            | 8.32   |
| $-10\%$ | $-1.00$     | 2.00            | 5.00   |
| $-30\%$ | $-3.00$     | 4.00            | 2.50   |
| $-40\%$ | $-4.00$     | 5.00            | 2.00   |
| $-70\%$ | $-7.00$     | 8.00            | 1.25   |
| $-100\%$| $-10.00$    | 11.00           | 0.909  |

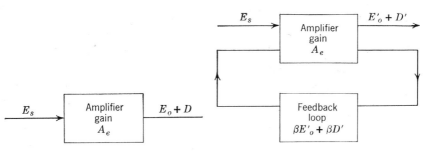

**Figure  17–3**  Block  diagram  of  amplifier with distortion.

**Figure 17–4**  Block diagram of amplifier with feedback and distortion.

The results of Table II show that negative feedback reduces the over-all gain of an amplifier.  Since negative feedback reduces the gain, it is often called *degenerative* feedback.

Lest any misconceptions of the magnitude of the effect of a negative feedback arise, let us determine the gain under conditions of a negative feedback of 1% for an amplifier that has a gain of 400 without feedback:

$$A'_e = \frac{A_e}{1 - \beta A_e}$$

$$= \frac{400}{1 + 0.01 \times 400} = \frac{400}{1 + 4} = \frac{400}{5} = 80$$

A 1% negative feedback on this amplifier reduces the gain by a factor of five.  A 1% feedback on the amplifier with a gain of 10 used in the table reduced the gain from 10 to 9.09.

In Fig. 17–3, a signal is amplified by the factor $A_e$.  At the same time, the amplifier creates a distortion $D$ in the output.  With a feedback loop (Fig. 17–4) not only is the output fed back into the input, but also the fractional part of the distortion which is $\beta D'$ appears in the input.  The total distortion in the output $D'$ must comprise not only the amplified value of $\beta D'$ but also the original distortion of $E_s$ which is produced by the amplifier.  The input signal is so arranged that $E_o$ equals $E'_o$.  This may be expressed as

$$D' = D + (\beta D') A_e$$

$$D' - \beta A_e D' = D$$

$$(1 - \beta A_e) D' = D$$

$$D' = \frac{D}{1 - \beta A_e} \tag{17–2}$$

When the feedback is positive, the distortion with feedback becomes greater than the distortion without feedback. When the feedback is negative, $D'$ is less than $D$. In other words, regenerative feedback increases distortion whereas degenerative feedback reduces distortion in the same proportion that it reduces gain.

As an example, taking the amplifier having a gain of 10 without feedback, assume that the inherent distortion of the amplifier is 20%. With a 10% feedback, the gain is 5, and the distortion is 10%. With a 40% negative feedback, the gain is 2, and the distortion is 4%. If two amplifiers are connected in cascade, one with the 10% feedback and the other with a 40% feedback, the over-all gain is the product of the two gains which is 5 × 2 or 10. The over-all distortion is approximately

$$1.10 \times 1.04 - 1 = 0.144 \text{ or } 14.4\%$$

If we take two amplifiers, each with a gain of 10 without feedback and with a distortion of 20%, when these amplifiers are in cascade, we have similarly:

$$\text{Over-all gain } A_e = 10 \times 10 = 100$$

$$\text{Over-all distortion } D = 1.20 \times 1.20 - 1 = 0.44 \text{ or } 44\%$$

When 9% negative feedback is used over both stages, the gain reduction and distortion reduction factors $(1 - \beta A_e)$ are both 10. Now the over-all gain is 10, and the over-all distortion is 4.4%. By this example, we can show that feedback over a number of stages, instead of feedback on each individual stage alone, produces the same gain but produces a much lower distortion. It is standard practice to use feedback in a single loop over several stages rather than feedback on each stage.

In the feedback formula

$$A'_e = \frac{A_e}{1 - \beta A_e}$$

If we divide the numerator and denominator by $A_e$, we find

$$A'_e = \frac{A_e/A_e}{1/A_e - \beta A_e/A_e} = \frac{1}{1/A_e - \beta}$$

When the value of the feedback $\beta$ is large compared to $1/A_e$ (i.e., when a heavy negative feedback is used on a high-gain amplifier), the term $1/A_e$ may be neglected, and

$$A'_e = -\frac{1}{\beta} \qquad (17\text{--}3)$$

We consider only negative feedback in this expression as we have shown that positive feedback would cause this circuit to oscillate. When a 10% negative-feedback loop is applied to an amplifier with a gain of 4000, the gain with feedback is 1/0.1 or 10. This value of gain is independent of tube variations, component changes (except the feedback loop), and power-supply variations. The over-all gain with feedback is determined by the feedback network alone provided the feedback does not depend upon the parameters of the tube. This circuit is very important in its application as a *decade amplifier* used in servo amplifiers, in computers, and as instrument multipliers.

By a similar process of analysis, it may be shown that the application of negative feedback, while reducing the gain of an amplifier, not only reduces distortion but also improves the frequency response and the signal-to-noise ratio. It should be remembered that this improvement is confined to the circuit within the feedback loop. Also, amplifiers using negative feedback are less dependent on power-supply voltage variations, tube characteristics, and component changes.

When the frequency response of an amplifier is examined, it is noted that, although the gain is reduced, the response is flatter and broader. However, when high values of feedback are used, the effect of the phase shifts at the low- and high-frequency ends may tend to make the feedback regenerative (Fig. 17–5).

As an example to show this effect, in the Williamson-type high-fidelity amplifier circuit (Fig. 15–19) a negative feedback loop is con-

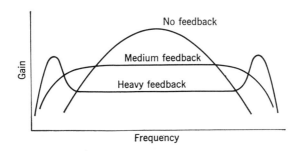

**Figure 17–5**   Response curves of an amplifier with different values of feedback.

nected over-all from the output back to the input. There is a tendency for the circuit to oscillate at a very high ultrasonic frequency. This oscillation absorbs power, causing the circuit to deliver a reduced output power with high distortion when used as an audio amplifier. To cure this condition, a low-pass L filter (a resistor and a mica bypass capacitor) is placed in the feedback loop. Then, feedback at this very high frequency is reduced sufficiently to prevent the circuit from oscillating.

**Section 17–4   Negative-Voltage Feedback Circuits**

In Fig. 17–6, a feedback loop, $R_2$ and $R_1$, with a blocking capacitor is added to a simple amplifier. Assume that the impedance of the signal source $R_s$ is much greater than $R_1$ and that it may be neglected. The output voltage appears across the feedback network of $R_1$ and $R_2$. The capacitor $C$ merely blocks the direct voltage on the plate from the grid. The feedback resistors $R_1$ and $R_2$ act as a voltage divider and the fraction $\beta$ of the output voltage which appears in the grid circuit is

$$\beta = \frac{R_1}{R_1 + R_2}$$

The feedback is negative because the plate voltage is 180° out of phase with the grid signal. If the resistance of the source $R_s$ were to be considered, the parallel combination of $R_s$ and $R_1$ would be used as $R_1$ in the equation. Figure 17–7 shows another circuit arrangement for voltage feedback, but the circuit has the disadvantage of requiring

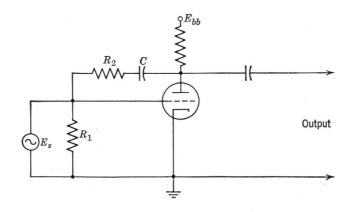

**Figure 17–6**   Simple voltage feedback.

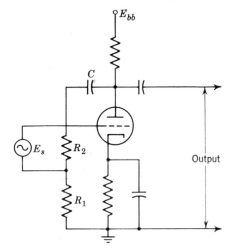

**Figure 17–7** Alternate method of voltage feedback.

a *floating* signal which is not connected to ground or to a common return. Figure 17–8 shows the application of voltage feedback to a multistage amplifier.

In the block diagram showing the feedback loop (Fig. 17–2) the actual amplifier input impedance is $Z_{in}$ and is equal to

$$Z_{in} = \frac{E'_o / A_e}{I_s} = \frac{E'_o}{A_e I_s}$$

The source voltage $E_s$ is greater than the actual amplifier input by

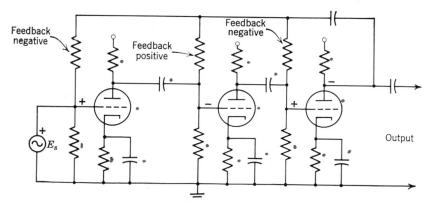

**Figure 17–8** Feedback in a multistage amplifier.

the amount of the feedback voltage $\beta E'_o$ and may be written

$$E_s = \frac{E'_o}{A_e} - \beta E'_o$$

The negative sign for $\beta$ is retained in accordance with the original sign convention used for the general feedback equation. The input impedance with feedback is $Z'_{in}$ and is

$$Z'_{in} = \frac{E'_o/A_e - \beta E'_o}{I_s}$$

$$Z'_{in} = \frac{E'_o - \beta A_e E'_o}{A_e I_s}$$

$$Z'_{in} = \frac{E'_o}{A_e I_s} - \beta A_e \frac{E'_o}{A_e I_s}$$

but

$$\frac{E'_o}{A_e I_s} = Z_{in}$$

Then

$$Z'_{in} = Z_{in}(1 - \beta A_e) \qquad (17\text{--}4)$$

The significance of Eq. 17–4 is that the input impedance to an amplifier increases with negative feedback in the same amount that the gain is reduced. This is very important in transistor circuits since one of the severe problems in transistor-amplifier design is the inherent low input impedance to the stage.

Figure 17–9a is the equivalent circuit of the amplifier output by using Thévenin's theorem. The impedance $Z_o$ is the conventional output impedance of the amplifier itself without feedback. When the signal $E_s$ is turned off and a voltage $E'_o$ is applied to the circuit to measure the back impedance (Fig. 17–9b), the internal voltage of the

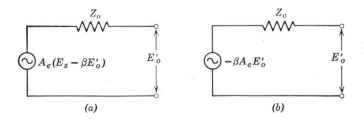

(a)                                   (b)

**Figure 17–9**  Equivalent output circuit by Thévenin's theorem.   (a) With input signal.   (b) Without input signal.

equivalent circuit is not zero but it is $-\beta A_e E'_o$. This situation results because there is an input voltage produced by $E'_o$ through the feedback loop. By the voltage equation, the current $I'_L$ in $Z_o$ is

$$I'_L = \frac{E'_o - \beta A_e E'_o}{Z_o}$$

$$I'_L = \frac{E'_o (1 - \beta A_e)}{Z_o}$$

Solving for $E'_o/I'_L$ which is $Z'_o$, the effective output impedance with feedback, we have

$$\frac{E'_o}{I'_L} = Z'_o = \frac{Z_o}{1 - \beta A_e} \tag{17-5}$$

The significance of Eq. 17–5 is that the (internal) output impedance of an amplifier with negative feedback is reduced directly as the gain and the distortion are reduced. One advantage of a reduction in output impedance is that the output voltage has less regulation and is more nearly constant when the external load-impedance changes. In transistor circuits, the combined effect of an increased input impedance and a decreased output impedance simplifies the matching problem with $RC$ coupling.

The general voltage feedback equation (Eq. 17–1) is

$$A'_e = \frac{A_e}{1 - \beta A_e}$$

The basic gain equation for an amplifier (Eq. 10–2b) is

$$A_e = \frac{\mu Z_L}{r_p + Z_L}$$

Substituting this in the general feedback equation, we have

$$A'_e = \frac{\mu Z_L/(r_p + Z_L)}{1 - \beta \dfrac{\mu Z_L}{r_p + Z_L}}$$

Cross-multiplying, we have

$$A'_e = \frac{\mu Z_L}{r_p + Z_L - \beta \mu Z_L}$$

Rearranging the terms gives

$$A'_e = \frac{\mu Z_L}{r_p + (1 - \mu\beta)Z_L}$$

Dividing each term in the numerator and denominator by $(1 - \mu\beta)$, we find

$$A'_e = \frac{\left(\dfrac{\mu}{1 - \mu\beta}\right) Z_L}{r_p/(1 - \mu\beta) + Z_L}$$

This expression is in the same form as the basic gain equation (Eq. 10–2b), and we may write

$$A'_e = \frac{\mu' Z_L}{r'_p + Z_L} \tag{17–6a}$$

and

$$\mu' = \frac{\mu}{1 - \mu\beta} \tag{17–6b}$$

and

$$r'_p = \frac{r_p}{1 - \mu\beta} \tag{17–6c}$$

In this form, we may interpret the voltage feedback as reducing both the amplification factor and the internal a-c plate resistance of the tube. This is another approach in showing that, in an amplifier with feedback, the internal impedance is reduced at the expense of the gain.

### Section 17–5   Current Feedback

If a resistance $R_3$ which is not used to develop output voltage, is inserted in series with the load (Fig. 17–10), the equivalent circuit is:

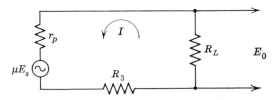

Then the loop current is

$$I = \frac{\mu E_s}{r_p + R_3 + R_L}$$

Since

$$E_o = I R_L$$

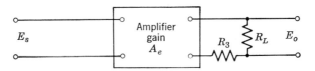

**Figure 17–10**   Block diagram of a current feedback circuit as an amplifier without feedback.

Substituting gives
$$E_o = \frac{\mu E_s R_L}{r_p + R_3 + R_L}$$

Divide both sides by $E_s$:

$$\frac{E_o}{E_s} = A_e = \frac{\mu R_L}{r_p + R_3 + R_L}$$

When $R_3$ is used as a current feedback which is defined as the case where the voltage fed back is proportional to the load current, the block diagram is modified to Fig. 17–11.   The new gain $A'_e$ is

$$A'_e = \frac{E'_o}{E'_s} = \frac{E'_o}{E_i + I'R_3}$$

but
$$I' = \frac{E'_o}{R_L}$$

Substituting gives

$$A'_e = \frac{E'_o}{E_i + (R_3/R_L)E'_o} = \frac{1}{E_i/E'_o + R_3/R_L}$$

but $E'_o/E_i$ must be the voltage gain without feedback which was evaluated from Fig. 17–10 as

$$A_e = \frac{\mu R_L}{r_p + R_3 + R_L}$$

Substituting this relation, we have

$$A'_e = \frac{1}{1/A_e + R_3/R_L}$$

$$= \frac{A_e}{1 + A_e(R_3/R_L)}$$

$$= \frac{\mu R_L}{(\mu + 1)R_3 + r_p + R_L} \tag{17-7a}$$

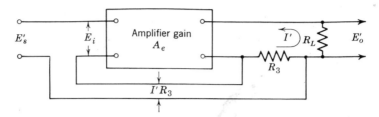

**Figure 17–11**   Block diagram of current feedback.

When $\beta$ is defined as $-R_3/R_L$, the gain equations become

$$A'_e = \frac{A_e}{1 - \beta A_e} \qquad (17–7b)$$

where $\beta = -R_3/R_L$.   This $\beta$ has the same sense in current feedback as the $\beta$ used in voltage feedback.

Harmonic reduction may be expressed in the same manner as before:

$$D' = \frac{D}{1 - \beta A_e} \qquad (17–2)$$

A very common and widely used circuit employing current feedback is shown in Fig. 17–12.   This circuit is merely a conventional amplifier which has the cathode bypass capacitor omitted.   In this circuit, the feedback voltage is developed across $R_K$.

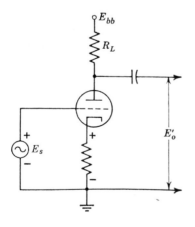

**Figure 17–12**   Circuit using current feedback.

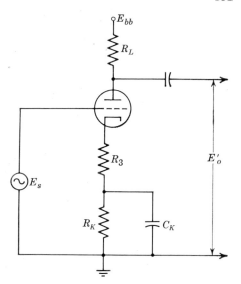

**Figure   17–13**   Current   feedback.

As an example, assume that for a triode $R_L$ is 100,000 ohms, $r_p$ is 20,000, $\mu$ is 20, and $R_K$ is 2000 ohms.   Then, from Eq. 17–7a,

$$A'_e = \frac{\mu R_L}{(\mu + 1)R_K + r_p + R_L}$$

$$= \frac{20 \times 100,000}{(20 + 1)2000 + 20,000 + 100,000}$$

$$= 12.35$$

An alternative circuit arrangement which accomplishes this current feedback is shown in Fig. 17–13.   In this circuit, the feedback $\beta$ is not as large as in Fig. 17–12, but we do have a d-c bias developed across the cathode resistor $R_K$, which is properly bypassed by $C_K$.

## Section 17–6   The Cathode Follower

A cathode follower is a circuit (Fig. 17–14) in which the feedback is 100% and is negative.   If there were no feedback, the gain would be

$$A_e = \mu \frac{R_K}{r_p + R_K}$$

But, as the feedback is negative and unity,

$$A'_e = \frac{A_e}{1 - \beta A_e} = \frac{\left(\mu \dfrac{R_K}{r_p + R_K}\right)}{1 + \left(\mu \dfrac{R_K}{r_p + R_K}\right)}$$

$$= \frac{\mu R_K}{r_p + R_K + \mu R_K} = \frac{\mu R_K}{(1 + \mu) R_K + r_p}$$

This may be rearranged to either

$$A'_e = \frac{\mu}{\mu + 1} \frac{R_K}{R_K + r_p/(\mu + 1)} \tag{17-8a}$$

or

$$A'_e = \frac{R_K}{\left(\dfrac{\mu + 1}{\mu}\right) R_K + \dfrac{r_p}{\mu}} \tag{17-8b}$$

or

$$A'_e = \frac{R_K}{\left(\dfrac{\mu + 1}{\mu}\right) R_K + \dfrac{1}{g_m}} \tag{17-8c}$$

Any one of these three forms for the voltage gain is valid, but, if a pentode is employed in the circuit, the amplification factor is so much greater than unity that the equation may be written as

$$A'_e = \frac{R_K}{R_K + 1/g_m} = \frac{g_m R_K}{1 + g_m R_K} \tag{17-8d}$$

In any case, the gain of the cathode follower must be less than one.

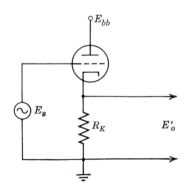

**Figure 17–14** The basic cathode follower.

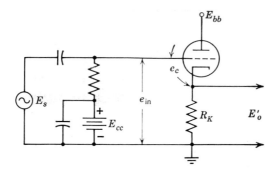

**Figure 17–15**    Voltage relations in a cathode follower.

When the form

$$A'_e = \frac{\mu}{\mu + 1} \frac{R_K}{R_K + r_p/(\mu + 1)} = \frac{E'_o}{E_s}$$

is used, then, the output voltage is

$$E'_o = \frac{\mu}{\mu + 1} E_s \frac{R_K}{R_K + r_p/(\mu + 1)}$$

From this expression, when the cathode-follower circuit is used to deliver power to a load, a maximum power transfer takes place when

$$r_p = (\mu + 1)R_K \qquad (17\text{–}8e)$$

This means that, for a particular load resistance $R_K$, a tube should be selected in which the plate resistance is of such a value as to permit a proper impedance match.

To determine a load line for a cathode follower (Fig. 17–15) it is evident that

$$E_{bb} = e_b + i_b R_K$$

If $R_K$ is assumed to be 10,000 ohms, using a 6S4 with a supply voltage of 400 volts, selection of assumed values of plate current enables the corresponding values of plate voltage to be determined by subtraction. Then the corresponding values of grid voltage $e_c$ are picked off the plate characteristics for the tube. The input voltage $e_{in}$ is obtained from

$$e_{in} = e_c + i_b R_K$$

The necessary data and calculations for the example are given in Table III.

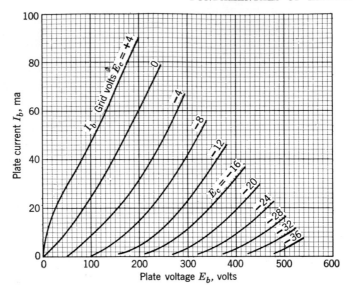

Average plate characteristics.

TABLE III

| $\dot{\imath}_b$ | $\dfrac{e'_0}{\imath_b R_k}$ | $e_b$ | $e_c$ | $e_{\text{in}}$ |
|---|---|---|---|---|
| 0 | 0 | 400 | −32 | −32 |
| 5 | 50 | 350 | −23 | +27 |
| 10 | 100 | 300 | −17 | +83 |
| 15 | 150 | 250 | −11 | +139 |
| 20 | 200 | 200 | −6 | +194 |
| 25 | 250 | 150 | −3 | +247 |
| 28 | 280 | 120 | −0.5 | +279.5 |
| 29 | 290 | 110 | 0 | +290 |
| 30 | 300 | 100 | +1 | +301 |

The results from this table are plotted as output voltage against input voltage in Fig. 17–16. This circuit can accept a very large and wide-range input signal in contrast to the conventional vacuum-tube amplifier. The optimum bias $E_{cc}$ should be located at the mid-point between cutoff (−32 volts) and grid-current flow (+290 volts) or at +129 volts. Under these conditions, this circuit can accept without a cutoff or a grid current all values of sinusoidal signal from zero to a peak value of 161 volts. A peak value of 161 volts corresponds to an rms value of 114 volts. The slope of the load line in

Fig. 17–16 determines the gain of the circuit:

$$A'_e = \frac{290 - 0}{290 - (-32)} = \frac{290}{322} = 0.900$$

In many vacuum-tube voltmeter circuits, the normal full-scale input is 5 volts rms. If this cathode-follower circuit is used as an input stage to the meter, it can withstand an overload of 114/5 or almost 23 times the rated value. Another valuable feature of the cathode follower is its ability to handle all signals from zero frequency (d-c) up. In the circuit of Fig. 17–15, the value of the grid resistance $R_g$ is independent of the value of the cathode resistance $R_K$. This property enables the cathode follower to be used as an ideal device for impedance matching in which $R_g$ can be set to match the source and $R_K$ can either match the load or even be the load itself. Another feature of the cathode-follower circuit is its high impedance which makes it very useful as a high-impedance probe for metering circuits. Because of the low output impedance, cathode followers are often used as drivers for class-AB and class-B amplifiers.

A grounded-collector transistor amplifier is the analog of the cathode-follower circuit arrangement. The analysis of this circuit was described in Section 11–3. The reason for including the analysis in Chapter 11 instead of in this chapter is that the mathematics of the development of the circuit in terms of hybrid parameters parallels the common-base and the common-emitter analysis. A load line for the common-collector amplifier would have to be developed in a manner very similar to the load line for the vacuum-tube cathode-follower circuit. The application and advantages of the common-

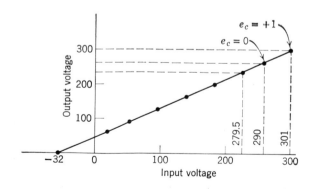

**Figure 17–16**   Dynamic-response curve for a cathode follower.

collector circuit are very similar to the uses of the cathode-follower stage. In the process of "transistorizing" circuits, the cathode follower is replaced by the grounded-collector amplifier.

### Section 17–7   Feedback in Transistor Circuits

The discussion in Section 17–1 through 17–3 on feedback is fully applicable to transistor circuits. A quantitative approach to feedback in transistor circuits is beyond the scope of this textbook. A mathematical analysis of feedback becomes very complex. The gain of a transistor amplifier is a function of both the input and the output impedances. A feedback loop on a transistor amplifier changes both the input impedance and the output impedance. It is necessary to re-evaluate the $h$ parameters of the circuit in terms of the application of the feedback loop. Accordingly, the discussion in this section is restricted to a qualitative approach to feedback.

As in the vacuum-tube amplifier, two general classifications of feedback are used. Since a transistor circuit can have both current and voltage amplification, it is preferable to use the term *shunt feedback* for the feedback loop, which corresponds to voltage feedback in the vacuum-tube circuit, and the term *series feedback* for the corresponding current feedback in the vacuum-tube circuit.

In the transistor circuit using shunt feedback (Fig. 17–17), the feedback resistance $R_f$ not only is used to establish the feedback, but it also serves to provide the proper operating bias. The feedback resistance $R_f$ acts as if it were in parallel with the load resistance $R_L$ as far as the voltage gain $A_e$ is concerned. The voltage gain decreases, not because of a feedback action, but because of this shunting effect.

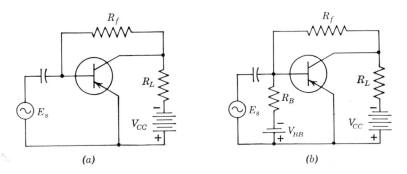

(a)                                             (b)

**Figure 17–17**   Shunt (voltage) feedback.   (a) Simple feedback.   (b) Feedback with a bias voltage divider.

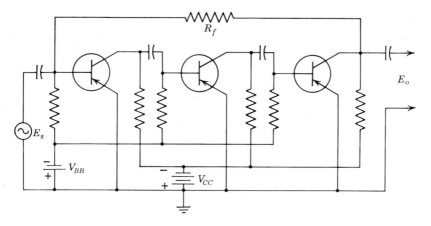

**Figure 17–18**   Multistage shunt feedback.

The current which is fed back from the collector to the base circuit is degenerative, and, as a result, the current gain $A_i$ is reduced by this feedback.   Both the input impedance $R_{\text{in}}$ and the output impedance $R_{\text{out}}$ are reduced by shunt feedback.

This circuit is often used to stabilize the operating point of a transistor circuit.   When the ambient temperature rises, the collector-current curves rise.   When the collector current rises, there is an increased voltage drop in the load resistance, $R_L$, and the direct voltage at the collector falls.   The direct bias current flow through $R_f$ decreases, and the operating point remains at a stable value on the load line.

A shunt feedback loop is often used on a multistage amplifier (Fig. 17–18).   The number of grounded-emitter stages within the loop must be an odd number in order to preserve the out-of-phase relation which

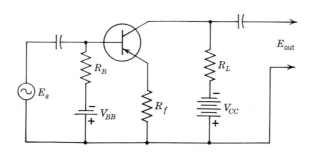

**Figure 17–19**   Series (current) feedback.

is required for negative feedback. As with the vacuum-tube circuits, one feedback loop, used over several stages, is preferable to several stages, each with an individual feedback arrangement. The required stability and frequency response is secured with less sacrifice of gain.

The action of a series feedback (Fig. 17–19) in a transistor circuit is very similar to the current feedback that is obtained by leaving the cathode resistor unbypassed. The low value of $R_f$ as compared to the magnitude of $R_L$ does not materially affect the value of the current gain $A_i$ of the circuit. The voltage drop across $R_f$ does develop a negative feedback as far as the voltage amplification $A_e$ is concerned, and the voltage gain is reduced by this feedback. With series feedback, both the input impedance $R_{in}$ and the output impedance $R_{out}$ are increased. When $R_f$ is bypassed with a capacitor, a feedback is produced as far as the d-c network is concerned, and by this action it serves as the stabilization network.

Series feedback may be applied to a multistage amplifier (Fig. 17–20). This form of feedback is less common than shunt feedback on a multistage amplifier.

In Fig. 17–21, a common-base amplifier has a series feedback developed across the feedback resistor $R$. For a positive signal, the directions of increasing currents are shown by $I_1$ and $I_2$. The current in the input circuit produces a voltage drop $V_1$, across the feedback resistor equal to $I_1R$. The collector current develops a voltage $V_2$ in this resistor equal to $I_2R$. The polarity of $V_2$ opposes $V_1$. The polarity of the voltage $V_1$ is such as to produce negative feedback, whereas $V_2$ produces a positive feedback. In the junction transistor,

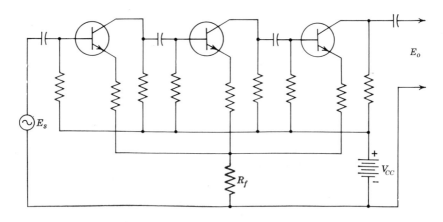

**Figure 17–20** Multistage series feedback.

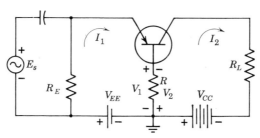

**Figure 17–21** Series feedback in a common-base amplifier.

$I_1$ must be greater than $I_2$, with the result that the net effect must produce a resultant degenerative feedback. By this reasoning, we find that a junction transistor must be stable and does not oscillate when used as an amplifier. In the point-contact transistor, $I_2$ is usually greater than $I_1$ in a circuit, and a positive feedback is produced. If this positive feedback is sufficient in magnitude, the circuit oscillates. There are three factors that control the stability of this point-contact transistor circuit. If $I_1$ is reduced sufficiently, the circuit becomes unstable. This means that there is a critical value for $R_E$ (or $R_g$) above which the circuit oscillates. Increasing the value of $R$ increases the positive feedback by increasing $(V_1 - V_2)$. When $R$ is in excess of a certain value, the circuit oscillates. When $R_L$ is reduced, the magnitude of $I_2$ increases to increase the positive feedback. It is very difficult to use the point-contact transistor in a stable amplifier circuit. On the other hand, it is very simple to use the point-contact transistor as an oscillator. Increasing the input resistance ($R_g$ or $R_E$), increasing the base resistance ($R$), or decreasing the collector resistance ($R_L$) increases the positive feedback to the point where the circuit breaks into oscillation. The point-contact transistor is not used extensively except as an oscillator because of this inherent instability.

## Section 17–8   Decoupling

When a d-c power supply has an internal resistance (Fig. 17–22), the instantaneous changing current demand on the load creates an a-c drop across this internal resistance of the supply $R_{\text{in}}$. The output voltage of the supply is no longer a pure direct voltage, but it contains a variation which is a function of the signal. When the instantaneous load-current demand increases, $E_{bb}$ falls, and, when the instantaneous load current decreases, $E_{bb}$ increases.

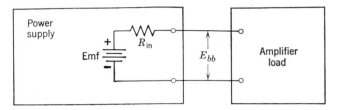

**Figure 17-22**   Effect of power-supply internal impedance.

In the circuit of Fig. 17-23, if the instantaneous polarity of the signal $E_s$ is as shown on the diagram, the signal at the grid of tube $B$ is 180° out of phase with $E_s$, and the signal at the grid of tube $C$ is in phase with the polarities as indicated.   Assume that stages $A$ and $B$ are voltage amplifiers requiring low values of plate current and that stage $C$ is a power amplifier drawing a large value of plate current.   If the polarity of the grid signal of stage $C$ is positive, the tube instantaneously demands an increase in plate current from the supply, and the effect of the internal resistance of the supply causes $E_{bb}$ to decrease. This decrease of $E_{bb}$ on tube $A$ causes an unwanted negative signal to appear on the grid of tube $B$, and this decrease of $E_{bb}$ on tube $B$ also produces an unwanted negative signal on the grid of tube $C$. The unwanted signal on the grid of tube $B$ is regenerative, whereas the unwanted signal on the grid of tube $C$ is degenerative.

This regenerative effect, if severe, can produce a low-frequency oscil-

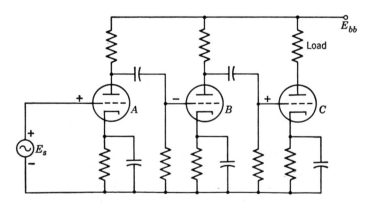

**Figure 17-23**   Three-stage amplifier operating from a common power supply.

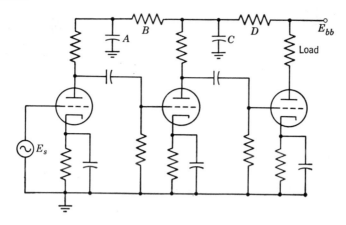

**Figure 17–24**  Three-stage amplifier using decoupling filters.

lation known as *motorboating* which sounds like a "putt putt putt" in a loudspeaker.   When an extra filter is placed in the power supply, this condition of motorboating may be cured.   However, the best solution to the problem is to place individual filter circuits in each sensitive lead to make the sensitive stages independent of this inter-stage coupling through the power supply.   These filters are called *decoupling filters* because they prevent signal from appearing on tubes except from normal sources.   This same circuit is redrawn in Fig. 17–24, using the decoupling filters, $AB$ and $CD$.

The time constant of the decoupling filter must be longer than the period of the lowest frequency that the circuit is to handle.   A rule of thumb states that, in order to have sufficient decoupling, the value of capacitive reactance should be one-tenth the value of the resistance at the lowest frequency.   This rule of thumb was used for calculating

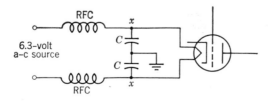

**Figure 17–25**  Decoupling in a heater circuit.

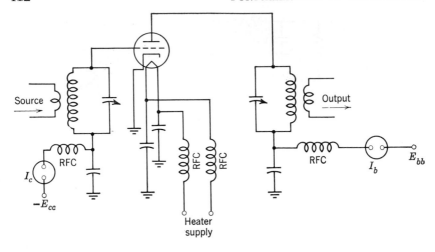

**Figure 17–26**   Class-C amplifier with decoupling filters.

the value of the cathode bypass capacitor which is actually a decoupling filter.

In Fig. 12–10, a three-stage transistor amplifier is given, using these decoupling filters. All the networks, $C_1$ and $R_1$, $C_2$ and $R_2$, $C_3$ and $R_3$, $C_4$ and $R_4$, $C_5$ and $R_5$, and $C_6$ and $R_6$ may be considered as decoupling filters used to provide the proper bias and, at the same time, prevent interaction between the stages.

In radio-frequency applications, particularly in transmitters, all leads are often decoupled: plates, screens, meters, heaters, and filaments. A radio-frequency choke (RFC) is usually substituted for the resistor. In transmitter circuits or in high-power industrial applications, the problem is to keep RF energy which is developed within a tube from escaping out into the supply circuits. Energy coming out from the filaments of the tube in Fig. 17–25 finds two paths at the junction $x$. A low-impedance path leads to ground through the capacitor $C$, and there is a high-impedance path to the main heater line through the RF choke. A properly selected decoupling filter shunts this energy to ground. Likewise any residual RF energy in the supply is kept from the stage.

In Sections 16–6 and 16–8, we discussed the procedure for tuning a class-C amplifier. In order for a class-C amplifier stage to function at all, certain necessary decoupling filters must be incorporated in the circuit. Figure 16–12 is redrawn as the circuit in Fig. 17–26 to include the usual decoupling filters.

## Section 17–9    Electronic-Regulated Power Supplies

In order to reduce power-supply coupling to a negligible point, the internal resistance of the power supply must approach zero. In Section 2–4, we discussed the application of a voltage-regulator tube to power-supply regulation. The voltage-regulator tube operates at a fixed voltage, and its operation is limited as to the load-current variation. A basic circuit which does not have the restrictions of the voltage-regulator tube is presented in a basic form in Fig. 17–27.

A battery $E_K$ fixes the cathode voltage of $V1$ so that it is constant, regardless of the variations in the load or in the input. The potentiometer $P$ is set so that the bias of $V1$ is negative but not below cutoff. When the load voltage falls, the voltage between the grid and ground of $V1$ falls, and the bias on $V1$ becomes more negative. The plate current through $V1$ decreases, and the voltage drop in $R$ decreases. A decreasing voltage drop across $R$ decreases the bias on $V2$. The tube drop of $V2$ now decreases, forcing the load voltage back up to its original value. This circuit not only is insensitive to load-voltage variations, as we have explained, but it also automatically compensates for an input voltage variation in the same manner.

The selection of proper values for the circuit components can give a perfect compensation, which results in an exact zero voltage regulation. It is possible to obtain an overcompensation which gives a negative voltage regulation. A manual change in the setting of $P$ changes the output load voltage.

Another approach to the understanding of the operation of the circuit is to use the feedback approach. A variation in load voltage is a signal which is fed into the grid of $V1$. $V1$ amplifies this signal and

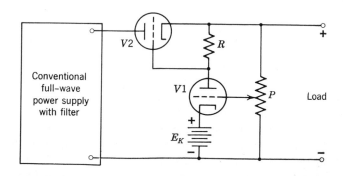

**Figure 17–27**    Basic electronic voltage-regulator circuit.

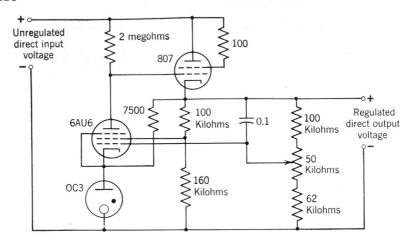

**Figure 17–28**   Electronic voltage-regulator.

reverses its phase.   The output of $V1$ controls the grid of $V2$.   $V2$ acts as a variable d-c resistance in series with the load.   Thus $V1$, by controlling the d-c resistance of $V2$, counteracts by negative feedback the output-voltage change.   In a practical extention of this circuit, a number of modifications are necessary.   The battery $E_K$ is replaced by a neon lamp or by a voltage-regulator tube.   The tube current of $V1$ is usually insufficient to fire a voltage-regulator tube.   To increase this current, a bleeder is added in parallel with $V1$.   The amplifier tube is usually a high-gain sharp cutoff tube to give a maximum control gain.   When a pentode is used, a screen supply circuit is necessary. If $V2$ does not have sufficient capacity to handle the load, a second tube is added in parallel to $V2$.   Small resistances must be placed in the grids, in the screens, and in the plates of each of these two tubes to prevent any interaction or an unequal division of currents.   The interaction effects are called *parasitic oscillations*, and the inserted damping resistors are called *parasitic suppressors* (Section 19–8).

A typical voltage-regulator circuit is shown in Fig. 17–28.   At a constant 50-ma load, an input variation from 500 to 700 volts causes the load voltage to increase from 299.9 to 300.1 volts.   An increase in load from 0 to 40 ma at 300 volts does not produce a measurable change in the load voltage.   Changing the potentiometer can vary the regulated output voltage from 150 to 400 volts for a 600-volt input supply.

A transistor version of the electronic voltage regulator is shown in Fig. 17–29.   In this circuit, the output voltage $E_o$ exceeds the reference

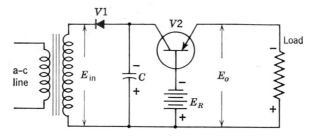

**Figure 17–29** Transistor voltage regulator.

voltage $E_R$ by the amount of the forward voltage drop of the emitter to base voltage of the transistor. Usually this voltage drop is of the order of a fraction of a volt in the forward direction. This makes the output voltage slightly higher than the reference voltage at all times. Since the transistor is a junction-type unit, the collector current is slightly less than the emitter current by the amount of the base current. In the characteristic curves for a transistor, the collector-current curves are very flat and independent of the collector voltage. As a result, variations of input voltage are variations in collector voltage and do not change the load voltage. The battery $E_K$ may be varied to control the output direct voltage. Also, the battery $E_K$ may be replaced by a Zener diode in order to avoid the use of dry batteries in an actual circuit application.

When the CBS 2N256 junction transistor is used, the load current may be varied from zero to 700 ma. For this transistor, when the

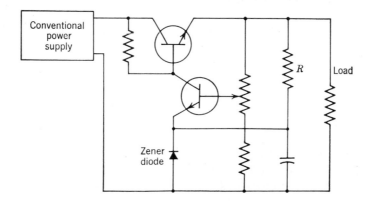

**Figure 17–30** Transistor equivalent of electronic regulator.

input voltage $E_{in}$ is 18 volts rms, when the reference voltage $E_R$ is 6 volts, and when the filter capacitor $C$ is 500 $\mu f$, the per cent regulation of the output voltage is 5.2 and the ripple is 0.16 of 1%.

The vacuum-tube electronic-regulator circuit is convertible to a completely transistorized circuit (Fig. 17–30). The two $NPN$ transistors function in the same manner as the power tube and the amplifier. The voltage-regulator tube is replaced by a Zener diode. The function of the resistor $R$ is to maintain enough reverse current in the Zener diode to insure that the stable breakdown voltage is maintained at all times.

#### . . . . Suggested References for Further Study

1. F. Langford-Smith, *Radiotron Designer's Handbook*, 4th ed., Chapters 7 and 33, RCA, Harrison, N. J., 1953.
2. R. B. Hurley, *Junction Transistor Electronics*, Chapters 7 and 11, John Wiley & Sons, New York, 1958.
3. L. B. Arguimbau, and R. B. Adler, *Vacuum-Tube Circuits and Transistors*, Chapter 10, John Wiley & Sons, New York, 1956.
4. E. J. Angelo, *Electronic Circuits*, Chapter 17, McGraw-Hill Book Co., New York, 1958.

#### . . . . QUESTIONS

1. Define or explain each of the following terms: (*a*) decade amplifier, (*b*) feedback factor, (*c*) regeneration, (*d*) degeneration, (*e*) voltage feedback, (*f*) current feedback, (*g*) feedback loop, (*h*) ultrasonic, (*i*) motorboating, (*j*) parasitic suppressor.
2. Under what conditions does feedback increase distortion? Reduce distortion?
3. Under what conditions does a negative-feedback loop produce an increase in gain?
4. What is the effect of negative feedback on input impedance? On output impedance? On equivalent amplification factor? On equivalent plate resistance?
5. What are the advantages and disadvantages of a cathode follower?
6. What are the vacuum-tube equivalents of a common-base amplifier, of a common-emitter amplifier, and of a common-collector amplifier?
7. Explain shunt feedback in terms of a transistor amplifier.
8. Explain series feedback in terms of a transistor amplifier.
9. Explain how feedback takes place across $R$ in Fig. 17–21.
10. Explain how an internal impedance in a power supply can produce regeneration and degeneration in an amplifier circuit.

11. Explain how an RFC can serve in a decoupling filter.

12. Point out the decoupling filters in Fig. 17–26.

13. Explain the operation of the regulator circuit shown in Fig. 17–28.

14. Explain the operation of the regulator circuit shown in Fig. 17–29.

15. Explain the operation of the regulator circuit shown in Fig. 17–30.

16. Give the use of each circuit component shown in Fig. 17–28.

17. Referring to Fig. 15–19, trace out the feedback loop.

18. Referring to Fig. 15–19, locate three decoupling filters.

## . . . . PROBLEMS

1. Using the amplifier shown in Fig. 17–6, the plate load is 47,000 ohms, the amplification factor is 35, and the transconductance is 2800 micromhos. The sum of $R_2$ and $R_1$ is 100,000 ohms.   Plot a curve of gain with the value of the feedback in per cent as the independent variable.

2. Solve problem 1 if the plate load resistance is increased to 150,000 ohms.

3. For the example given in problem 1, plot input impedance against the value of feedback in per cent as the independent variable.

4. From the data of problem 2, determine $\mu'$ and $r'_p$ when the feedback is 15%.

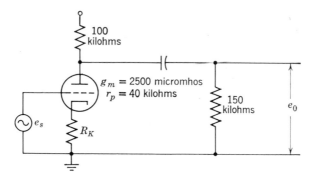

**Prob. 17–5**

5. Determine the gain for the circuit shown when the cathode resistance is 2500 ohms.

6. Solve problem 5 for a cathode resistance of 1500 ohms.

7. Solve problem 5 for a cathode resistance of 1000 ohms.

8. Using the 6S4 characteristic in the text, determine the dynamic-response curve for a cathode follower that has a 7500-ohm resistance in the cathode and operates from a 300-volt supply.   Determine the operating point that accepts the maximum peak-to-peak input signal.   Determine the gain.

# Feedback oscillators

$\bullet \, \bullet \, \bullet \, \bullet \, \bullet \, \bullet \, \bullet \, \bullet \, \bullet \, \bullet \, \bullet \, \bullet \, \bullet \, \bullet \, \bullet \, \bullet \, \bullet \, \bullet \, \bullet \, \bullet$ CHAPTER $18$

Before studying feedback oscillators, it is particularly important to review two topics previously studied: the mechanism of the operation of the grid-leak bias circuit (Section 16–1) and the function of the tank circuit which produces a sinusoidal oscillation when pulsed by plate current (Section 16–2). The method of starting an oscillation, the waveform, and the equivalent circuit of the basic oscillator (Section 18–1) lead to the familiar circuit arrangements of resonant feedback oscillators known as the Armstrong (Section 18–2). The Hartley (Section 18–3), the Colpitts (Section 18–4) and the electron-coupled (Section 18–5) oscillators are also discussed. The chapter concludes (Section 18–6) with a discussion of the various factors involved in the limitations of these oscillators.

### Section 18–1   Basic Oscillator Theory

In Section 17–2 of the previous chapter, in discussing positive feedback, we set forth two requirements that must be met in order to maintain a sustained oscillation:

1. The feedback must be positive, and
2. The amount of feedback must be large enough to make the feedback factor unity.

When an air-core transformer is connected to a triode as an oscillator (Fig. 18–1), a tuning capacitor $C$ must be placed across either the grid coil $L_g$, as shown in the diagram, or across the plate coil $L_p$, in order to have a single stable frequency of operation. The positive feedback is

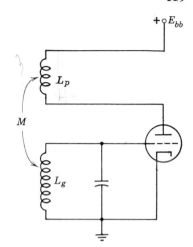

**Figure 18–1**   The basic oscillator.

determined by the relative polarity of the coils.   If an oscillator is constructed and fails to oscillate, the first check is a reversal of one of two windings to make sure that the feedback actually is positive and not negative.   The amount of the feedback is controlled by the mutual inductance $M$ between the plate and the grid coils.   An increase in the coefficient of coupling $k$ increases the feedback and is accomplished by bringing the coils closer together physically.   It should be remembered that most small coils are so wound that the coupling is determined and fixed during manufacture.

When the circuit is first turned on, a rush of plate current develops an increasing flux in the plate coil.   This increasing flux produces a secondary voltage in the grid winding.   The polarity of the grid voltage drives the tube positive and at the same time charges the tuning capacitor $C$.   The tank starts to oscillate, and, when the capacitor voltage becomes negative, this negative voltage on the grid reduces the plate current.   The reversed direction of the changing plate current through the plate winding induces a voltage in the grid winding which makes the current reduction a cumulative process. It takes a few cycles to accomplish the building up of the amplitude of the oscillation to a final value.   The limits of the amplitude of the oscillation must be examined.   The plate current in the tube is limited by cutoff at one extreme and by the saturation of the tube at the other. We expect, then, to have a square-current waveform.   Excessive grid drive and grid current not only prevent a sinusoidal waveform in the tank circuit, but also, under normal conditions, cause an overload within the tube.

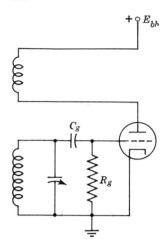

**Figure 18–2**   Oscillator with grid leak bias.

In order to maintain a sinusoidal waveform and to prevent excessive currents from destroying the tube, a class-C bias arrangement is necessary.   If the class-C bias is obtained by use of a fixed-bias battery, the tube is permanently cut off at the onset, and oscillations cannot possibly develop from self-excitation.   An automatic or grid-leak bias comprising a grid-leak resistor $R_g$ and a grid leak capacitor $C_g$, must be used as in Fig. 18–2.   Now, as the amplitude of the oscillation increases, the negative bias increases from zero and reduces the angle of plate-current flow during each cycle.   The oscillator stabilizes at that point where the losses of the circuit equal the developed a-c power output of the tube.   The losses in this circuit, beside the tube itself, include the plate coil, the grid tank, and the grid leak.

An approximate equivalent circuit (Fig. 18–3), which is sufficient to serve the needs of this discussion, retains only those circuit elements that contribute to the a-c aspect of the oscillator.   Thus, the grid leak, $R_g$ and $C_g$, does not appear in this equivalent circuit since it is used only as a means of obtaining the proper operating bias.   We shall use this equivalent circuit as a fundamental feedback oscillator and from it develop as variations of the prototype the several well-known oscillators.   The three circuit elements in Fig. 18–3 are considered, for the derivation, pure reactances, $jX_1$, $jX_2$, and $jX_3$ and grid current is considered to be negligible.   The external load on the plate is

$$Z_L = \frac{jX_2(jX_3 + jX_1)}{jX_1 + jX_2 + jX_3} = \frac{-X_1X_2 - X_2X_3}{jX_1 + jX_2 + jX_3}$$

The gain without feedback is

$$A_e = \frac{-\mu Z_L}{r_p + Z_L}$$

The negative sign associated with the amplification factor signifies the inherent 180° phase shift of the tube as an amplifier. The feedback is determined by the voltage-dividing network formed by $jX_1$ and $jX_3$ and is given by

$$\beta = \frac{jX_1}{jX_1 + jX_3} = \frac{X_1}{X_1 + X_3}$$

In order to have sustained oscillations, the feedback factor $\beta A_e$ must be unity. Substituting the values we have established for $Z_L$, $A_e$, and $\beta$, we find that

$$\beta A_e = \frac{-\mu X_1 X_2}{X_2(X_1 + X_3) - jr_p(X_1 + X_2 + X_3)}$$

In order for $\beta A_e$ to be unity, the $j$ term must be zero or

$$X_1 + X_2 + X_3 = 0$$

This condition reduces the expression for the feedback factor to

$$\beta A_e = \frac{-\mu X_1 X_2}{X_2(X_1 + X_3)}$$

Then

$$\beta A_e = -\mu \frac{X_1}{X_1 + X_3}$$

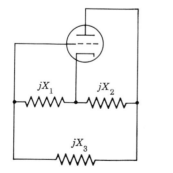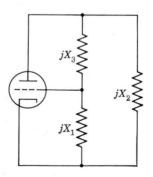

**Figure 18-3**  Equivalent circuit of the feedback oscillator.

Since

$$X_1 + X_2 + X_3 = 0$$

$$-X_2 = X_1 + X_3 \tag{18-1}$$

and substituting

$$\beta A_e = \mu \frac{X_1}{X_2} \tag{18-2}$$

In the derivation of the equations, we used $jX_1$, $jX_2$, and $jX_3$ for the reactances. In the final equation an inductive reactance $\omega L$ is used as a positive number, and a capacitive reactance $1/\omega C$ is substituted as a negative number $(-1/\omega C)$. In order to make the feedback factor $+1$, in Eq. 18–2, $X_1$ and $X_2$ must have the same sign; that is, both are either capacitive reactances or inductive reactances. From Eq. 18–1 it is evident then that $X_2$ and $X_3$ are opposite in sign. These relations are listed in Table I.

TABLE I

| $X_1$ | $X_2$ | $X_3$ | Name of Basic Oscillator |
|---|---|---|---|
| Inductance | Inductance | Capacitance | Hartley |
| Capacitance | Capacitance | Inductance | Colpitts |
| Inductively tuned tank | Inductively tuned tank | $C_{gp}$ | Tuned grid–tuned plate |
| Inductive crystal | Inductively tuned tank | $C_{gp}$ | Miller crystal oscillator |
| $C_{gk}$ | $C_{pk}$ | Inductive crystal | Pierce crystal oscillator |

When a tank circuit operates slightly below its natural frequency, it is inductive. The term "inductively tuned tank" used in Table I describes this condition. The amount off resonance at which the tank operates is very small for a high-$Q$ circuit and is that amount needed to fulfill the conditions of Eq. 18–1 and 18–2. Since the $Q$ of a crystal is very high, the operation of an "inductive crystal" is extremely close to its natural parallel-resonant frequency.

The mathematical criteria for self-sustained oscillation in terms of $g_m$ and circuit components are given in Appendix I.

### Section 18–2   The Armstrong Oscillator

The Armstrong oscillator is the basic oscillator which we have discussed in Section 18–1. The feature by which it may be quickly recognized is that the oscillator coil has two windings with four terminals (Fig. 18–4). If the tuning capacitor is placed in the grid circuit, the plate winding is referred to as the *feedback* or *tickler winding*. The tuning capacitor may be placed in the plate circuit, and the grid winding becomes the feedback winding. This latter connection has the material disadvantage that the tuning capacitor is "hot." Not only must the tuning capacitor be insulated from the chassis, but also its shaft must be insulated to prevent a short circuit on, or an electric shock from, the supply voltage.

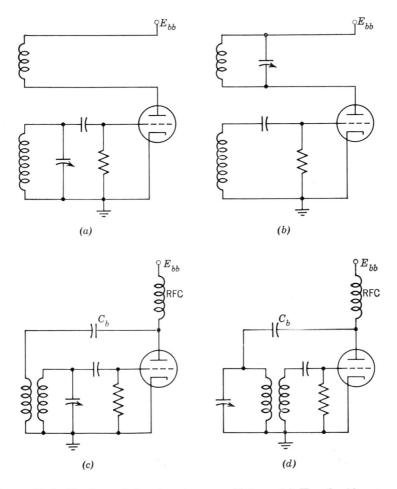

**Figure 18–4** Versions of the Armstrong oscillator. (*a*) Tuned-grid–untuned-plate series feed. (*b*) Tuned-plate–untuned-grid series feed. (*c*) Tuned-grid–untuned-plate shunt feed. (*d*) Tuned-plate–untuned-grid shunt feed.

In a *series-feed* circuit, the plate current flows *through* at least part of the oscillator coil. In a *shunt feed* or *parallel feed*, the plate current is kept out of the coil by means of a blocking capacitor $C_b$. An RF choke must be placed in series with the plate to maintain the plate at a high a-c impedance with respect to ground. These four basic versions of the Armstrong oscillator are shown in Fig. 18–4.

In oscillator circuits using transistors (Fig. 18–5), the proper operating bias to insure a sinusoidal waveform is obtained by limiting the

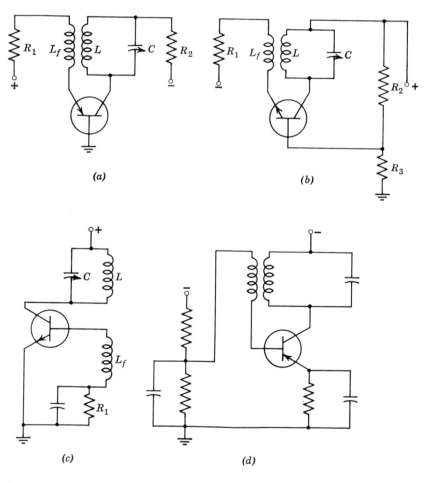

**Figure 18–5** Armstrong oscillators using transistors. (*a*) Grounded base. (*b*) Grounded collector. (*c*) Grounded emitter. (*d*) Oscillator using emitter stability.

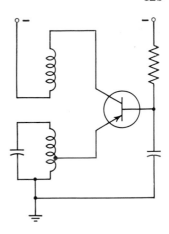

**Figure 18-6**  Armstrong oscillator using a
tap on the oscillator tank.

operating currents. In the common-base oscillator (Fig. 18-5a),
$R_1$ establishes the sinusoidal oscillation by controlling the emitter
current. The resistor in the collector $R_2$ limits the collector current to
a safe value when the polarity on the collector reverses during the half-
cycle when the emitter is reverse biased. The tuning capacitor may
be placed in either winding of the oscillator coil.

In the development of transistor theory, we showed that a transistor
is a relatively low-impedance device when compared to the vacuum
tube. Very often we find that the connection of the tank circuit in
series with a transistor electrode causes the $Q$ of the tank circuit to be
reduced to too low a value. It is a common practice in transistor
circuits to avoid this situation by not using the full tank circuit for the
electrode lead, but by using a tap on the oscillator coil. An example of
this arrangement is shown in Fig. 18-6. The oscillator coil of this
circuit, although it has not four but five terminals, is used in a true
Armstrong-type oscillator circuit.

### Section 18-3    The Hartley Oscillator

In the table at the end of Section 18-1, we defined the Hartley
oscillator as having the elements of Fig. 18-3 inductive for $X_1$ and $X_2$
and capacitive for $X_3$. A tapped coil is used to provide $X_1$ and $X_2$
and the tuning capacitor serves as the feedback element $X_3$. When an
operating circuit is drawn from this equivalent circuit (Fig. 18-7),
inspection reveals that it is shunt-fed. This shunt-fed oscillator also
has the material disadvantage of a floating tuning capacitor which is
not at ground potential.

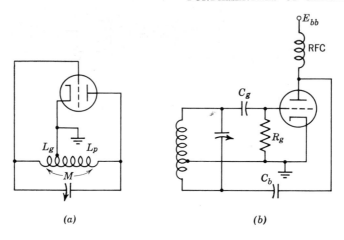

(a)                                          (b)

**Figure 18–7**   Shunt-fed Hartley oscillator.   (a) Equivalent circuit.   (b) Actual circuit.

When the ground in the equivalent circuit is moved from the cathode to the plate (Fig. 18–8), a much simpler circuit version of the Hartley oscillator may be developed.   This form of the Hartley which is series-fed is very widely used because of its simplicity in requiring a minimum number of circuit elements.   The cathode tap is generally made at about 10% from the bottom of the coil.   Experimentation with the exact location of the tap often can improve the operation of the oscillator circuit.   A Hartley oscillator circuit may be quickly

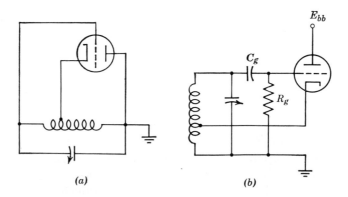

(a)                                          (b)

**Figure 18–8**   Series-fed Hartley oscillator.   (a) Equivalent circuit.   (b) Actual circuit.

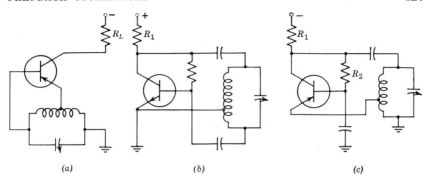

**Figure 18-9** Hartley oscillators using transistors. (*a*) Simple low-frequency oscillator. (*b*) Shunt-fed oscillator. (*c*) Series-fed oscillator.

recognized by the fact that the oscillator coil is tapped and has three terminals.

The circuit in Fig. 18–8 does have a drawback. The cathode of the vacuum tube is not at ground potential. When this circuit is used at high frequencies, there is energy transfer between the heater and the cathode which results in the presence of a line-frequency hum in the output of the oscillator.

The transistor Hartley oscillator circuits (Fig. 18–9) are very similar to the vacuum-tube circuits. Again stabilization of the oscillator to procure a sinusoidal waveform is accomplished by adjusting the current-limiting and the bias resistors. The transistor oscillator has the advantage over the vacuum-tube circuit that a series feed does not create the problem of a hum pickup.

The tank circuit of a Hartley oscillator may be tapped in order to prevent the low impedance of the transistor from lowering the $Q$ of the tank. A method of doing this is shown in the oscillator in Fig.

**Figure 18-10** Hartley oscillator using a tap on the oscillator tank.

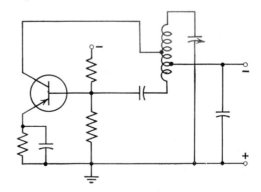

18–10.   The oscillator coil used in this circuit has four terminals. Care must be taken not to confuse this circuit with the Armstrong oscillator in which the oscillator coil also has four terminals.

### Section 18–4   The Colpitts Oscillator

Referring again to the table at the end of Section 18–1, we have defined the Colpitts oscillator in terms of the circuit elements, $X_1$, $X_2$, and $X_3$.   $X_1$ and $X_2$ are small mica capacitors placed in the circuit, and $X_3$ is an inductively tuned tank circuit (Fig. 18–11b).   Since the oscillator is most effective at high frequencies, the cathode must be grounded to prevent a hum pickup, and an RF choke is used in the plate supply lead.   In some applications, in order to obtain a mechanical symmetry, both $C_g$ and $C_b$ are used.   Actually, either one could be

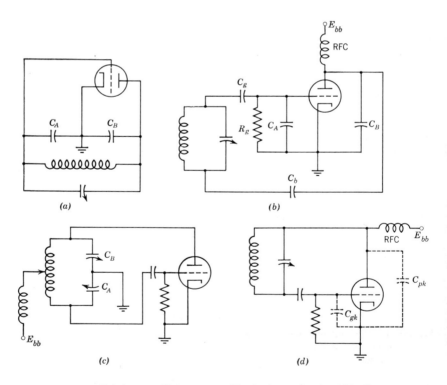

**Figure 18–11**  Colpitts oscillators.  (*a*) Equivalent circuit.  (*b*) Conventional circuit.  (*c*) Circuit with split-stator tuning capacitance.  (*d*) Ultra-audion oscillator.

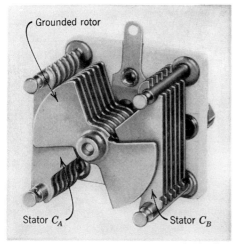

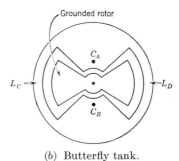

(a) Split-stator capacitor.                    (b) Butterfly tank.

**Figure 18–12** Special capacitors used for high-frequency oscillators. (*Courtesy Hammarlund Mfg. Co.*)

omitted because the other can serve the dual function of blocking the plate voltage and acting as the grid-leak capacitor.

Very often, a special split-stator capacitor (Fig. 18–12a) is used with the form of the Colpitts oscillator shown in Fig. 18–11c. The capacitor has two stators and a grounded rotor. When the rotor is turned, there is a simultaneous increase or decrease in both $C_A$ and $C_B$. This capacitor used in the Colpitts oscillator provides both the required tuning and the voltage division.

Another special tank circuit which is suited to the Colpitts oscillator is the butterfly (Fig. 18–12b), which is used at very high frequencies. When the rotor plates are meshed with the stator plates, the capacitors $C_A$ and $C_B$ are a maximum. The inductances of the supporting frames, $L_C$ and $L_D$, are also a maximum. When unmeshed, the rotor plates tend to short-circuit the inductance of $L_C$ and $L_D$ by a close capacitance effect. In this tuning circuit both capacitance and inductance vary. Since the resonant frequency of a tuned circuit is

$$f_0 = \frac{1}{2\pi \sqrt{LC}}$$

a simultaneous change of $L$ and $C$ give a much greater range of frequency variation than if $C$ alone is variable.

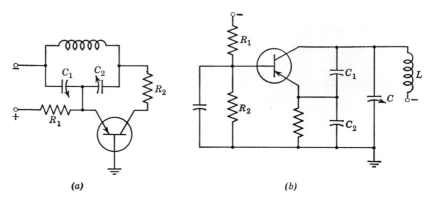

**Figure 18–13** Colpitts oscillators using transistors. (a) Circuit using two supplies. (b) Circuit using one supply.

One version of the Colpitts circuit which is used at very high frequencies is the *ultra-audion* oscillator (Fig. 18–11d). In this circuit, the voltage-dividing capacitors are the interelectrode capacitances, grid-to-cathode and plate-to-cathode, of the tube itself. The grid-to-plate capacitance becomes part of the tuning capacitance. This circuit is commonly used in television receivers as the main oscillator.

The Colpitts oscillator may be recognized readily by its two-terminal, single-winding coil or by the split capacitor.

The transistor versions of the Colpitts oscillator (Fig. 18–13) are very similar to the vacuum-tube circuits. The tank arrangement, which may be either a fixed capacitance divider or a split-stator tuning capacitor, is dictated by the use and function of the circuit. Resistors serve to set the operating bias and to limit the current to safe values.

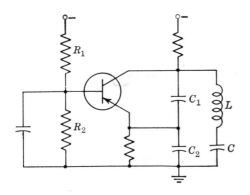

**Figure 18–14** The Clapp oscillator.

The Colpitts oscillator of Fig. 18–13b has a parallel-tuned tank circuit. When the tank circuit is reconnected as a series-resonant circuit (Fig. 18–14), the new circuit is called a *Clapp* oscillator.

### Section 18–5    The Electron–Coupled Oscillator (ECO)

A series-fed Hartley oscillator (Fig. 18–8) is the basic circuit for the electron-coupled oscillator. The triode is replaced by a tetrode or a pentode, and the screen is used as the plate of the oscillator section of the tube. The electron stream from the cathode, by the time it passes through the screen mesh, is varying in accordance with the fundamental frequency of the oscillator tank circuit. The screen-to-plate region of the tube is used for power amplification, and isolation of the load from the actual oscillator is obtained. Because of the shielding action of the screen, a change in the load does not affect the oscillator. In the circuit diagram for the electron-coupled oscillator (Fig. 18–15), we show the load as a block rather than as a specific circuit component. This load may be a tuned circuit which is adjusted either to the fundamental frequency or to a harmonic frequency. In the latter case, the electron-coupled oscillator serves the dual purpose of an oscillator and a frequency multiplier. In many applications, the load is resistive or reactive, depending on the nature of the use of the circuit. Several variations of this circuit are used, but they all have the same basic principle of operation.

The electron-coupled oscillator is so named because energy is transferred from the oscillator to the load through the electron stream of the tube. The shielding action of the screen (and also of the suppressor if a pentode is used) prevents interaction between the oscillator and the load. The load may be adjusted or varied without upsetting the electrical conditions within the oscillator section of the circuit.

**Figure 18–15**   The electron-coupled oscillator.

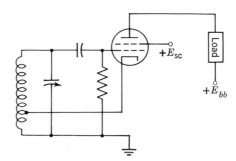

### Section 18–6    Limitations of Oscillators

With the exception of the electron-coupled oscillator, we have not discussed any of the methods for taking power or voltage from an oscillator circuit. Very often, the power drain by the load on an oscillator is very small, and a "gimmick" loop (A in Fig. 18–16) may be used. Two wires twisted together is another variety of "gimmick" which also uses a capacitive coupling between the two wires (B in Fig. 18–16). A coupling capacitor (C in Fig. 18–16) which is not large enough to interfere with the action of the oscillator grid-leak capacitor may be used. A secondary winding (D in Fig. 18–16) is added to the oscillator coil when larger amounts of power are required.

If too much power is demanded from the oscillator, the over-all circuit Q will fall to the point where the flywheel effect of the tank circuit will not be able to maintain a sinusoidal waveform. Certain design factors have been established limiting the output that may be taken from an oscillator. One consideration states that the ratio of stored energy to output energy per cycle must be at least two. Another approach requires that the effective Q of the loaded oscillator tank circuit must be at least $4\pi$. These two factors are mentioned to give the reader a rule of thumb. For the development of these relations, reference should be made to textbooks on circuit design.

When an oscillator is operated at a high power and if the circuit should fail and oscillations cease, the tube immediately draws excessive plate current. In order to protect the tube, a fuse, a resistor, or a panel lamp is often placed in the cathode or in the plate circuit. The panel lamp offers an increased resistance in the circuit when the lamp current increases.

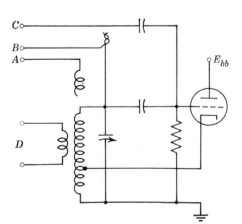

**Figure 18–16**  Methods of obtaining an output from an oscillator.

The operation of an oscillator may be effectively monitored by a properly bypassed d-c milliammeter which reads the grid current. The product of this direct grid current times the value of the grid-leak resistance $R_g$ gives the value of the d-c bias which is nearly the peak of the alternating voltage. When the plate current is metered, we find that a strong oscillation develops a large bias and produces a low value of plate current.

Very often, a rapid means of checking is desired on the operation of an oscillator that does not have permanent metering circuits. One may use an RF vacuum-tube voltmeter which reads the alternating voltage directly. Radio-frequency voltmeters are often unavailable because of their cost and limited usefulness. When an ordinary d-c voltmeter is used to measure the value of the direct grid-leak bias voltage, the capacitance of the meter and of the meter leads either detunes the oscillator so far that the reading is worthless or it loads the circuit to the point where the oscillation ceases. When a resistor of the order of a megohm is placed in series with the "hot" meter lead *at* the point of measurement, the meter will not detune the circuit appreciably, and an accurate reading can be taken of the grid bias. In order to eliminate the need for correcting the meter reading for the probe resistance drop, commercial vacuum-tube voltmeters have this resistor built in as an integral part of the d-c lead and are calibrated with the probe in place. A neon lamp is often used to check a radio frequency oscillator for operation.

The frequency of oscillation may be measured by an absorption-type wave meter, by a grid dip meter or by tuning in a radio receiver to the oscillation. The frequency range of the oscillator is determined by the ratio of the maximum to the minimum capacitance of the tuning capacitor by calculation from the resonant-frequency equation:

$$f_0 = \frac{1}{2\pi \sqrt{LC}}$$

When the inductance is constant, the frequency ratio is inverse to the square root of the capacitance ratio. As an example, assume that a tuning capacitor has a range from 30 to 450 $\mu\mu$f. Assume that the total stray capacitance of the coil, the tube, and the wiring is 20 $\mu\mu$f. The total capacitance ratio is $(450 + 20)$ to $(30 + 20)$ or 470/50, and the frequency coverage ratio is $\sqrt{470/50}$ or 3.06 to 1. In a butterfly circuit, if the inductance change is the same as the change in capacitance, say 470/50, the frequency range would be 470/50 or 9.36 to 1 which is much greater than the frequency ratio in the conventional tank circuit.

The output voltage of one of these oscillator circuits is not constant over the entire range of tuning. The design of the coil and the $L/C$ ratio are the primary factors. In many applications, if the variation in the amplitude of the oscillator output is within 2:1 over the band of tuning, it is generally considered satisfactory.

The factors that involve the stability of an oscillator warrant special consideration. A variation in supply voltage and in heater voltage can produce variations in frequency and in output level. Very often a voltage-regulator tube is used to control the supply voltage within close limits. At the very least, a decoupling filter should be used. The circuit components should be ruggedly mounted, lest mechanical vibrations produce a varying capacitance or inductance. Proper values of $R_g$ and $C_g$ in the grid-leak bias circuit aid in oscillator stability. Changes in temperature produce mechanical contractions and expansions within the coil and capacitor which cause frequency and output variations. Many oscillators have temperature-compensating capacitors placed in parallel with the tank circuit. These capacitors are available with different temperature coefficients and are rated in micromicrofarads change per micromicrofarad of capacitance per degree centigrade ($\mu\mu f/\mu\mu f/°$ C). Humidity variations can also affect the stability of an oscillator.

In addition to these factors, it must be remembered that a high effective $Q$, a low $L/C$ ratio, and a light loading are the three prerequisites for oscillator stability. With great care the frequency of a feedback oscillator can be held to a few thousandths of one per cent.

#### . . . . Suggested References for Further Study

1. F. E. Terman, *Radio Engineer's Handbook*, Section 2, McGraw-Hill Book Co., New York, 1943.
2. W. A. Edson, *Vacuum-Tube Oscillators*, John Wiley & Sons, New York, 1953.
3. R. F. Shea, editor, *Principles of Transistor Circuits*, Chapter 13, John Wiley & Sons, New York, 1953.
4. K. R. Sturley, *Radio Receiver Design*, Part I 2nd ed., Chapter 6, John Wiley & Sons, New York, 1954.

#### . . . . QUESTIONS

1. Define or explain each of the following terms: (*a*) coefficient of coupling, (*b*) class C, (*c*) tickler winding, (*d*) series feed, (*e*) shunt feed, (*f*) split stator, (*g*) butterfly, (*h*) loading, (*i*) detuning, (*j*) VFO.

2. State two conditions required for oscillation.

3. In terms of the feedback factor, what determines the condition for oscillation?

4. Why is a grid-leak bias required to limit the strength of oscillations?

5. Explain the build-up process of the oscillation.

6. Compare series and shunt feed.

7. Show a circuit for the vacuum-tube version of the Clapp oscillator.

8. What is the advantage of a butterfly oscillator tank?

9. What is the advantage of the ECO?

10. What are the approximate frequency ranges for the various oscillator circuits?

11. How can an ECO be used as a frequency tripler? What are the steps in oscillator adjustment?

12. Why is a panel lamp preferred to a resistor in the cathode of an oscillator?

13. How are $I_b$, $I_c$, $E_c$, and $E_g$ related in an oscillator circuit?

14. What methods are used to obtain power from an oscillator?

15. Why does an ordinary d-c voltmeter detune an oscillator when it is used to measure the direct grid voltage?

16. What limits the frequency range of an oscillator design?

17. Why is an oscillator detuned when a person's hand is placed close to the oscillator tank?

18. What units are used to describe the temperature coefficient of an oscillator drift?

19. Name three requisites to good oscillator design.

# Negative-resistance
# oscillators

• • • • • • • • • • • • • • • • • • • CHAPTER **19**

The principles of a negative-resistance oscillator are discussed (Section 19–1) and followed by the direct applications; the dynatron (Section 19–2) and the point-contact transistor oscillators (Section 19–3). The tuned-plate–tuned-grid oscillator is considered in detail (Section 19–4). The quartz crystal (Section 19–5) is used in the crystal oscillator (Section 19–6). The crystal oscillator, which is effectively a tuned-plate–tuned-grid oscillator, may be arranged in the form of an electron-coupled oscillator, the tri-tet (Section 19–7). Negative-resistance effects developing in circuits and in tubes cause unwanted parasitic oscillations (Section 19–8).

### Section 19–1  General Principles

The parallel impedance of a tank circuit (Section 7–2) at resonance is

$$Z_o = QX_c$$

From this equation we may consider that the equivalent circuit of a tank circuit at resonance (Fig. 19–1) is an ideal tank of pure inductance and pure capacitance acting in parallel with a pure resistance of value $QX_c$. This parallel resistance represents all the losses of the actual tank circuit.

A "negative" resistance of magnitude $-R$ placed in parallel to this equivalent circuit cancels the "positive" resistance $QX_c$ of the tank circuit. Then, once an oscillation starts in the tank, it continues

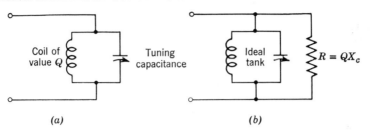

**Figure 19-1** The parallel-resonant circuit. (*a*) Actual circuit. (*b*) Equivalent circuit.

indefinitely without damping. "Negative" resistance as such in the form of physical circuit elements does not exist. An electronic circuit which exhibits the characteristic of negative resistance can be used in conjunction with a tank circuit to provide a continuous sinusoidal oscillation. In the study of electronics up to this point, several instances of negative resistance have been encountered: the arc drop in a gas discharge (Section 1-9) the plate characteristic of a tetrode, (Section 4-2) the point-contact transistor (Section 5-7), and the Miller effect in an amplifier (Section 13-4).

Any volt-ampere relation that has a negative slope has the property of negative resistance. In Fig. 19-2, both curves between points 1 and 2 have a positive slope. An increase in voltage or current produces an increase of current or voltage, respectively. In the region between 2 and 3, an increase in voltage or current results in a *decrease* in current or voltage, respectively. The curves between 3 and 4 again show a positive resistance. The value of negative resistance in the region of the curves between 2 and 3 may be determined by the slope of the curve in the same manner as the method of finding the plate resistance $r_p$ from the tube characteristics.

### Section 19-2 The Dynatron Oscillator

The plate characteristics of a tetrode have a negative-resistance region between $a$ and $b$ in Fig. 19-3. This negative resistance is caused by the absorption by the screen of the secondary emission which occurs at the plate, as explained in Section 4-2. This negative-resistance effect occurs only when the plate voltage is less than the screen voltage.

A dynatron oscillator is formed by placing an appropriate tank circuit in series with the plate lead and maintaining the plate voltage

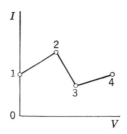 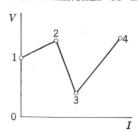

**Figure 19-2**   Volt-ampere curves showing negative resistance.

less than the screen voltage (Fig. 19–4). The variable direct voltage on the grid controls the amplitude of the oscillation. Dynatron oscillators are usually low-frequency oscillators and exhibit good stability characteristics.

### Section 19-3   Point-Contact Transistor Oscillators

In Sections 5–7 and 17–7 we showed that the point-contact transistor is inherently unstable as an amplifier under many different conditions of operation. Although this situation is a material disadvantage in using the transistor as an amplifier, it facilitates its use as an oscillator. Usually, the transistor is made unstable by increasing the base impedance above the critical value at which point the input resistance to the transistor circuit becomes negative. In Fig. 19–5a, the tank circuit at resonance provides a very high base impedance. The resistor $R_1$ limits the emitter current, and $R_2$ limits the collector current to safe values which maintain a pure sinusoidal waveform. In Fig. 19–5b, the base lead is connected to a tap on the tank coil. This tap by preventing the transistor from loading the tank excessively, allows a high $Q$ to be maintained in the tank circuit. In

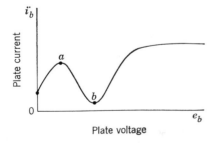

**Figure 19-3**   Negative resistance characteristic of a tetrode.

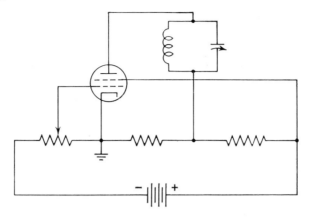

**Figure 19-4** The dynatron oscillator.

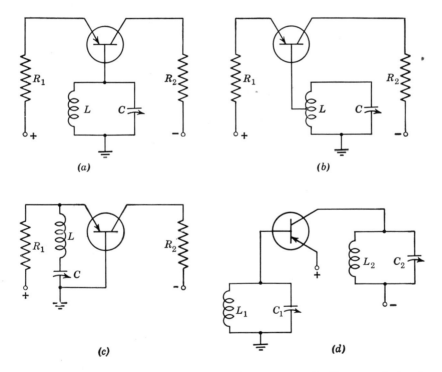

**Figure 19-5** Point-contact transistor oscillators. (*a*) Oscillator tank in the base lead. (*b*) Oscillator tank with tap. (*c*) Oscillator using series resonance. (*d*) Transistor equivalent of an electron-coupled oscillator.

Fig. 19–5c, the base impedance and the low impedance of the series tank circuit both cause the transistor to become unstable and oscillate. Since the input impedance to a transistor is low and since the input resistance to the transistor is negative when the resistance of the input circuit is below a certain critical value, a series-resonant tank is used instead of a high-impedance parallel tank circuit.

Figure 19–5d is the nearest transistor equivalent to the vacuum-tube electron-coupled oscillator. The fundamental oscillator tank is $L_1$ and $C_1$. This resonant tank circuit oscillates because it is in the base lead of the point-contact transistor, and its high impedance causes the transistor to act as a negative resistance. As we can see from Fig. 19–5a, this is the only tank circuit necessary for oscillation. In place of a resistor in the collector circuit, this circuit uses a tuned circuit. If this collector-tuned circuit, $C_2$ and $L_2$, is tuned to a harmonic of the frequency of the tank in the base, the circuit serves the same purpose as the electron-coupled oscillator. The collector tank is usually tuned to the second, the third, or the fourth harmonic of the fundamental frequency.

### Section 19–4   Tuned-Grid–Tuned-Plate Oscillator

In Section 13–4 we showed, in studying the input impedance of a vacuum-tube amplifier, that when the plate load on an amplifier is inductive the input impedance to the grid comprises, in part, a negative resistance. Thus, if a parallel-resonant tank is placed in the grid circuit, this tank can be made to sustain oscillations provided the proper load conditions exist in the plate circuit. In the circuit of Fig.

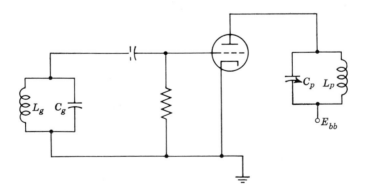

**Figure 19–6**   The tuned-grid–tuned-plate oscillator.

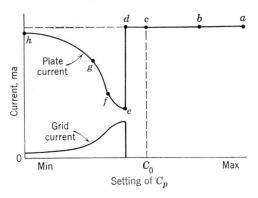

**Figure 19-7**   Characteristics of a tuned-grid–tuned-plate oscillator.

19–6, a grid leak is used to provide the self-excited class-C bias necessary for an oscillator. The frequency of the oscillation is determined by the resonant frequency of the grid tank, $L_g$ and $C_g$. There is a tank circuit in the plate only because a tank circuit is very convenient to adjust at radio frequencies. This plate tank must be so adjusted that it is inductive with respect to the resonant frequency of the grid circuit.

Assume that an alternating voltage of fixed frequency is applied to the parallel combination of a fixed inductance and a variable capacitor. The line current is the sum of the two currents in the branches. If the inductive current is 5 ma and the capacitive current is 7 ma, the line current is 2 ma and it is capacitive. Since the current in the capacitive branch of the circuit is proportional to the value of the capacitance, when the value of the tuning capacitor is greater than that required for resonance, the line current is capacitive, and the over-all plate load is capacitive. Similarly, in order to have the plate load inductive, the setting of the plate-tuning capacitor $C_p$ must be less than that value of $C_p$ that is required to resonate the tank circuit at the resonant frequency of the grid tank.

For the circuit of the tuned-grid–tuned-plate oscillator (Fig. 19–6), assume that the resonant frequency of the grid tank is $f_0$ and that, if the plate tank is set to resonate at $f_0$, the value of $C_p$ is $C_0$. When we plot the plate- and the grid-current readings obtained for this oscillator when $C_p$ is the only variable, we obtain the curves of Fig. 19–7. In the region $ab$ of the curve, the load (the plate tank) is capacitive with respect to $f_0$, and the circuit does not oscillate. There is no bias and, consequently, no grid current. The plate current is a maximum.

When the plate-tank capacitor is set at $C_0$, the reflected load from the plate circuit back into the grid circuit is, by the Miller effect, a pure resistance, and the circuit still does not oscillate. It is only when the plate circuit is detuned to the point $d$ that the plate tank is sufficiently inductive to produce oscillation. The current jumps sharply from point $d$ which is no oscillation to point $e$ which is a strong oscillation. When the plate tank is detuned still further away from $f_0$, its impedance with respect to $f_0$ falls, and the strength of the oscillation diminishes, as indicated by the path from $e$ to $h$. It is often stated that, in order to obtain an oscillation in the tuned-grid–tuned-plate oscillator, the plate circuit is tuned to a higher frequency than the grid tank.

The plate tank is set for normal operation, not at point $e$, but at point $f$. If there is any small circuit change or disturbance at $f$, the operation shifts slightly toward $e$ or $g$. If the point of operation is at $e$, a small disturbance could easily cause the circuit to go out of oscillation. The small power loss accepted by operating at $f$ instead of at $e$ is well worth the assurance of continued operation.

The whole point of the preceding discussion was to establish very clearly and precisely the current characteristics shown in Fig. 19–7. If we refer back to the table at the end of Section 18–1, we note that, for the tuned-grid–tuned-plate oscillator, *both* tuned circuits must be slightly inductive for the circuit to function at all. Both the plate circuit and the grid circuit are detuned off the resonant frequency of operation. Also, it should be noted carefully that the grid tank and the plate tank are physically separated, that there is no mutual inductance between the coils of the tanks, and that the feedback occurs solely through the grid-to-plate interelectrode capacitance of the tube.

It is very inconvenient to use this circuit as a variable-frequency oscillator (VFO). At each new setting for the grid-tuning capacitor, the plate circuit would have to be readjusted. As a result, this circuit is primarily intended as a fixed-frequency oscillator. The circuit is the basis of operation of the Miller-type crystal oscillator, and, as such, it must be very carefully considered.

An application of this oscillator is widely used in the instrumentation field. To understand the circuit operation, assume that the grid tank resonates at 500 kc and that the plate tank resonates at 540 kc. The oscillator is greatly detuned and weakly oscillates at 500 kc. The plate current is near the maximum (point $h$ on Fig. 19–7). An aluminum vane is brought close to part of the grid coil. The nearness of the vane reduces the inductance of the coil (Section 6–3) and causes the resonant frequency of the grid tank to increase in value and come much closer to the resonant frequency of the plate-tank coil. Let us assume that the oscillator frequency rises to 530 kc. The plate current of the oscillator drops to point $f$ (Fig. 19–7). This change in direct plate current is used to operate a relay circuit. The mechanical power used to move the vane is very small, making it possible to use such signal sources as gas thermometers.

## Section 19–5   Crystals

Among a number of crystalline substances, quartz, Rochelle salt, barium titanate, and tourmaline are the most important that exhibit *piezoelectric* properties. If a slab of one of these crystalline substances is properly cut, a mechanical stress produces an emf across the slab. Conversely, an applied emf produces a mechanical stress. Rochelle salt produces the greatest piezoelectric reaction and is widely used in audio components such as microphones and phonograph pickups. Quartz has the best properties for radio-frequency work. It has a good mechanical strength, a high $Q$, a low-temperature drift, and a high degree of electrical stability.

A quartz crystal, when properly cut and ground, acts like a parallel-resonant circuit of high $Q$ and can be used as a tank circuit in many applications. A quartz crystal also has a series resonance which is frequently used in crystal filters. The principal uses of quartz plates are in oscillators and in filter circuits. The crystal must be mounted in a special holder (Fig. 19–8) and, since it is quite brittle, it must be treated in the same careful manner as a glass microscope slide.

A typical 430-kc crystal is $2.75 \times 3.33 \times 0.636$ cm in size. The values for the equivalent circuit for this crystal are:

$$C_1 \quad 5.8 \ \mu\mu\text{f} \qquad C_2 \quad 0.042 \ \mu\mu\text{f}$$
$$L \quad 3.3 \ \text{henrys} \qquad Q \quad 23,000$$

The resonant frequency of a crystal is inversely proportional to its size and thickness. Although the normal upper limit for crystals is about 10 Mc some are ground for use up to 30 Mc. These, however, are very thin and cannot take overloading without fracturing.

There are many ways of cutting a quartz plate from a crystal. The orientation of the cutting to the optical ($Z$) axis, the crystal faces (the $Y$ or mechanical axis), and the corners (the $X$ or electrical axis) determine the electrical properties of the crystal. Some of the characteristics of the different cuts are:

1. Suitability for different frequency ranges.
2. Suitability for filters.

3. Suitability for oscillators.

4. Different or zero temperature coefficients.

Certain cuts have a great deal of waste and, as a result, are more expensive. The different cuts from a natural quartz crystal are illustrated in Fig. 19–9.

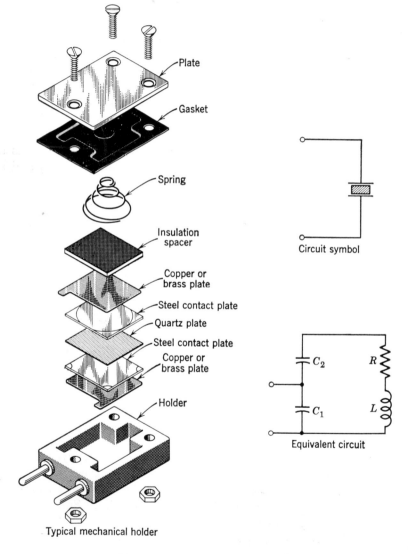

Circuit symbol

Equivalent circuit

**Figure 19–8** The quartz crystal.

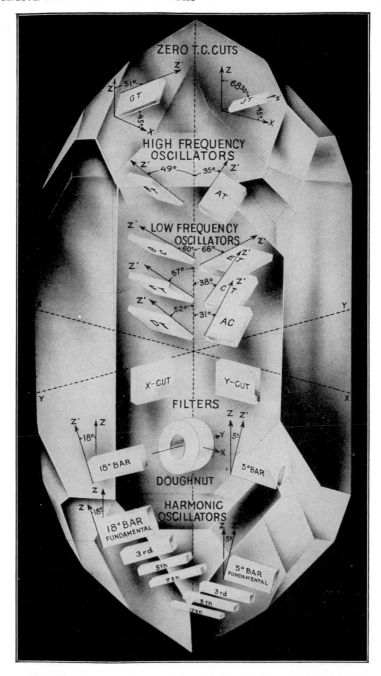

**Figure 19–9** Different cuts from a quartz crystal. (*Courtesy Bendz and Scarlott, Electronics for Industry*)

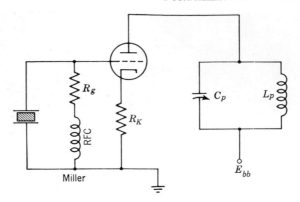

**Figure 19–10**   The Miller crystal oscillator.

## Section 19–6   The Crystal Oscillator

In the last section, we discussed the adaptability of the quartz crystal as an equivalent for a parallel circuit tuned for a particular frequency.   In Section 19–4, we developed the operation of the tuned-grid-tuned-plate oscillator in detail.   Now the two are combined to form the Miller crystal oscillator (Fig. 19–10).

The plate-tuning capacitor $C_p$ controls the action of this circuit in the same manner as the plate-tuning capacitor in the tuned-grid-tuned-plate oscillator.   The curves in Fig. 19–7 are also valid for the crystal oscillator with the same conditions of tuning in the plate circuit.   A cathode resistor $R_K$ may be used as a safety element, should the crystal fail to function.   The RF choke and the grid resistor limit the alternating grid voltage (and the RF crystal current) to a safe value.   Too large an alternating voltage across a crystal can cause the crystal to shatter from excessive mechanical vibrations. The crystal itself normally serves as the grid-leak capacitor.

A small variable capacitor is sometimes placed in parallel with the crystal.   It is possible to adjust the frequency of a crystal oscillator up to 50 or 100 cycles per megacycle by varying this capacitor. If a particular frequency must be exact, the grinding process becomes too critical, and this method of fine adjustment is often used.

Very often the temperature variation of a crystal causes the crystal to drift beyond the allowable limits of the required tolerance.   Then it is necessary to maintain the crystal in a temperature-controlled oven (Fig. 19–11).   When the oven is at operating temperature, the contacts of the bimetallic strip are open.   At the time the alternating

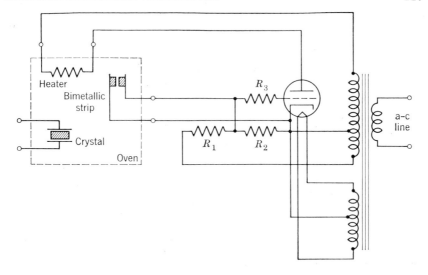

**Figure 19–11** Crystal in temperature-controlled oven.

voltage is positive on the plate, the grid is held below cutoff by the voltage drop across $R_2$. On the other half of the a-c cycle, when the grid voltage is positive, the plate voltage is negative. The limiting resistance $R_3$ prevents an excessive grid current when the grid is positive. When the oven falls in temperature, the contacts of the bimetallic strip close, short-circuiting the bias. The resistor $R_1$ prevents a short circuit on the line transformer. Plate current flows, allowing the heater element to develop an $I^2R$ heating in the oven. The fact that the waveform of the plate-current flow in the

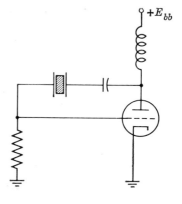

**Figure 19–12** The Pierce crystal oscillator.

heater element is that of a half-wave rectifier does not affect the operation of the crystal.

With great care the frequency of a 100-kc crystal oscillator can be maintained closer than one part in ten million.

Again referring to the table at the end of Section 18–1, the Pierce crystal oscillator is a crystal version of the Colpitts oscillator. The feedback element is a crystal which operates inductively, and the two elements, $X_1$ and $X_2$, are the interelectrode capacitances of the tube, $C_{gk}$ and $C_{pk}$. The circuit for this oscillator is given in Fig. 19–12.

The oscillator circuits for the point-contact transistor shown in Fig. 19–5 can be readily converted to a crystal oscillator by replacing

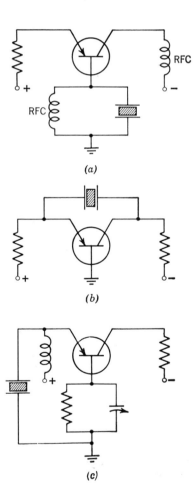

(a)

(b)

**Figure 19–13** Crystal oscillators using point-contact transistors.

(c)

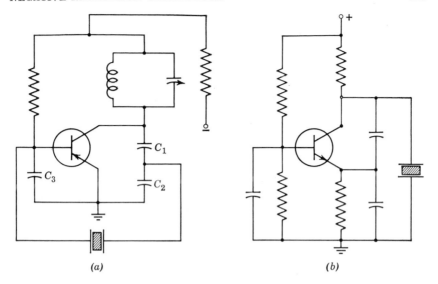

**Figure 19–14** Crystal oscillators using junction transistors. (a) Feedback oscillator. (b) Clapp oscillator.

the tank circuit by a crystal. Some typical point-contact transistor–crystal-oscillator circuits are shown in Fig. 19–13.

In the crystal oscillator of Fig. 19–14a, using a junction transistor, the crystal establishes the feedback between the collector and the base. The capacitors $C_1$ and $C_2$ serve as a voltage divider to reduce the alternating voltage to the crystal. The capacitor $C_3$ is added to balance $C_2$ so that the proper phase relation of the feedback voltage from the crystal is maintained. This particular circuit was developed to serve as a secondary standard at 100 kc. The circuit demands very little power from the battery and, as a result, does not drift from heating. When the supply is a single mercury cell, the current drain of the oscillator is of the order of 100 $\mu$a, and a battery life of many weeks is obtained under conditions of continuous operation.

A crystal oscillator can be formed by replacing the series-resonant circuit with a crystal in the Clapp oscillator circuit (Fig. 19–14b). The feedback is obtained by the dividing capacitors $C_1$ and $C_2$.

### Section 19–7  The Tri-Tet Oscillator

Since it is found that a change in plate load conditions changes the crystal-oscillator frequency slightly, an electron-coupled version of

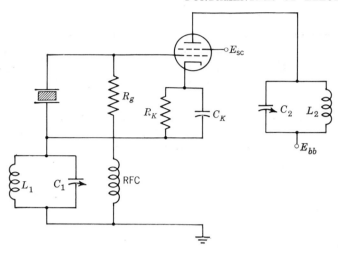

**Figure 19 15** The tri-tet oscillator.

the crystal oscillator (Fig. 19–15) is very useful to isolate the load from the oscillator.

The crystal is the grid tank, and $C_1 - L_1$ is the plate tank of the tuned-grid–tuned-plate oscillator. The screen of the tetrode serves as the oscillator plate in the same manner that the screen serves as the oscillator plate in the electron-coupled oscillator. The tank circuit, $C_2 - L_2$, is the tuned circuit of the electron-coupled load. The RF choke and the grid-leak resistor $R_g$ limit the grid current to a suitable value. The cathode resistor $R_K$, which is bypassed by $C_K$, prevents excessive tube currents when the circuit is not oscillating. The tank circuit in the cathode is detuned for oscillation by making the circuit capacitive as was done in the simple crystal-oscillator circuit.

It is very difficult to tune the output tank circuit, $C_2 - L_2$, to the fundamental frequency of the crystal. This tank is usually tuned to a harmonic of the crystal frequency. In this manner, the tri-tet circuit performs both the function of the crystal oscillator using an electron-coupled load and the function of a frequency-multiplier circuit.

### Section 19–8   Parasitic Oscillations

Many times in electronic circuits undesired negative-resistance phenomena establish conditions where unwanted, spurious oscillations

occur.   These oscillations are termed *parasitics*.   Typical sources of
negative resistances that are encountered are gas discharges and arcs,
interactions between the screen and the plate when tetrodes and pentodes are connected as triodes, and interactions within the parallel
operation of tubes.   The inductance and capacitance of the leads and
of the tube electrodes themselves provide a very high-frequency tank
circuit which can oscillate in conjunction with this negative resistance.

A parasitic oscillation consumes power which otherwise might be
converted into useful a-c power output.   A parasitic oscillation which
occurs within the tube envelope increases the heating of the tube.
Very often the parasitic oscillations radiate energy into space.   This
radiation can severely hamper the operation of commercial services
which are properly allocated to that part of the frequency spectrum
which suffers the interference.

In most cases, the elimination of the parasitic is insured by inserting
in the offending lead a small resistance which is sufficient to overcome
the negative-resistance effect.   These parasitic suppressors are usually
of the order of 10 or 100 ohms.   Because of the unwanted radiations
that occur, gas tubes are generally avoided where possible in communications equipments.   When they are used, they are very carefully
shielded to prevent stray radiation.


### . . . . Suggested References for Further Study

1. F. E. Terman, *Radio Engineer's Handbook*, Section 2, McGraw-Hill Book Co.,
   New York, 1943.
2. W. A. Edson, *Vacuum-Tube Oscillators*, John Wiley & Sons, New York, 1953.
3. R. F. Shea, *Principles of Transistor Circuits*, Chapter 13, John Wiley & Sons,
   New York, 1957.
4. T. L. Martin Jr., *Electronic Circuits*, Chapter 10, Prentice-Hall, Englewood
   Cliffs, N. J., 1955.

### . . . . QUESTIONS

1. Describe or explain each of the following terms: (*a*) negative resistance,
   (*b*) damping, (*c*) piezoelectric, (*d*) grinding, (*e*) holder, (*f*) oven, (*g*) mercury cell, (*h*) frequency multiplication, (*i*) cut, (*j*) parasitic.

2. Why does a negative resistance produce an oscillation?

3. Explain the difference between the two graphs shown in Fig. 19–2.

4. What is the advantage of the dynatron oscillator?

5. What property of a point-contact transistor enables it to be used as an oscillator?

6. Carefully explain the shape of the curves in Fig. 19–7.

7. Name four materials suitable for use as piezoelectric materials.

8. What are the functions of a crystal holder?

9. Explain the operation of the crystal oven (Fig. 19–11).

10. What is the difference between the Miller and the Pierce crystal oscillators?

11. Explain in detail the process in aligning the tri-tet oscillator.

12. What causes parasitic oscillations?

13. How do parasitic suppressors function?


# . . . . SPECIAL PROBLEMS

1. From an outside reference, explain the operation of a transitron oscillator.

2. From an outside reference, list the various crystal cuts, and describe the circuit advantages of each.

# Miscellaneous sine-wave oscillators

Balanced-bridge oscillators are widely used in applications of electronics. The basic concept of the balanced-bridge oscillator can best be understood from a study of the phase relations in a bridge and from a generalized block diagram (Section 20–1). The Wien bridge is analyzed as a bridge circuit (Section 20–2), and then it is applied to the electronic circuit to form an oscillator (Section 20–3). Phase-shift oscillators are discussed (Section 20–4). The Meissner oscillator which is a feedback oscillator (Section 20–5), furnishes the background for understanding the operation of a magnetostriction oscillator (Section 20–6). The tuning-fork oscillator (Section 20–7) is often used as a stable source of an audio-frequency signal.

### Section 20–1  Basic Concepts of the Bridge Oscillator

Consider a Wheatstone bridge (Fig. 20–1a) in which the resistances $R_1$ and $R_2$ are equal. The fixed arm of the bridge is $R_3$, and $R_4$ is the variable arm. When $R_3$ equals $R_4$, the bridge is balanced. Figure 20–1b shows the phasor diagram for the bridge at balance. Point $A$ which is the junction of $R_3$ and $R_4$ must be at the same potential as point $B$ because a condition of bridge balance requires that there is zero potential across the output terminals of the bridge, $A$ and $B$.

When $R_4$ is not equal to $R_3$, the bridge is unbalanced and a voltage exists across the output. When $R_4$ is less than $R_3$, point $A$ is at a lower potential than point $B$ as seen in the phasor diagram for the

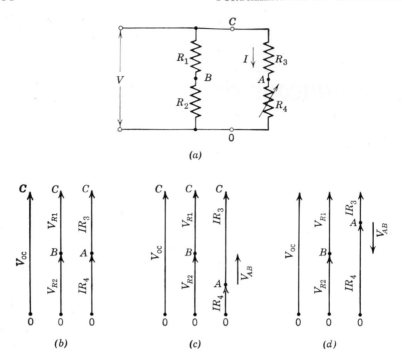

*(a)*

*(b)*                    *(c)*                    *(d)*

**Figure 20–1** The Wheatstone bridge. (*a*) Circuit. (*b*) Vector diagram at balance. (*c*) Vector diagram when $R_4 < R_3$. (*d*) Vector diagram when $R_4 > R_3$.

unbalance (Fig. 20–1*c*). The bridge output voltage, when measured *from A to B* is in phase with the applied voltage $V_{oc}$ since it acts in the same direction as the total applied bridge voltage, $V_{oc}$. When $R_4$ is greater than $R_3$, the potential of point $A$ is higher than the potential of point $B$, (Fig. 20–1*d*), and the voltage *from A to B* is 180° out of phase with $V_{oc}$ since it acts in the opposite direction to $V_{oc}$.

Let us connect this bridge into a two stage-amplifier (Fig. 20–2) which has a 180° phase shift in each stage or a total phase shift of 360°. This 360° total phase shift means that the input voltage and the output voltage are in phase. If the circuit is to function as an oscillator, the feedback must be positive, and, as a result, the bridge network cannot introduce a phase shift. Thus, when $R_4$ is greater than $R_3$, the input voltage $V_{AB}$ is 180° out of phase with the output voltage $V_{oc}$, and the circuit *cannot* oscillate. At balance, when $R_4$ equals $R_3$, there is zero output, and the circuit certainly cannot oscillate. When $R_4$ is less than $R_3$, the cathode-to-grid voltage $V_{AB}$ is in phase with the output voltage $V_{OC}$, providing positive feedback. The circuit now oscillates if the signal is strong enough, that is, if there is a sufficient amount of bridge unbalance. Reference to Fig. 20–1 shows that $V_{AB}$ is a certain fraction of $V_{OC}$. For example, if $V_{AB}$ is one-seventh the magnitude of $V_{OC}$, an amplifier gain of 7 is needed to set the circuit in oscillation. If the amplifier gain is 5, the circuit does not oscillate since $V_{AB}$ is only $\frac{1}{7} V_{OC}$. In order to have an oscillation exist, the magnitude of $V_{AB}$ must increase from $\frac{1}{7}$ to $\frac{1}{5} V_{OC}$.

Even if the unbalance of the bridge and the gain of the amplifier were proper for oscillation, we do not, as yet, have the automatic bias arrangement that is necessary to establish and to maintain a sinusoidal waveform. If we use a resistance panel lamp as the element $R_4$ in the bridge, we find that its nonlinear volt-ampere characteristic can provide this required variable amplitude control. When the voltage across a panel lamp increases, the resistance of the lamp increases. When the amplitude of the output of the oscillator increases, the voltage across the panel lamp increases, and its resistance increases accordingly. This increase in resistance brings the bridge closer to balance. The bridge output voltage decreases, and this causes the amplitude of the oscillation to decrease. When the output voltage of the oscillator decreases, the resistance of the lamp decreases, and this provides stronger oscillations to restore the output voltage to a fixed and stable value. By using this lamp, the amplitude of the oscillation is constant over a very wide range of frequencies.

If the circuit is to provide oscillations at a particular frequency, the resistance network of $R_1$ and $R_2$ must be replaced by a network that is frequency-selective. Then $R_1$ and $R_2$ are the equivalent circuit of this frequency-selective network "at resonance." At fre-

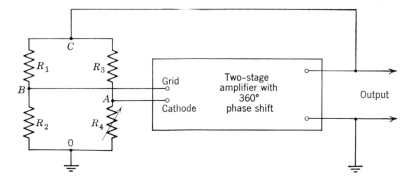

**Figure 20–2** Block diagram of bridge oscillator.

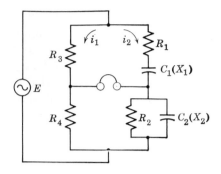

**Figure 20–3**   The Wien bridge.

quencies other than the resonant frequency, there is a reduced voltage $V_{AB}$ and a phase angle that differs from the desired inphase relationship.   There are a number of a-c bridges which may be used for this purpose.

### Section 20–2   The Wien Bridge

The Wien bridge (Fig. 20–3) is a frequency-selective network that does not use inductances.   Most bridges require an inductance arm. High-$Q$ inductances at low frequencies are both expensive and heavy. On the other hand, by using the Wien bridge, the inductance is not required, and capacitors are readily available that have negligible resistance.   This bridge circuit can be constructed quite easily and is both light in weight and compact.

At balance the bridge equations are as follows:

$$i_1 R_3 = i_2 (R_1 - jX_1)$$

$$i_1 R_4 = i_2 \frac{R_2(-jX_2)}{R_2 - jX_2}$$

Dividing one by the other, we get

$$\frac{R_3}{R_4} = \frac{(R_1 - jX_1)(R_2 - jX_2)}{-jR_2 X_2}$$

Expanding gives

$$\frac{R_3}{R_4} = \frac{R_1 R_2 - X_1 X_2 - jX_1 R_2 - jX_2 R_1}{-jR_2 X_2}$$

$$\frac{R_3}{R_4} = \frac{X_1 R_2 + X_2 R_1}{R_2 X_2} + j\frac{R_1 R_2 - X_1 X_2}{R_2 X_2}$$

If we equate the $j$ parts of this equation, we obtain

$$0 = j \, \frac{R_1 R_2 - X_1 X_2}{R_2 X_2}$$

or

$$R_1 R_2 = X_1 X_2 = \frac{1}{2\pi f_0 C_1} \frac{1}{2\pi f_0 C_2}$$

Then

$$f_0 = \frac{1}{2\pi \sqrt{R_1 R_2 C_1 C_2}}$$

By equating the "real" parts, we obtain the other balance equation:

$$\frac{R_3}{R_4} = \frac{X_1 R_2 + X_2 R_1}{R_2 X_2} = \frac{X_1 R_2}{R_2 X_2} + \frac{X_2 R_1}{R_2 X_2} = \frac{X_1}{X_2} + \frac{R_1}{R_2}$$

$$= \frac{\left(\dfrac{1}{2\pi f_0 C_1}\right)}{\left(\dfrac{1}{2\pi f_0 C_2}\right)} + \frac{R_1}{R_2}$$

Then

$$\frac{R_3}{R_4} = \frac{C_2}{C_1} + \frac{R_1}{R_2}$$

When $R_1 = R_2 = R$ and $C_1 = C_2 = C$, the final results for balance are

$$f_0 = \frac{1}{2\pi R C}$$

and

$$\frac{R_3}{R_4} = 2$$

We have developed this bridge derivation as an example of the analysis of a typical true a-c bridge circuit. This bridge circuit is found in a capacitance checker where a tuning-ray indicator is used as a balance detector. When we use this circuit in an oscillator, the fundamental bridge circuit is modified somewhat. In the next section we show these modifications in its adaptation to the oscillator circuit.

### Section 20–3  The Bridge Oscillator

In using this bridge in an oscillator circuit, the analysis of the bridge itself is not sufficient for an understanding of the complete oscillator

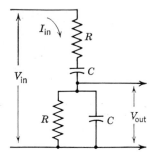

**Figure 20–4**  The modified Wien bridge circuit.

circuit.   We consider that part of the bridge circuit which contains the capacitors (Fig. 20–4) and use the simplifications from the bridge-balance equations wherein $R_1 = R_2 = R$ and $C_1 = C_2 = C$.   The total impedance of the circuit is

$$Z_{\text{in}} = R - jX + \frac{R(-jX)}{R - jX}$$

$$= \frac{R^2 - j2RX - X^2 - jRX}{R - jX}$$

$$= \frac{R^2 - X^2 - j3RX}{R - jX}$$

The total current is

$$I_{\text{in}} = \frac{V_{\text{in}}}{Z_{\text{in}}}$$

Then the output voltage is

$$V_{\text{out}} = I_{\text{in}} \left[ \frac{R(-jX)}{R - jX} \right] = \frac{V_{\text{in}}}{Z_{\text{in}}} \left( \frac{-jRX}{R - jX} \right)$$

Substituting the expression for $Z_{\text{in}}$, we have

$$V_{\text{out}} = \frac{V_{\text{in}}(R - jX)}{R^2 - X^2 - j3RX} \frac{-jRX}{R - jX}$$

Simplifying

$$V_{\text{out}} = \frac{-jRX}{R^2 - X^2 - j3RX} V_{\text{in}}$$

But at resonance which is bridge balance we have established that $R$ equals $X$, and this relation simplifies to

$$V_{\text{out}} = \frac{-jRX}{-j3RX} V_{\text{in}} = \tfrac{1}{3}V_{\text{in}}$$

If we plot the output voltage for a fixed input voltage over a range of frequencies and obtain the corresponding phase angles, we find that at resonance the output voltage is a maximum ($\tfrac{1}{3}V_{\text{in}}$) and the phase angle is zero. These results are shown in Fig. 20–5.

When this circuit is used in an oscillator (Fig. 20–6), the grid-to-ground signal is the output voltage of Fig. 20–4. The resistance $R_4$ is a panel lamp. Since the value of $V_{\text{out}}/V_{\text{in}}$ is one-third for the capacitive branch at balance, the value of $R_4$ must be less than one-half the value of $R_3$ to sustain the oscillations. We recall at this point that the balance equations for the Wein bridge require that $R_3$ is twice the value of $R_4$ at balance. The oscillation occurs at that frequency at which $V_{\text{out}}/V_{\text{in}}$ is a maximum and at which the phase angle is zero in the bridge arm. When the frequency of the circuit is to be continuously variable, switched values of the resistors $R$ give the different frequency ranges and the capacitors, $C$ are ganged as a continuously variable tuning capacitor. If the two-stage amplifier is wide-band, this oscillator can cover, for example, a frequency range

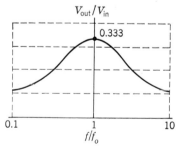

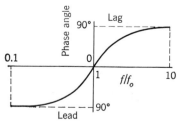

**Figure 20–5** Response of the network of Fig. 20–4.

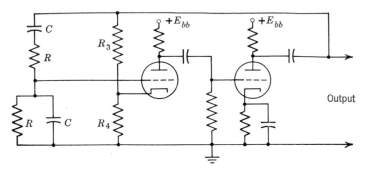

**Figure 20-6**   The basic Wien bridge oscillator.

from 20 cycles to 200,000 cycles with a distortion of less than 1%. Transistors may be used in this circuit in place of the vacuum tubes.

Other types of a-c bridges may be used in place of the Wien bridge. For example, a resonance bridge consists of three resistive arms with the fourth arm comprising $R$, $L$, and $C$. At balance, $X_L$ equals $X_C$, and a simple Wheatstone bridge-balance relation exists for the four resistances. When this bridge is incorporated in a vacuum-tube oscillator circuit, it is known as the Meacham oscillator.

### Section 20-4   The Phase-Shift Oscillator

In a phase-shift oscillator (Fig. 20-7) the amplifier usually consists of a single-stage circuit using a vacuum tube or a transistor in which the output is 180° out of phase with the input. The output is fed back into the input through a phase-shift network. The phase-shift network must produce a 180° phase shift at one particular frequency to develop the required positive feedback. When the gain of the amplifier is $A_e$, the loss through the phase-shift network can be no greater than $1/A_e$ in order to maintain the oscillation.

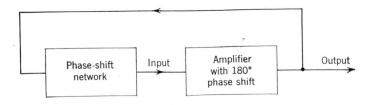

**Figure 20-7**   Block diagram of a phase-shift oscillator.

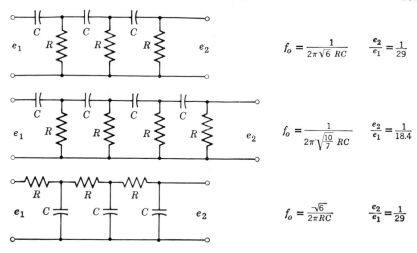

$$f_o = \frac{1}{2\pi \sqrt{6}\ RC} \qquad \frac{e_2}{e_1} = \frac{1}{29}$$

$$f_o = \frac{1}{2\pi \sqrt{\frac{10}{7}}\ RC} \qquad \frac{e_2}{e_1} = \frac{1}{18.4}$$

$$f_o = \frac{\sqrt{6}}{2\pi RC} \qquad \frac{e_2}{e_1} = \frac{1}{29}$$

**Figure 20-8** Typical phase-shift oscillator networks.

The usual networks developed for these oscillators are simple resistance–capacitance arrangements. Some of these networks are shown in Fig. 20–8.

The parallel-T network configuration is widely used for developing a frequency discrimination without the use of inductances. This network as used in the phase-shift oscillator is shown in Fig. 20–9.

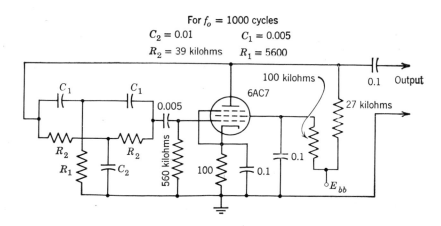

**Figure 20-9** Phase-shift oscillator using parallel–T network.

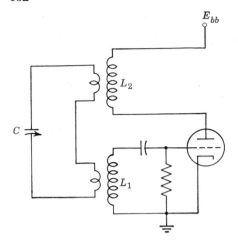

Figure 20–10 The Meissner oscillator.

## Section 20–5   The Meissner Oscillator

A discussion of the Meissner oscillator properly belongs with the feedback oscillators in Chapter 19. However, since it is a special form of the basic oscillator, we are using it here as a simple approach to understanding the action of the mechanical oscillator. In the Meissner circuit (Fig. 20–10) coupling between the plate and the grid coils is made not by a direct mutual inductance, but by means of a *link*.

A link is, in effect, the complete network of a secondary winding of a transformer, the connecting wires, and the primary winding of another transformer. A link is used to transfer energy from one point on a chassis to another, and it is most often used to transfer energy from one class-C tank to another. In this latter application, the connecting wires of the link are usually twisted to prevent radiation from the wires of the link. Normally, in a class-C application, the link does not discriminate between energies of different frequencies since a tuned tank circuit reflects into the link as a resistance.

In this Meissner circuit, a tuning capacitor is inserted in series with the link. The tuning capacitor resonates with the values of the inductance of the coils, $L_1$ and $L_2$, reflected into the link by transformer action. Now there is a maximum energy transfer in the link at one particular frequency, and this circuit oscillates at that frequency.

## Section 20–6   The Magnetostriction Oscillator

Certain substances, such as cobalt, nickel, and stainless steel, expand and contract when they are placed in an a-c magnetic field.

A rod made of a magnetostrictive substance can be used to take the place of the tuned link in the Meissner circuit. The contraction or expansion in the material as a wave at the speed of sound along the bar is resonant at a frequency that depends on the length of the bar (Fig. 20–11). This mechanical resonance acts in the same manner as the tuned link in the Meissner oscillator.

The magnetostriction oscillator is used principally to generate ultrasonic frequencies. The bar is connected to a form of loudspeaker called a *transducer* which produces ultrasonic "audio." Ultrasonic frequencies are used industrially in such varied applications as product inspection, smoke control, liquid emulsification, cutting, cleaning, and germ-control processes.

## Section 20–7   The Tuning-Fork Oscillator

The tuning-fork oscillator or "microphone hummer" as it is sometimes called (Fig. 12–12) is used as a very stable single-frequency source. The natural frequency of the fork determines the frequency of the oscillator. The vibrations of the tuning fork drive the carbon-microphone diaphragm (Section 25–1) in and out. This changing position of the diaphragm causes the current through the solenoid to vary with the mechanical position of the tuning fork. The changing current through the solenoid coil produces a magnetic coupling between the solenoid and the tuning fork which serves as the positive feedback which is necessary for an oscillator.

The tuning-fork oscillator is often used as the signal source for self-contained a-c bridges. The circuit is also used in telephone equipment as a source of fundamental and harmonic test and ringing frequencies.

**Figure  20–11**  The  magneto-striction oscillator.

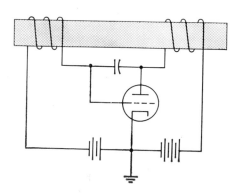

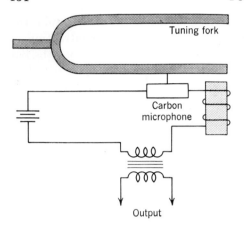

Tuning fork

Carbon microphone

**Figure 20–12**   The tuning-fork oscillator

Output

# . . . . Suggested References for Further Study

1. T. L. Martin Jr., *Electronic Circuits*, Chapter 10, Prentice Hall, Englewood Cliffs, N. J., 1955.
2. F. E. Terman, *Radio Engineer's Handbook*, Section 6, McGraw-Hill Book Co., New York, 1943.
3. W. A. Edson, *Vacuum-Tube Oscillators*, John Wiley & Sons, New York, 1953.

# . . . . QUESTIONS

1. Describe or explain each of the following terms: (*a*) bridge, (*b*) bridge balance, (*c*) thermal element, (*d*) link, (*e*) magnetostriction, (*f*) tuning fork, (*g*) ultrasonic, (*h*) transducer, (*i*) microphone hummer, (*j*) solenoid.

2. Show how inphase and out-of-phase voltage can be produced by a Wheatstone bridge.

3. Answer question 2 if the variable arm of the bridge is a lamp.

4. Why can two equations be obtained from one equation in an a-c bridge circuit?

5. When the response of the Wien bridge is that given in Fig. 20–5, show that the bridge tends to return to the center instead of drifting off.

6. Explain the action of the panel lamp, $R_4$, in Fig. 20–6.

7. What are the gain requirements for the circuits to be used with the phase-shift networks of Fig. 20–8.

8. What is the frequency response of the parallel–T network included in the circuit of Fig. 20–9?

9. Explain the operation of the Meissner oscillator.

10. Show how the magnetostriction oscillator is a Meissner oscillator.

11. What are the advantages and disadvantages of the tuning-fork oscillator?

## . . . . SPECIAL PROBLEMS

1. Derive the equations for the networks shown in Fig. 20–8.

2. Derive a general balance equation for the parallel–T network shown in Fig. 20–9.

# Nonsinusoidal oscillators

• • • • • • • • • • • • • • • • • • • CHAPTER 21

A relaxation oscillator is a circuit in which a tube is first "on" and then "off," producing a self-sustained oscillation. The principles of the relaxation oscillator can be demonstrated by the use of a neon lamp (Section 21–1). The replacement of the neon lamp by a thyratron in the circuit improves the operation (Section 21–2). It is usually desired to lock-in or synchronize this circuit to an outside source (Section 21–3). These principles of synchronization may also be applied to the blocking oscillator (Section 21–4) and to the multivibrator (Section 21–5). A variation of the basic multivibrator circuit is the cathode-coupled multivibrator (Section 21–6). These relaxation oscillators can produce a sawtooth output by use of a discharge circuit (Section 21–7). Transistor power supplies are examined (Section 21–8).

### Section 21–1   The Neon-Lamp Oscillator

A neon lamp (Section 2–4) ionizes at approximately 65 volts and deionizes at approximately 50 volts. It is used in the basic relaxation circuit (Fig. 21–1). If the neon lamp is not in the circuit, when the supply voltage is turned on, the voltage across the capacitor rises from zero and builds up exponentially to the value of the supply voltage along curve 0–1–$a$. With the neon lamp in the circuit, when the capacitor voltage reaches the ionization potential, 65 volts (point 1), the neon lamp fires and discharges the capacitor. When the discharging capacitor voltage falls to 50 volts, point 2, the neon lamp deionizes because $R$ is sufficiently large to limit the current below the minimum level needed to maintain the ionization in the gas. As

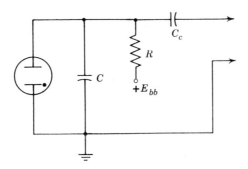

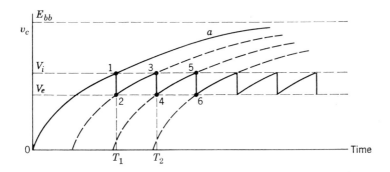

**Figure 21-1**   The neon-lamp relaxation oscillator.

soon as the neon lamp completely deionizes, the capacitor begins to recharge following path 2–3 and the cycle repeats.  The output is, for the numerical values we have used, a 15-volt peak-to-peak saw-tooth wave.

The resistance–capacitance charging curve for the exponential rise is represented by

$$v_c = E_{bb}[1 - \epsilon^{-t/RC}] = E_{bb} - E_{bb}\epsilon^{-t/RC}$$

The ionization potential $V_i$ occurring on this curve at point 3, which is $T_2$, is

$$V_i = E_{bb} - E_{bb}\epsilon^{-T_2/RC}$$

and the extinction potential $V_e$, occurring at point 2, which is $T_1$, is

$$V_e = E_{bb} - E_{bb}\epsilon^{-T_1/RC}$$

Solving each for $T_1$ and $T_2$, we have

$$\epsilon^{-T_2/RC} = \frac{E_{bb} - V_i}{E_{bb}} \quad \text{and} \quad \epsilon^{-T_1/RC} = \frac{E_{bb} - V_e}{E_{bb}}$$

Then

$$-\frac{T_2}{RC} = \ln \frac{E_{bb} - V_i}{E_{bb}} = \ln (E_{bb} - V_i) - \ln E_{bb}$$

and

$$-\frac{T_1}{RC} = \ln \frac{E_{bb} - V_e}{E_{bb}} = \ln (E_{bb} - V_e) - \ln E_{bb}$$

Subtracting the first from the second gives

$$\frac{T_2}{RC} - \frac{T_1}{RC} = \ln (E_{bb} - V_e) - \ln (E_{bb} - V_i)$$

or

$$T_2 - T_1 = RC \ln \frac{E_{bb} - V_e}{E_{bb} - V_i}$$

Since $(T_2 - T_1)$ is the period of the wave, the frequency of the sawtooth is

$$f = \frac{1}{T_2 - T_1} = \frac{1}{RC \ln \dfrac{E_{bb} - V_e}{E_{bb} - V_i}} \tag{21-1}$$

A discussion of the operation of the circuit may be made from either the waveform of Fig. 21-1 or from this equation.    When the value of the capacitor or resistor is increased, the charging action is slower and the frequency decreases.    When the supply voltage is increased, the time between $T_2$ and $T_1$ decreases and the frequency increases. Also, when the supply voltage is increased, the amount of curvature between $V_e$ and $V_i$ decreases, and the sawtooth output approximates the ideal waveform.

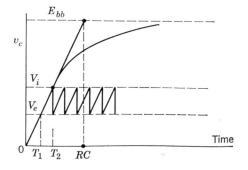

**Figure 21-2** Waveform assuming linear charging rate.

Figure 21–3  Output waveform at high frequency.

If the supply voltage is much higher than the ionization potential, the waveform may be taken as a pure sawtooth waveform, and the charging action of the capacitor may be assumed a straight line. This straight line, when extended, reaches the supply voltage $E_{bb}$ at that value of time which is the time constant $RC$ (Fig. 21–2). An increase in $E_{bb}$ increases the frequency of the sawtooth and an increase in either $R$ or $C$ decreases the frequency.

Any discharging tube used in a relaxation-oscillator circuit has a peak current limitation. If the limit on the neon lamp used in this circuit is 3 ma, in order to protect the tube, a series current-limiting resistance is required. Taking the normal tube drop as 53 volts and the peak potential (ionization) as 65 volts, a resistance must be used across which the voltage drop is 12 volts for 3 ma or 4000 ohms. This means that, in addition to the normal deionization time, there is also a discharge time-constant made up of this protective resistance and the capacitor. The time of ionization, although shorter than the time of deionization, is nevertheless finite. When the frequency of these gas-tube relaxation oscillators becomes high, in the order of 10 kc to 50 kc, these factors cannot be neglected and do become an appreciable part of the cycle, and the deviation from a sawtooth waveform is pronounced, Fig. 21–3.

The application of the neon lamp as a relaxation oscillator is limited. The small peak-to-peak voltage is the most serious disadvantage of the circuit. The operation of the tube is relatively high on the charging curve and results in an excessive curvature of the sawtooth output. Also the ionization and deionization potentials of a neon lamp are not particularly stable.

### Section 21–2  The Thyratron Relaxation Oscillator

By using a thyratron, such as an 884, in place of the neon lamp (Fig. 21–4), a lower value of deionization potential is obtained (approximately 16 to 20 volts), and the ionization potential can be controlled by the direct bias voltage. The gas mixture of small thyratrons has

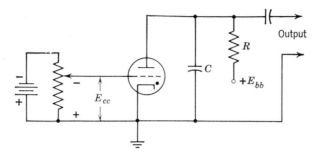

**Figure 21-4**   The thyratron relaxation oscillator.

shorter ionization and deionization times than the neon lamp.   The higher peak-current ratings of thyratrons improves the waveform at high frequency.

The waveform (Fig. 21–5), by operating on the lower part of the charging curve, is more linear.   The limitations of linearity, of peak-current protection and of high-frequency use are similar to the limitations of the neon lamp circuit.   The equation for frequency is valid, also, for this circuit.

If the charging current of the capacitor $C$ were constant, the waveform of the increasing voltage across the capacitor would be a perfect sawtooth without curvature.   Since the plate current of a pentode is constant and independent of plate voltage over a wide range of voltage, circuits have been devised in which the pentode is in series with the charging circuit to produce this ideal sawtooth wave.

Switched values of fixed capacitors for $C$ give the frequency ranges, and a potentiometer in series with a fixed resistor for $R$ gives smooth

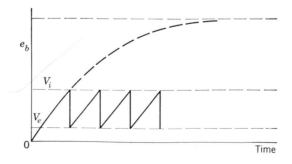

**Figure 21-5**   Output waveform of the thyratron relaxation oscillator.

frequency variations in applications of this circuit. The circuit is usually used to provide the timing or the sweep voltage for a cathode-ray-tube oscilloscope (Chapter 26).

The type of tube used in the circuit determines the extinction voltage $V_e$. The d-c bias $-E_{cc}$ determines the ionization potential $V_i$. Thus, $R$ and $C$ alone control the resulting frequency, and variations in $R$ and $C$ do not affect the amplitude of the sawtooth output. When everything is fixed in the circuit except the supply voltage, an increase in $E_{bb}$ results in a shorter charging time and, thus, increases the output frequency without changing the amplitude. When the only variable is the d-c bias, an increase in negative bias increases the ionization potential $V_i$. This results in an increase in the amplitude of the output wave and also causes a decrease in the frequency.

### Section 21-3   Synchronization

To *synchronize* or *sync* a free-running oscillator means to lock it in to an external signal source. If the outside signal frequency changes slightly, a properly synchronized circuit changes its frequency accordingly. The synchronized circuit now operates at a *forced frequency* instead of at a *free-running frequency*.

Let us assume that, in this thyratron circuit, the fixed bias is set at $-10$ volts. From the firing or control characteristic (Fig. 21-6), the thyratron fires at 100 volts and goes out at 20 volts. Then, the free-running waveform is 0-1-2-3-4-5. At the instant the plate voltage is 80 volts, let us introduce a sharp $+2$-volt pulse into the grid. Then, the net bias is $-8$ volts, and the tube fires at $T'_A$. Again, when the plate voltage rises to 80 volts, another $+2$-volt pulse fires the tube. If these pulses are a continuous train, the new output waveform is 0-1'-2'-3'-4'-5'.

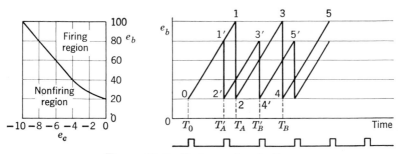

**Figure 21-6**   Basic synchronization.

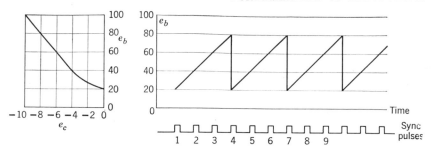

**Figure 21–7**   Synchronization at a higher frequency.

If these synchronizing pulses were less than $+2$ volts, they would not fire the thyratron each time. Thus, one requirement for synchronization is that *the synchronizing voltage must be sufficiently large to synchronize.* If the synchronizing pulses arrive after the tube has already fired, they are too late. In other words, the time interval $(T'_A - T_0)$ must be less than the time interval $(T_A - T_0)$. Or *the synchronizing frequency must be greater than the free-running frequency of the oscillator.* A third requirement for the synchronizing pulse is peculiar to gas tubes: The duration of the synchronizing pulse must be at least the ionization time; otherwise the thyratron cannot fire.

We have indicated that the sync voltage is a series of short-duration square pulses. This waveform is the ideal. The action of synchronization is clearly and sharply defined. It should be understood that a sine wave or an irregular waveform may be used, and the synchronization functions in the same manner.

Very often it is desirable to synchronize a low-frequency oscillator to a high-frequency signal, for example, a 1000-cycle oscillator to a 3000-cycle signal. Thus, in this example, every third cycle is to synchronize. Again, taking the same circuit as before with a fixed bias of $-10$ volts, a $+2$-volt synchronizing signal fires the oscillator on pulses 1, 4, and 7 in Fig. 21–7. When pulses 3 and 6 appear at the grid, the plate voltage is 60 volts. For 60 volts, the firing grid potential is $-6$ volts, whereas we have $-8$ volts which does not allow the tube to fire. When pulses 2 and 5 come to the grid, the plate voltage is 40 volts. For 40 volts on the plate, the firing grid potential is $-4$ volts. Thus, pulses 2, 3, 5, and 6 "miss." With a $-10$-volt bias and a 3000-cycle synchronizing train of $+2$-volt pulses, the oscillator is locked in at 1000 cycles to the 3000–cycle synchronization.

The level of the sync pulses can be raised from $+2$ volts to $+3.99$ volts with no effect. When the sync pulse level is raised to $+4$ volts, the net bias becomes −6 volts during the duration of the pulse.    For a bias of −6 volts, the tube fires at a plate voltage of 60 volts.    Now, the tube fires on pulses 1, 3, 5, and 7.    Thus, the oscillator frequency changes suddenly from 1000 cycles to 2000 cycles.    If the pulse level is raised again, at a +6-volt pulse level the tube fires on each pulse. Now the thyratron circuit is driven at 3000 cycles although its own free-running frequency is less than 1000 cycles.

It is not desirable to have this wide difference between the free-running and the lock-in frequency.    Not only is the amplitude of the circuit reduced, but there is also the possibility of a bad distortion of the waveform.    Thus, a general rule should be observed: *Use only enough synchronizing voltage to obtain good synchronization.*

Figure 21–8 shows a thyratron relaxation circuit with a provision for sync voltage injection.    When the sync voltage-control potentiometer is set at the center, the synchronizing voltage on the thyratron grid is zero, and the oscillator is free running.    This circuit arrangement of the potentiometer provides a positive synchronizing voltage at the grid for either polarity of the incoming pulse, up for positive and down for negative.    When the sync input is a sine wave, the circuit may now be synchronized on either the positive or the negative half of the wave.

We have shown in detail the process of synchronization by the use of a grid-voltage injection.    A positive pulse fed into the plate circuit would also provide synchronization, or a negative pulse fed into the cathode could be used.    In a screen circuit, a positive pulse is required for synchronization.    We have discussed synchronization as the process where the cycle is "started" by means of a pulse.    It is also possible (more easily in vacuum-tube circuits than in gas-tube circuits)

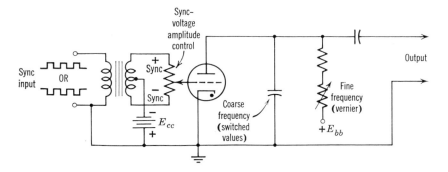

**Figure 21–8**    Relaxation oscillator with provision for synchronization.

to "stop" a cycle of the oscillation by the use of a pulse of opposite polarity. For instance, a large negative pulse on a grid or on a plate "stops" current flow.

### Section 21–4  The Blocking Oscillator

The circuit of the blocking oscillator (Fig. 21–9) is a modified Armstrong oscillator. The Armstrong oscillator uses an air-core transformer which has a low coefficient of coupling of the order of a few per cent. A large alternating voltage in $L_p$ induces only a few volts in $L_s$, the grid winding. The grid-leak bias action establishes a stable sinusoidal condition where just enough voltage is fed back into the grid circuit to maintain the oscillation. In the blocking oscillator, the coefficient of coupling is raised by means of a carefully designed core to almost unity. If the turns ratio of the transformer, $N_s/N_p$, is three, a 100-volt plate signal produces 300 volts in the grid winding. This 300-volt signal violently drives the grid positive and establishes a high direct voltage on the grid leak. This d-c bias cuts off the tube completely and abruptly ends and "blocks" further current flow. The tube remains "blocked" until the direct grid-leak bias voltage discharges to the cutoff point of the tube. Now the oscillator tries to oscillate and is, again, immediately "blocked."

There is a stray winding capacitance within the turns of the blocking transformer which determines a particular resonant frequency for the transformer. When the oscillator is cut off, the plate voltage is the supply voltage $E_{bb}$. When the grid discharges to cutoff, plate current starts to flow, inducing a positive voltage on the grid of the tube through the transformer. The circuit shuts off at the peak value of

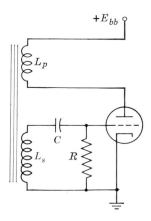

**Figure 21–9**  The blocking oscillator.

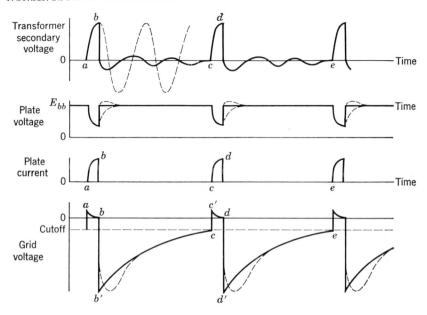

**Figure 21-10** Waveforms of the blocking oscillator.

the cycle. Thus, the normal oscillator action of the circuit as an Armstrong oscillator is limited to a quarter of one cycle. This "on" time of the blocking oscillator is established by the transformer design. The "off" time of the blocking oscillator is a function of the time constant of the grid-leak circuit, $R$ and $C$.

With these "on–off" circuits, a specific reference to *frequency* could prove confusing as there are different times involved. To avoid this, a new term is introduced, *pulse-repetition rate*. With the blocking oscillator, a pulse-repetition rate of 400 means that there are 400 "on" and 400 "off" conditions per second. The blocking oscillator and the multivibrator are standard integral parts of television receivers and, in this application, have reached many people whose electronic knowledge is centered on radio. As a result, the term *pulse-repetition rate* for these two circuits is dropped and the term *frequency* is used indescriminately. In equipment where these circuits are used as pulse generators, the term *pulse-repetition rate* is retained.

The waveforms for the blocking oscillator are shown in Fig. 21–10. The solid lines are for ideal conditions which are considered first. The vacuum tube is "on" during the intervals *ab* and *cd* and is "off" during *bc* and *de*. The transformer secondary voltage has a very high amplitude which is usually several hundred volts. The transformer secondary voltage is purely alternating, and, by definition of an a-c wave, the area under the curve above the zero axis must be equal to the area below the zero axis. Another approach to this waveform is to consider that from $a$ to $b$ energy is stored up in the magnetic field within the transformer. When the tube is cut off at $b$, this energy must be dissipated and produces a high "back voltage." This release of stored energy in the transformer causes an oscillation within the secondary winding of the transformer which dies out rapidly. This "die-away" is seen on the waveform. The amount of damping in the transformer and in the circuit controls the amplitude of this transient oscillation. If the circuit did not block, the transformer secondary waveform would be the dotted sine wave.

When the tube goes into the start of an oscillation, $ab$ and $cd$, the plate voltage falls, the plate current rises, and the grid is driven positive. The positive grid draws grid current which tends to flatten the bottom of the plate-voltage waveform and the top of the plate-current pulse. As the grid-leak capacitor charges up, the positive voltage on the grid drops to zero, giving rise to the positive tip on the grid-voltage waveform. At $b$ and $d$, the oscillator blocks and the circuit is abruptly cut off. The plate current drops to zero, the plate voltage rises to $E_{bb}$, and the grid becomes very strongly cut off, $b'$ and $d'$. The circuit remains cut off until the grid-leak capacitance voltage discharges through the grid-leak resistor $R$, and the second-

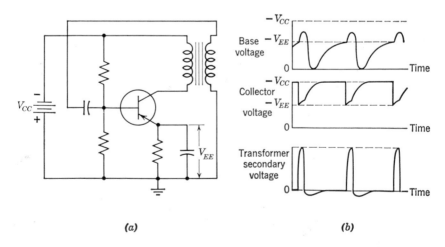

*(a)*          *(b)*

**Figure 21-11** The transistor blocking oscillator. *(a)* Circuit. *(b)* Waveforms.

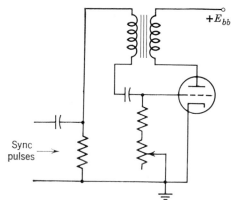

$+E_{bb}$

**Figure 21–12** Blocking oscillator with provision for synchronization.

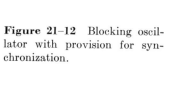

Sync pulses

ary winding of the transformer to the cutoff value of grid voltage, $c$ and $e$. Then the cycle repeats.

The effect of the release of the stored energy in the transformer changes these waveforms slightly to the dotted waveforms. The plate voltage does not return to $E_{bb}$ at $b$ and $d$, but usually returns with a time delay, although at times the circuit values are such to cause an overshoot. The effect of the induced voltage in the secondary winding is more pronounced in the grid-voltage waveform. The sharp points at $b'$ and at $d'$ are lost, and the grid wave exhibits a negative loop instead. When the secondary is loaded by a damping resistor or by another tube, as shown in Fig. 21–22$a$, the waveforms approach the ideal.

Normally, there is no control over the time intervals, $ab$ and $cd$. The natural resonant frequency of the blocking-oscillator transformer determines this time. The time intervals, $bc$ and $de$ are easily controlled by making part of the grid-leak resistance $R$ a variable resistor.

A transistor blocking-oscillator circuit and the waveforms are shown in Fig. 21–11. The vertical axis of the waveforms shows negative voltage increasing upward, in order to keep the phase relations consistent with the vacuum-tube blocking-oscillator circuit. A voltage-divider network establishes a d-c bias on the base, and it is very slightly greater in magnitude than $V_{EE}$. If the base voltage falls below $V_{EE}$, the transistor is cut off. Then the reference axis for the waveform in this circuit is $V_{EE}$, whereas in the vacuum-tube circuit the reference was the cutoff voltage on the grid. The waveforms and the explanation for the waveforms are the same as for the vacuum-tube circuit.

Vacuum-tube blocking oscillators are readily synchronized by positive pulses of the order of 10 to 20 volts. The positive pulse brings the grid to and above cutoff earlier than cutoff would be reached for the *RC* grid-leak discharge action alone. For transistor circuits, the polarity of the sync pulse depends on whether a *PNP* or an *NPN* transistor is used. In a television receiver the variable resistance in the grid adjusts the free-running pulse-repetition rate so that it is slightly slower than the pulse-repetition rate of the incoming sync signals from the program transmitter. This control in the television receiver is labeled "hold."

### Section 21–5   The Multivibrator

The multivibrator, devised by H. Abraham and E. Block in 1918, was one of the earliest developed forms of the vacuum-tube oscillator. This circuit (Fig. 21–13) consists of a two-stage *RC*-coupled amplifier, which is fed back on itself. Since each stage provides a 180° phase shift, the over-all feedback is positive. The circuit arrangement does not limit the resultant oscillation to a sine wave, but allows the amplitude to rise to the limits of the tubes. One limit is tube cutoff, and the other is the effect of driving the grids positive. Both these limits clip the sine wave and produce a square wave. The plate voltage of tube *V*1 is 180° out of phase with tube *V*2. The plate waveforms are shown in Fig. 21–14.

Unfortunately this simple explanation does not give us an understanding of the grid-voltage waveform which is most necessary for this circuit. We will use a process of reasoning which is accepted in

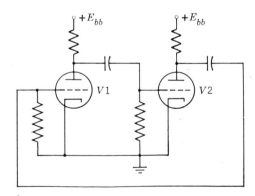

**Figure 21–13**   The basic multivibrator.

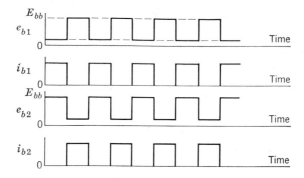

**Figure 21–14**  Basic waveforms of a multivibrator.

mathematics: We assume that the circuit does work, and then we show that it must so function.

Assume that $V1$ (in Fig. 21–15) has plate current and that the plate current in $V2$ is zero. Also assume that, with current flow, the plate voltage of tube $V1$ is 50 volts. Since $V2$ is cut off, its plate voltage is the supply voltage, 250 volts. The polarity of the voltages on the capacitors is indicated on the circuit diagram. The magnitude of the voltage on $C_1$ is 50 volts, and the voltage on $C_2$ is 250 volts.

Now, assume that plate current starts to flow in $V2$. This current flow produces an $IR$ drop in $R_{L2}$, and the plate voltage of $V2$ decreases. The potential from plate to ground of $V2$ is now less than 250 volts. The value of the charge on $C_2$ produced by the 250 volts cannot change immediately—it must take time—there is a time constant involved in $R_{g1}$ and $C_2$. If the right side of $C_2$ drops to, say, $+200$ volts with respect to ground, since the voltage on $C_2$ is set at 250 volts, then, the left side of $C_2$ must now be $-50$ volts with respect to ground. Thus, a lowered and falling voltage on the plate of $V2$ causes a lowered and falling negative voltage on the grid of $V1$. This negative voltage on the grid of $V1$ cuts off $V1$. These last three sentences are the key to understanding the operation of this circuit. The plate of $V1$ tries to rise to $+250$ volts, but, as $C_1$ cannot change from its original 50 volts instantaneously, the grid of $V2$ is forced positive. Forcing the grid of $V2$ positive speeds up the action of $V2$ in going from a condition of zero plate current to maximum plate current. Because of grid current from $V2$, both $e_{b1}$ and $C_1$ quickly come to 250 volts.

When the plate of $V2$ falls to 50 volts, the grid of $V1$ is simultaneously driven to $-200$ volts. Now the circuit conditions are: $V2$ has plate current, and $V1$ is cut off. The tubes have switched.

$V1$ stays cut off until $C_2$ discharges through $R_{g1}$ down to the cutoff value. When $C_2$ discharges sufficiently to allow a plate current on $V1$, the action switches back between the two tubes in the same manner as we have described.

The complete waveforms are shown in Fig. 21–16. The tips or tails marked $x$ are caused by grid-current flow. The curvature marked $y$ is caused by the time constant involved when the coupling capacitors recharge to the supply voltage. The grid discharge from $z$ to cutoff has the same curvature as the $RC$ discharge in the grid of the blocking-oscillator circuit. If the output is taken in push–pull, the tips $x$ tend to cancel the curvatures $y$, and a much cleaner square-wave shape results. When the push–pull wave is fed into a clipping circuit arrangement, a very good square wave is produced.

The time that $V1$ is cut off is determined by the time constant of $R_{g1}$ and $C_2$. The time that $V2$ is cut off is determined by $R_{g2}$ and $C_1$. This assumes that the equivalent plate-to-cathode resistances of the tubes when plate currents flow are small compared to the values of $R_{g1}$ and $R_{g2}$. These times are also a function of the supply voltage, of the cutoff voltage, and of the plate voltage existing when full plate current flows. These last three factors are the same for the two tubes and are usually fixed for a particular circuit. At high frequencies, the interelectrode capacitances must be considered in the time constant. The period of the fundamental frequency of the multivibrator is the sum of these two discharge times.

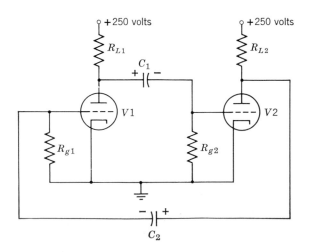

**Figure 21–15** The action of a multivibrator.

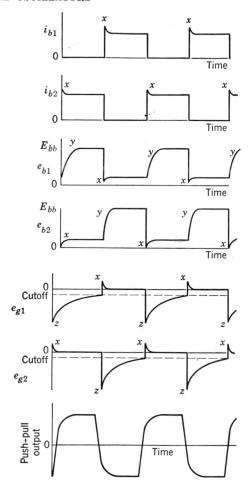

**Figure 21-16**  Complete waveforms for the multivibrator.

When a multivibrator is unbalanced, the circuit produces both long and short pulses.  A typical circuit and the waveforms are shown in Fig. 21-17.

The circuit and the waveforms for a multivibrator using transistors are shown in Fig. 21-18.  The vertical axis of the waveforms, as with the waveforms of the transistor blocking oscillator, is drawn to present the waveforms in that phase relation which enables them to be compared to the conventional waveforms of the vacuum-tube circuit. Again, in the circuit, a cutoff condition exists for the transistor when

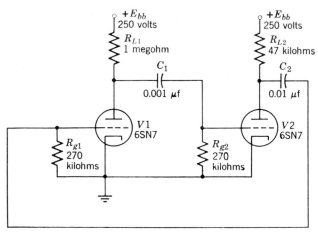

$R_{L1} \neq R_{L2}$ or $C_1 \neq C_2$ or $R_{g1} \neq R_{g2}$ or
a combination of these inequalities.

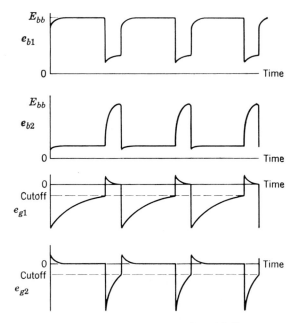

**Figure 21–17** The unbalanced multivibrator.

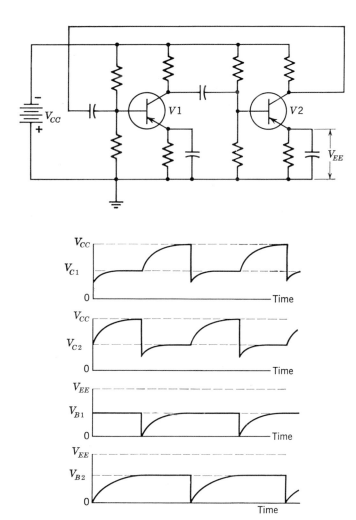

**Figure 21–18** The transistor multivibrator.

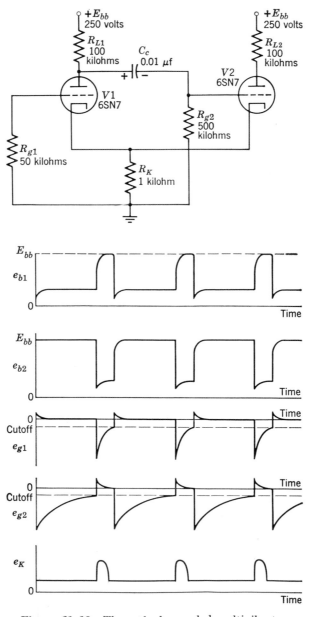

**Figure 21-19**   The cathode-coupled multivibrator.

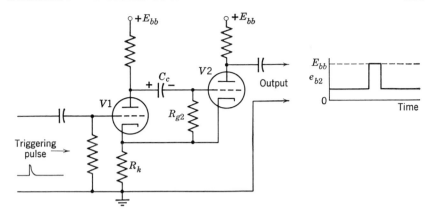

**Figure 21-20**  The single-shot multivibrator.

the base voltage falls below $V_{EE}$. The very low impedance of the base input in the forward direction prevents the formation of a tip on the base waves which was observed on the grid of the vacuum tube. These waveforms otherwise do not differ from those obtained in the vacuum-tube circuit arrangement.

This is a circuit of many uses. It is the fundamental square wave or pulse generator for many direct applications. Although the free-running frequency is unstable, it is very readily and easily synchronized to an outside source. Since the square-wave pattern of the multi-vibrator contains many harmonics (useful up to the 150th), when it is synchronized to a frequency standard, it produces many high-frequency harmonics which may be used also as frequency standards. When the synchronizing frequency is a multiple of the fundamental

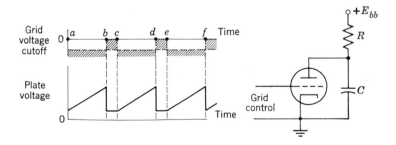

**Figure 21-21**  The discharge circuit.

frequency of the multivibrator, the circuit is termed a frequency divider. Frequency dividers are used in frequency-modulation transmitters and in "frequency standards" to obtain accurate time measured on an electric clock. Multivibrators (and blocking oscillators), when used with a discharge circuit (explained in Section 21–7), produce the sawtooth sweep voltages needed in the cathode-ray-tube deflection circuits in oscilloscopes and in television receivers. Multivibrators are useful from about 1 cycle to 150 kc at fundamental frequency.

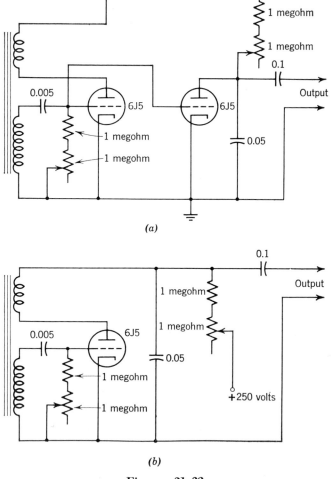

Figure 21–22

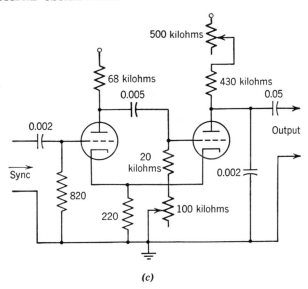

500 kilohms

68 kilohms
0.005

430 kilohms
0.05

Output

0.002

Sync

20 kilohms

0.002

820

100 kilohms

220

*(c)*

**Figure 21–22** Typical composite oscillator–discharge circuits. (*a*) Blocking oscillator with separate discharge tube. (*b*) Blocking oscillator and discharge circuit combined. (*c*) Combined multivibrator and discharge circuit.

## Section 21–6 Cathode-Coupled Multivibrators

To understand the operation of the cathode-coupled multivibrator (Fig. 21–19), a different approach will be taken than was used for the standard multivibrator. Assume that the heaters are turned off and that the supply voltage is applied to the circuit. The coupling capacitor $C_c$ is charged to 250 volts with the indicated polarity. When the heaters are turned on, both tubes show plate current. The plate current in $V1$ causes its plate voltage to decrease. Since the 250-volt charge on $C_c$ cannot change instantly, the grid of $V2$ is driven negative by the amount that the plate voltage of $V1$ falls from 250 volts.

The second tube $V2$ stays cut off until $C_c$ discharges to cutoff through the circuit of $R_{g2}$, $R_k$ and the equivalent d-c resistance of $V1$. When plate current starts to flow in $V2$, there is an increased $IR$ drop in the cathode resistor $R_k$. This increasing voltage across $R_k$ decreases the plate current in $V1$. The plate voltage of $V1$ rises consequently, and now the low-voltage charge on $C_c$ creates a positive grid on $V2$. A now large current flows in $V2$ and causes a sufficient $IR$ drop in $R_k$ to cut off $V1$. $C_c$ charges rapidly to 250 volts since

$R_{g2}$ is in the discharge circuit but not in the charge circuit. As soon as $C_c$ recharges, grid current in $V2$ ceases, and $V1$ starts to have plate current. Now the cycle repeats as we have described.

The cathode-coupled multivibrator produces a pulse-type waveform and not a square wave. If a synchronizing pulse is fed into the grid of $V1$, it must be negative as its function is to cut off $V1$. When the pulse is fed into the grid of $V2$, it must be positive in order to initiate current flow in $V2$.

Another form of the cathode-coupled multivibrator is the *univibrator* or *single-shot multivibrator* (Fig. 21–20). In this circuit, $V2$ has no self-bias whereas $V1$ has a d-c bias, the $IR$ drop across the cathode resistor $R_k$. If the plate load of $V2$ is properly adjusted, there is enough drop across $R_k$ due to plate current in $V2$ to cut off $V1$. Then, $C_c$ is charged to full supply voltage. A positive initiating or triggering pulse coming in to the grid of $V1$ overcomes the cutoff condition caused by the normal cathode voltage and produces a plate current in $V1$. The plate voltage of $V1$ drops, and the voltage resulting from the fixed charge on $C_c$ cuts off $V2$. Since $V2$ is cut off, $V1$ continues to have plate current flow beyond the time the initiating pulse ceases. When $C_c$ discharges through $R_{g2}$ sufficiently (to the cutoff point of $V2$), the plate current begins to flow in $V2$. This cuts off $V1$, putting the circuit back to the original state.

This action takes place only once for each trigger. The circuit is useful for such applications as counting or for developing a single-sweep trace across the face of a cathode-ray tube.

### Section 21–7   Discharge Circuits

A vacuum tube may be used in place of the thyratron in the $RC$ sawtooth generating circuit (Fig. 21–21). However, the vacuum-tube circuit is not a self-sustaining oscillator; it must be driven. During the time of the capacitor charge, $a$ to $b$, $c$ to $d$, and $e$ to $f$, the grid must be kept below cutoff. When the capacitor is being discharged, $b$ to $c$ and $d$ to $e$, the grid voltage must be above cutoff. The grid waveforms present in the blocking oscillator and unbalanced multivibrator are ideally suited for this use. In these applications, the frequency is determined by the repetition rate of the blocking oscillator or multivibrator. Then, $R$ and $C$ serve to establish the amplitude of the sawtooth output. A variation in $R$ or $C$ does not affect the frequency but only the amplitude of the waveform.

Representative composite circuits are shown in Fig. 21–22. It is possible to combine the discharge circuit with the oscillator circuit. **This combination simplifies the over-all circuit by eliminating a tube.**

### Section 21–8    Transistor Power Supplies

Two power transistors can be arranged as a multivibrator to produce a square-wave power source (Fig. 21–23).    The feedback is obtained from the ends of a center-tapped transformer winding.    The same winding can be used for both the bases and the collectors by cross-connecting the base leads, or a separate winding can be used as a feedback winding.    There is a resistor in series with the base leads to limit the current to safe values.    If the circuit were adjusted to establish sinusoidal oscillation, we could call these circuits push–pull oscillators of the Armstrong type.    Often a capacitor is placed across one of the windings to "tune" the transformer to a particular frequency.

The transformers are usually step-up power transformers providing a high alternating voltage in the secondary winding.    The circuit can then be used as a source of power frequencies in portable equipment.

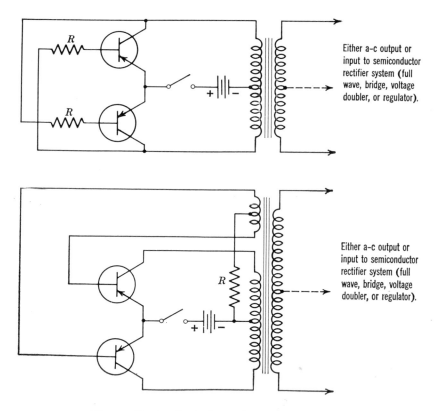

Figure 21–23    Typical transistor power supplies.

The rectifier system which is used to convert the high alternating voltage into direct voltage depends upon the application. Conventional rectifier circuits (Sections 9–1 to 9–8) or transistor voltage regulators (Section 17–9) may be used with either circuit.

## . . . . Suggested References for Further Study

1. W. A. Edson, *Vacuum-Tube Oscillators*, John Wiley & Sons, New York, 1953.
2. D. DeWitt and A. L. Rossoff, *Transistor Electronics*, Chapter 13, McGraw-Hill Book Co., New York, 1957.
3. T. L. Martin Jr., *Electronic Circuits*, Chapters 17 and 18, Prentice Hall, Englewood Cliffs, N. J., 1955.
4. O. S. Puckle, *Time Bases*, 2nd ed., John Wiley & Sons, New York, 1951.

## . . . . QUESTIONS

1. Define or explain each of the following terms: (*a*) ionization, (*b*) deionization, (*c*) nonlinearity, (*d*) forced frequency, (*e*) free-running frequency, (*f*) on–off circuit, (*g*) block, (*h*) pulse-repetition rate, (*i*) damping resistance, (*j*) cathode-coupled.

2. Explain the action of a neon-lamp relaxation oscillator.

3. What are the advantages and disadvantages of a neon-lamp relaxation oscillator?

4. Explain how the grid controls the operation of a thyratron relaxation oscillator?

5. Explain the effect on the frequency of the thyratron relaxation-oscillator output by varying (*a*) grid bias, (*b*) plate voltage, (*c*) decreasing $R$, (*d*) increasing $C$.

6. Explain the effect on peak-to-peak output voltage of the thyratron relaxation oscillator by varying (*a*) grid bias, (*b*) plate voltage, (*c*) decreasing $R$, (*d*) increasing $C$.

7. What are the advantages of the thyratron relaxation oscillator?

8. What are the disadvantages of the thyratron relaxation oscillator?

9. What is the purpose of synchronization?

10. Show how a 3000-cycle sync signal can lock in a 1000-cycle oscillator.

11. Show how increasing the amplitude of a 3000-cycle sync signal can change a 1000-cycle oscillator to 3000 cycles.

12. Explain the operation of a blocking-oscillator circuit, and give the waveforms.

13. Show why the reference level of the waveforms in a transistor blocking-oscillator circuit is $V_{EE}$.

14. Show why grid synchronization is obtained by positive pulses in a vacuum-tube blocking-oscillator circuit, and how either positive or negative pulses can lock in transistor circuits.

15. Explain the operation of a balanced multivibrator vacuum-tube circuit, and include waveforms.

16. Answer question 15 for a transistor circuit.

17. What is an unbalanced multivibrator?

18. Show the waveforms for an unbalanced vacuum-tube multivibrator circuit.

19. Answer question 18 for a transistor circuit.

20. What is the advantage of a cathode-coupled multivibrator?

21. Explain the operation of a cathode-coupled multivibrator.

22. Explain the operation of a single-shot multivibrator.

23. What is the purpose of a discharge circuit?

24. Using Fig. 21–22, explain the effect on the operation of the circuit of varying each resistance in turn, and show the waveforms.

25. Discuss the uses of the transistor power-supply circuits shown in Fig. 21–23.


. . . . PROBLEMS


1. In Fig. 21–1, assume that the supply voltage is 400 volts, $R$ is 1 megohm, and $C$ is 0.05 $\mu$f. Using an ionization potential of 65 volts and a deionization potential of 55 volts for the neon lamp, determine the frequency of operation.

2. Solve problem 1 if the supply voltage is reduced to 350 volts.

3. Solve problem 1 for $R$ equal to 470,000 ohms and $C$ equal to 1250 $\mu\mu$f.

4. Solve problem 3 if the supply voltage is reduced to 350 volts.

5. A thyratron is used in place of the neon lamp. Its ionization potential is adjusted to 65 volts, and its deionization potential is 20 volts. Solve problems 1 through 4 for this new condition.

# High-frequency amplifiers

• • • • • • • • • • • • • • • • • • • • • CHAPTER 22

This chapter is concerned with small-signal amplifiers at high frequencies. A single-tuned circuit (Section 22–1) or a double-tuned transformer (Section 22–2) can be used in an amplifier. The modifications that are necessary when these tuned circuits are used with transistors are considered (Section 22–3).

### Section 22–1    Single-Tuned Amplifiers

A single-tuned amplifier using capacitive coupling is shown in Fig. 22–1. In an equivalent circuit, the parallel tank circuit is shunted by the plate resistance of the tube $r_p$ and by the grid-leak resistor $R_g$ of

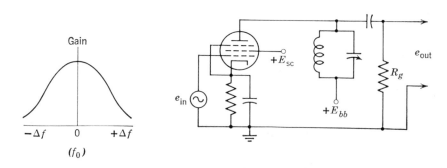

**Figure 22–1**    Single-tuned amplifier using capacitive coupling.

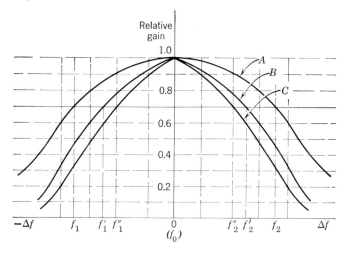

**Figure 22–2**   Relative gain for a two-stage amplifier.

the following stage.   The $Q$ of the tank circuit is reduced by these loading resistances, and this new net equivalent circuit $Q$, $Q'$, can be found from the method outlined in Section 7–2.   The gain of the circuit is determined from the pentode gain equation

$$A_e = g_m Z_L$$

The total load in the circuit at resonance is $Q'X$, where $X$ is either the capacitive or the inductive reactance of the components of the tank at resonance.   With this substitution, the gain equation becomes

$$A_e = g_m Q'X \qquad (22\text{--}1)$$

The bandwidth which is defined as the frequency spread between the $-3$-db response frequencies is given by

$$BW = f_0/Q' \qquad (7\text{--}5)$$

It should be noted that, in this circuit, the tank and the grid-leak resistor $R_g$ may be interchanged without changing the gain as long as $g_m$ and $r_p$ are not affected.   In some circuits it is more convenient to have the tuned circuit in the grid, and in others it is placed in series with the plate.   Usually, the tuned circuit is in series with the plate when $R_g$ is high.   In a broad-band amplifier where a low $Q$ is obtained by shunting the tank with a low value of $R_g$, the tank is in the grid circuit.   When the tank is in the grid circuit, there are no high direct voltages on the components which are tuned.

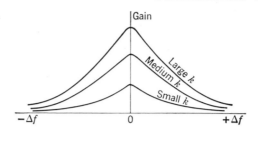

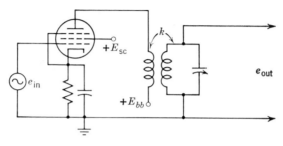

**Figure 22–3** Amplifier using an untuned-primary-tuned-secondary air-core transformer.

The gains of two amplifiers, $A$ and $B$, are plotted on the basis of unity gain at resonance in Fig. 22–2. Amplifier $A$ has a bandwidth of $f_2 - f_1$, and amplifier $B$ has a bandwidth of $f'_2 - f'_1$. When these two amplifiers are connected in cascade, the over-all gain is the product of the gains of the two stages (curve $C$). When the gain of stage $A$ is 0.40 and the gain of stage $B$ is 0.30, the combined gain is 0.12. The bandwidth of the composite curve is $f''_2 - f''_1$.

It is evident, from this example that, when tuned amplifiers are cascaded, the over-all bandwidth depends on the bandwidths of the several individual stages. Also, the over-all bandwidth is less than the bandwidth of any one stage.

In Section 7–5 we discussed the action of an untuned-primary–tuned-secondary air-core transformer. This transformer connected in an amplifier circuit is shown in Fig. 22–3. This circuit does not require a grid resistor for the next stage since there is a d-c path through the secondary winding of the transformer to ground. The response curve for this amplifier is very similar to the response curve of the previous circuit. The gain of this amplifier at the resonant frequency is given by

$$A_e = g_m Q' X_m \qquad (22\text{–}2)$$

$Q'$ is the effective circuit $Q$, taking into consideration the shunting effect of the plate resistance. $X_m$ is the value of the reactance of the mutual inductance between the primary and the secondary. The mutual inductance is directly proportional to the coefficient of coupling $k$, and the gain can be varied, if necessary, by varying the coefficient of coupling.

### Section 22-2    Double-Tuned Amplifiers

A circuit using a double-tuned air-core transformer is shown in Fig. 22–4. Each of the two tuned circuits is adjusted to the same resonant frequency. The equivalent circuit for this amplifier is given in Fig. 22–5$a$. The source $g_m e_g$ and the circuit elements $r_p$ and $C_1$ may be replaced by Thévenin's theorem to yield a series circuit of $E$, $C$, and $R$. This series circuit is combined into a new equivalent circuit (Fig. 22–5$b$). If the plate resistance is high, it may be neglected in relation to the rest of the circuit. The plate resistance $r_p$

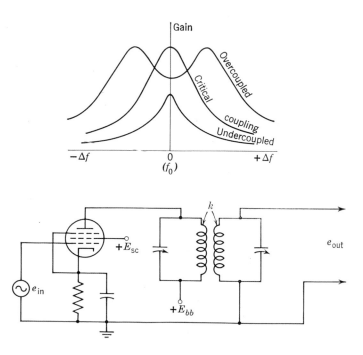

**Figure 22-4**  Amplifier using a tuned-primary–tuned-secondary air-core transformer.

converts into the series circuit as the resistance $R$. In a series circuit the value of $R$, in order to be negligible, must be very small, and it can be combined with the resistance of the primary for the purpose of calculations.

When the primary coil of the circuit is arranged in series, and the secondary is in parallel, we can use the analysis that was developed in Section 7–6. In this analysis we showed that, as the coefficient of coupling increases from zero, the gain increases and the bandwidth decreases. The gain increases until the critical coupling is reached. At this point the gain is for high $Q$ coils

$$A_e = \frac{g_m \omega_0 M}{k_c^2} = g_m \frac{\omega_0 \sqrt{L_p L_s}}{k_c} \qquad (22\text{--}3)$$

When the coefficient of coupling is increased beyond the value of critical coupling, the response curves expand to produce the double humped characteristic. The gain of the amplifier at the two peaks is given by Eq. 22–3, and the separation of the two peaks is given by Eq. 7–11.

In Fig. 22–6, the response curve for a single-tuned circuit is shown as $B$, and a double-tuned amplifier response curve is shown as $A$. The product of the two gain curves is curve $C$. Curve $C$ has a wide

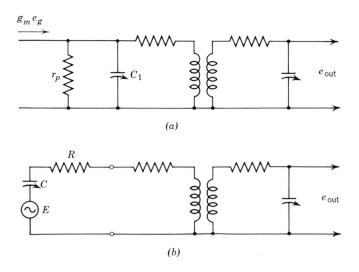

*(a)*

*(b)*

**Figure 22–5** Equivalent circuits for the double-tuned amplifier. (*a*) Equivalent circuit. (*b*) Equivalent circuit transformed by Thévenin's theorem.

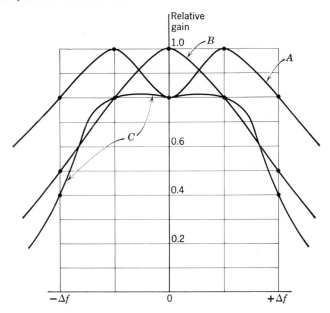

**Figure 22-6**   Response of a combined two-stage amplifier.

bandwidth, and it has almost constant gain over this region.   In this manner of combining two circuit arrangements, a steep slope is obtained on the sides of a flat response curve.

## Section 22-3   Transistor Considerations in High-Frequency Amplifiers

The principles of the tuned circuits used in vacuum-tube amplifiers also apply to transistor circuits.   As we have found in low-frequency amplifiers, it is necessary to modify the circuits to take care of the low-impedance characteristics of the transistor.   In the vacuum-tube circuit, we employed pentodes instead of triodes to minimize the high shunting capacitance of the Miller effect.   The transistors that are most often used because of their lower cost are the three-element types. Since these transistors are comparable to vacuum-tube triodes, it is necessary to neutralize the circuit.

The double-tuned circuit is not common in transistor circuits because the input impedance to a transistor is so low.   Instead, the usual circuit is an air-core transformer which has the tuning in the

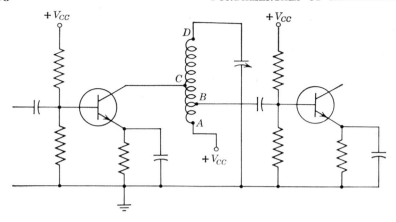

**Figure 22–7**   Single-tuned transistor amplifier using capacitive coupling.

primary instead of in the secondary to take advantage of the relatively high impedance in the collector circuit.

A transistor amplifier using a single-tuned circuit with capacitive coupling is shown in Fig. 22–7.   The tuning capacitor is placed across the entire coil to provide a high $Q$.   The collector is tapped into the

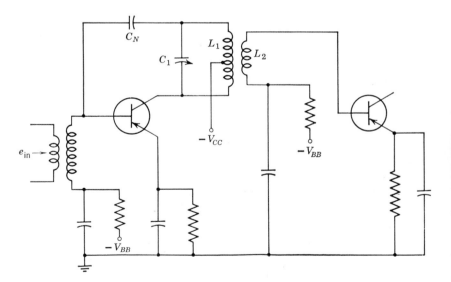

**Figure 22–8**   Transistor amplifier using a single-tuned transformer.

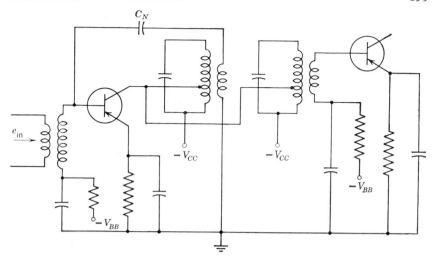

**Figure 22-9**   Circuit using two tuned circuits.

coil at $C$, and the coupling capacitor which connects to the input of the next stage is also tapped into the coil.   The impedance between $A$ and $C$ matches the impedance of the collector, and the impedance between $A$ and $B$ matches the base input impedance of the next stage. Each of these impedances is very low compared to the total impedance of the tuned circuit.   If either connection were made across the entire tank circuit, the $Q$ of the tank would be lowered to the point where there would be no peaking effect at all.

A typical transistor circuit using a single-tuned air-core transformer is shown in Fig. 22–8.   The tuning is accomplished in the primary winding of the transformer.   The low-impedance take-off winding $L_2$ of the transformer matches the input impedance of the base of the next stage.   The collector supply is brought into a tap on the primary winding $L_1$.   This arrangement serves two purposes.   The tap enables the tank impedance to be much higher than the value required for matching to the collector.   Also a 180° out-of-phase voltage is available for neutralization.   The energy required for neutralization is fed back into the base through the neutralizing capacitor $C_N$.   This circuit is very similar to the Hazeltine neutralizing circuit used in vacuum-tube circuits (Fig. 16–14b).

Another circuit arrangement which is used to secure the required bandwidth makes use of two tuned circuits (Fig. 22–9).   The secondary of one transformer is used to provide the neutralization, and the secondary of the other provides the driving energy for the next stage.

## . . . . Suggested References for Further Study

1. F. Langford-Smith, *Radiotron Designer's Handbook*, 4th ed , Chapters 23 and 26, RCA, Harrison, N. J., 1953.
2. E. J. Angelo, *Electronic Circuits*, Chapter 15, McGraw-Hill Book Co., New York, 1958.
3. S. Seely, *Electron-Tube Circuits*, Chapter 10, McGraw-Hill Book Co., New York, 1950.

## . . . . QUESTIONS

1. Define or explain each of the following terms: (*a*) tank, (*b*) bandwidth, (*c*) tuning core, (*d*) trimmer, (*e*) effective Q, (*f*) coefficient of coupling, (*g*) critical coefficient of coupling, (*h*) Miller effect, (*i*) neutralization, (*j*) driving energy.

2. What is the advantage of a single-tuned circuit?

3. What is the effect of a shunt-resistance load on bandwidth and on gain?

4. How is a single-tuned circuit arranged in series feed and in shunt feed?

5. What is the method of coupling when an untuned-primary–tuned-secondary transformer is used?

6. How does a variation in the coefficient of coupling affect the response of a double-tuned amplifier stage?

7. Show how a square band pass can be obtained from a two-stage amplifier.

8. Under what conditions is neutralization required in vacuum-tube circuits?

9. Why are taps used on tuned circuits in transistor amplifiers?

10. How is neutralization accomplished in a transistor amplifier?

11. Describe the Hazeltine neutralization circuit as used for a vacuum-tube amplifier.

## . . . . PROBLEMS

1. In the given circuit, $C$ is 75 $\mu\mu f$ and $L$ is 800 $\mu h$. The $Q$ of the coil itself is 170. $R_g$ is 270,000 ohms. Determine the voltage gain of the circuit at the resonant frequency, and determine the bandwidth of the response curve.

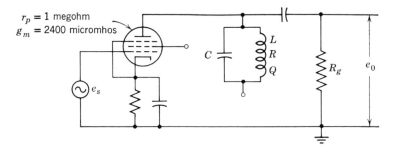

**Prob. 22-1**

2. Solve problem 1 for the following circuit values:

$$C = 125 \ \mu\mu\text{f}, \qquad Q = 140$$
$$L = 1.2 \ \text{mh}, \qquad R_g = 330,000 \ \text{ohms}$$

3. Solve problem 1 for the following circuit values:

$$C = 30 \ \mu\mu\text{f}, \qquad Q = 65$$
$$L = 180 \ \mu\text{h}, \qquad R_g = 20,000 \ \text{ohms}$$

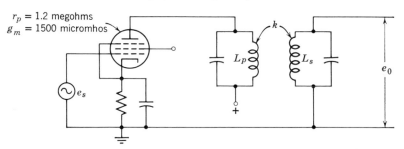

**Prob. 22-4**

4. In the circuit diagram, $L_p$ and $L_s$ are each 130 $\mu$h with a $Q$ of 70 at the resonant frequency, 900 kc. The coefficient of coupling is critical. Determine the value of the capacitors needed to resonate the coils. Determine the gain at the resonant frequency. Determine $k_c$.

# Modulation

• • • • • • • • • • • • • • • • • • • • • CHAPTER 23

The fundamental purpose of modulation is to superimpose the desired intelligence signals on a high-frequency carrier for transmission at that high frequency (Section 23–1). Amplitude modulation (Section 23–2) and amplitude-modulation circuits (Section 23–3) are discussed. The general considerations of frequency modulation (Section 23–4) are followed by a study of two methods of producing frequency modulation, the reactance tube (Section 23–5) and the balanced modulator (Section 23–6). Pre-emphasis and de-emphasis are considered (Section 23–7).

## Section 23–1   The General Problem of Modulation

A signal is transmitted from one point to another for a variety of purposes. The most common example is telephone communication within a geographic area. A remote-metering problem is another form of signal transmission that is in the same classification. For a telephone circuit existing between two distant cities, the physical equipment involves an enormous quantity of poles, cross-arms, insulators, and wires. When the demand on the circuit becomes large, it is necessary to add additional facilities. Now the problem resolves into the method of providing the additional circuit. The situation is similar in the remote-metering problem when it becomes necessary to add further metering circuits.

One method of increasing the facility of a circuit is to use a method of modulation. Let us assume that a voice-frequency band from 200 to 3000 cycles is required for telephone communications. If we take bands of frequencies, 0 to 3 kc, 3 to 6 kc, 6 to 9 kc, 9 to 12 kc, and 12 to

502

15 kc a total band of 0 to 15 kc apparently could provide five separate *channels* for five separate telephone circuits over one pair of wires, provided that the original band of 200 to 3000 cycles can be transferred to each of the high-frequency bands. The process of superimposing the information contained within a frequency band onto another frequency band is called *modulation*. The process of decoding or converting the signal back to its original form is called *demodulation* or *detection*. The problems of detection are considered in Chapter 24.

The energy medium by which the signal is to be transferred is called the *carrier*. The signal is often termed the *modulating frequency*. If we consider a single-frequency carrier, we may write

$$e_o = E_m \cos (\omega_0 t + \theta)$$

or

$$e_o = E_m \cos (2\pi f_0 t + \theta)$$

When the amplitude of the carrier $E_m$ is varied in accordance with the signal information, we have *amplitude modulation*. When the frequency of the carrier $f_0$ is varied in accordance with the signal, we have *frequency modulation*. When the phase angle $\theta$ is varied in accordance with the signal, we have *phase modulation*. There are also a number of special methods of modulation which are in use but are beyond the scope of this textbook. For example, if a series of short-duration pulses are transmitted, the signal information can vary the width of the pulse (*pulse-width modulation*), or the signal can vary the height of the pulses (*pulse-amplitude modulation*), or the signal can vary the exact starting point of each pulse (*pulse-position modulation* or *pulse-time modulation*).

### Section 23–2  Amplitude Modulation

A carrier signal may be represented by

$$e_0 = E_m \cos 2\pi f_0 t \tag{23-1}$$

where $f_0$ is the frequency of the carrier wave (Fig. 23–1*a*). The phase angle is taken as zero because it does not contribute to amplitude modulation, and its retention complicates the algebra unnecessarily. In amplitude modulation, the magnitude of the carrier $E_m$ is varied in accordance with the signal (Fig. 23–1*b*). Amplitude modulation produces a modulation envelope on the carrier waveform. This modulation envelope follows the signal waveform, and it should be noted quite carefully that, when the envelope increases in the positive direction, it also increases in the negative direction. The amplitude

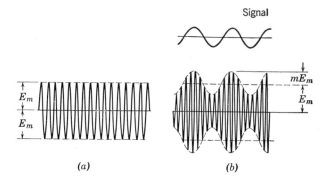

**Figure 23-1**   Amplitude modulation.   (*a*) Unmodulated wave.   (*b*) Modulated wave.

of the modulation envelope is a fraction *m* of the amplitude of unmodulated wave.  This fraction *m* is called the *modulation* and is usually given in per cent and, in this form, is termed *per cent modulation*. Based on this definition for modulation, we may write the equation for the information signal $e_s$ as

$$e_s = mE_m \cos \omega_s t$$

or

$$e_s = mE_m \cos 2\pi f_s t$$

When a carrier is amplitude-modulated by a sine-wave signal, the amplitude of the carrier contains the sinusoidal variations as expressed by

$$(1 + m \cos \omega_s t)E_m$$

The instantaneous voltage of the resultant wave is

$$e = (1 + m \cos \omega_s t)E_m \cos \omega_0 t$$

Expanding this expression yields

$$e = E_m \cos \omega_0 t + mE_m \cos \omega_0 t \cos \omega_s t$$

From trigonometry, we have the expansion formula

$$\cos x \cos y = \tfrac{1}{2} \cos (x + y) + \tfrac{1}{2} \cos (x - y)$$

Substituting

$$e = E_m \cos \omega_0 t + \frac{mE_m}{2} \cos (\omega_0 + \omega_s)t + \frac{mE_m}{2} \cos (\omega_0 - \omega_s)t \quad (23\text{-}2)$$

or

$$e = E_m \cos 2\pi f_0 t + \frac{mE_m}{2} \cos 2\pi (f_0 + f_s)t + \frac{mE_m}{2} \cos 2\pi (f_0 - f_s)t$$

By this derivation, we show that the equation of an amplitude-modulated wave contains three terms. The first term is identical with Eq. 23–1 which is the unmodulated wave. Thus, it is apparent that the process of amplitude modulation does not change the original wave but *adds* to it by producing two additional terms. The frequency of the second term is $(f_0 + f_s)$, and the frequency of the third term is $(f_0 - f_s)$. As an example, when the carrier is 5000 cycles and the signal is 100 cycles, the frequencies of the three terms are 5000 cycles, 5100 cycles and 4900 cycles. The term that is at 5100 cycles $(f_0 + f_s)$ is called the *upper sideband* and the term that is at 4900 cycles $(f_0 - f_s)$ is called the *lower sideband*. In this example, the signal is 100 cycles, but the total bandwidth required is from 4900 cycles to 5100 cycles, or 200 cycles. The very important conclusion to be made at this point in the discussion is that *the bandwidth required in amplitude modulation is twice the frequency of the modulating signal.* In standard broadcast transmission, the carriers of the stations are allocated at intervals of 10 kc: for example, 960 kc, 970 kc, 980 kc. Thus each station would appear to have a bandwidth allocation of 10 kc and a maximum permissible modulating frequency of 5000 cycles. Actually, the Federal Communications Commission (FCC) imposes a limit of 7500 cycles only when justifiable complaints of interference are received and proved.

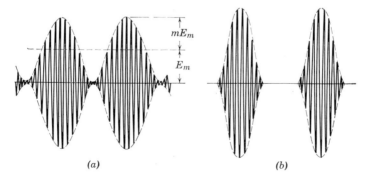

(a)                                   (b)

**Figure 23–2** 100% modulation and overmodulation. (a) 100% modulation ($m = 1$). (b) Overmodulation ($m > 1$).

From Eq. 23–2, we can see that the sidebands go to zero when the modulation $m$ is zero and the equation is that of the carrier alone, (Eq. 23–1). When the modulation is 100% (Fig. 23–2a), the maximum instantaneous voltage is $2E_m$ and the minimum instantaneous voltage of the envelope is zero. The condition of overmodulation is shown in Fig. 23–2b. The waveform is clipped, and, since the envelope is discontinuous, it cannot be represented by Eq. 23–2. Under conditions of overmodulation, the envelope is no longer sinusoidal, but is represented by a fundamental and many harmonics. These harmonics also produce sidebands. When the modulation is 98%, there are only two sidebands. When the modulation is 105%, there are many sidebands. This condition of overmodulation produces a sideband *splattering* by requiring a bandwidth much greater than the normal bandwidth for modulations not exceeding 100%. This splattering creates interference for the stations in the adjacent channel assignments.

The modulation patterns of Fig. 23–1b and Fig. 23–2a are called *modulated continuous waves* (*MCW*). The simplest method of radio transmission is accomplished by turning a radio transmitter on and off by means of a telegraph key. The modulation pattern (Fig. 23–3) is a sequence of square dots and dashes. This method of transmission is called *interrupted continuous waves* (*ICW*). The time duration of a dot is called a *baud*. The length of a dash is three bauds, and the space between the dots and the dashes of the code for a letter is one baud. The space between successive letters is three bauds. If a word is taken as five letters and each letter is taken as 10 bauds including the spacing interval, the word is 50 bauds long. If the spacing between words is nine bauds, ten words require $10(50 + 9)$ or 590 bauds. Since a baud corresponds to either a positive half-cycle or a negative half-cycle, 590 bauds represents 295 cycles. When the speed of transmission of signals is ten words per minute, this figure becomes 295/60 cycles of bauds per second. In order to produce a dot or a dash, a square-wave modulation is needed and requires a harmonic content of all harmonics up to the eleventh to obtain a clean wave form. With this modification, ten words per minute requires a modulation con-

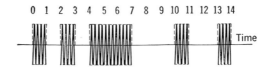

**Figure 23–3**   Waveform of radio telegraphy (ICW).

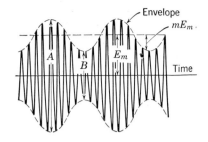

**Figure 23-4** Details of modulated wave.

taining frequencies up to

$$\tfrac{295}{60} \times 11 = 54.1 \text{ cycles per second}$$

Since amplitude modulation requires both an upper sideband and a lower sideband, the total bandwidth necessary to transmit code at ten words per minute is 108.2 cycles.

Very often it is necessary to determine the modulation from the waveform (Fig. 23-4). The maximum peak-to-peak amplitude is $A$, and the spread between the minimum points is $B$. These values may be determined easily from an oscilloscope pattern. From this information, the peak of the unmodulated waveform is

$$E_m = \frac{A/2 + B/2}{2} = \frac{A + B}{4}$$

The peak of the modulating signal, $mE_m$, is

$$mE_m = \frac{A/2 - B/2}{2} = \frac{A - B}{4}$$

When these two expressions are taken as a ratio

$$\frac{mE_m}{E_m} = \frac{(A - B)/4}{(A + B)/4}$$

$$m = \frac{A - B}{A + B} \qquad (23\text{-}3)$$

When the total modulation is fed into the vertical or the $Y$-deflection terminals of an oscilloscope and the modulating signal is fed into the horizontal or $X$-deflection terminals, a trapezoidal pattern results (Fig. 23-5). Several different patterns are in the diagram, including one that shows the pattern $f$ of a developed second harmonic in the modulating circuit. The values of the per cent modulation may

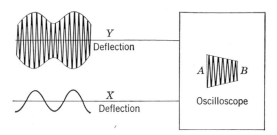

Test equipment.

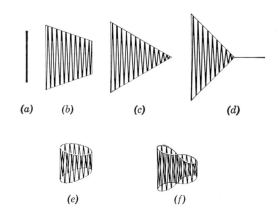

(a)      (b)                (c)                     (d)

(e)                    (f)

**Figure 23–5** Visual observation of modulation. Trapezoidal modulation patterns. (a) $m = 0\%$. (b) $m = 25\%$. (c) $m = 100\%$. (d) $m > 100\%$. (e) Phase
·shift not proper to produce trapezoid. (f) Second harmonic distortion.

be determined from these figures by use of Eq. 23–3. The pattern is
quite useful in checking the operation of a modulator and is often used
in monitoring the operation of a transmitter.

The coefficients of the terms of Eq. 23–2 are

$$E_m \qquad \frac{mE_m}{2} \qquad \frac{mE_m}{2}$$

and are in the ratio

$$1 \quad m/2 \quad m/2$$

Since power may be expressed as $E^2/R$, these terms can be converted
to a power ratio:

$$1 \quad \frac{m^2}{4} \quad \frac{m^2}{4}$$

The total power is in the ratio

$$1 + \frac{m^2}{4} + \frac{m^2}{4} = 1 + \frac{m^2}{2}$$

We may state this in the form of an equation:

$$\frac{P_T}{P_o} = 1 + \frac{m^2}{2} \qquad (23\text{--}4a)$$

where $P_o$ is the carrier power, and $P_T$ is the total power for a modulation $m$. If $R$ is the resistance,

$$\frac{P_T}{P_o} = \frac{I_T{}^2 R}{I_0{}^2 R} = 1 + \frac{m^2}{2}$$

and

$$I_T = I_0 \sqrt{1 + m^2/2} \qquad (23\text{--}4b)$$

When the modulation is 100%, $m$ is unity and the total power ratio becomes 1.5.

As an example, when the carrier power is 500 watts, the total power, under conditions of 100% modulation, becomes $1.5 \times 500$ or 750 watts. The additional 250 watts represents the energy content of the sidebands. There are 125 watts in the upper sideband and 125 watts in the lower sideband. The sideband energy represents the signal content, and the unchanged carrier-energy content of 500 watts is that energy which is required as the means of transmission. As a further example, if the antenna or load current for an unmodulated transmitter is 8 amperes, when the modulation is 40%, the current rises to

$$I_T = I_0 \left(1 + \frac{m^2}{2}\right)^{\frac{1}{2}}$$

$$= 8 \left(1 + \frac{0.40^2}{2}\right)^{\frac{1}{2}}$$

$$= 8(1.08)^{\frac{1}{2}}$$

$$= 8.32 \text{ amperes}$$

When the average power of an unmodulated transmitter is 1000 watts, the peak instantaneous power is 2000 watts. Since the peak voltage of a wave at 100% modulation is twice the peak of the unmodulated wave, the peak power at 100% modulation is 4000 watts.

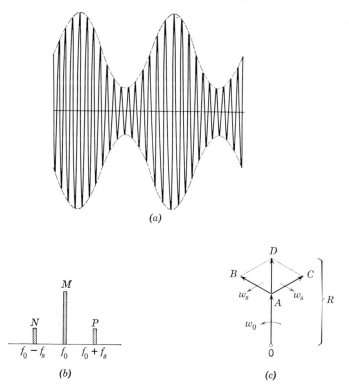

*(a)*

*(b)*                                          *(c)*

**Figure 23-6**   Three representations of an AM wave.   *(a)* Time axis.   *(b)* Frequency axis.   *(c)* Phasor diagram.

We found from Eq. 23-2 that an amplitude-modulated wave may be expressed as

$$e = E_m \cos \omega_0 t + \frac{mE_m}{2} \cos (\omega_0 + \omega_s)t + \frac{mE_m}{2} \cos (\omega_0 - \omega_s)t$$

This wave may be represented graphically in three forms (Fig. 23-6). The waveform (Fig. 23-6a) showing the instantaneous total value of the carrier and the sidebands is the conventional form of representing the modulated wave.   The horizontal axis in this case is time.   When the horizontal axis is frequency (Fig. 23-6b), energy appears only at three places, the lower sideband, the carrier, and the upper sideband. The amplitudes of the representations $N$, $M$, and $P$ are proportional either to the voltage or to the power content of the three frequencies.

The separation between $N$ and $P$ is the bandwidth. When the modulation changes, the amplitude of $M$ is fixed, but the amplitudes of $N$ and $P$ vary. When the modulating frequency changes, $N$ and $P$ are nearer to or further from $M$, depending on whether the modulating frequency decreases or increases.

In the phasor diagram (Fig. 23–6c), $OA$ represents the carrier and has a length proportional to $E_m$. This carrier rotates about point $O$ counterclockwise at the angular velocity of the carrier $\omega_0$. Two phasors, $AB$ and $AC$, are added to the carrier. The length of these phasors is proportional to $mE_m/2$, and they represent the sidebands. The phasor $AC$ rotates about point $A$ clockwise, and the phasor $AB$ rotates about point $A$ counterclockwise, both at the angular velocity of the signal $\omega_s$. The relative speed of $AC$ about point $O$ is $(\omega_0 - \omega_s)$, and the relative speed of $AB$ about point $O$ is $(\omega_0 + \omega_s)$. Thus, $AB$ is the upper sideband, and $AC$ is the lower sideband. The phase relation of the phasors must be such that the sum of the three phasors is $R$, and $R$ must at all times be in phase with the carrier phasor $OA$. When the projection of $R$ is traced out as it rotates about point $O$, the modulation pattern of Fig. 23–6a is developed.

In discussing the three terms of Eq. 23–2, we pointed out that the signal content of the total was the sideband energy alone. It is possible to have communications systems that do not transmit the energies of all the three terms, but suppress all or part of the carrier term and/or one of the sidebands. These methods have been developed into systems of great importance in modern communications equipment which fall into a general classification called *single-sideband transmission*. These systems are quite complex in both the circuitry and in the theory of operation.

### Section 23–3  AM Circuits

Some typical modulation circuits are shown in Fig. 23–7. In these circuits, all RF decoupling networks are omitted for simplicity of illustration. Amplitude modulation is obtained by increasing the gain of an RF amplifier when the audio signal is positive and by decreasing the gain when the audio signal is negative. Amplitude modulation may be accomplished by any of several forms: *grid modulation, screen modulation, plate modulation,* or, if the modulator tube is a pentode, *suppressor grid modulation.* When these circuits are arranged for push–pull operation, the bias is class AB or class B to improve the over-all operating efficiency. At high-power levels, class-B operation is standard practice in order to obtain the greatest

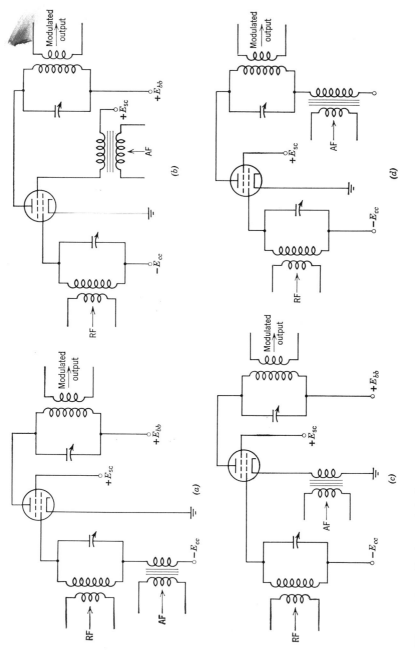

**Figure 23-7** Basic modulation circuits. (a) Grid modulation. (b) Screen modulation. (c) Cathode modulation. (d) Plate modulation.

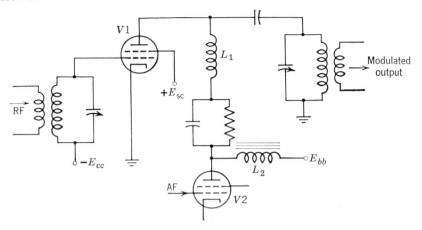

**Figure 23-8**   The Heising modulator.

efficiency.   Very often the RF amplifiers in the modulator are triodes
which require an additional neutralizing circuit.

An example of a modulating circuit is an adaptation of plate modulation called the *Heising* method of modulation.   The plate tank is
shunt-fed, using an RF choke $L_1$.   The plate current for $V1$ comes
from the supply through $L_1$ and through $L_2$, an audio choke, both of
which have a low d-c resistance.   The series resistor creates a direct
voltage drop which maintains the plate voltage of $V1$ at a lower voltage than the plate of $V2$ in order to improve the over-all efficiency.
The capacitor bypasses the resistor for audio frequencies.   The
inductance of $L_1$ at radio frequencies prevents the RF from entering
the modulator tube $V2$.   When the instantaneous polarity on $V2$ is
positive, $V2$ demands an increase in plate current.   Since $L_2$ is an
audio-frequency choke, the current through it cannot change, and the
increase in current is obtained by a decrease of plate current in $V1$.
When the grid signal on $V2$ is negative, its plate current decreases,
forcing the plate current of $V1$ to increase.   Since the current in $L_2$ is
constant, this method of modulation is also called *constant-current
modulation*.

## Section 23-4   Frequency Modulation

The invention and development of frequency modulation by Major
Edwin H. Armstrong (*Proceedings of the Institute of Radio Engineers,*
May 1936) was the result of his search for a method of reducing the

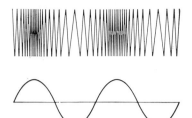

**Figure 23-9**   Frequency modulation.

static and noise present in home reception of the standard AM broadcasts.   Since most natural and manmade electrical noise is in the form of amplitude-modulated signals, a method of keeping the amplitude $E_m$ constant while incorporating the signal into variations of the carrier frequency $f_0$ accomplishes the initial objective.

The terms and definitions used in frequency modulation and the principles of frequency modulation can be shown best by a numerical example.   Let the carrier frequency $f_0$ be 1000 kc, the audio-signal frequency $f_s$ be 1 kc, and the amplitude of the audio signal $E_s$ be 1 volt. At the instant the audio is zero, the FM wave is 1000 kc.   When the audio increases in a positive direction, let us assume that the output wave increases its frequency, and, when the audio signal cycle is negative, the output wave decreases in frequency.   Assume that at the instant the signal is +1 volt, the instantaneous frequency of the output is 1010 kc, and that, at the instant the audio cycle is −1 volt, the output frequency is 990 kc.   This concept is shown in Fig. 23-9.

For each complete cycle of audio, the instantaneous frequency of the output follows:

| Signal | 0 | +1 | 0 | −1 | 0 |
|---|---|---|---|---|---|
| Output frequency, kc | 1000 | 1010 | 1000 | 990 | 1000 |

If this relation is linear, a 2-volt signal changes these figures to

| Signal | 0 | +2 | 0 | −2 | 0 |
|---|---|---|---|---|---|
| Output frequency, kc | 1000 | 1020 | 1000 | 980 | 1000 |

When the audio signal is reduced to 0.5 volt, we find

| Signal | 0 | +0.5 | 0 | −0.5 | 0 |
|---|---|---|---|---|---|
| Output frequency, kc | 1000 | 1005 | 1000 | 995 | 1000 |

It is evident that the amplitude of the audio signal determines the *frequency deviation* $f_d$ from the carrier.   For a 0.5-volt signal, the deviation is 5 kc.   For a 1-volt signal, $f_d$ is 10 kc, and, for a 2-volt signal $f_d$ is 20 kc. It should be noted that $f_d$ is measured *one way* from the carrier. It is not a total spread of frequency. The limit on $f_d$ is established by the application. For FM broadcasting, the Federal Communications Commission limits $f_d$ to a maximum of 75 kc, and, in television broadcasting, it limits $f_d$ to 25 kc for the sound portion of the program.

We may summarize by stating that the deviation frequency $f_d$ contains the information on the amplitude or volume of the signal $f_s$.

If we take the original conditions where $f_s$ is 1 kc and $E_s$ is 1 volt, the deviation is 10 kc. This indicates that the output is changing between 1010 kc and 990 kc at the rate of 1000 times a second. If the audio is kept at one volt, and if the audio frequency is changed from 1 kc to 2 kc, the deviation stays the same at 10 kc, but the output frequency changes between 1010 kc and 990 kc 2000 times a second instead of 1000 times a second. From this, we see that the frequency of the signal is the *rate of change* of the output frequency.

In order to correlate these two concepts, we define a new term, *index of modulation*, $m_f$, as

$$m_f = \frac{f_d}{f_s} \qquad (23\text{--}5)$$

In the original example, $m_f$ is 10 kc/1 kc, or 10. When the signal is increased to 2 volts, the index of modulation changes from 10 to 20 since the deviation is doubled. When the signal is 0.5 volt, the index of modulation is 5. An infinite number of combinations of signal and amplitude can produce the same index of modulation. If a 1-volt signal at 1 kc produces a deviation of 10 kc, the index of modulation is 10. A 2-volt signal at 2 kc produces a deviation of 20 kc. The index of modulation is still 10. A 1-volt signal at 2 kc produces a deviation of 10 kc, and the index of modulation is 5. Using this assumed data, Fig. 23–10 shows the relation among $f_s$, $f_d$ and $m_f$. It should be remembered that $f_d$ is proportional to the signal and that the vertical axis of this graph could be labeled $E_s$ instead of $f_d$.

In FM broadcasting, 15 kc is the maximum allowed audio frequency. The maximum allowed deviation is a swing of 75 kc above and below the carrier frequency. These two limiting figures give a particular index of modulation which is 75 kc/15 kc, or 5. This index of modulation is called the *deviation ratio.* When the deviation ratio is larger than unity, we have *wide-band* frequency modulation and, when the deviation ratio is less than unity, the classification *narrow-band frequency modulation* is used.

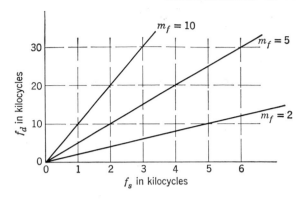

**Figure 23–10**   Plot showing relationship of $f_d$, $f_s$, and $m_f$.

The discussion up to this point uses the instantaneous time wave of an FM signal (Fig. 23–9).   In order to illustrate frequency modulation by means of a frequency axis and by a phasor diagram, a mathematical development must be formed in order to present the FM output wave as a carrier with sidebands.   The general equation of a sine wave, neglecting the phase angle, is

$$e = E_m \cos \omega t$$

In frequency modulation, as we have shown, the instantaneous frequency is a function of $f_0$, $f_d$, $f_s$, and $E_s$.   Since the index of modulation $m_f$ joins together $f_d$, $f_s$, and $E_s$, we can reduce the variables to $f_0$, $f_s$, and $m_f$.   The equation for the instantaneous frequency $f_i$ of the FM wave may be expressed as

$$f_i = f_0 + f_d \cos 2\pi f_s t$$

$$2\pi f_i = 2\pi f_0 + 2\pi f_d \cos 2\pi f_s t$$

$$\omega_i = \omega_0 + \omega_d \cos \omega_s t$$

The expression for $\omega_i$ may be converted by means of calculus* to an

$$* \ e(t) = E_m \cos \left[ \int \omega_i(t) \ dt \right]$$

$$= E_m \cos \left[ \int (\omega_0 + \omega_d \cos \omega_s t) \ dt \right]$$

$$= E_m \cos \left( \omega_0 t + \frac{\omega_d}{\omega_s} \cos \omega_s t \right)$$

$$= E_m \cos \left( \omega_0 t + m_f \sin \omega_s t \right)$$

expression for instantaneous voltage:

$$e = E_m \cos (\omega_0 t + m_f \sin \omega_s t)$$

or
$$\frac{e}{E_m} = \cos (\omega_0 t + m_f \sin \omega_s t) \tag{23-6}$$

This expression is similar to $\cos (x + y)$, and, from the expansion formula of trigonometry, we have

$$\cos (x + y) = \cos x \cos y + \sin x \sin y$$

which enables us to write

$$\frac{e}{E_m} = \cos \omega_0 t \cos (m_f \sin \omega_s t) + \sin \omega_0 t \sin (m_f \sin \omega_s t)$$

The expressions $\cos (\sin x)$ and $\sin (\sin x)$, although they appear to be quite simple, are, in fact, very complex and require advanced methods of mathematical analysis for their evaluation.* When the last equation for $e/E_m$ is expanded, we find

$$\frac{e}{E_m} = J_0(m_f) \cos \omega_0 t$$
$$+ J_1(m_f) \cos (\omega_0 + \omega_s)t - J_1(m_f) \cos (\omega_0 - \omega_s)t$$
$$+ J_2(m_f) \cos (\omega_0 + 2\omega_s)t + J_2(m_f) \cos (\omega_0 - 2\omega_s)t$$
$$+ J_3(m_f) \cos (\omega_0 + 3\omega_s)t - J_3(m_f) \cos (\omega_0 - 3\omega_s)t$$
$$+ J_4(m_f) \cos (\omega_0 + 4\omega_s)t + J_4(m_f) \cos (\omega_0 - 4\omega_s)t$$
$$+ \cdots \tag{23-7}$$

From Eq. 23-7, it is evident that in frequency modulation there are many sidebands whereas in amplitude modulation there were only two sidebands. The sidebands in frequency modulation occur in pairs. There are an upper sideband and a lower sideband for the signal frequency, for the second harmonic of the signal frequency, for the third harmonic of the signal frequency, for the fourth harmonic of the signal frequency, and so on. As in amplitude modulation there is a term that represents energy at the carrier frequency—the $J_0$ term. Since the equation is for $e/E_m$, the vector sum of the coefficients of the carrier and sideband terms must add to unity. The coefficients [$J_0(m_f)$, $J_1(m_f)$, $J_2(m_f)$, etc.] of the terms are called *Bessel functions of the first kind*. The subscript of the $J$ is called the *order*. Thus the fourth-order Bessel function is the coefficient of the fourth sidebands which are located at $(f_0 + 4f_s)$ and at $(f_0 - 4f_s)$. These Bessel functions may

* E. Jahnke and F. Emde, *Tables of Functions* (Leipzig: Teubner, 1938); (New York: Dover Publications, 1943).

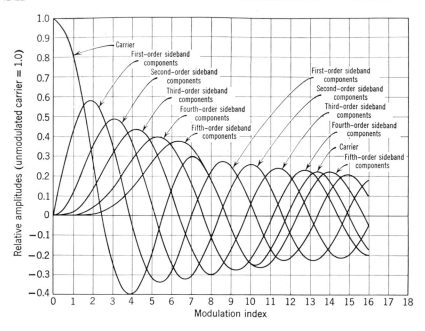

**Figure 23-11**    Bessel functions.

be evaluated numerically and are plotted as a function of the index of modulation in Fig. 23–11.

It is apparent from Fig. 23–11 that the magnitude of the sideband coefficients varies with the index of modulation $m_f$. When the index of modulation is zero, all the energy is contained within the carrier. The graph shows that $J_0(m_f)$ is unity and all higher-order coefficients are zero. When modulation is applied, the index of modulation increases to finite values. The coefficient of the $J_0$ term decreases, and other sideband coefficients appear. Thus, it is evident that the energy content of the carrier decreases and energy shifts into the side-bands. As we stated in the original presentation of the material on frequency modulation, the amplitude of the final output wave is constant. One of the main advantages of the FM transmitter is that, unlike the AM transmitter, the output power is at all times constant. The process of frequency modulation reduces the carrier power and puts this decreased energy into useful signal carrying sideband energy. In an AM transmitter rated at 1000 watts, the circuit must be capable of handling 1500 watts average and 4000 watts peak at 100% modulation. On the other hand, an FM transmitter has an average power, for the same conditions, of 1000 watts at any modulation level.  As a result, smaller equipment can be used in the FM transmitter.

We note from Fig. 23–11 that, as the order of modulation $m_f$ increases, there appear a greater number of sidebands.  As an example, for an index of modulation of 3, we find from the graph:

$$J_0(m_f) = -0.260 \quad \text{carrier}$$
$$J_1(m_f) = +0.339 \quad \text{first-order sideband}$$
$$J_2(m_f) = +0.486 \quad \text{second-order sideband}$$
$$J_3(m_f) = +0.309 \quad \text{third-order sideband}$$
$$J_4(m_f) = +0.132 \quad \text{fourth-order sideband}$$
$$J_5(m_f) = +0.043 \quad \text{fifth-order sideband}$$
$$J_6(m_f) = +0.011 \quad \text{sixth-order sideband}$$

Higher-order sidebands are negligible.

An index of modulation of 3 can be produced by a 4 kc signal at a sufficient level to cause a deviation frequency of 12 kc.  The fifth-order sideband means that energies exist at 5 × 4 or 20 kc, above and below the carrier.  This energy distribution can be represented on a frequency axis (Fig. 23–12a) in the same fashion as was done with the AM signal (Fig. 23–6b).  From this energy spectrum, we can see that, for this index of modulation of three, the second-order sideband contains the greatest amount of energy.  At high modulation levels where the index of modulation is large, the energy spectrum contains a great many sidebands.  If the deviation is 25 kc and the signal is 1 kc, the index of modulation is 25.  The energy distribution is shown in

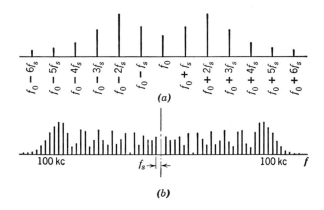

*(a)*

*(b)*

**Figure 23–12**  Sideband energy distribution.  (a) Frequency distribution for $m_f = 3$.  (b) Frequency distribution for $m_f = 25$.  (*Courtesy Gray, Applied Electronics*)

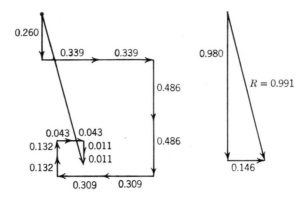

**Figure 23-13**   Addition of sideband phasors to show total energy.

Fig. 23-12*b*. Sidebands are present up to the 30th order. In this case a total bandwidth of 60 kc is required to transmit the complete signal.

A phasor diagram may be established for frequency modulation as was done for amplitude modulation, and we can show this by using the coefficients determined for the index of modulation of three. The resultant phasor is the sum of the carrier and the sideband terms, which are added to each other at right angles. Each phasor is at a right angle to the preceding phasor and the phasor is shifted 90° clockwise from the previous one. By the term phasor, we mean the sum of the coefficients for each sideband pair. When a coefficient is negative, the phasor is reversed from the normal positive direction. Each coefficient is represented twice since there are two sidebands for each coefficient. The resulting phasor diagram is shown in Fig. 23-13. The resultant phasor $R$, which is the sum of the carrier and sidebands up to the sixth order, is 0.991, whereas it should be 1.000. This small error is brought about by error in reading the graph and by neglecting the higher-order terms. When the sixth-order sideband is also neglected, $R$ is 0.979.

It is possible to transmit frequency modulation without some of the higher-order sideband pairs. The resultant phasor is not exactly unity, but varies slightly in length. A variation in length is an amplitude modulation. In a receiver, a circuit that restores the constant amplitude by clipping or limiting the amplitude to a fixed level is called a *limiter* (Section 24-4), and the process is called *limiting*. In this sense, the action of the limiter is to restore the sidebands which are needed to produce a pure FM wave without amplitude variation.

We have shown in developing the results of Eq. 23–7 that the result-ant phasor $R$ of the carrier and sidebands in frequency modulation is a phasor of constant amplitude. This brings us back to the initial premise illustrated in the time wave of frequency modulation (Fig. 23–9), that the signal is independent of a variation in the amplitude of the output.

If we show the resultant phasor $R$ in reference to the unmodulated carrier $OY$ in Fig. 23–14, the locus of the tip of $R$ is a circle. $R$ advances and falls behind the carrier phasor $OY$. $OY$ rotates at a speed $\omega_0$, whereas $R$ has a varying speed $\omega_i$. When $\omega_i$ is greater than $\omega_0$, $R$ advances ahead of $OY$, and, when $\omega_i$ is less than $\omega_0$, $R$ falls behind $OY$. The rate of change of $\omega_i$ in frequency modulation is the signal $\omega_s$. At all times there exists a phase angle $\theta$ between $R$ and $OY$. If the method of modulation provides that $\theta$ is proportional to the amplitude of the signal $e_s$, and if it provides that the rate of change of $\theta$ is proportional to the frequency of the signal $f_s$, we have *phase modulation*. Phase modulation and frequency modulation are neces-sarily simultaneous. Whether we call the system frequency or phase modulation is determined by whether the modulation is proportional to frequency or to phase angle.

It is quite possible and reasonable to bring the discussion of fre-quency modulation to this point without mention of the complex concept of the Bessel function. However, an electronic technician should know how to check out an FM transmitter, and, without an appreciation of the sideband concepts of frequency modulation, the technique is meaningless.

We note that in Fig. 23–11 the carrier energy, the $J_0$ term, goes to zero at successive values of the index of modulation. These null points occur at

$$
\begin{array}{lll}
\text{Number 1} & m_f = & 2.4048 \\
\text{Number 2} & m_f = & 5.5201 \\
\text{Number 3} & m_f = & 8.6537 \\
\text{Number 4} & m_f = & 11.7915 \\
\text{Number 5} & m_f = & 14.9309 \\
\text{Number 6} & m_f = & 18.0711 \qquad \text{etc.}
\end{array}
$$

**Figure 23–14** Phasor diagram showing fre-quency and phase modulation.

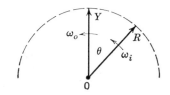

As an example, assume that a 0.1-volt signal at 1000 cycles produces a deviation of 2404.8 cycles. The index of modulation is 2.4048, and the carrier energy is zero. If the signal frequency is raised to 2000 cycles, if the amplitude of the audio signal is increased, when the carrier energy is again zero, the index of modulation does not change, and the deviation must be doubled, or 4809.6 cycles. If the modulation is linear, the signal level must be 0.2 volt. If the voltage of the signal is held fixed at 0.1 volt, and if the frequency of the signal is varied, we can, by observing the audio frequencies at which the carrier energy disappears, determine if the modulation is linear. Now, if the initial conditions produce a null at 0.1 volt and 1000 cycles, and this null is the first null as the signal level is raised from zero, the second null should occur at an audio frequency of (2.4048/5.5201) × 1000 cycles, the third null occurs at (2.4048/8.6537) × 1000 cycles, the fourth null occurs at (2.4048/11.7915) × 1000 cycles, etc.

If the original condition calls for the first null at 1000 cycles and 0.1 volt for the audio signal, maintaining the frequency and increasing the signal level increases the deviation. At (5.5201/2.4048) × 0.1 volt, we obtain the second null. At (8.6537/2.4048) × 0.1 volt we find the third null. Any deviation from these values of signal levels indicates that there is a nonlinearity in the modulation.

Unfortunately, there is no other method of checking the linearity of a source of frequency modulation. This indirect procedure must be followed and the results analyzed to see whether they correspond to the proper cross-over or null points of the carrier term. There are several methods in use for determining the null of the carrier term. The laboratory technique for the procedure is involved. If the principles are understood, a demonstration of the actual procedure on test equipment becomes meaningful.

### Section 23–5    The Reactance-Tube Modulator

The reactance-tube oscillator is a method of producing frequency modulation directly. The reactance tube itself is first analyzed, and then it is incorporated in a complete oscillator circuit. The elementary circuit is shown in Fig. 23–15. The reactance network is the capacitor $C$ and the resistor $R$. This circuit for a vacuum tube is not conventional because an external voltage is *applied to* the plate circuit, and the action of the tube is evaluated. The capacitor $C_c$ is merely a blocking capacitor and the reactance of the RF choke is sufficiently high that its effect can be neglected. The applied voltage $e_p$ produces a current $i$ in the reactance network. The component values in the

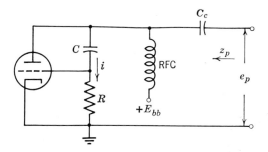

**Figure 23–15** The basic reactance tube circuit.

reactance network are such that

$$X_c \gg R$$

Then the current $i$ is determined solely by $X_c$:

$$i = \frac{e_p}{-jX_c} = j\frac{e_p}{X_c} = j2\pi fCe_p$$

The grid voltage on the tube is

$$e_g = iR = j2\pi fRCe_p$$

Since the plate current in a vacuum tube is $g_m e_g$,

$$i_p = g_m e_g = j2\pi f g_m RCe_p$$

The impedance presented by the tube to the external voltage is

$$z = \frac{e_p}{i_p}$$

Substituting, we get

$$z = \frac{e_p}{j2\pi f g_m RCe_p}$$

$$= -j\frac{1}{2\pi f(g_m RC)}$$

The final form of this equation is that of a capacitive reactance in which the term in parentheses is an equivalent capacitance. In this manner, the circuit arrangement acts as a capacitance $C_{eq}$, which is given by

$$C_{eq} = g_m RC$$

This equivalent capacitance is often described as an *injected capacitance* since the circuit places across the source of $e_p$ a parallel capacitance.

This equivalent capacitance is directly proportional to $g_m$. When a remote cutoff tube is used, the transconductance is proportional to the instantaneous bias voltage. If an audio signal is fed into this grid, the equivalent capacitance of the circuit changes according to the instantaneous value of the signal. The reactance-tube circuit is connected in parallel to the tank of an oscillator which in Fig. 23–16 is an electron-coupled oscillator.

The equivalent capacitance of the reactance tube is in parallel with the oscillator tank, $L_1$ and $C_1$. When there is an audio signal on the grid of the reactance tube, the instantaneous $g_m$ varies, and $C_{eq}$ changes. Since the total tuning capacitance of $L_1$ includes $C_{eq}$, the frequency of the electron-coupled oscillator changes. In this manner, the output of the electron-coupled oscillator is an FM signal. Usually, the reactance tube is a remote-cutoff multigrid tube because these tubes have very large variations in the transconductance with changing bias. When a multigrid tube is used, the junction of the $R$ and $C$ of the reactance network is connected to either the grid or the cathode, and the signal is fed into one of the electrodes which is not used by the reactance network. In practice, a reactance tube modulator must be compensated to produce a linear modulation.

The capacitor and the resistor of the reactance network may be interchanged, or inductance $L$ and resistance $R$ may be used. The four basic circuit arrangements are shown in Fig. 23–17. These basic diagrams do not show the required blocking capacitors, the grid-leak resistors, or the power-supply sources which are necessary in an actual

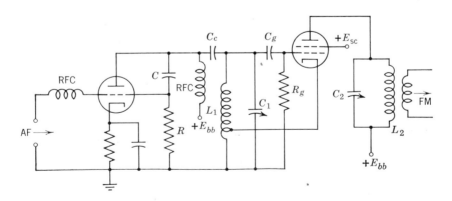

**Figure 23–16**   The reactance-tube modulator.

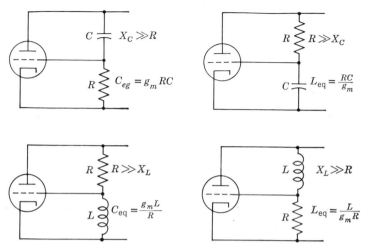

**Figure 23–17** Basic forms of a reactance tube.

circuit. The relative magnitudes of the parts of the reactance networks are specified in the diagrams, and equations for the resulting values of injected capacitance or inductance are given. The derivation of the other three forms of the circuit is left as an exercise.

### Section 23–6 The Balanced Modulator

The original FM transmitter developed by Major Armstrong was not the direct FM system using the reactance-tube modulator, but was an indirect method using a *ring* or *balanced modulator*. First we develop the relations between the input and the output of the widely used balanced modulator, and then we apply this circuit to the generation of an FM signal.

The balanced modulator (Fig. 23–18) is essentially a push–pull circuit with two inputs, $A$ and $B$, and one output, $C$. If input $B$ did not exist, the circuit would be an ordinary push–pull amplifier. Since the signal $B$ simultaneously appears on both grids at the same phase angle, the input $B$ is called a *push–push* input.

Let us assume for the derivation that the frequency of signal $B$ is greater than the frequency of signal $A$. In a specific application, the input $B$ is radio frequency and the input $A$ is audio frequency. The signal $A$ produces a voltage on the grid of tube $V1$ which may be given as $\sin A$. Since the circuit is in push–pull, the signal from $A$ on the

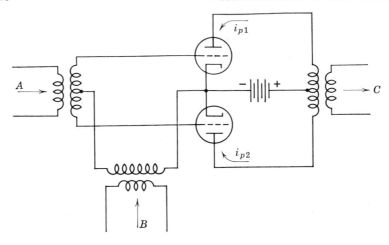

**Figure 23–18**    The balanced or ring modulator.

grid of $V2$ is $-\sin A$. The signal from the push–push input, $\sin B$, is simultaneous on both grids. The total signals on the grids are

$$e_{g1} = \sin B + \sin A$$

and $\qquad\qquad e_{g2} = \sin B - \sin A$

A power series is used to represent the plate currents of the tubes, and, since the tubes are identical, the coefficients of corresponding terms are the same for the two tubes:

$$i_{p1} = a_0 + a_1 e_{g1} + a_2 e^2{}_{g1} + a_3 e^3{}_{g1} + \cdots$$

$$i_{p2} = a_0 + a_1 e_{g2} + a_2 e^2{}_{g2} + a_3 e^3{}_{g2} + \cdots$$

The push–pull output is the difference of these two plate currents

$$C = i_{p1} - i_{p2}$$

The algebraic procedure at this point is to substitute the equations for the grid voltages into the power series and then to examine the results of the push–pull difference of the two expansions.

$$i_{p1} = a_0 + a_1(\sin B + \sin A) + a_2(\sin B + \sin A)^2$$
$$+ a_3(\sin B + \sin A)^3 + \cdots$$

$$i_{p2} = a_0 + a_1(\sin B - \sin A) + a_2(\sin B - \sin A)^2$$
$$+ a_3(\sin B - \sin A)^3 + \cdots$$

Expanding gives

$$i_{p1} = a_0 + a_1 \sin B + a_1 \sin A + a_2 \sin^2 B + 2a_2 \sin B \sin A$$
$$+ a_2 \sin^2 A + a_3 \sin^3 B + 3a_3 \sin^2 B \sin A$$
$$+ 3a_3 \sin B \sin^2 A + a_3 \sin^3 A + \cdots$$

$$i_{p2} = a_0 + a_1 \sin B - a_1 \sin A + a_2 \sin^2 B - 2a_2 \sin B \sin A$$
$$+ a_2 \sin^2 A + a_3 \sin^3 B - 3a_3 \sin^2 B \sin A$$
$$+ 3a_3 \sin B \sin^2 A - a_3 \sin^3 A + \cdots$$

Upon subtraction, we find that the difference is

$$i_{p1} - i_{p2} = 2a_1 \sin A + 4a_2 \sin B \sin A + 6a_3 \sin^2 B \sin A$$
$$+ 2a_3 \sin^3 A$$

This last equation contains a number of terms. We are not interested in the magnitude of these terms but only in their frequency content. For example, if the term is $2a_1 \sin A$, the energy content is at $f_A$.

By using the trigonometric expansion formula

$$2 \sin x \sin y = \cos (x + y) - \cos (x - y)$$

it is evident that the energy content of the term $4a_2 \sin B \sin A$ is at frequencies $(f_B + f_A)$ and $(f_B - f_A)$.

In considering the term $6a_3 \sin^2 B \sin A$, we neglect the coefficient and write the term as

$$(\tfrac{1}{2} - \tfrac{1}{2} \cos 2B) \sin A$$

Expanding, it becomes

$$\tfrac{1}{2} \sin A - \tfrac{1}{2} \cos 2B \sin A$$

But

$$2 \cos x \sin y = \sin (x + y) - \sin (x - y)$$

Substituting, we have

$$\tfrac{1}{2} \sin A - \tfrac{1}{4} \sin (2B + A) + \tfrac{1}{4} \sin (2B - A)$$

This means that the term $\sin^2 B \sin A$ contains energies at

$$f_A, \quad (2f_B + f_A), \quad \text{and} \quad (2f_B - f_A)$$

The remaining term, $2a_3 \sin^3 A$, may be treated by considering $\sin^3 x$:

$$\sin^3 x = \sin x (\sin^2 x)$$
$$= \sin x (\tfrac{1}{2} - \tfrac{1}{2} \cos 2x)$$
$$= \tfrac{1}{2} \sin x - \tfrac{1}{2} \sin x \cos 2x$$
$$= \tfrac{1}{2} \sin x - \tfrac{1}{4} \sin 3x - \tfrac{1}{4} \sin x$$
$$= \tfrac{1}{4} \sin x - \tfrac{1}{4} \sin 3x$$

Thus, the term contains energy at $f_A$ and at $3f_A$.

When the energy terms are collected and duplications are ignored, we find that the push–pull output $C$ contains energies at

$$f_A, \quad (f_B + f_A), \quad (f_B - f_A), \quad (2f_B + f_A), \quad (2f_B - f_A), \quad 3f_A$$

If the output transformer is an RF transformer tuned to $f_B$, the audio frequencies, $f_A$ and $3f_A$, are attenuated completely. Since $(2f_B + f_A)$ and $(2f_B - f_A)$ are very close to the second harmonic, $2f_B$, of $f_B$, these frequencies are also not present in the output. The output, then, from this tuned circuit consists only of energies at $(f_B + f_A)$ and at $(f_B - f_A)$. The output *does not* contain the carrier $f_B$. Hence, *the dual function of the ring modulator is to develop amplitude modulation and to separate the sidebands from the carrier.*

In the phasor diagram for amplitude modulation (Fig. 23–19*a*), the resultant phasor $R$ is at all times in phase with the carrier. If the sidebands are rotated 90° with respect to the carrier, the resultant phasor is not in phase with the carrier phasor and represents phase modulation (Fig. 23–19*b*). This resultant phasor does vary in length, but, if the resultant wave is amplified in a limiter circuit, the output of the limiter has a constant amplitude (Fig. 23–19*c*), and, together with frequency-response correction networks in the audio input stages, produces a pure FM wave.

The block diagram of the Armstrong transmitter (Fig. 23–20) shows how these principles are joined together in the complete circuit. The audio and the radio frequency from the crystal drive a balanced

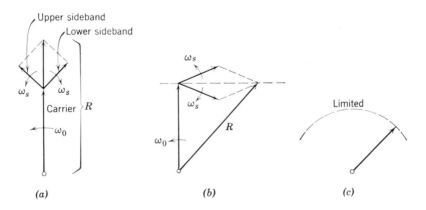

(a)                          (b)                          (c)

**Figure 23–19** Phasor diagrams for the Armstrong method of producing frequency modulation. (*a*) Phasor diagram of amplitude modulation. (*b*) Sidebands rotated 90°. (*c*) Pure frequency modulation.

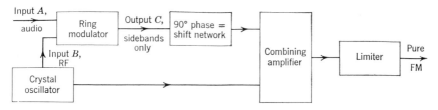

**Figure 23–20**   Block diagram of the Armstrong transmitter.

modulator which produces the sidebands only in the output. The output coupling circuit gives the required 90° phase shift to the sidebands, and this sideband signal is fed into the combining amplifier. A signal from the crystal oscillator is also fed into the combining amplifier. The amplitude modulation present in the output of the combining amplifier is removed in the limiter stage to produce a pure FM output.

The reactance-tube modulator cannot be crystal-controlled, and various complicated methods are used in later amplifier stages to provide the necessary close frequency stability. The Armstrong method provides crystal control of the output signal as a part of the balanced-modulator circuit itself.

There are other methods used to develop frequency modulation, but, since their application is limited to FM transmitters, they are not considered here. These circuits can be found in the specialized textbooks on frequency modulation that are in print.

## Section 23–7   Pre-emphasis and De-emphasis

In FM broadcasting and receiving systems, the volume of the high-frequency audio signals is increased for transmission and is corrected within the audio stages of the receiver. The increase of the level of the high frequencies which is termed *pre-emphasis* increases the energy content of the high-order sidebands, with the result that reception can be made with lower signal-to-noise values than without pre-emphasis. In the audio amplifiers of the transmitter, a simple high-pass $L$ filter made up of a resistor and an inductor is used. The time constant of this filter is 75 $\mu$sec.

It is necessary to use in the receiver the inverse, or *de-emphasis*, characteristic. The de-emphasis must have the same time constant, 75 $\mu$sec, as the pre-emphasis.

## . . . . Suggested References for Further Study

1. F. E. Terman, *Radio Engineer's Handbook*, Section 7, McGraw-Hill Book Co., New York, 1943.
2. A. Hund, *Frequency Modulation*, McGraw-Hill Book Co., New York, 1942.
3. C. E. Tibbs and G. G. Johnstone, *Frequency Modulation Engineering*, 2nd ed. rev. John Wiley & Sons, New York, 1956.
4. L. B. Arguimbau, and R. B. Adler, *Vacuum-Tube Circuits and Transistors*, Chapter 12, John Wiley & Sons, New York, 1956.

## . . . . QUESTIONS

1. Define or explain each of the following terms used in the development of the theory of amplitude modulation: (a) upper sideband, (b) per cent modulation, (c) overmodulation, (d) splattering, (e) peak power, (f) MCW, (g) ICW, (h) baud, (i) SSB, (j) trapezoidal pattern.

2. Define or explain each of the following terms used in the development of the theory of frequency modulation: (a) index of modulation, (b) deviation frequency, (c) deviation ratio, (d) wide-band FM, (e) narrow-band FM, (f) multiple sidebands, (g) reactance tube, (h) push–push, (i) ring modulator, (j) signal-to-noise ratio.

3. What is the purpose of a modulation?

4. Distinguish among AM, FM and PM.

5. How can the per cent modulation be determined from a screen pattern on an oscilloscope?

6. Describe four methods of producing amplitude modulation.

7. How does the sideband energy content vary with audio signal in AM?

8. Compare AM and FM based on bandwidth considerations.

9. Compare AM and FM based on power considerations.

10. Explain in detail the method of checking an FM transmitter or oscillator for linearity.

11. What is meant by "linearity" in an AM modulator and in an FM modulator?

12. What are the advantages and disadvantages of a reactance tube?

13. What is the advantage of a balanced modulator circuit in producing FM?

14. Describe the operation of the balanced-modulator circuit.

15. Explain pre-emphasis and de-emphasis.

16. Using Fig. 23–11, explain how the first-order sidebands could be used to check out the linearity of a frequency modulator.

## . . . . **PROBLEMS**

1. A high-speed radio-telegraph system operates at 300 words per minute, transmitting five-letter code words. Determine the bandwidth required for AM transmission of the signals.

2. Solve problem 1 for a transmission speed of 450 words per minute.

3. The carrier strength of an AM signal is 600 watts. When the modulation is 20%, determine the average sideband power.

4. Solve problem 3 for 40% modulation.

5. Solve problem 3 for 60% modulation.

6. Solve problem 3 for 80% modulation.

7. Solve problem 3 for 100% modulation.

8. Assume that the peak-to-peak value of a carrier wave is 50 volts. What are the values of $A$ and $B$ in Fig. 23–5a when the modulation is 20%? 40%? 60%? 80%? 100%?

9. The power delivered to a 72 ohm-antenna is 100 watts with no modulation. Determine the antenna current when the modulation is zero. Repeat for modulations of 20%, 40%, 60%, 80% and 100%.

10. The current in an antenna is 7.2 amperes when the modulation is 45%. Determine the modulation when the antenna current rises to 7.9 amperes.

11. In an FM system, when the audio frequency is 500 cycles and the audio voltage is 2.4 volts, the deviation is 4.7 kc. When the audio is changed to 6.7 volts, what is the deviation? What is the index of modulation in each case?

12. In an FM system, if the carrier vanishes when the audio is 4 kc and 6 volts, what voltage at 250 cycles causes the carrier to go to zero. Assume that the operation is at the first cross-over point for the $J_0$ term. Repeat if the second cross-over is causing the condition.

13. In an FM system, as the voltage is increased from zero at 400 cycles, the carrier first goes to zero when the audio level is 0.31 volt. At what successive audio levels does the carrier energy go to zero? When the frequency is changed to 1000 cycles, at what audio voltages will the carrier go to zero? Assume, that the modulation is linear.

14. Derive the equations for the reactance-tube circuits shown in Fig. 23–17.

# Detection

• • • • • • • • • • • • • • • • • • • CHAPTER **24**

In a receiving device, it is necessary to convert a modulated wave, AM or FM, back to the audio signal. At the same time it is necessary to remove the high-frequency carrier from the composite wave. The *detector* is the electronic device that restores the audio, and the *filter section* separates the signal from the carrier.

A mathematical approach to the problem of detection is very complex, and a quantitative treatment is sufficient for the needs of the technician. The diode (Section 24–1) and the triode (Section 24–2) are both used in AM detection. Automatic volume control (Section 24–3) is a fundamental circuit used in the radio receiver. The limiter–discriminator circuit (Section 24–4) and the ratio detector (Section 24–5) are alternative methods of FM detection. Frequency converters (Section 24–6) are also forms of the detector. An automatic frequency-control circuit (Section 24–7) combines several basic circuits to provide a stabilized frequency source.

### Section 24–1  AM Detectors--Diodes

A modulated carrier wave is shown in Fig. 24–1a. When this signal is fed into a diode rectifier, only one-half the composite signal is passed to the load (Fig. 24–1b). When this rectifier output is filtered, the high frequency is removed and the audio is retained. The resultant wave corresponds to the envelope of the original input signal (Fig. 24–1c). The action of rectification produces a simultaneous direct voltage in the filtered output, $E_{dc}$. A blocking capacitor removes the direct voltage leaving the pure a-c audio signal shown in Fig. 24–1d.

**532**

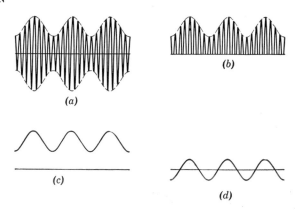

**Figure 24–1** The mechanism of diode detection. (*a*) Modulated carrier wave. (*b*) Waveform resulting from half-wave rectification. (*c*) Envelope of the output of half-wave rectification. (*d*) D-c value removed by blocking capacitor.

A circuit that accomplishes this detection is shown in Fig. 24–2. The incoming modulated AM signal is fed into the detector from a tuned circuit, $L_1$ and $C_1$. This tuned circuit is resonant at the frequency of the carrier, and its response is broad enough to pass the sideband energy content of the modulated wave. Since a diode is a unilateral device, it rectifies this modulated wave and allows one half, in this case the positive half, to pass on to the filter circuit. The filter section comprising $C_2$, $R_1$, and $C_3$ is a low-pass $\pi$ filter. Its cutoff frequency is adjusted by component selection to attenuate the high carrier and sideband frequencies. The audio frequencies and the direct current pass through the $\pi$ filter and appear across the load resistor $R_2$. The coupling capacitor $C_4$ blocks the direct voltage and a pure a-c audio signal appears across $R_3$.

There are several sources of distortion in this circuit. The d-c load on the diode, neglecting the resistance of the transformer secondary

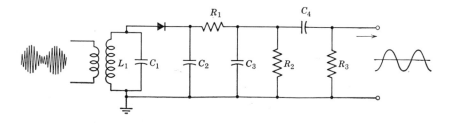

**Figure 24–2** The simple diode detector.

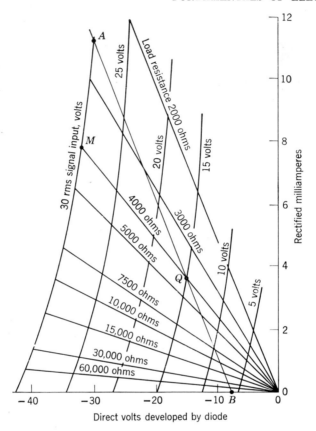

**Figure 24–3** Rectification characteristics of a 6AL5.

and $R_1$, is $R_2$. The a-c load on the diode is the parallel combination of $R_2$ and $R_3$. This difference can cause the diode to operate in a nonlinear fashion.

The rectification characteristic of a typical diode under dynamic conditions is shown in Fig. 24–3. If we assume in Fig. 24–2 that $R_1$ is zero and that $R_3$ is infinite resistance, the action of the circuit for different values of the load resistance $R_2$ is shown in Fig. 24–3. This load line is somewhat different from the concepts of the amplifier load line. When $R_2$ is 4000 ohms, the load line is $OM$. The operating point is not fixed, but it is determined by the level of the incoming carrier signal. When the carrier signal is 15 volts rms, the operating point is $Q$. If the carrier-signal strength increases, the operating point shifts toward $M$, and, if the carrier drops to zero, the operating point moves along the load line from $Q$ to $O$.

When the coupling network, $R_2$, $C_4$ and $R_3$, exists in Fig. 24–2, both a d-c and an a-c load line must be considered. If we assume that both $R_2$ and $R_3$ are 4000 ohms, the d-c load line for 4000 ohms is used, and an a-c load line for 2000 ohms, the parallel combination, must be drawn through the operating point in the same manner as was done with the voltage amplifier a-c load line. In this circuit, the operating point $Q$ is valid only for a specific input rms signal. In Fig. 24–3, the load line $AQB$ is drawn through point $Q$ with a slope of 2000 ohms. A carrier signal of 15 volts rms or 21 volts peak establishes the operation at $Q$. When the carrier signal is modulated, the modulation causes the instantaneous operation to shift along $AQB$. The distance from $Q$ to $A$ is 15 volts rms or 21 volts peak. The distance from $Q$ to

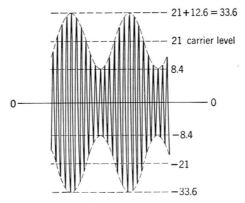

$B$ is 9 volts rms or 12.6 volts peak. When the modulation is 100%, the envelope rises from the carrier level of 21 volts to 42 volts and falls to zero. The load line $AQB$ can accommodate the modulation peak of 42 volts, but, when the modulation envelope falls below (21–12.6) or 8.4 volts, the diode cuts off at point $B$.

Using Eq. 23–3, we have, for this condition, a modulation of

$$m = \frac{A - B}{A + B} \times 100 = \frac{2 \times 33.6 - 2 \times 8.4}{2 \times 33.6 + 2 \times 8.4} \times 100$$

$$= \frac{25.2}{42.0} \times 100 = 60\%$$

Thus, for this carrier input and these specific values of $R_2$ and $R_3$, the action of the detector clips the lower part of the modulation envelope when the modulation exceeds 60%.

In order to minimize this distortion, it is necessary to make $R_3$ much greater than $R_2$. Since $R_3$ usually serves as the grid resistor for the first audio amplifier tube, the value of $R_3$ that can be used has a practical upper limit of the order of one half, or one megohm for most tubes.

A detailed examination of the input to the filter (Fig. 24–4a) shows that the input capacitor charges to the peak of the cycle and then discharges until the next positive half-cycle. As a result, the output of the filter (Fig. 24–4b) is not exactly smooth, but is serrated. If the signal abruptly drops from a high level to a low level (Fig. 24–4c), the time constant of the filter prevents the filter output from following this change exactly (Fig. 24–4d) and introduces a distortion. This distortion, called *diagonal clipping*, cannot occur when the abrupt change is from a low level to a high level because the capacitor voltage rises with the first positive half-cycle to the peak value. If the time constant of the filter is decreased, this distortion decreases, but the magnitude of the serrations or sawteeth increases in the output. Since these serrations occur at the frequency of the carrier, an increase in the magnitude indicates that the filtering action is reduced. An actual circuit design is a compromise between these two factors.

Another source of distortion arises from the fact that the a-c load for the audio frequency is the parallel combination of $R_2$ and $R_3$ (Fig. 24–2). This loading is not the same as the a-c load at the carrier frequency. The load impedance on the transformer is essentially the low impedance of the filter at the carrier frequency.

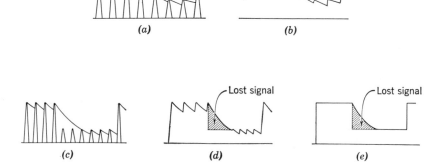

**Figure 24–4** Effect of filter time constant on diode output. (*a*) Input to filter. (*b*) Output of filter. (*c*) Input to filter for square-wave signal. (*d*) Output of filter for square-wave signal. (*e*) Signal output.

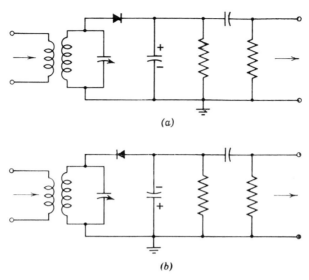

*(a)*

*(b)*

**Figure 24–5**  Polarity of detector load voltage.  *(a)* Positive direct voltage.
*(b)* Negative direct voltage.

As far as the alternating signal output voltage is concerned (Fig.
24–5), a reversed diode has no effect on the magnitude of the output
wave.   One diode connection rectifies the top envelope, and the other
diode connection rectifies the bottom envelope.   These two envelopes
are equal in magnitude but opposite in phase.   This means that the
only difference between the two circuits is a phase difference which is
usually not at all important.   The two diode connections produce
different direct voltage polarities across the load.   This direct voltage
is proportional to the magnitude of the incoming carrier and is not a
function of the modulation.   The direct voltage can be used to measure the carrier level and is employed in many applications for this
purpose.   The specific application of the circuit determines whether
a positive or a negative voltage is required.   The connection that
develops a negative direct voltage is used to provide the voltage for
automatic volume control (Section 24–3).

### Section 24–2   AM Detectors—Triodes

The dynamic-transfer characteristic for a triode is shown in Fig.
24–6.   It is possible to obtain detection at three places on this characteristic, *A*, *B*, or *C*.   Waveforms *a*, *b*, and *c* represent an incoming

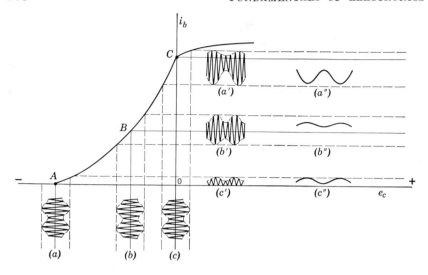

**Figure 24-6** Waveforms for plate detection.

modulated carrier. Waveforms $a'$, $b'$, and $c'$ are the plate-current waves before filtering, and waveforms $a''$, $b''$, and $c''$ show the result of the smoothing effect of the filter.

When the bias is held at cutoff $A$, the action is very similar to the diode, but, in this circuit, a voltage gain is obtained. A cutoff bias is not obtained from a fixed external battery, but from a cathode bias (Fig. 24–7). The cathode resistor $R_K$ is very high, of the order of 100,000 ohms or 1 megohm. This very high cathode resistance does not quite cut off the tube, but it is near enough to cutoff that the operation is effectively at cutoff.

When the circuit is biased at $B$, the values of $R_K$ and $C_K$ are those of a normal amplifier. Since the action of the detection depends on the degree of nonlinearity of the transfer characteristic at $B$, the difference between the top half of the waveform $b'$ and the bottom half cannot be large. The output $b''$, which is the average of the top envelope and the bottom envelope, is not a large signal. Normally, operation at point $B$ is avoided.

When the plate detector is operated at zero bias (point $C$), the value of the cathode resistance $R_K$ is zero. The grid current produced when the instantaneous input signal to the grid is positive causes a plate-current saturation effect. The output waveforms are $a'$ and $a''$. This circuit connection gives the greatest output and gain, but, by demanding grid current, it loads down the input transformer. Grid current is not flowing when the operation is at points $A$ or $B$. These last conditions do not load down the input transformer and are often called *infinite impedance detectors.*

The circuit for grid-leak detection is shown in Fig. 24–8. The grid leak combination, $C_g$ and $R_g$, develops a d-c bias in the manner explained in Section 16–1. The time constant of the grid leak is such that the d-c bias follows the envelope of the modulation. For example, assume that the maximum peak-to-peak value of the incoming modulated wave is 10 volts and that the minimum peak-to-peak value is 6 volts. The d-c bias follows the envelope. Each cycle drives the grid very slightly positive to develop a direct voltage on the capacitor $C_g$ equal to the peak value of the voltage of the cycle. In this example, the d-c bias varies between $-3$ and $-5$ volts. Except at the time when the capacitor is recharging, the wave is at all times negative measured *down from zero.* As can be seen from the grid waveform on Fig. 24–8, the relocated amplitude of the envelope is 4 volts instead of 2 volts. This action of the grid leak provides a gain of two in addition to the amplification within the triode, which serves as the detector amplifier. The waveforms within the tube (Fig. 24–9) are very similar to those obtained from the plate detector.

When a schematic for a piece of equipment is examined, the detector stage may be either a diode or a triode. If the triode is used, it is either a grid-leak detector or a plate detector. The presence of a grid-leak resistor and capacitor without a cathode resistor identifies the circuit as a grid-leak detector. If it does not meet these identifications, it must be a plate detector.

A common use of the grid-leak detector is in the circuit of the one-tube regenerative receiver. A signal from the antenna is fed to an

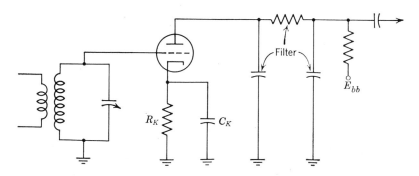

**Figure 24–7**   Circuit for plate detection.

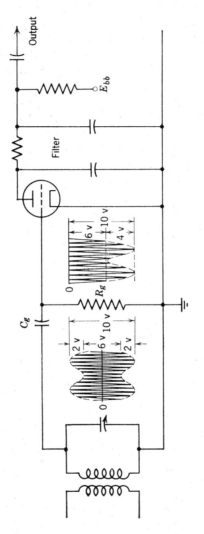

**Figure 24-8**  Circuit for grid-leak detection.

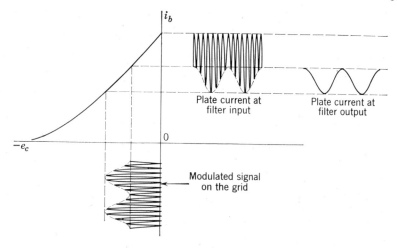

**Figure 24–9** Waveforms of grid-leak detection.

untuned-primary–tuned-secondary transformer in which $C_1$ tunes the circuit to the desired station signal. Grid-leak detection using $C_g$ and $R_g$ is employed. The filter in the plate circuit removes the carrier-frequency energy so that the energy in the headphones is an audio signal. The winding $L_f$ is a feedback winding from the plate circuit back to the grid circuit. When the feedback is positive, as we showed in Section 17–2, the gain approaches infinity when the feedback factor approaches $+1$. This receiver is extremely sensitive, but care must

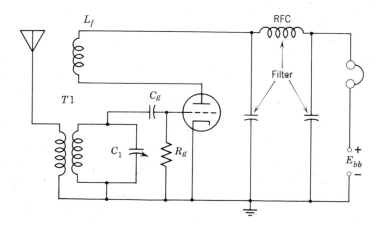

**Figure 24–10** The regenerative receiver.

be taken to prevent it from breaking into oscillation.   The feedback may be controlled in several ways:

1. Vary mechanically the coupling of $L_f$ into $T1$.
2. Detune $L_f$ with an additional tuning capacitance.
3. Vary the supply voltage which varies $A_e$ instead of $\beta$ in the feedback factor.
4. Load down $L_f$ with a variable resistance.

It should be noted that detectors of this type produce a high distortion at high modulation levels.

## Section 24-3   Automatic Volume Control

If we have a radio receiver tuned to a station which induces a signal of 50 $\mu$v in the antenna, a proper setting of the volume control produces a pleasing output sound level.   When the receiver is tuned in to a strong station which induces a signal of 50,000 $\mu$v in the antenna, the input signal has increased by a factor of 1000.   If the sound level in the speaker is increased by a factor of 1000 also, the listener would be extremely discomforted.   It is necessary to provide an *automatic volume-control* (*AVC*) circuit which reduces the gain of the receiver on strong signals.

The direct voltage at the detector is proportional to the strength of the carrier level that is being detected.   If this direct voltage is filtered, it can be used to bias remote-cutoff tubes which amplify the signal. A negative direct voltage proportional to the carrier level is developed across the load resistor $R_L$ from $A$ to ground in Fig. 24–11.   This direct voltage is well filtered in the L filter comprised of $R$ and $C$. This L filter is called the AVC filter, and its time constant is longer than the lowest audio frequency.   If the time constant of this filter were too short, the AVC action would tend to suppress the audio signal itself.   The AVC voltage is applied to each grid of the preceding amplifiers.   A decoupling filter is usually placed in each grid to prevent motorboating.   The amplifier tubes must be remote-cutoff tubes. A large bias on a remote-cutoff tube lowers the transconductance and lowers the stage gain.   A weak AVC voltage lowers the bias and allows the transconductance and the stage gain to increase.

In transistor circuits, an AVC voltage (or current) reduces the forward bias toward zero and lowers the gain.   The polarity of the automatic volume control may be either positive or negative, depending on whether the transistor is *NPN* or *PNP*.   A typical circuit is shown in Fig. 24–12.   The action of the detector $V3$ is very similar to the plate

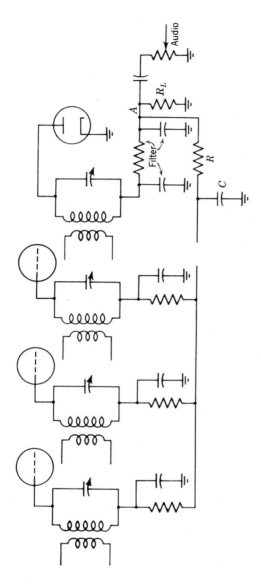

**Figure 24–11** Automatic volume control (AVC) circuit.

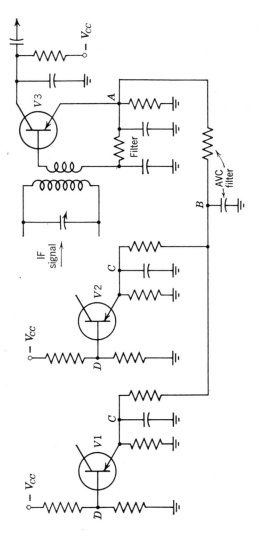

**Figure 24-12**   AVC circuit using transistors.

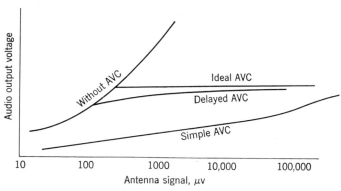

**Figure 24–13** Effects of AVC action.

detector. The forward bias on $V1$ and $V2$ is determined by the difference in voltage between $C$ and $D$, both of which are negative. Point $D$ is more negative than point $C$, giving a forward bias on the transistor. When the carrier level increases, the negative voltage at $A$ increases. This negative voltage is filtered in the AVC filter, and it causes the negative voltage at point $C$ to increase. An increased negative voltage on the emitters of $V1$ and $V2$ reduces the net forward bias and reduces the currents in these transistors. When the currents are reduced, the values of $z_{in}$ and $z_{out}$ increase. This increase in the input and output impedances creates a serious mismatch which lowers the gain of the transistors. In this manner, we find that the transistor can give the same results as the use of a variable-mu pentode. If $NPN$ transistors were used in this circuit, a positive AVC voltage would be necessary.

In Fig. 24–13, the effect of the automatic volume control is shown for different antenna signal strengths. Without automatic volume control, the audio signal increases rapidly to a point of distortion. Ideally, the gain should rise to a predetermined point and then remain fixed for all larger antenna signals. In the simple AVC circuits of Fig. 24–11 and Fig. 24–12, all signal levels produce an AVC voltage and a consequent reduction in gain. This situation decreases the gain when it is most needed—at the very weak signal levels. If a diode is used for automatic volume control and a separate diode is used for detection, the AVC diode can be biased in the manner of a gate or clamp so that it does not function until a certain signal level is reached. This circuit arrangement is known as *delayed automatic volume control, DAVC,* (Fig. 24–14).

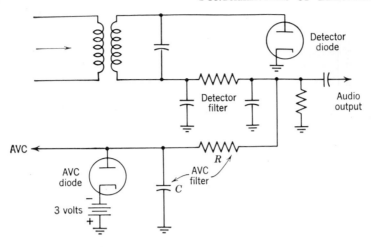

**Figure 24–14**   Delayed AVC circuit.

## Section 24–4   FM Detectors—The Limiter and Discriminator

The limiter (Fig. 24–15$a$) is a form of clipping circuit which, although widely used in the field of applied electronics, is usually associated with the Foster–Seeley discriminator circuit in FM detection.   The purpose of the limiter is to remove amplitude variations from an incoming FM signal before it is detected.   The distinguishing features of the limiter circuit are the use of a grid-leak bias and a very low plate and screen voltage of the order of 25 to 40 volts using a sharp cutoff pentode. The action of the grid leak levels off the top of the signal as shown in the waveforms for the grid-leak detector (Fig. 24–8).   The low voltage of the plate and the screen provide a plate saturation and a cutoff of the signal at low signal levels.   A weak signal ($A$ in Fig. 24–15$b$) is clipped on one side by the action of the grid leak, but the amplitude variations are present in the plate circuit.   When the signal level reaches the level shown at $B$ in the diagram, clipping occurs on both sides of the signal, and amplitude variations are removed.   A still larger signal $C$ does not produce a greater output, and the limiting is complete.   The response characteristic (Fig. 24–15$c$) shows that limiting does not occur until point $B$ is reached and that the output remains constant for increasing signal to point $C$.   At very high incoming signal levels beyond $C$, the curve may tend to droop.   The sharp characteristic of the tube used as a limiter is necessary to provide proper clipping, and a high-gain tube insures saturation at low-input signal levels.

Obviously, the concept of conventional gain cannot be used for a limiter. If limiting occurs at point $B$ for a 1-volt signal and if the limiter output is 10 volts, the voltage gain is 10. When the input voltage is increased to 30 volts (point $C$) the output is still 10 volts. If the usual concept of gain is used, the gain at point $C$ is 10/30 or 0.33. In order to eliminate the difficulty of this gain concept, the term *threshold limiting* is introduced. Threshold limiting occurs at point $B$ on the response curve. The action of a limiter is usually specified by stating the minimum signal that is required to produce this limiting action.

It is possible to improve the action of the limiting by using a

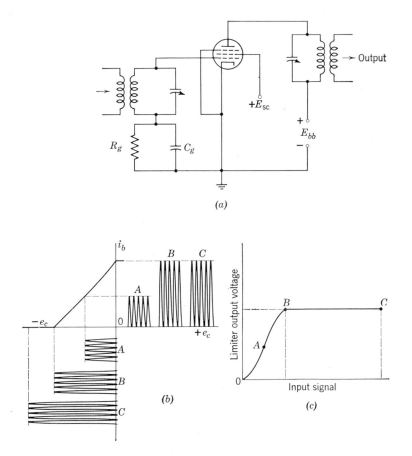

(a)

(b)

(c)

**Figure 24–15** The limiter. (a) Circuit. (b) Waveforms on transfer characteristic. (c) Response characteristic.

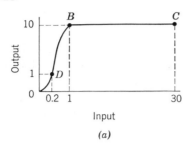
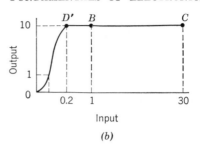

Figure 24–16  Action of a double limiter. (a) Single limiter. (b) Double limiter.

*double limiter.* In a double-limiter circuit, two limiters are connected in cascade. The coupling between the two stages is usually *RC* coupling. Let us assume that threshold limiting in each stage occurs at a 1-volt signal (Fig. 24–16a). When a 0.2-volt signal is fed into the first limiter grid, the output is 1 volt. This 1-volt signal on the grid of the second limiter produces a 10-volt output. In this double-limiter circuit, threshold limiting is accomplished at an input level of 0.2 volt, whereas a single limiter requires 1 volt. In other words, in this example, the use of a double limiter increases the limiting sensitivity of the circuit by a factor of five.

In a discriminator circuit (Fig. 24–17a), a constant level signal from a limiter is impressed across the primary winding of a double-tuned transformer. Both the primary $L_1$ and the secondary $L_2$ are carefully tuned to the same resonant frequency. The key to the operation of this circuit is the phase relation between the primary and the secondary voltages. The angle between the primary and secondary voltages is 90° at resonance (Fig. 24–17b). When the incoming frequency goes above the resonant frequency, the angle between these phasors increases. When the frequency shifts below the resonant frequency, the angle decreases. Over a range of frequencies near resonance, this phase-angle change is linear with a change in frequency.

The supply voltage (point $A$ in the circuit) is at a-c ground potential because the supply voltage is properly bypassed. A coupling capacitor $C_3$ electrically ties the tip of the primary voltage phasor (point $B$) to the center tap of the transformer secondary winding (point $D$). The alternating voltage on the top diode $V2$ is the sum of the primary voltage $AB$ plus one half the secondary voltage $DE$, producing the phasor $M$ in Fig. 24–17c. The alternating voltage on the bottom diode $V1$ is the sum of the primary voltage $AB$ plus the other half of the secondary voltage $DC$. This is shown as the phasor $N$. The load resistors, $R_1$ and $R_2$, are equal. Since the rectifier plate voltages, $M$ and $N$, are equal, the direct output voltages across $R_1$ and $R_2$ are equal. The direction of rectification of the diodes produces direct voltages across $R_1$ and $R_2$ which are opposing in polarity. The net output voltage across the total load is zero. This value is represented as point $o$ in Fig. 24–17$f$. The RF choke provides a return path for the

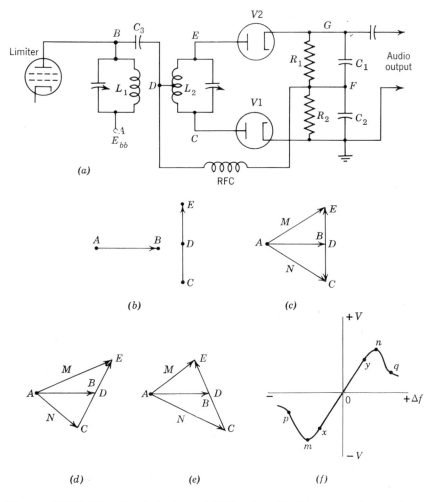

**Figure 24–17** The discriminator. (*a*) Circuit. (*b*) Primary and secondary-voltage-phasors at resonance. (*c*) Phasor diagram at $f = f_0$. (*d*) Phasor diagram at $f > f_0$. (*e*) Phasor diagram at $f < f_0$. (*f*) Discriminator characteristic.

direct currents. This choke is often replaced by a resistor in order to reduce the cost of the circuit components.

When the incoming frequency is greater than the resonant frequency, the magnitudes of $AB$ and $CE$ remain constant because of limiter action, and only the phase angle changes. The voltage $M$ to the top diode is greater than the voltage $N$ on the bottom diode (Fig. 24–17$d$), and the net output across both load resistors is positive, locating point $y$ on the discriminator characteristic. When the frequency of the signal is less than the resonant frequency, the secondary phasor shifts in a leading direction (Fig. 24–17$e$), and a negative output voltage is developed which is point $x$ on the characteristic. There are maximum output values that can be obtained, and these are shown as points $m$ and $n$ on the characteristic. When the frequency changes beyond the deviation corresponding to $m$ and $n$, we are working beyond the range of the tuned transformer, and the output falls off toward zero (points $p$ and $q$). The over-all characteristic (Fig. 24–17$f$) is the so-called S curve of the discriminator.

It is necessary that complete and exact symmetry be maintained in the S curve. An examination of Fig. 24–17$c$ shows that the magnitude of the phasor $N$ is a direct function of the length of $AB$. The length of $N$ can be monitored by measuring the direct voltage across $R_2$. When the transformer primary winding is properly tuned to resonance, the voltage across $R_2$ is a maximum. When the direct voltage across the full discriminator load is metered, it should be zero at the resonant frequency. When $L_2$ is properly tuned to resonance, this meter reading is zero. It is necessary to work back and forth between the primary and the secondary windings several times since the tuning of one affects the other slightly.

It can be seen from Fig. 24–17$f$ that a varying frequency produces a changing voltage across the full diode load. Thus a frequency modulated wave can be detected into audio. An increase in deviation which is proportional to volume produces greater swings on the S curve, giving the required greater amplitudes of output signal. The rate of deviation or the rate of changing frequency from above resonance to below resonance is the frequency of the signal and produces the frequency of the alternating current in the output of the discriminator.

### Section 24–5  FM Detectors—The Ratio Detector

The basic ratio detector (Fig. 24–18) is similar in form to the discriminator. The diodes are connected in series to produce an additive

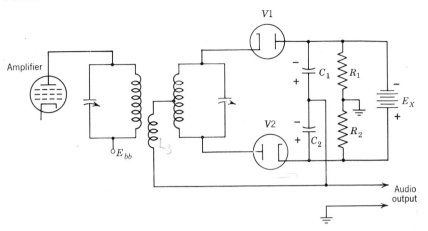

**Figure 24–18**   The basic ratio detector.

d-c polarity across the load resistors, $R_1$ and $R_2$.   The primary voltage is added to the secondary voltage by means of a tertiary winding $L_3$.   When the peak-to-peak incoming signal is less than the battery voltage $E_x$, the diodes cannot conduct and a signal does not appear across the load.   A load voltage exists only when the incoming peak-to-peak signal is greater than the battery voltage.   In any case, the load voltage cannot be greater than $E_x$.   This limiting action of the battery serves the purpose of a limiter in the circuit.   Threshold limiting is that point at which the diodes begin to rectify.

The sum of the voltages across $C_1$ and $C_2$ must equal the limiting voltage $E_x$ for amplitude-limited conditions:

$$e_a + e_b = E_x$$

The voltage across $C_1$ is $e_a$ and is the peak of the incoming signal on $V1$.   The voltage across $C_2$ is $e_b$ and is the peak of the a-c signal on $V2$.   When the incoming signal is at center frequency, the two voltages $e_a$ and $e_b$ are equal, and the output voltage taken between the junction of the resistors $R_1$ and $R_2$ and the junction of the capacitors is zero.   When the incoming frequency is above the center frequency of the transformer, the alternating voltage on $V1$ exceeds the alternating voltage on $V2$, and $e_a$, is larger than $e_b$, producing an instantaneous positive voltage.   When the incoming signal is below the center frequency, $e_b$ is larger than $e_a$, and an instantaneous negative output voltage results.   The total voltage of ($e_a + e_b$) is a constant,

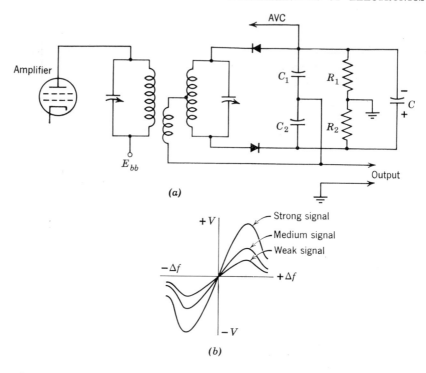

**Figure 24–19**    The ratio detector.    (*a*) Circuit.    (*b*) Frequency response.

and a change in voltage between $e_a$ and $e_b$ must divide proportionally; hence the name ratio detector.

Assume that $E_x$ is 10 volts. At the center frequency, $e_a$ and $e_b$ are each 5 volts. When the deviation above the center frequency is sufficient, $e_a$ becomes 7 volts and $e_b$ is 3 volts. The output voltage for this condition is +2 volts. The reference point of measurement is the center of the 10 volts that is established by the fixed voltages across $R_1$ and $R_2$. If we consider these voltages in regard to the discriminator circuit of Fig. 24–17, the voltage across $R_1$ is 7 volts and the voltage across $R_2$ is 3 volts. In the discriminator, the output is the *difference* voltage between the two load voltages, or +4 volts. From these figures, we find that the output of the ratio detector is one-half the output of the discriminator for the same conditions.

It is very inconvenient to use a fixed battery across the ratio detector to provide limiting. When the battery is replaced by an electrolytic capacitor $C$ in Fig. 24–19, the long time constant of $(R_1 + R_2)$ and $C$ has the same energy storage effect as the battery to eliminate the variations in the amplitude of the incoming signal. The use of a battery to provide limiting produces the same S curve that is the characteristic of the discriminator circuit. When a capacitor is used to provide the limiting, the magnitude of the S curve depends on the amplitude of the incoming signal since the equivalent $E_x$ depends on the direct voltage on the capacitor, which is the peak-to-peak carrier level. In order to prevent a distortion which may occur when changing from a small S curve to a large S curve, an AVC circuit is usually used with the ratio detector. The negative voltage from the limiting capacitor $C$ is used for the automatic volume control since the voltage across the capacitor is produced by and is proportional to the incoming carrier-signal strength.

The ratio-detector transformer may be tuned to the carrier frequency by using a visual alignment procedure in which the test equipment is an FM signal generator and an oscilloscope. If it is desired to align the circuit with a d-c voltmeter, resistors are temporarily placed in parallel with $C_1$ and $C_2$. These resistors provide a d-c circuit for the voltmeter and should be much higher in value than $R_1$ and $R_2$. When the incoming signal is set to the carrier frequency, the primary winding of the ratio detector transformer is tuned for a maximum voltage across the limiting capacitor $C$. The secondary is tuned for a zero reading on the d-c voltmeter connected between the junction of the temporary resistors and the junction of $R_1$ and $R_2$. As in the case of discriminator alignment, this sequence of tuning must be repeated several times in order to eliminate detuning from the coupling of one winding of the transformer into the other.

A number of simple versions of this circuit have been developed for use in television receivers wherein a reduced cost is the primary consideration.

### Section 24-6 Frequency Conversion

*Frequency conversion* or *heterodyning* is used to produce a *beat* or difference frequency and can be accomplished by using any nonlinear device. In a nonlinear device, the current is represented by a power series in terms of the voltage:

$$i = a_0 + a_1e + a_2e^2 + a_3e^3 + \cdots$$

The input signal is the sum of two sinusoidal signals:

$$e = A \sin \omega_1 t + B \sin \omega_2 t$$

It is only necessary to use the first three terms of the power series for the expansion, and, by substitution, we have

$$i = a_0 + a_1(A \sin \omega_1 t + B \sin \omega_2 t) + a_2(A \sin \omega_1 t + B \sin \omega_2 t)^2$$

$$= a_0 + a_1 A \sin \omega_1 t + a_1 B \sin \omega_2 t + a_2 A^2 \sin^2 \omega_1 t$$

$$+ 2a_2 AB \sin \omega_1 t \sin \omega_2 t + a_2 B^2 \sin^2 \omega_2 t$$

This expression is reduced by using the relations

$$\sin^2 x = \tfrac{1}{2} - \tfrac{1}{2} \cos 2x$$

and $$\sin x \sin y = \tfrac{1}{2} \cos (x + y) - \tfrac{1}{2} \cos (x - y)$$

The substitutions are made, and the terms that correspond are collected. The exact coefficients are not needed for the discussion, and they are simplified to give

$$i = k_0 + k_1 \sin \omega_1 t + k_2 \sin \omega_2 t + k_3 \cos 2\omega_1 t + k_4 \cos 2\omega_2 t$$

$$+ k_5 \cos (\omega_1 + \omega_2)t + k_6 \cos (\omega_1 - \omega_2)t$$

The $k_1$ and $k_2$ terms are the signal frequencies present in the output, and the $k_3$ and $k_4$ terms represent the second harmonics. The energy at the sum of the two frequencies $(f_1 + f_2)$ is the $k_5$ term, and the energy at the difference frequency $(f_1 - f_2)$ is the $k_6$ term. The $k_1$, the $k_5$, and the $k_6$ terms taken together represent amplitude modulation.

The objective of frequency conversion is to separate from the composite output the difference or beat frequency, the $(f_1 - f_2)$ term. The simplest circuit to accomplish this is called a *diode mixer* (Fig. 24–20). The output circuit is tuned to the difference frequency $(f_1 - f_2)$ in order to eliminate the undesired products of mixing. If the input waveforms are added, point by point, a waveform results that varies at the difference frequency. This difference frequency is shown in the diagram as the envelope of the sum. This composite envelope is rectified by the diode, and by filtering action of the tuned circuit, the output is a pure sine wave whose frequency is $(f_1 - f_2)$.

A triode can be used as a mixer for heterodyning (Fig. 24–21). In this circuit, a voltage from the oscillator at frequency $f_2$ beats with a signal at frequency $f_1$ to produce the difference frequency $(f_1 - f_2)$ in the output. If both $f_1$ and $f_2$ are radio frequencies, $f_2$ can be greater than $f_1$. In this case, the frequency of the output is $(f_2 - f_1)$. The triode has a circuit advantage in comparison to the diode, because a voltage gain is obtained in the amplifying action of the triode. As an ordinary amplifier, the gain may be calculated by using the value of the transconductance $g_m$. When a tube is used in a mixing circuit,

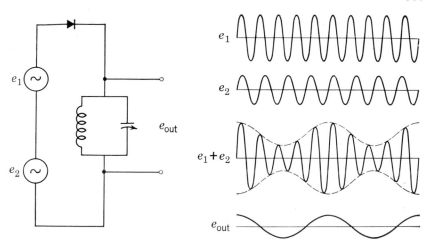

**Figure 24–20**   Diode mixing.

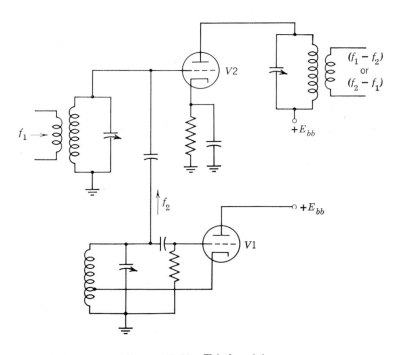

**Figure 24–21**   Triode mixing.

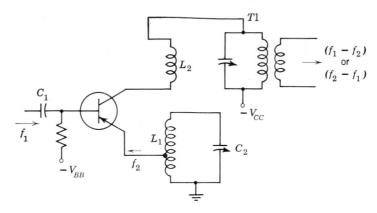

**Figure 24–22**   Heterodyning in a transistor circuit.

the gain is less than the gain obtained as a straight amplifier. This lowered gain is accounted for in gain calculations by using a different form of transconductance called *conversion transconductance*. The gain of the stage as a mixer is called *conversion gain*.

In Fig. 24–22, $L_1$, $L_2$, and $C_2$ form an Armstrong-type oscillator operating at frequency $f_2$. A signal frequency $f_1$ is fed into the base. As far as the signal $f_1$ is concerned, the transistor serves as a grounded-emitter amplifier. The collector load $T_1$ is tuned to the difference frequency.

In Fig. 24–21, the oscillator is a separate triode $V1$, and the mixing takes place in $V2$. In Fig. 24–22, the oscillation takes place in the same electronic amplifier that does the mixing. When this simultaneous action takes place within a tube or a transistor, the term *conversion* or *converter* is used to distinguish this circuit arrangement from the mixer which uses a separate oscillator.

A special five-grid tube has been developed for use as a converter. This pentagrid tube combines the action of an electron-coupled oscillator with the mixing (Fig. 24–23). The cathode, the first grid, and the second grid form the oscillator section. The signal $f_1$ is fed into the third grid. The third grid, the fourth grid, and the fifth grid function as the three grids of an ordinary pentode in which the cathode is the equivalent of the oscillator section of the tube. The load in the plate circuit is tuned to the difference frequency.

When interrupted continuous-wave (ICW) telegraph signals are picked up on an ordinary receiver, the dots and dashes cannot be interpreted since the original transmitted signal does not have an audio

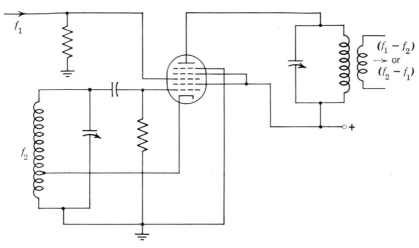

**Figure 24–23**  The converter.

modulation.   In order to produce an audible signal a *beat-frequency oscillator* (*BFO*) is used.   Assume that the incoming code-signal carrier frequency is $f_x$.   Energy from the beat-frequency oscillator at a frequency $f_y$ is also injected into the final detector circuit.   The detector acts as a mixer, and its output is $(f_x - f_y)$ or $(f_y - f_x)$.   The frequency of the beat-frequency oscillator is such that the difference frequency is audible.   A control that varies the frequency of the beat-frequency oscillator $f_y$ controls the beat output frequency and is called the *pitch* control.

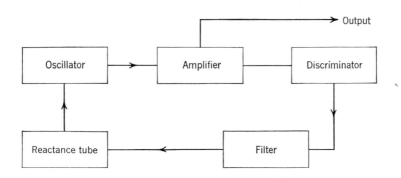

**Figure 24–24**  Block diagram for automatic frequency control (AFC).

## Section 24–7    Automatic Frequency Control

The objective of *automatic frequency control* (*AFC*) is to stabilize an oscillator to close tolerance in circuits where a crystal cannot be used. A block diagram of the AFC system is shown in Fig. 24–24. The oscillator is one of the conventional forms, usually a Hartley circuit. An amplifier between the oscillator and the discriminator may or may not be necessary, according to the needs of the application. When the frequency of the oscillator is correct, the output from the discriminator is zero. When the oscillator is off the frequency at which the control is made, an output is developed in the discriminator load. This output voltage is negative or positive, according to which way from the center frequency the oscillator has changed. This direct output voltage is filtered carefully and adds or subtracts to a d-c bias on the reactance tube. A changing bias on the reactance tube changes the transconductance of the tube, and, since the reactance tube is connected in parallel with the oscillator, the oscillator returns to the proper frequency.

In order to align this circuit, the reactance tube must be left in the circuit at all times since it places a "static" capacitance in the tank circuit. The connection between the filter and the reactance tube is opened, and the normal no-signal bias is maintained on the reactance tube. Now there can be no correcting action by the reactance tube. The oscillator is set to the desired frequency, and the discriminator circuit is carefully aligned to give zero output. When the d-c circuit from the filter to the reactance tube is restored, there is no additional bias on the reactance tube, and the oscillator will maintain the stable frequency. When one of these circuits is constructed, it should be remembered that, if the phasing of the detector is reversed, the tendency of the AFC action is to change the oscillator as far as possible away from the desired frequency.

When the oscillator is replaced by a converter or mixer–oscillator circuit, the automatic frequency control can be used to provide automatic tuning for a radio or a television receiver.

### . . . . Suggested References for Further Study

1. F. E. Terman, *Radio Engineer's Handbook*, Section 7, McGraw-Hill Book Co., New York, 1943.
2. A. Hund, *Frequency Modulation*, McGraw-Hill Book Co., New York, 1942.
3. C. E. Tibbs and G. G. Johnstone, *Frequency Modulation Engineering*, 2nd ed. rev., John Wiley & Sons, New York, 1956.

# . . . . QUESTIONS

1. Define or explain each of the following terms: (a) diode filter, (b) diagonal clipping, (c) AVC, (d) DAVC, (e) limiter, (f) threshold limiting, (g) S curve, (h) mixer, (i) converter, (j) conversion transconductance.
2. Explain how a diode filter separates the audio and the RF.
3. Show how a diode detector is nonlinear, owing to a shifting of the operating point on Fig. 24–3.
4. Explain how diode clipping produces distortion.
5. Explain the operation of the two plate detector circuits and the grid-leak detector circuit.
6. Explain the tuning and the adjustment procedure for a regenerative receiver.
7. Develop the need for AVC in a radio receiver.
8. What determines the time constant for an AVC filter?
9. What is the characteristic of a vacuum tube if it is to be controlled by an AVC voltage?
10. Compare simple AVC to delayed AVC and to ideal AVC.
11. Explain the operation of a limiter circuit.
12. Compare a single limiter with a double limiter.
13. What is the essential characteristic of a tube if it is to be used as a limiter?
14. Explain how a discriminator functions.
15. Explain how a ratio detector functions.
16. Point out the ways in which the discriminator and the ratio detector are similar.
17. Point out the ways in which the discriminator and the ratio detector are not similar.
18. Give the alignment procedure in detail for the limiter–discriminator circuit.
19. Give the alignment procedure in detail for the ratio-detector circuit.
20. What is the difference between a mixer and a converter?
21. Compare conversion gain with normal gain.
22. Show how a BFO detects ICW telegraph signals.
23. Explain the principles of an AFC circuit.
24. Explain in detail the steps that must be taken to align an AFC circuit.

# . . . . SPECIAL PROBLEM

1. From an outside reference, find the circuit of a superregenerative receiver and explain its operation.

## . . . . PROBLEMS

1. In the circuit, $R_1$ is 7500 ohms and $R_2$ is 10,000 ohms.   The carrier level $e_{in}$ is 20 volts.   Determine, by the use of the rectifier characteristic shown in Fig. 24–3, at what modulation level distortion occurs.

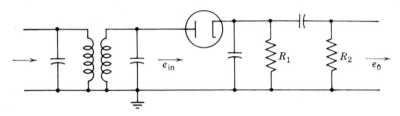

**Probs. 24–1 and 24–2**

2. Solve problem 1 for $R_1$ 15,000 ohms and $R_2$ 20,000 ohms.

# Audio elements

• • • • • • • • • • • • • • • • • • • CHAPTER 25

A microphone is a device that is used to convert sound energy into electric energy for use with electronic circuitry. A short discussion is given on the operation of several forms of commercial microphones (Section 25–1). The general problem of converting electric energy back into sound energy requires a unique solution to obtain a practical reproducer (Section 25–2). In order to secure a large audio volume, some form of the loudspeaker is necessary (Section 25–3). A short discussion of pickup and recording devices concludes the chapter (Section 25–4).

## Section 25–1    Microphones

The *carbon microphone* was originally developed as a telephone transmitter, and it has been continually used and improved in that application. The sound-wave front impinges on a diaphragm (Fig. 25–1), which is rigidly clamped to prevent any lateral motion. The diaphragm can move only in a direction that is perpendicular to the plane of the diaphragm. The vibration of the diaphragm squeezes together and releases the carbon granules contained in the *button* at the rate of the incoming sound waves. The resistance of these carbon granules changes and allows a varying current to flow in the primary winding of the transformer. The local battery $E$ is required with this microphone. Actually, the action of a changing resistance of the granules to the battery circuit serves as a power amplifier, and a high sensitivity is obtained in comparison with other types of microphones. The impedance of the carbon microphone is very low, and a transformer that combines isolation and step-up is required when this

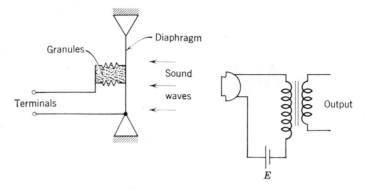

**Figure 25-1**   The single-button carbon microphone.

microphone is used with vacuum-tube and transistor circuits.   The random contacting of the carbon particles gives rise to a relatively high background noise called a *hiss*.   As a result this microphone is limited to voice communications systems.   The large mass of the button and the carbon granules do not respond to the high frequencies necessary for high-quality music programming.

Another version of this microphone is the double-button carbon microphone (Fig. 25–2).   Two buttons are used, and they are connected in a push–pull circuit which gives a greater output and at the same time reduces the total harmonic content in the output by eliminating the developed even harmonics.

A *capacitor microphone* is essentially two parallel metallic diaphragms or disks about 0.001 inch apart.   One disk is fixed, and the other moves in response to sound-pressure impulses.   When a high potential of the order of several hundred volts is applied between the

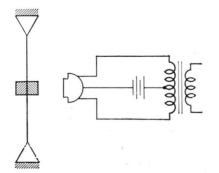

**Figure 25–2**   The double-button carbon microphone.

**Figure 25–3** The input circuit for the
capacitor microphone.

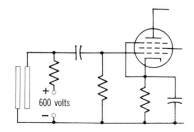

disks, a charge is placed on the disks.  Sound-pressure changes vary
the disk capacitance and change this charge.  This changing charge
develops a voltage drop in the resistor which is amplified in a vacuum-
tube circuit (Fig. 25–3).  A blocking capacitor is used to keep the
high d-c microphone bias voltage off the grid.  Stray capacitance
effects must be kept at a minimum, and, in order to accomplish this,
the physical location of the amplifier must be as close to the microphone as possible.  This microphone has a very high output impedance.  It is used widely in broadcast and motion picture studios and
as a test microphone for such purposes as a sound-level meter.

A cylindrical tube on which there are turns of wire is mounted on one
side of the diaphragm of the *dynamic* or *moving-coil microphone* (Fig.
25–4).  When sound waves cause the diaphragm to move, the conductors of the coil cut the flux of the magnetic field of the permanent
magnet, generating an emf in the turns of the coil.  This voltage is
stepped up through a transformer to the input of the first amplifier
stage.  The microphone is classified as a low-impedance type.  This
microphone can be designed to give a good frequency response and is

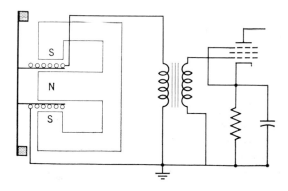

**Figure 25–4** The dynamic microphone.

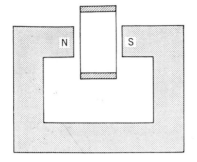

**Figure 25–5**   The ribbon microphone.

mechanically rugged.   The dynamic microphone is used widely as a general-purpose microphone.

A *ribbon* or *velocity microphone* operates on the principle of the dynamic microphone.   An aluminum ribbon is placed in a plane parallel to the magnetic field of a permanent magnet (Fig. 25–5). The sound pressure is applied to the front of the ribbon, and the difference between the front and the back air pressure causes the ribbon to vibrate at the rate of the intensity and pitch of the sound.   The vibrating ribbon generates a small emf between the ends of the ribbon. The ribbon microphone, naturally, is a low-impedance microphone, and it is used in the same circuit as the dynamic microphone.   This microphone has a very good frequency response.   When the microphone is used outdoors, it often tends to vibrate in the wind, producing a high background noise.   Also, a large sound impulse can destroy the sensitive aluminum element.

A *crystal microphone* functions by making use of the piezoelectric effect of a crystal.   A mechanical pressure on a crystal develops an emf across the face of the crystal proportional to the pressure.   Two Rochelle salt crystals are used for microphone construction (Fig. 25–6).   When the sound pressure is increased, one crystal expands while the other contracts lengthwise.   This differential arrangment is

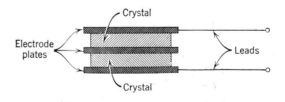

**Figure 25–6**   The crystal microphone.

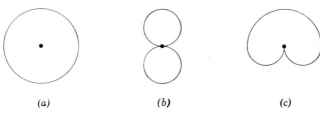

*(a)*                          *(b)*                          *(c)*

**Figure 25–7** Directional characteristics of microphones. (*a*) Nondirectional or omnidirectional. (*b*) Bidirectional. (*c*) Cardiod.

termed a *bimorph* crystal unit. The impedance of the microphone is very high, and, since it does not have a d-c path, the microphone is connected directly across the grid resistor of the input amplifier tube. The crystal microphone is available with a very good frequency response and is used interchangeably, except for impedance, with a ribbon microphone in its application.

An important property of a microphone is its directional characteristic (Fig. 25–7). The microphone can be nondirectional, bidirectional, or unidirectional in its response. The pattern of a unidirectional microphone is equivalent to the locus of the cardiod and is often advertised and sold as a *cardiod*. The basic pattern, as an example, for the ribbon microphone is bidirectional. By a proper design of the reflecting baffles and ports, the microphone can be adapted to have a cardiod response pattern. The specifications for a microphone should give the fundamental type, the electric output rating (Section 8–6), the impedance, and the directional characteristics. As prices on microphones can vary from a few dollars to several hundred dollars, it is important to be able to interpret the meaning of the specification in order to determine the suitability of a particular microphone for a specific application.

## Section 25–2   The General Problem of Sound Reproduction

A major difficulty that Alexander Graham Bell faced in his development of a working model of a telephone was the solution to the problem of converting electric energy back into sound energy. In the first receiver (Fig. 25–8), a circular diaphragm of soft steel is held rigidly at the rim. The signal current passing through a coil $L$ produces a flux which exerts a force on the diaphragm in the manner of an electromagnet. If the signal current is sinusoidal, it may be represented as

$$i = A \sin \omega t$$

The flux density in the coil is proportional to the current if the magnetic circuit is linear and may be written as

$$B = B_m \sin \omega t$$

From elementary magnetic-circuit analysis, the force $W$ in an electromagnet is proportional to the square of the flux density:

$$W = kB^2$$

$$= k(B_m \sin \omega t)^2$$

$$= kB_m{}^2 \sin^2 \omega t$$

Substituting the trigonometric relation

$$\sin^2 x = \tfrac{1}{2} - \tfrac{1}{2} \cos 2x$$

we have

$$W = \frac{kB_m{}^2}{2} - \frac{kB_m{}^2}{2} \cos 2\omega t$$

The first term, $kB_m{}^2/2$, is the average displacement of the diaphragm with signal and the second, $(kB_m{}^2/2) \cos 2\omega t$, represents the a-c motion of the diaphragm. This a-c motion is twice the frequency of

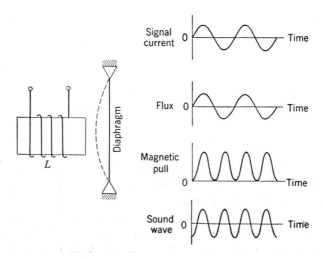

**Figure 25–8**   The elementary receiver.

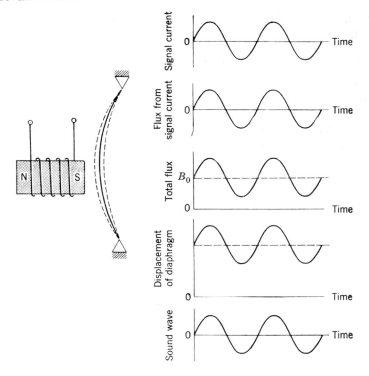

**Figure 25–9** Receiver using a permanent magnet.

the electric signal and accordingly raises the pitch of the reproduced signal by one octave. This result shows that this method of sound reproduction is useless.

This same result can be obtained from an examination of the waveforms in Fig. 25–8. As far as the diaphragm is concerned, a reversed flux direction in the electromagnet does not exert a "push"; it still attracts. Thus, for each full flux cycle, there are two "pulls" on the diaphragm. Two "pulls" on the diaphragm produce two sound waves instead of the desired single sound-wave cycle.

Bell solved this difficulty by using a permanent magnet as a core for the coil (Fig. 25–9). The permanent magnet gives an initial displacement to the diaphragm so that the addition of an a-c flux merely increases or decreases the displacement about the no-signal position. At all times a "pull" is exerted on the diaphragm. A reversed signal flux, by only decreasing the "pull," enables a correspondence to be maintained between the a-c signal and the developed sound wave.

If the value of the flux density in the permanent magnet is $B_0$, the total flux under signal conditions is

$$B = B_0 + B_m \sin \omega t$$

This is substituted in $\quad W = kB^2$
to give

$$W = k(B_0 + B_m \sin \omega t)^2$$

$$= kB_0{}^2 + 2kB_0B_m \sin \omega t + kB_m{}^2 \sin^2 \omega t$$

The term containing $\sin^2 \omega t$ can be reduced by expansion to give

$$W = kB_0{}^2 + 2kB_0B_m \sin \omega t + \frac{kB_m{}^2}{2} - \frac{kB_m{}^2}{2} \cos 2\omega t$$

The first term in this equation is the initial displacement of the diaphragm produced by the flux of the permanent magnet. The second term is the useful sound-reproducing force. The third term is a d-c term and represents a fixed displacement which occurs only when a signal is present. It is similar in concept to the rise of plate current in a power tube with signal (Section 10–5). The last term is a displacement at double frequency and represents a second-harmonic distortion introduced in the process of converting electric energy into sound energy. The per cent second harmonic is found from the ratio of the coefficient of this term to the coefficient of the fundamental term and is

$$A_2 = \frac{kB_m{}^2/2}{2kB_0B_m} \times 100 = \frac{B_m}{4B_0} \times 100\%$$

The only way in which the second harmonic can be decreased is to make $B_0$ as large as possible in comparison to the signal flux $B_m$. In order to do this, special steels are used such as Alnico V, and the air gaps in the transducer are kept as low as possible. Very often loudspeakers are compared by noting the weights of the permanent magnets.

### Section 25–3  Loudspeakers

The construction of a conventional loudspeaker is shown in Fig. 25–10. Energy is delivered from a power amplifier through a step-down transformer, the output transformer, to the low-impedance voice coil winding. The voice coil impedances are usually from 2 to 16 ohms. Loudspeakers are rated in either maximum average or peak

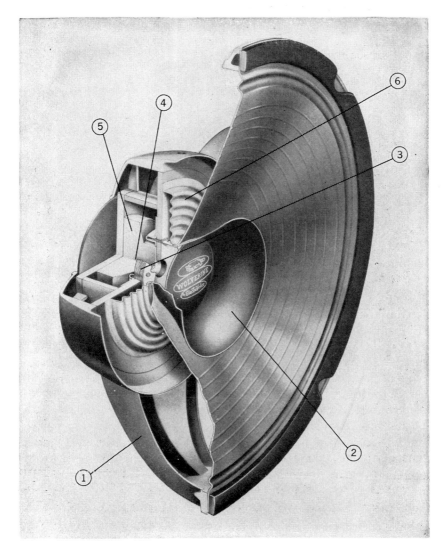

**Figure  25–10**  The  loudspeaker.  (1) Diecast  frame.  (2) Cone.  (3) Voice coil.  (4) Glass coil form.  (5) Slug-type magnet.  (6) Spider.  (*Courtesy Electro-Voice Inc.*)

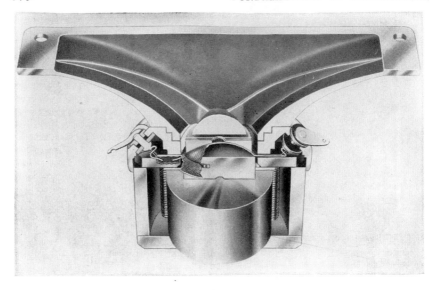

**Figure 25–11**   The driver and horn.   (*Courtesy Electro-Voice Inc.*)

electric input powers.   When a loudspeaker is overdriven, the limits
of linear travel of the cone are exceeded, and severe distortion results.
If the travel of the cone is limited by striking a solid metal surface, a
speaker rattle results.   The design of loudspeakers has been extended
to great lengths to meet the requirements of high fidelity.   The
mechanical design of the loudspeaker enclosure or *baffle* has a very
important effect on the over-all frequency response of a reproducer.

Quite often two speakers are used.   One speaker called the *woofer*
handles the low-frequency energy, and the other, a *tweeter*, handles
the high-frequency energy.   The point at which the energy shifts
from one speaker to the other is called the *cross-over frequency*.   The
combination low-pass–high-pass filter which divides the energy from
the power amplifier to the woofer and to the tweeter is the *crossover
network*.

The conventional loudspeaker is not used for large audio power
applications such as outdoor stadiums.   For these large powers, a
*driver* is used with a *horn* (Fig. 25–11).   The driver is used to convert
electric energy into a high-pressure, low-velocity sound energy.   The
design of the horn is such that it slowly expands the energy to a low
pressure and high velocity.   These horns are highly directional, and
in an outdoor application they usually are used in multiple to cover
the desired terrain.

### Section 25–4   Recorders and Tape Recorders

The elementary diagrams of a pickup or recording head are shown in Fig. 25–12. When playing a record, the variations in the grooves mechanically varies the position of the needle. In the magnetic unit, a changing needle position varies the magnetic flux in the air gap, and this changing flux induces an emf in the output coil. In the crystal pickup head, the vibrations of the needle exert a varying pressure on a bimorph crystal. By the piezoelectric effect, this mechanical pressure is converted into an output signal voltage. The magnetic pickup is a low-impedance device usually requiring an impedance-matching transformer to the first amplifier stage. The crystal pickup has a high impedance and requires a grid-leak resistor in the first amplifier grid circuit to provide a d-c path to ground.

There are many refinements in actual commercial units which have been brought about by the adaptation of "high fidelity" as a part of the American home entertainment habits. These as well as loud-speakers are specialized, and the reader who wishes to pursue the subject further has many available reference books and magazines to consult.

These pickup heads, when used for recording, are operated directly in reverse. Energy is fed into the pickup head from the recording

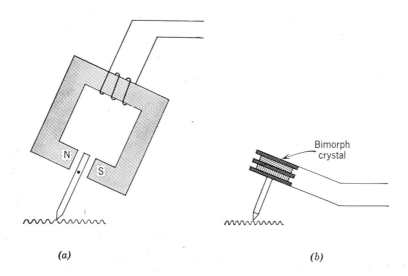

(a)                                                    (b)

**Figure 25–12**   Elementary pickup and recording heads.  (a) Magnetic pickup. (b) Crystal pickup.

amplifier, and the needle displacement caused by this energy input cuts the required grooves in the record.

Tape recorders have, in recent years, expanded beyond the radio and entertainment fields. They have become a vital part of the very large segment of the electronics industry which is devoted to computers. The tape recorder is used as a compact means of information storage which is available when required. If a complex computer is devoted, for example, to payroll work, one reel of tape can be used for each department of a large company. Since the tapes can be easily duplicated, the information can be used with different machines.

The surface of a flexible plastic tape is coated with a magnetic material. The magnetic material on the surface of the tape passes through a *recording head* and is magnetized in accordance with the flux formed from a signal current. When the tape passes through the *playback head*, the magnetism in the tape which was put on by the recording head induces a voltage in the pickup coil, duplicating the original recording signal. When the speed of the tape, given in inches per second, is increased, the frequency response of the tape is improved.

The erasing operation is accomplished in an *erasing head* by subjecting the tape to a high-intensity a-c field which goes to zero as the tape moves out from under the head, leaving the tape free of any residual magnetism, and enabling the tape to be re-used. The frequency of the erase oscillator is higher than the highest signal frequency that is placed on the tape. The erase frequency is usually of the order of 50 to 100 kc.

Experimental procedure has determined that the stored information on a tape does not deteriorate with time provided certain elementary precautions are maintained.

A single head and amplifier may be used both for recording and for playback by a suitable switching circuit. The erase head is usually a separate head. On most recorders a single tape is used to record on two or more *tracks*. In a recorder using dual heads, one head takes care of the top half of the tape and the other head of the lower half of the tape.

**. . . . Suggested References for Further Study**

1. F. Langford-Smith, *Radiotron Designer's Handbook*, 4th ed., Chapters 17, 18, and 20, RCA, Harrison, N. J., 1953.
2. H. F. Olson, *Acoustical Engineering*, Chapters 6 through 9, D. Van Nostrand Co., Princeton, N. J., 1957.

3. L. L. Beranek, *Acoustics*, Chapters 6 through 9, McGraw-Hill Book Co., New York, 1954.
4. H. G. M. Spratt, *Magnetic Tape Recording*, The Macmillan Co., New York, 1958.

## . . . . QUESTIONS

1. Define or explain each of the following terms: (*a*) hiss, (*b*) bimorph, (*c*) cardoid, (*d*) baffle, (*e*) Alnico, (*f*) spider, (*g*) voice coil, (*h*) cone, (*i*) crossover, (*j*) driver.

2. Explain the operation of a single-button carbon microphone.

3. Explain the operation of a double-button carbon microphone.

4. Explain the operation of a capacitor microphone.

5. Explain the operation of a dynamic microphone.

6. Explain the operation of a crystal microphone.

7. Compare the characteristics of the five basic microphones.

8. Why is a d-c magnetic flux necessary in a loud-speaker?

9. Compare the use of the loudspeaker with that of a horn.

10. Sketch the fundamental principles of tape recording.

11. Why is the erase frequency an ultrasonic frequency?

# The cathode-ray oscilloscope

• • • • • • • • • • • • • • • • • • • •  CHAPTER **26**

The principles of the cathode-ray tube (Section 26–1), the power supply (Section 26–2), the display of a signal on the screen (Section 26–3), and of amplifiers and synchronization (Section 26–4) are sufficient for understanding the basic operation of an oscilloscope. Frequency measurements can be made by means of the oscilloscope (Section 26–5). Gain and waveform measurements can be made directly from the screen pattern (Section 26–6). Z-axis signals (Section 26–7) have special applications. The chapter concludes with a discussion of typical commercial oscilloscopes (Section 26–8).

## Section 26–1  The Cathode-Ray Tube

If we consider a simple diode (Fig. 26–1), we see that an electron released at the cathode by thermionic emission is attracted to the plate in the path shown on the diagram. The positive voltage on the plate

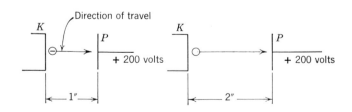

**Figure 26–1**  Electron travel from cathode to plate.

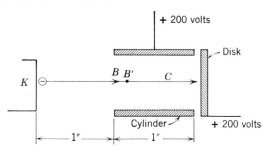

**Figure 26–2**   Travel of an electron within a cylindrical plate.

produces a *force* on the electron which has a *mass*. By Newton's law of motion, the combined action of a force and a mass produces by

$$Force = mass \times acceleration$$

an acceleration on the electron toward the plate. The equations of distance, time, and motion can be used, and the position, the velocity, the acceleration, and the energy of the electron can be calculated for any point in its path. We recall that *voltage* is a unit of work per unit charge. This means that the work done on the electron for a 1-inch travel is identical with the work done on the electron for a 2-inch travel when the potential difference between the cathode and the plate is the same (Fig. 26–1). If the work done on the electron is the same in the two cases, the kinetic energies of impact ($\frac{1}{2}mv^2$) on the plates are the same, and the final velocities of the electrons are also equal. Accordingly, the acceleration of the electron is greater for the short path than for the long path.

In Fig. 26–2, the single plate of Fig. 26–1 is replaced by two plates. One is a hollow cylinder, and the other is a flat disk. Both plates are maintained at the same potential. The electron liberated at $A$ is accelerated to its final velocity at $B'$. From $B'$ to $C$, there is no change in potential, and consequently there is no acceleration from $B'$ to $C$. The velocity of the electron does not change from $B'$ to $C$. In a cathode-ray tube, the region between $A$ and $B'$ is used to concentrate the electron stream into a narrow beam and to provide acceleration, focus, and brightness. Within this "drift" region from $B'$ to $C$, the beam of electrons is deflected up and down and from left to right to provide the desired visual pattern.

The disk plate of Fig. 26–2 is the *screen material* coated on the inside of the *face* of a cathode-ray tube. The release of kinetic energy produced by the impact of the high-velocity electrons on the screen develops a light output from the screen material. The general term given to this property of conversion of energy into light is *luminescence*. There are two forms of luminescence: *fluorescence* and *phosphorescence*. Fluorescence is the property of converting energy into light directly, whereas phosphorescence is the release of stored energy into light over a period of time. It is not possible to have one form without the other. Actually, one may predominate almost to the exclusion of the other. As an example, there is no material afterglow when a fluorescent lamp is turned off. The gadgets that "glow in the dark" do not noticeably fluoresce when the room is normally illuminated. The different materials that are used for cathode-ray-tube screens produce different colors and different *persistence* times for the visible signal. The characteristics of different screen materials in common use are listed in Table I.

TABLE I. PHOSPHORS

| Material | Fluorescence | Phosphorescence | Persistence |
|----------|--------------|-----------------|-------------|
| P1  | Green       | Green  | Medium      |
| P2  | Blue–Green  | *Green*  | Long        |
| P4  | *White*     | Yellow  | Medium      |
| P7  | Blue–White  | *Yellow*  | Long        |
| P11 | Blue        | Blue  | Short       |
| P12 | Orange      | Orange  | Medium long |

The predominate color is italicized.

The tube-type numbers for a cathode-ray tube give information on the screen characteristic. For example, 5ADP7 indicates that the screen is 5 inches in diameter and has the characteristic of the P7 phosphor material.

Let us consider two cylindrical plates ($G2$ and $G3$ in Fig. 26–3), which are at different positive potentials. Curved electrostatic field lines are drawn from the lower potential to the higher potential. An

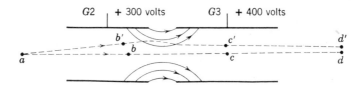

**Figure 26–3**  The electron lens.

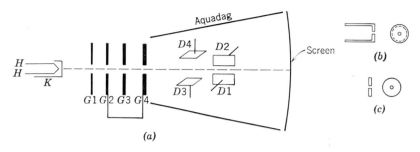

**Figure 26–4** The cathode-ray tube. (*a*) Tube elements. (*b*) Cylindrical anode. (*c*) Disk anode.

electron crossing one of these electrostatic lines is deflected in the direction of the higher potential by a force that acts in the direction of the line. An electron that passes from $a$ to $d$ axially (path $abcd$) is not deflected by this electrostatic field. An electron that enters the field at an angle $ab'$ is influenced by this field twice, producing a double-curved path, $ab'c'd'$. When the potential difference between the cylinders $G2$ and $G3$ is varied, the location of $d'$ changes. In providing focus control, this potential difference is controlled by a potentiometer. Proper focus occurs when $d'$ coincides with $d$ and when both $d$ and $d'$ are located at the screen phosphor. The action of this curved electric field on an electron is very similar to the effect of a lens on a light beam. This correspondence has resulted in the use of the terms *electron lens* and *electron optics*.

The grid and anode structure of the cathode-ray tube is shown in Fig. 26–4. The grids, $G1$, $G2$, $G3$, and $G4$ are actually not conventional grid structures but hollow cylinders or disks, each having a small hole to allow axial travel of the electron stream. Thermionic electron emission is produced at the cathode $K$. The cathode receives its energy from the heater, $H$–$H$. The first grid $G1$ is negative with respect to the cathode. The amount of this negative voltage controls the number of electrons per second in the electron beam. When this flow or *beam current* is varied, the illumination level on the screen changes. The potentiometer which controls this negative bias voltage is called the *intensity* control. The first and third anodes, $G2$ and $G4$, provide the high positive potential which is required to accelerate the electron stream. The second anode $G3$, placed between $G2$ and $G4$, operates at a lower potential which can be varied. This variable voltage changes the shape of the electron lens and varies the *focus* of the beam on the screen.

The inside surface of the cathode-ray tube between the anode $G4$ and the screen is coated with a graphite-conducting paint called *Aquadag* or *Dixonac*. This coating also has the shape of a cylindrical anode. The potential on the Aquadag may be the same as that on $G4$ or at a much higher voltage. In any case, the electrons do not receive axial acceleration in this region, but travel to the screen at a fixed velocity.

In this region the deflection plates, $D1$, $D2$, $D3$, and $D4$, are mounted. When $D4$ is positive with respect to $D3$, the beam is deflected upward, and, then $D4$ is negative with respect to $D3$, the beam shifts downward. Correspondingly, the plates $D1$ and $D2$ provide deflection to the sides. The plates $D3$ and $D4$ produce *vertical* or *Y-axis* deflection. The plates $D1$ and $D2$ produce *horizontal* or *X-axis* deflection.

The axial velocity of the electrons in the beam is determined by the Aquadag potential. When the Aquadag potential is increased, the electron-stream velocity increases. When there is a fixed deflection voltage on a pair of plates, an increase in Aquadag potential decreases the amount of the beam deflection on the screen. An increase in Aquadag potential does not change the acceleration and velocity caused by the voltage on the deflecting plates, because the two act at right angles to each other. The increase in Aquadag potential decreases the time during which the deflecting force acts on the beam and produces less deflection on the screen. An increase in Aquadag potential increases the kinetic energy of the electrons impinging on the screen. The brightness of the spot on the screen increases, but it is at a sacrifice in deflection.

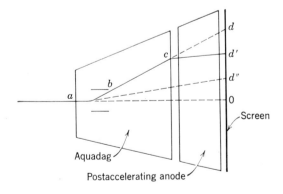

**Figure 26–5**   The postaccelerating or intensifier anode.

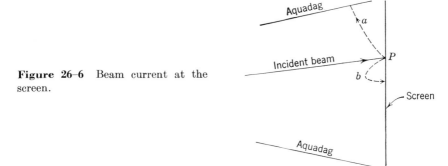

**Figure 26–6** Beam current at the screen.

The Allen B. DuMont Laboratories have developed a tube which uses an *intensifier* or *postaccelerating* anode (Fig. 26–5). The normal Aquadag coating ends before the screen, and a narrow ring of Aquadag extends to the screen. The Aquadag is at a relatively low potential of the order of 1500 volts. Wide deflection angles are obtained with low deflection voltages on the deflection plates. The postaccelerating anode is held at a higher voltage, approximately 3000 volts. The electron stream at $c$ is violently drawn into the screen at $d'$, producing a very bright spot. If there were no intensifier anode, the spot would appear at $d$ with much less brightness. If the Aquadag where at the same potential as the intensifier, the deflection would only be $d''$.

Usually the Aquadag is internally connected to the last anode which is $G2$–$G4$ in Fig. 26–4. Accordingly, the Aquadag is not shown as a separate element in the schematic representation. In many forms of cathode-ray-tube construction, a simpler grid structure is used. The control grid is $G1$, and the first anode $G2$ is the focusing anode. The second anode $G3$ is the accelerating anode and is internally connected to the Aquadag.

When an electron from the beam hits the screen at point $P$ (Fig. 26–6), one or more electrons are released from the surface of the screen by secondary emission. The beam current cannot return to the Aquadag along the surface of the phosphor because the screen phosphor material is an insulator. The positive Aquadag attracts secondary-emission electrons along path $a$. The total number of secondary-emission electrons attracted to the Aquadag must be equal to the number of electrons in the incident beam current. When more than one electron is knocked off the screen at point $P$ for each incident electron, the screen is left with a positive charge at $P$. This positive charge on the screen causes the extra electrons of secondary emission

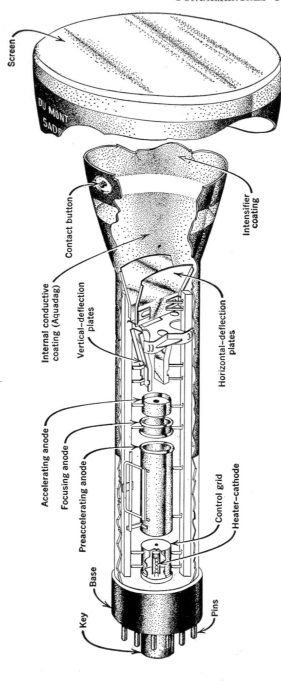

Screen

Contact button

Intensifier coating

Internal conductive coating (Aquadag)

Vertical–deflection plates

Horizontal–deflection plates

Accelerating anode

Focusing anode

Preaccelerating anode

Control grid

Heater–cathode

Key

Base

Pins

**Figure 26–7** Cross-sectional view of a typical commercial cathode-ray tube. (*Courtesy Allen B. DuMont Laboratories*)

to return into the screen. When the intensity is increased to the point where the spot intensity could *burn* a hole in the screen material, the *rain* of these secondary-emission electrons back into the screen also produces illumination. This illumination shows up as a visible *ring* or *halo*. The term used to describe this effect is *halation*.

A cross section of a typical commercial cathode-ray tube is shown in Fig. 26–7.

### Section 26–2 The Cathode-Ray-Tube Power Supply

The various anodes of the cathode-ray tube draw currents which are of the order of microamperes. These low drains allow a half-wave rectifier to be used in the power supply. The various different voltages are obtained from a voltage-divider network. The unknown signals which are to be observed are connected to the deflection plates. In order to prevent serious shock hazard, these deflection plates are held as close to ground potential as possible. By keeping the plates near ground potential, the electric fields are maintained without changes produced by stray causes. Since the deflection plates are located within the electric field of the Aquadag, the Aquadag also is maintained at or close to ground potential. We indicated that the Aquadag is of the order of 1500 volts positive with respect to the cathode. In order to meet both these requirements, the cathode potential is $-1500$ volts when the Aquadag is at or near zero potential. When an intensifier anode is used, its potential is approximately $+1500$ volts with respect to ground (the Aquadag).

The circuit shown in Fig. 26–8a contains a full-wave power supply used for the amplifiers of the cathode-ray oscilloscope. A winding of 575 volts is connected in series with one-half the full-wave secondary, producing a total alternating supply voltage for the half-wave rectifier of 890 volts. The half-wave connection produces an output of $-1200$ volts for the cathode-ray tube. When a cathode-ray tube with an intensifier anode is used, an additional output voltage is required for the postaccelerating anode (Fig. 26–8b).

The circuit of Fig. 26–9 shows the connection of a cathode-ray tube to the voltage divider. The Aquadag, $G2$, and $G4$ are internally joined together within the cathode-ray tube, and the lead is grounded. One side of each pair of deflection plates is also grounded. A variable direct voltage is supplied to each of the other deflection plates. When the variable arms of the vertical-centering and the horizontal-centering controls are set at the centers of the potentiometers, the voltages from the wiper arms to ground are zero. The electron beam hits

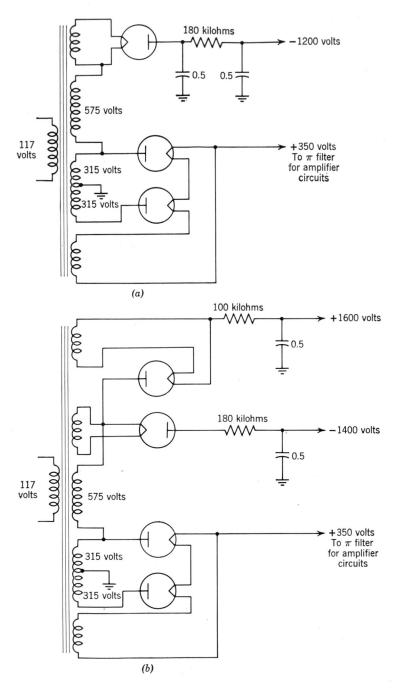

**Figure 26–8** Cathode-ray-tube power supplies. (*a*) Rectifier circuit for cathode-ray tube without intensifier. (*b*) Rectifier circuit for cathode-ray tube with intensifier.

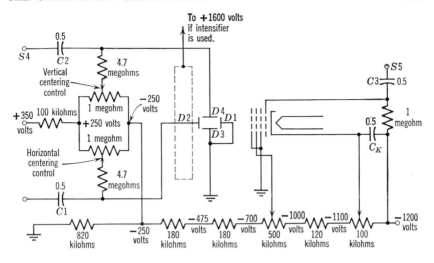

**Figure 26–9**  Voltage-divider circuit for cathode-ray-tube power supply.

the screen at the exact center if the mechanical position of the various anodes is exactly in line axially.  A shift in the position of the sliders on the centering controls places a d-c bias on the ungrounded deflection plates.  A positive voltage attracts the beam and a negative voltage repels the beam.  In this manner, the beam can be moved up and down and from side to side in the amount determined by the voltage from the centering controls.  $S4$ is the input terminal for a signal to the vertical-deflection plate $D4$, and $S2$ is the input terminal for a signal to the horizontal-deflection plate $D2$.  A signal can be fed into the control grid $G1$ through terminal $S5$.  $C_1$, $C_2$, and $C_3$ serve as blocking or coupling capacitors.

An intensifier anode is indicated by the dotted lines in Fig. 26–9. The connection to the intensifier is a metallic button contact on the glass envelope, and it connects a positive 1600-volt supply to the ring.

### Section 26–3  The Display of a Signal on the Screen

The specific purpose of a complete cathode-ray oscillograph is to give the user a visual display of the waveform that is under study. In the discussion of a-c theory and electronic circuits, waveforms are used freely for illustration.  The action of an oscilloscope can be analyzed by considering one cycle (Fig. 26–10$a$) of a continuous sine-wave voltage signal.  If the signal is applied to the vertical deflection

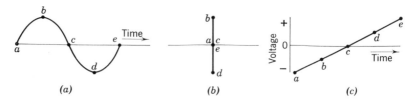

*(a)*　　　　　　　　*(b)*　　　　　　　　*(c)*

**Figure 26–10**　Display of a sine wave on the cathode-ray-tube screen. (*a*) Original signal. (*b*) Signal applied to the vertical plates only. (*c*) Horizontal signal required to display the sine-wave signal.

plates, the beam is displaced up and down, producing a vertical line (Fig. 26–10*b*) on the screen.　In order to develop the two-dimensional pattern of Fig. 26–10*a*, a simultaneous displacement of the beam in the horizontal direction is required.　The original sine wave is given on a linear time axis, and, since the reproduced waveforms must also be linear with time, the voltage applied to the horizontal deflection plates must be directly proportional to time (Fig. 26–10*c*).

The position $P$ of the beam spot on the screen is determined by the Cartesian coordinate values of the $X$ deflection and the $Y$ deflection. When both the $X$-deflection signal and the $Y$-deflection signal are positive, the spot is located in the first quadrant (point $P$, Fig. 26–11*a*).

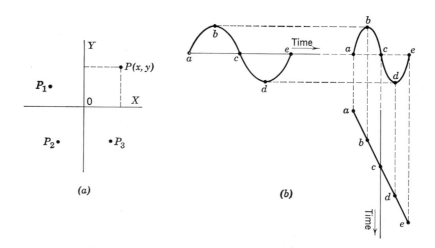

*(a)*　　　　　　　　　　　　　　　*(b)*

**Figure 26–11**　Beam deflection on the screen. (*a*) Location of a point by means of coordinates. (*b*) The point-by-point development of an oscilloscope pattern by two waveforms.

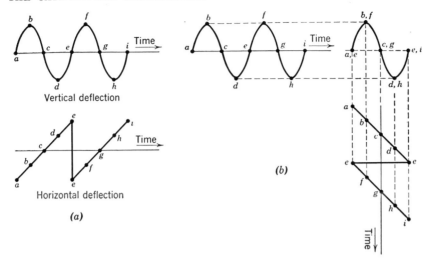

**Figure 26–12**  Development of a single-cycle oscilloscope pattern.  (*a*) Signal waveforms.  (*b*) Point-by-point development of beam deflection.

A positive $Y$-deflection voltage and a negative $X$-deflection voltage locate a point in the second quadrant $P_1$.  A negative $Y$-deflection voltage and a negative $X$-deflection voltage locate the point $P_2$ in the third quadrant.  A negative $Y$-deflection voltage and a positive $X$-deflection voltage locate point $P_3$ in the fourth quadrant.

In Fig. 26–11*b*, a trace on the screen is determined by locating a succession of points which forms the locus of simultaneous voltages on the deflection plates.  Each point is determined by considering the voltage of each waveform at an instant of time that is common to both waves.  The reason why we consider time as the common reference between the two signals is that the beam cannot create two spots in different places at the same time.  Successive points in the diagram of Fig. 26–11*b* are *a*, *b*, *c*, *d*, and *e*.

Let us consider two cycles of sine-wave signal and two cycles of horizontal *sawtooth* deflection voltage (Fig. 23–12*a*).  When these two waveforms are applied to the deflection plates and the trace is developed by the point-by-point method (Fig. 26–12*b*), a single sine-wave cycle is produced on the screen.  The second trace is superimposed over the first trace.  In this manner, when the two waveforms are continuous, all that we see on the screen is a single sine-wave cycle.  In order to develop this pattern, the transition from point *e* to point *e* on the horizontal sawtooth waveform must be instantaneous and occur in zero time. Actually it is impossible to have this transition occur in zero time because, if it did, the velocity of the spot across the screen from right to left would necessarily be infinite, which condition is impossible.

In certain applications, the *return trace* develops in an additional circuit a negative signal voltage which is applied to the first grid of the cathode-ray tube and cuts off the beam completely during retrace. This additional circuit arrangement is called *blanking.*

A finite return-trace time must exist for the sawtooth waveform. For the purposes of this discussion, let us assume that the retrace time is 1 $\mu$sec. If we are observing a 100-cycle signal, the return-trace time of 1 $\mu$sec is such a small part of the total time of one cycle, 10,000 $\mu$sec, that it is not visible on the screen. If a 100-kc signal is being observed, the return-trace time of one microsecond is 10% of the period of the wave, 10 $\mu$sec. Under these conditions, the return trace is very markedly noticeable (Fig. 26-13).

When the frequency of the horizontal sawtooth voltage is one-third the frequency of the vertical-deflection signal, three cycles are traced out on the screen (Fig. 26-14). When the horizontal frequency is one-half the frequency of the signal, two cycles are produced. The setting of the *sweep* frequency is controlled by two dials on the front panel of the cathode-ray oscillograph. One control, the *coarse frequency* or *range* establishes the range of the frequency of the horizontal-deflection voltage, and the other, the *fine frequency,* provides a con-

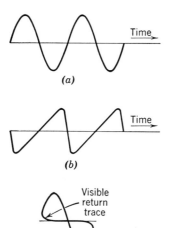

(a)

(b)

Visible return trace

(c)

**Figure 26-13**  Effect of a finite-return trace time.  (a) Signal.  (b) Horizontal-deflection waveform.  (c) Screen pattern.

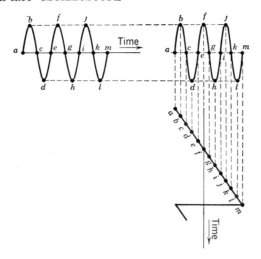

**Figure 26–14**   Point-by-point development of a three-cycle pattern.

tinuous variation between the overlapping range positions. The coarse control is obtained by switching fixed capacitors in the horizontal-oscillator time-constant circuit, and the fine-frequency control is a rheostat adjustment in the time constant circuit.

The horizontal-oscillator circuit develops the necessary sawtooth-voltage waveform.   A relaxation oscillator using a thyratron (Section 21–2) is commonly used.   The thyratron, a gas tube, is limited at high frequencies by ionization and deionization times.   These finite ionization and deionization times produce the return trace effect shown in Fig. 26–13.   A multivibrator (Section 21–5) and discharge circuit (Section 21–7) are often used in those instruments which require horizontal frequency sweeps greater than 30 kc.

### Section 26–4   The Amplifiers and Synchronization

When an a-c signal is placed directly on the deflection plates, a magnitude from 40 to 50 volts peak to peak is required to produce a 1-inch deflection on the screen.   Since many signals that are to be observed are much smaller than this level, it is necessary to use amplifiers and gain controls to adjust the pattern to a convenient size. The use of amplifiers reduces the input-level signal requirement to the order of a few millivolts peak-to-peak in order to produce a deflection of 1 inch on the screen.   In normal oscilloscope operation, it is

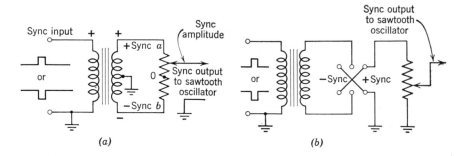

**Figure 26-15**   Input sync amplitude controls.   (*a*) Center-tapped transformer.
(*b*) Reversing switch.

unusual to require that the signal be connected directly to the plates
bypassing the amplifiers.

The gain control on each amplifier is one of two forms.   The simpler
oscillographs use a single gain control which is a potentiometer serving
as an ordinary "volume" control.   The other type of gain control is a
formal attenuator.   The over-all gain is adjusted by switching different input voltage-divider circuits which vary the gain in fixed steps,
usually in multiples of ten.   These decade attenuator steps are very
useful in setting the voltage calibration of the oscilloscope (Section
26–6).

The free-running frequency of the sawtooth generator is not particularly stable, making it necessary to use some form of *synchronization* (Section 21–3) to lock in the sweep frequency.   Let us assume
for this discussion that a positive pulse (or a positive signal)
is required to synchronize the sawtooth generator circuit.   When a
center-tapped transformer is used in the sync input circuit (Fig.
26–15*a*), the sync pulse output is zero when the sync amplitude potentiometer control arm is set at the center *o*.   When the transformer
input signal is a positive pulse, shifting the arm of the potentiometer
toward *a* produces an increasing positive output pulse for the sawtooth generator.   When the incoming input signal pulse is negative,
shifting the control arm from *o* toward *b* produces the positive output
pulse which is necessary to lock in the sawtooth generator.   An
alternative circuit arrangement uses a double-pole double-throw switch
to reverse the transformer secondary in order to maintain the actual
oscillator sync voltage positive at all times.

When the sawtooth oscillator is synchronized, the synchronizing
signal can be obtained from one of three sources as determined by the

position of the *sync selector* switch (Fig. 26–16).   The sawtooth can be locked into:

1. The signal that is being observed on the screen (Internal), or
2. An external, outside signal fed into a special binding post (External), or
3. The 60-cycle a-c power line (Line).

Under normal use, an oscilloscope should be set for *internal* synchronization.   It is not usual to set the oscilloscope on the *line* position or on the *external* position.   When a person is first learning the use of an oscilloscope, one of the most common mistakes is to have the sync selector control set to a position other than *internal*.

As we pointed out in Section 21–3, an increase in sync voltage beyond a certain point can cause the oscillator to lock in at a lower frequency. For example, if three cycles are being observed on the screen, when the sync amplitude is increased, the pattern can suddenly change to two cycles or even one cycle.   Usually this is accompanied by a severe distortion in the observed pattern.   As a general rule, only enough sync amplitude should be used just to stop or lock in the waveform under observation.

Usually a waveform can be locked in with either a positive or a negative sync amplitude.   The waveforms shown in Fig. 26–17 do require the proper sync polarity for stable observation.   The illustration shows that, for one polarity, an abrupt change occurs at regular intervals, whereas, on the other half of the waveform, the amplitude is very irregular and could produce an erratic synchronization.

At this point, the person seeking familiarity with the use of an oscilloscope should stop and obtain facility in the basic operation of the

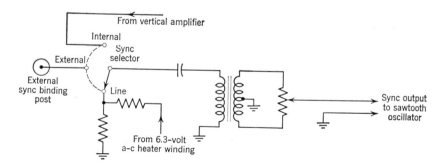

**Figure 26–16**   The sync-selector circuit.

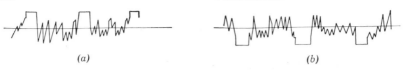

(a)          (b)

**Figure 26-17** Waveforms requiring different synchronizations. (a) Positive sync required. (b) Negative sync required.

instrument. An audio oscillator connected to the vertical input terminals can provide signals of unknown amplitude and unknown frequency for observation. The *intensity*, the *focus*, the *vertical centering*, and the *horizontal centering* establish the proper spot at the center of the screen. A setting of the horizontal-amplifier *gain* control in the *recurring sweep* position produces a horizontal line. The setting of the vertical *gain* control determines the height of the pattern, and the proper settings of the *range* and *fine*-frequency controls, together with the proper *sync amplitude* set on *internal*, give a centered, balanced pattern of one, two, or three cycles on the screen. This sequence should be repeated for as many different settings of frequency and voltage on the audio oscillator as are necessary to develop accuracy and speed in these adjustments.

### Section 26-5  Phase Measurements and Lissajous Patterns

When two voltages of equal frequency but different phase relations are connected to the deflection amplifiers, an elliptical pattern results. This pattern is established in Fig. 26–18 by the point-by-point method. These two voltages produce beam displacements which may be given by

$$y = A \cos \omega t$$

and          $$x = B \cos (\omega t + \theta)$$

By using the trigonometric expansion formula,

$$\cos (x + y) = \cos x \cos y - \sin x \sin y$$

to expand $\cos (\omega t + \theta)$, these equations become

$$y = A \cos \omega t$$
$$x = B \cos \omega t \cos \theta - B \sin \omega t \sin \theta$$

When $\omega t$ is 90°,

$$\sin \omega t = 1 \quad \text{and} \quad \cos \omega t = 0$$

Then

$$y = 0 \quad \text{and} \quad x = B \sin \theta$$

and, when $\omega t$ is 270°,

$$\sin \omega t = -1 \quad \text{and} \quad \cos \omega t = 0$$

Then $\qquad y = 0 \quad \text{and} \quad x = -B \sin \theta$

These two conditions locate points 1 and 7 on the ellipse of Fig. 26–18. The total distance between 1 and 7 is

$$2B' = 2B \sin \theta$$

Then $\qquad\qquad \sin \theta = \dfrac{2B'}{2B}$

Since the over-all width of the pattern is $2B$, we may write

$$\sin \theta = \frac{X\text{-axis intercept}}{\text{total width of ellipse}}$$

If the incoming wave on the horizontal-deflection plates is taken as the reference with the vertical input leading by the phase angle $\theta$,

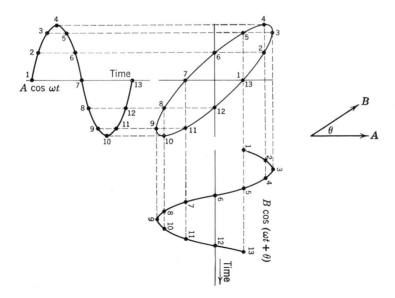

**Figure 26–18** Elliptical phase-shift pattern.

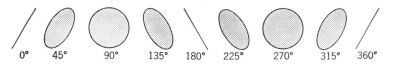

**Figure 26–19**   Phase-shift patterns between 0 and 360 degrees.

then, by the same process,

$$\sin \theta = \frac{Y\text{-axis intercept}}{\text{total height of ellipse}}$$

It is optional whether the data is taken along the $Y$ axis or along the $X$ axis because the same angle is being evaluated in each case.

The various phase-shift patterns which are obtained by this phase-shift method are shown in Fig. 26–19.   It should be noted that the

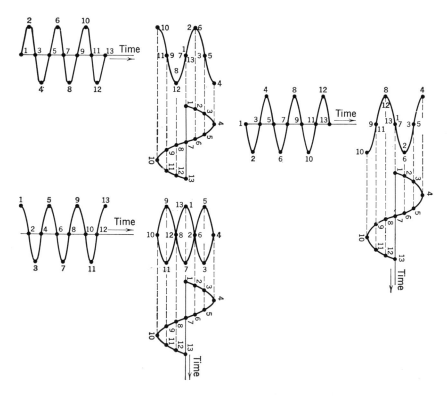

**Figure 26–20**   Lissajous patterns showing a 3–1 frequency ratio.

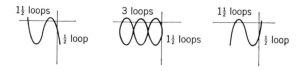

**Figure 26–21**   Method of determining frequency ratios.

patterns for 135° and for 225°, for example, are identical. It is important to have some previous data to determine whether the angle is 135° or 225°. Usually a set of sequential sketches taken with the data serves this need. It should be pointed out that, during the measurements, the horizontal sawtooth generator is not producing the horizontal deflection. The external $X$-deflection signal reaches the horizontal-deflection plates through the horizontal amplifier. A perfect circle is obtained at 90° and 270° only when the height and width of the screen pattern are equal.

In a Lissajous pattern, voltages of different frequencies are applied to the two amplifiers. When the frequency of one is a multiple or a fractional multiple of the other, a stable pattern results. This method enables a frequency to be measured very accurately and conveniently by comparing the unknown with a known frequency. The patterns of Fig. 26–20 are drawn point by point for two sine waves. The frequency on the vertical deflection is three times the frequency on the horizontal deflection. The different patterns result from different phase relations between the two voltages. The frequency ratio of a pattern can be determined easily by "slicing off" the top and side of a pattern (Fig. 26–21). A full loop counts as 1 and a partial loop counts as $\frac{1}{2}$. The number of loops cut by the horizontal slice gives the frequency on the vertical plates, and the number of loops cut by the vertical slice gives the frequency on the horizontal plates:

$$\frac{\text{Vertical-deflection frequency}}{\text{Horizontal-deflection frequency}}$$

$$= \frac{\text{number of loops in the horizontal cut}}{\text{number of loops in the vertical cut}}$$

In the example of Fig. 26–21, the ratio is

$$\frac{\text{Vertical-deflection frequency}}{\text{Horizontal-deflection frequency}} = \frac{1\frac{1}{2}}{\frac{1}{2}} = \frac{3}{1} = \frac{1\frac{1}{2}}{\frac{1}{2}} \quad \text{or 3 to 1}$$

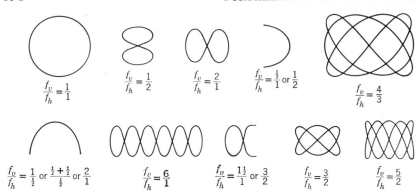

**Figure 26–22**   Typical Lissajous patterns.

Several typical patterns together with the frequency ratios are shown in Fig. 26–22.

### Section 26–6   Input Attenuators and Voltage Calibration

The principles of the input attenuator are shown in Fig. 26–23. When the input range selector is set at 0.1, the full signal is applied to the amplifier. When the input range switch is set at 1, the signal is reduced by a factor of 10. When the switch is set at 10, the reduction factor is 100, and, when the switch is set at 100, the reduction is 1000. The fine-gain control varies the gain from zero to maximum or from 0 to 100% and is independent of the range-switch setting. As an example, assume that with a maximum setting of the fine-gain control a 2-inch-high peak-to-peak signal pattern appears on the screen when the input signal is 12-mv rms and when the range switch is set at 0.1. When the range switch is turned to 1, a 120-mv or 0.12-volt signal is required to produce a 2-inch screen deflection. On the 10 position, a 1.2-volt signal is required to produce the 2-inch deflection, and, on the 100 position, a 12-volt signal is required. On the 100 position, an 18-volt signal proportionately produces a 3-inch-high pattern.

The trimmers on the attenuator network are used to compensate the circuit for a flat frequency response. A square-wave input signal (Fig. 26–24a) should produce a square-wave pattern on the screen. If the trimmers are not properly adjusted, the oscilloscope patterns will either undershoot or overshoot (Fig. 26–24b).

Many oscilloscopes have an internal vertical voltage-calibration signal which is independent of the attenuator network. The amplifier

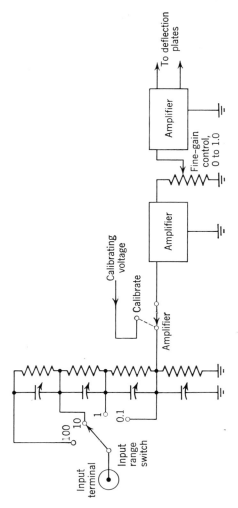

**Figure 26–23**   The input attenuator circuit.

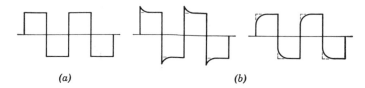

(a)                                                      (b)

**Figure 26–24**  Waveforms for adjusting the frequency response of the input attenuator.  (*a*) Input signal.  (*b*) Incorrect trimmer settings.

may be switched from the attenuator network to the calibrated voltage source (Fig. 26–23).   The calibrating voltage is so determined that a direct reading of observed waveforms can be made in terms of voltage. If the internal calibrating voltage is 1, adjustment of the fine-gain control to establish a pattern 1-inch high on the screen sets the calibration to a decimal pattern.   In observing an unknown signal, if the attenuator step is 10 and if the pattern on the screen is 2 inches high, this signal has a peak-to-peak voltage value of 20 volts.   Correspondingly, when the attenuator switch is set to 0.1, a pattern 3.4 inches high indicates that the peak-to-peak voltage of the waveform is 0.34 volt.

Once the calibration is established, the fine-gain control cannot be disturbed.   Some oscilloscopes have an internal calibration source which is 5.   When the fine-gain control sets the calibrating waveform to five divisions, oscilloscope patterns are then in decimal multiples of one volt per division.   If, for example, the input to an amplifier is monitored by an oscilloscope and the output is measured by a meter, one must remember that the oscilloscope reads peak-to-peak voltages and that the meter reads rms voltage.   The appropriate conversion, which is $2\sqrt{2}$ for sine waves, must be made.

As an example, let us assume that the output of an amplifier is 4.6 inches on the screen with an attenuator setting of 100 and that the amplifier input is 1.4 inches on the screen with the attenuator set to 1. The switching of the attenuator from 1 to 100 reduces the oscilloscope gain by 100.   In terms of the amplifier input voltage, the output pattern is $100 \times 4.6$, or 460 inches.   The amplifier gain is 460/1.4, or 328.6.

If an internal calibrating voltage is not available, an external known alternating voltage can be used.   The standard alternating outlet voltage is 320 volts peak to peak, and a 6.3-volt heater is slightly less than 18 volts peak to peak.

The input attenuator is arranged to permit the insertion or removal of a blocking capacitor in series with the input terminal.   When the connection from the terminal to the attenuator is direct, the oscilloscope amplifier accepts a d-c signal. The capacitor in the lead removes the direct current in the signal and allows only the a-c signal to pass through to the deflection plates. The d-c amplifier is very useful at times to show the relative location of the a-c signal to the d-c reference levels.

The application of the oscilloscope for observing the output of the amplifier in Fig. 26–25a illustrates the difference between the a-c and the d-c inputs. A fixed signal from the generator is set on the grid. When the cathode resistance $R_K$ is very large, the operating point is

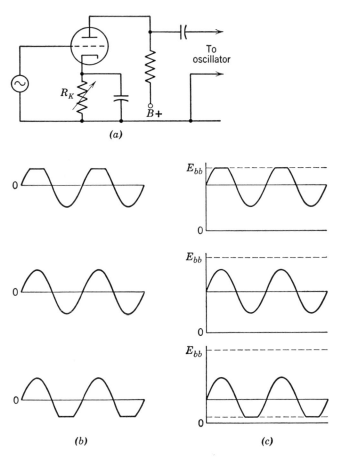

**Figure 26–25** Measurement of the output of an amplifier by means of an oscilloscope. (*a*) Circuit. (*b*) A-c amplifier waveforms. (*c*) D-c amplifier waveforms.

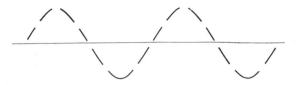

**Figure 26–26**   Intensity modulation of $Z$-axis pattern.

shifted toward cutoff, and the top of the output voltage waveform is clipped.   When the cathode resistance establishes the operating point at the center of the load line, the output is sinusoidal, and, when the cathode-resistance value is too low, grid-current flow distorts the output waveform.   The a-c position shows the clipping of the output wave, but the d-c position also shows the shift of the operating point.

## Section 26–7   $Z$-axis Patterns

The power-supply circuit of Fig. 26–9 show a terminal post $S5$ and a coupling capacitor $C_3$ leading to the control grid of the cathode-ray tube.   A signal placed between this terminal and ground *intensity modulates* the beam pattern on the screen.   A positive signal increases the beam current, and a negative signal decreases it.   Two cycles of a sine waveform produced by normal vertical deflection are shown in Fig. 26–26.   The signal into the $Z$ axis is a sine-wave voltage which is seven times the frequency of the two-cycle pattern.   The $Z$ axis input is often useful in case the conventional Lissajous pattern is too complex to be observed carefully.

Television is an example of $Z$-axis intensity modulation.   The conventional $X$ and $Y$ deflections are used to form the rectangular picture.   The picture information signal varies the intensity of the beam as it scans the rectangular deflection pattern to produce the light and dark elements of the complete picture.

## Section 26–8   Commercial Oscilloscopes and Controls

Two typical commercial oscilloscopes are shown in Fig. 26–27.   Both these instruments have a number of features that have not been discussed to this point.

The Weston oscilloscope has an *astigmatic* control which assists the focus control in obtaining a very fine trace on the screen.   The deflection amplifiers are arranged so that a positive signal produces an upward deflection on the vertical and a deflection to the right on the horizontal. The *normal-reverse* switches allow these deflection directions to be reversed. The sweep range also provides a 30 cycle (*TV-V*), and a 7875 cycle (*TV-H*) fixed-frequency sawtooth sweeps to expedite the observation of television signals. A *phase* control regulates the synchronized position of the waveform to the line frequency over a range of 170°.

The DuMont oscilloscope has an external binding post which connects to the plate of the relaxation oscillator. This terminal can be used as a source for the internal sawtooth signal, or an external capacitor can be placed from this terminal to ground, thereby permitting the frequency of the sawtooth to be established by the external capacitor. A relaxation oscillator is normally self-sustaining. However, if the sweep selector is set to *driven sweep*, the sawtooth occurs only when there is an incoming signal on the *Y* axis sufficient in amplitude to cause triggering of the relaxation oscillator. This

(a) Weston model 983. (*Courtesy Weston Instruments Division of Daystrom, Inc.*)

(b) DuMont model 304-A. (*Courtesy Allen B. DuMont Laboratories*)

**Figure 26–27**  Typical commercial cathode-ray oscilloscopes.

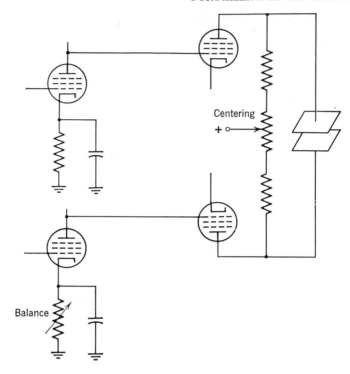

**Figure 26–28** Balance and centering controls in the d-c amplifier.

driven sweep is only used for certain specialized testing procedures. Here, again, it is important to advise the student to avoid this sweep position and to make sure that the oscilloscope is switched to the *recurring sweep* position.

Both oscilloscopes have *vertical-balance* and *horizontal-balance* controls which work in conjunction with the centering controls. A simplified schematic circuit which illustrates the principles of operation is shown in Fig. 26–28. Both the vertical and horizontal amplifiers are cascaded push–pull circuits and are direct-coupled to provide either d-c or a-c amplification. A potentiometer in the final plate circuit shifts the relative direct voltage on the two plates and centers the beam on the screen. A cathode rheostat in one of the earlier stages varies the over-all gain of one side of the push–pull system to match that on the other side. The proper balance setting is obtained when a rotation of the fine-gain control does not disturb the position of the spot on the screen.

## . . . . Suggested References for Further Study

### A. Electron ballistics and optics

1. T. S. Gray, *Applied Electronics*, 2nd ed., Chapter 1, John Wiley & Sons, New York, 1954.
2. W. G. Dow, *Fundamentals of Engineering Electronics*, 2nd ed., Chapter 1, John Wiley & Sons, New York, 1952.
3. K. R. Spangenberg, *Vacuum Tubes*, Chapter 13, McGraw-Hill Book Co., New York, 1948.

### B. Cathode-ray oscilloscope

1. J. Soller, M. A. Starr, and G. E. Valley Jr., *Cathode-Ray-Tube Displays*, Vol. 22, Radiation Laboratories Series, McGraw-Hill Book Co., New York, 1948.
2. K. R. Spangenberg, *Vacuum Tubes*, Chapter 15, McGraw-Hill Book Co., New York, 1948.
3. J. F. Rider and S. D. Ulsan, *Encyclopedia of the Cathode-Ray Oscilloscopes and Their Uses*, J. F. Rider, New York, 1950.
4. M. Bly, *A Guide to Cathode-Ray Patterns*, John Wiley & Sons, New York, 1943.

## . . . . QUESTIONS

1. Define or explain each of the following terms: (*a*) luminescence, (*b*) phosphorescence, (*c*) fluorescence, (*d*) persistence, (*e*) halation, (*f*) blanking, (*g*) retrace line, (*h*) Lissajous pattern, (*i*) Z-axis, (*j*) balance control.
2. Why is it necessary for the Aquadag to extend over a large part of the glass envelope?
3. Explain how focus is obtained from an electrostatic lens.
4. Why does the deflection of the beam decrease when the voltage on the aquadag is increased?
5. Explain how electrons from the beam get back to the power supply.
6. Why is the positive voltage grounded in the cathode-ray oscilloscope?
7. What filtering is used for the direct voltage for a cathode-ray tube?
8. Why is a sawtooth waveform needed for the horizontal deflection?
9. What is the purpose of blanking?
10. How is phase shift determined from a screen pattern?
11. Show how Lissajous patterns are produced.
12. How is a frequency ratio determined from a Lissajous pattern?
13. Explain how to measure gain using a cathode-ray oscilloscope.
14. Explain how to make calibrated voltage measurements using a cathode-ray oscilloscope.
15. How are Z-axis patterns produced?
16. Explain the step-by-step procedure in adjusting a cathode-ray oscilloscope.

# The mathematical analysis
## of oscillators

### The Tuned-Plate–Untuned-Grid Oscillator

$R_g$ does not enter into the equation since the grid current is essentially zero. The frequency of oscillation is

$$f = \frac{1}{2\pi \sqrt{L_p C_p}} \left( 1 + \frac{R_p}{r_p} \right)^{\frac{1}{2}}$$

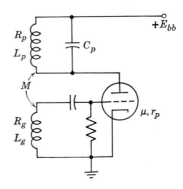

If $R_p$ is negligible, the expression becomes

$$f_0 = \frac{1}{2\pi \sqrt{L_p C_p}}$$

Then

$$f = f_0 \left( 1 + \frac{R_p}{r_p} \right)^{\frac{1}{2}}$$

and $f > f_0$, making the tuned circuit a capacitive impedance at the frequency of oscillation. The condition for stable oscillation is

$$g_m = \frac{\mu R_p C_p}{\mu M - L_p}$$

If $R_p$ is zero, the tank impedance is infinite and $A_e$ becomes $\mu$. Then

$$\mu = L_p/M$$

**603**

### The Tuned-Grid–Untuned-Plate Oscillator

$R_g$ now enters the equations since it directly determines the $Q$ of the tank circuit. The frequency of oscillation is

$$f = \frac{1}{2\pi \sqrt{L_g C_g} \left(1 + \dfrac{R_g}{r_p}\dfrac{L_p}{L_g}\right)^{1/2}}$$

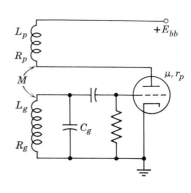

If $R_g$ is negligible, this expression becomes

$$f_0 = \frac{1}{2\pi \sqrt{L_g C_g}}$$

Then

$$f = f_0 \frac{1}{\left(1 + \dfrac{R_g}{r_p}\dfrac{L_p}{L_g}\right)^{1/2}}$$

and $f < f_0$, making the tuned circuit an inductive impedance at the frequency of oscillation. The condition for stable oscillation is

$$g_m = \frac{\mu R_g L_g C_g}{M(\mu L_p - M)}$$

### The Hartley Oscillator

Let $L_T = L_g + L_p + 2M$ in the equation for the frequency of oscillation:

$$f = \frac{1}{2\pi \sqrt{L_T C}} \left(1 + \frac{R_p}{r_p}\right)^{1/2}$$

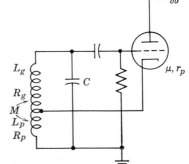

If $R_p$ is negligible compared to $r_p$, this equation becomes

$$f = f_0 \left(1 + \frac{R_p}{r_p}\right)^{1/2}$$

and $f > f_0$, making the tuned circuit a capacitive impedance at the resonant frequency. The condition for stable oscillation is

$$g_m = (R_g + R_p) \frac{L_T C}{(L_p + M)(L_g + M)}$$

## The Colpitts Oscillator

Let $1/C_T = 1/C_1 + 1/C_2$ or $C_T = C_1C_2/(C_1 + C_2)$ in the equation for the frequency of oscillation:

$$f = \frac{1}{2\pi \sqrt{LC_T}} \left(1 + \frac{R}{r_p} \frac{C_2}{C_1 + C_2}\right)^{\frac{1}{2}}$$

If $R$ is negligible compared to $r_p$, the equation becomes

$$f_0 = \frac{1}{2\pi \sqrt{LC_T}}$$

Then

$$f = f_0 \left(1 + \frac{R}{r_p} \frac{C_2}{C_1 + C_2}\right)^{\frac{1}{2}}$$

and $f > f_0$, making the tuned circuit a capacitive impedance at the resonant frequency. The condition for stable oscillation is

$$g_m = \frac{\mu R(C_1 + C_2)}{L(\mu - C_1/C_2)}$$

This condition for oscillation may be solved for $\mu$ to give

$$\mu = \frac{C_2}{C_1} + r_p R \left(\frac{C_1 + C_2}{L}\right)$$

## . . . . Suggested References for Further Study

1. K. R. Sturley, *Radio Receiver Design*, Part I, 2nd ed., Chapter 6, John Wiley & Sons, New York, 1954.
2. J. Millman, *Vacuum-Tube and Semiconductor Electronics*, Chapter 18, McGraw-Hill Book Co., New York, 1958.
3. S. Seely, *Electron-Tube Circuits*, Chapter 12, McGraw-Hill Book Co., New York, 1950.

# Transistor equivalent circuits

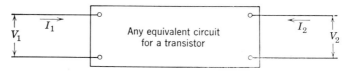

The analysis for a transistor in terms of the hybrid parameters $h$ was developed in Chapter 11. The set of $h$ parameters resulted from an analysis of the two equations developed from the "black-box" concept in Section 7–10. There are four variables, $V_1$, $I_1$, $V_2$, and $I_2$, which, when taken two at a time, produce sets of parameters. The hybrid parameters result from one of these combinations. Other sets of parameters can be established and are used in transistor literature. The sets, six in number, result from the following pairs of equations which apply to the "black box".

1. $a$ parameters:

$$V_1 = a_{11}V_2 - a_{12}I_2$$

$$I_1 = a_{21}V_2 - a_{22}I_2$$

2. $b$ parameters:

$$V_2 = b_{11}V_1 - b_{12}I_1$$

$$I_2 = b_{21}V_1 - b_{22}I_1$$

3. $g$ parameters:

$$I_1 = g_{11}V_1 + g_{12}I_2$$

$$V_2 = g_{21}V_1 + g_{22}I_2$$

**606**

4. $h$ parameters:

$$V_1 = h_{11}I_1 + h_{12}V_2$$

$$I_2 = h_{21}I_1 + h_{22}V_2$$

5. $y$ parameters:

$$I_1 = y_{11}V_1 + y_{12}V_2$$

$$I_2 = y_{21}V_1 + y_{22}V_2$$

6. $z$ parameters:

$$V_1 = z_{11}I_1 + z_{12}I_2$$

$$V_2 = z_{21}I_1 + z_{22}I_2$$

These equations can all be solved for $z_{\text{in}}$, $z_{\text{out}}$, $A_v$, $A_i$, $A_p$, $Z_{\text{in}}$, $Z_{\text{out}}$, and MAG. The method of application of the hybrid parameters to the transistor circuit is the major content of Chapter 11. It is a common practice for the manufacturer to give published transistor data in terms of the $z$ parameters. It is necessary to use the $z$-parameter values directly or to convert them to the $h$ parameter. The $z$ parameter itself implies a complex impedance, but, in order to simplify the procedure, the $z$ parameter is reduced in practice to the $r$ parameter. These $r$ parameters are adapted to an equivalent circuit of the "black box" which is in the form of a T network. The technical data comprise $r_e$ as the emitter resistance, $r_b$ as the base resistance, $r_c$ as the collector resistance, and $\alpha$ as the current gain.

### The Grounded-Base Amplifier

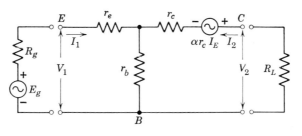

$$r_{11} = r_b + r_e \quad [= V_1/I_1 \text{ for } I_2 = 0]$$

$$r_{21} = r_b + \alpha r_c \quad [= V_2/I_1 \text{ for } I_2 = 0]$$

$$r_{22} = r_b + r_c \quad [= V_2/I_2 \text{ for } I_1 = 0]$$

$$r_{12} = \phantom{r_b +} r_b \quad [= V_1/I_2 \text{ for } I_1 = 0]$$

## The Grounded-Emitter Amplifier

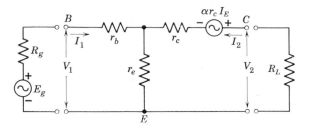

$$r_{11} = r_b + r_e \qquad\qquad [= V_1/I_1 \text{ for } I_2 = 0]$$

$$r_{21} = r_e - \alpha r_c \qquad\qquad [= V_2/I_1 \text{ for } I_2 = 0]$$

$$r_{22} = r_e + (1 - \alpha)r_c \quad [= V_2/I_2 \text{ for } I_1 = 0]$$

$$r_{12} = \qquad r_e \qquad\qquad [= V_1/I_2 \text{ for } I_1 = 0]$$

## The Grounded-Collector Amplifier

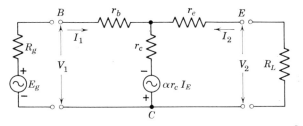

$$r_{11} = r_b + r_c \qquad\qquad [= V_1/I_1 \text{ for } I_2 = 0]$$

$$r_{21} = \qquad r_c \qquad\qquad [= V_2/I_1 \text{ for } I_2 = 0]$$

$$r_{22} = r_c(1 - \alpha) + r_e \quad [= V_2/I_2 \text{ for } I_1 = 0]$$

$$r_{12} = r_c(1 - \alpha) \qquad\qquad [= V_1/I_2 \text{ for } I_1 = 0]$$

Equations can be established for these parameters for the various end results listed in the summary of Chapter 11:

$$\Delta^r = r_{11}r_{22} - r_{12}r_{21}$$

$$r_{\text{in}} = \frac{\Delta^r + r_{11}R_L}{r_{22} + R_L}, \qquad r_{\text{out}} = \frac{\Delta^r + r_{22}R_G}{r_{11} + R_G}$$

$$R_{\text{in}} = \sqrt{\frac{r_{11}}{r_{22}}}\,\Delta^r, \qquad R_{\text{out}} = \sqrt{\frac{r_{22}}{r_{11}}}\,\Delta^r$$

$$A_i = \frac{r_{21}}{r_{22} + R_L}, \qquad A_v = \frac{r_{21}R_L}{\Delta^r + r_{11}R_L},$$

$$\text{MAG} = \frac{r_{21}{}^2}{(\sqrt{r_{11}r_{22}} + \sqrt{\Delta^r})^2}$$

The input impedances, the output impedances, the current gains, and the voltage gains for *any* value of $R_g$ and $R_L$ for these six sets of parameters are tabulated below:

$$\Delta = n_{11}n_{22} - n_{12}n_{21}$$

|   | $z_{\text{in}}$ | $z_{\text{out}}$ | $A_i$ | $A_v$ |
|---|---|---|---|---|
| a | $\dfrac{a_{11}Z_L + a_{12}}{a_{21}Z_L + a_{22}}$ | $\dfrac{a_{22}Z_g + a_{12}}{a_{21}Z_g + a_{11}}$ | $\dfrac{1}{a_{22} + a_{21}Z_L}$ | $\dfrac{Z_L}{a_{12} + a_{11}Z_L}$ |
| b | $\dfrac{b_{22}Z_L + b_{12}}{b_{21}Z_L + b_{12}}$ | $\dfrac{b_{11}Z_g + b_{12}}{b_{21}Z_g + b_{22}}$ | $\dfrac{\Delta}{b_{11} + b_{12}Z_L}$ | $\dfrac{\Delta Z_L}{b_{12} + b_{22}Z_L}$ |
| g | $\dfrac{g_{22} + Z_L}{\Delta + g_{11}Z_L}$ | $\dfrac{\Delta + g_{22}/Z_L}{g_{11} + 1/Z_L}$ | $\dfrac{g_{21}}{\Delta + g_{11}Z_L}$ | $\dfrac{g_{21}Z_L}{g_{22} + Z_L}$ |
| h | $\dfrac{\Delta + h_{11}/Z_L}{h_{22} + 1/Z_L}$ | $\dfrac{h_{11} + Z_g}{\Delta + h_{22}Z_g}$ | $\dfrac{-h_{21}/Z_L}{h_{22} + 1/Z_L}$ | $\dfrac{-h_{21}Z_L}{h_{11} + \Delta Z_L}$ |
| y | $\dfrac{y_{22} + 1/Z_L}{\Delta + y_{11}/Z_L}$ | $\dfrac{y_{11} + 1/Z_g}{\Delta + y_{22}/Z_g}$ | $\dfrac{-y_{21}/Z_L}{\Delta + y_{11}/Z_L}$ | $\dfrac{-y_{21}}{y_{22} + 1/Z_L}$ |
| z | $\dfrac{\Delta + z_{11}Z_L}{z_{22} + Z_L}$ | $\dfrac{\Delta + z_{22}Z_g}{z_{11} + Z_g}$ | $\dfrac{z_{21}}{z_{22} + Z_L}$ | $\dfrac{z_{21}Z_L}{\Delta + z_{11}Z_L}$ |

By permission: R. F. Shea, *Principles of Transistor Circuits*, John Wiley & Sons, 1953.

The parameters for one system can be converted to the parameters for another system. For example, $h$ parameters can be converted into $z(r)$ parameters, or $z(r)$ parameters can be converted into $h$ parameters. The interchanging equations are:

### Matrix Interrelations

| From →<br>To ↓ | $[z]$ | $[y]$ | $[h]$ | $[g]$ | $[a]$ | $[b]$ |
|---|---|---|---|---|---|---|
| $[z]$ | $\begin{matrix} z_{11} & z_{12} \\ z_{21} & z_{22} \end{matrix}$ | $\begin{matrix} \dfrac{y_{22}}{\Delta^y} & \dfrac{-y_{12}}{\Delta^y} \\[6pt] \dfrac{-y_{21}}{\Delta^y} & \dfrac{y_{11}}{\Delta^y} \end{matrix}$ | $\begin{matrix} \dfrac{\Delta^h}{h_{22}} & \dfrac{h_{12}}{h_{22}} \\[6pt] \dfrac{-h_{21}}{h_{22}} & \dfrac{1}{h_{22}} \end{matrix}$ | $\begin{matrix} \dfrac{1}{g_{11}} & \dfrac{-g_{12}}{g_{11}} \\[6pt] \dfrac{g_{21}}{g_{11}} & \dfrac{\Delta^g}{g_{11}} \end{matrix}$ | $\begin{matrix} \dfrac{a_{11}}{a_{21}} & \dfrac{\Delta^a}{a_{21}} \\[6pt] \dfrac{1}{a_{21}} & \dfrac{a_{22}}{a_{21}} \end{matrix}$ | $\begin{matrix} \dfrac{b_{22}}{b_{21}} & \dfrac{1}{b_{21}} \\[6pt] \dfrac{\Delta^b}{b_{21}} & \dfrac{b_{11}}{b_{21}} \end{matrix}$ |
| $[y]$ | $\begin{matrix} \dfrac{z_{22}}{\Delta^z} & \dfrac{-z_{12}}{\Delta^z} \\[6pt] \dfrac{-z_{21}}{\Delta^z} & \dfrac{z_{11}}{\Delta^z} \end{matrix}$ | $\begin{matrix} y_{11} & y_{12} \\ y_{21} & y_{22} \end{matrix}$ | $\begin{matrix} \dfrac{1}{h_{11}} & \dfrac{-h_{12}}{h_{11}} \\[6pt] \dfrac{h_{21}}{h_{11}} & \dfrac{\Delta^h}{h_{11}} \end{matrix}$ | $\begin{matrix} \dfrac{\Delta^g}{g_{22}} & \dfrac{g_{12}}{g_{22}} \\[6pt] \dfrac{-g_{21}}{g_{22}} & \dfrac{1}{g_{22}} \end{matrix}$ | $\begin{matrix} \dfrac{a_{22}}{a_{12}} & \dfrac{-\Delta^a}{a_{12}} \\[6pt] \dfrac{-1}{a_{12}} & \dfrac{a_{11}}{a_{12}} \end{matrix}$ | $\begin{matrix} \dfrac{b_{11}}{b_{12}} & \dfrac{-1}{b_{12}} \\[6pt] \dfrac{-\Delta^b}{b_{12}} & \dfrac{b_{22}}{b_{12}} \end{matrix}$ |
| $[h]$ | $\begin{matrix} \dfrac{\Delta^z}{z_{22}} & \dfrac{z_{12}}{z_{22}} \\[6pt] \dfrac{-z_{21}}{z_{22}} & \dfrac{1}{z_{22}} \end{matrix}$ | $\begin{matrix} \dfrac{1}{y_{11}} & \dfrac{-y_{12}}{y_{11}} \\[6pt] \dfrac{y_{21}}{y_{11}} & \dfrac{\Delta^y}{y_{11}} \end{matrix}$ | $\begin{matrix} h_{11} & h_{12} \\ h_{21} & h_{22} \end{matrix}$ | $\begin{matrix} \dfrac{g_{22}}{\Delta^g} & \dfrac{-g_{12}}{\Delta^g} \\[6pt] \dfrac{-g_{21}}{\Delta^g} & \dfrac{g_{11}}{\Delta^g} \end{matrix}$ | $\begin{matrix} \dfrac{a_{12}}{a_{22}} & \dfrac{\Delta^a}{a_{22}} \\[6pt] \dfrac{-1}{a_{22}} & \dfrac{a_{21}}{a_{22}} \end{matrix}$ | $\begin{matrix} \dfrac{b_{12}}{b_{11}} & \dfrac{1}{b_{11}} \\[6pt] \dfrac{-\Delta^b}{b_{11}} & \dfrac{b_{21}}{b_{11}} \end{matrix}$ |
| $[g]$ | $\begin{matrix} \dfrac{1}{z_{11}} & \dfrac{-z_{12}}{z_{11}} \\[6pt] \dfrac{z_{21}}{z_{11}} & \dfrac{\Delta^z}{z_{11}} \end{matrix}$ | $\begin{matrix} \dfrac{\Delta^y}{y_{22}} & \dfrac{y_{12}}{y_{22}} \\[6pt] \dfrac{-y_{21}}{y_{22}} & \dfrac{1}{y_{22}} \end{matrix}$ | $\begin{matrix} \dfrac{h_{22}}{\Delta^h} & \dfrac{-h_{12}}{\Delta^h} \\[6pt] \dfrac{-h_{21}}{\Delta^h} & \dfrac{h_{11}}{\Delta^h} \end{matrix}$ | $\begin{matrix} g_{11} & g_{12} \\ g_{21} & g_{22} \end{matrix}$ | $\begin{matrix} \dfrac{a_{21}}{a_{11}} & \dfrac{-\Delta^a}{a_{11}} \\[6pt] \dfrac{1}{a_{11}} & \dfrac{a_{12}}{a_{11}} \end{matrix}$ | $\begin{matrix} \dfrac{b_{21}}{b_{22}} & \dfrac{-1}{b_{22}} \\[6pt] \dfrac{\Delta^b}{b_{22}} & \dfrac{b_{12}}{b_{22}} \end{matrix}$ |
| $[a]$ | $\begin{matrix} \dfrac{z_{11}}{z_{21}} & \dfrac{\Delta^z}{z_{21}} \\[6pt] \dfrac{1}{z_{21}} & \dfrac{z_{22}}{z_{21}} \end{matrix}$ | $\begin{matrix} \dfrac{-y_{22}}{y_{21}} & \dfrac{-1}{y_{21}} \\[6pt] \dfrac{-\Delta^y}{y_{21}} & \dfrac{-y_{11}}{y_{21}} \end{matrix}$ | $\begin{matrix} \dfrac{-\Delta^h}{h_{21}} & \dfrac{-h_{11}}{h_{21}} \\[6pt] \dfrac{-h_{22}}{h_{21}} & \dfrac{-1}{h_{21}} \end{matrix}$ | $\begin{matrix} \dfrac{1}{g_{21}} & \dfrac{g_{22}}{g_{21}} \\[6pt] \dfrac{g_{11}}{g_{21}} & \dfrac{\Delta^g}{g_{21}} \end{matrix}$ | $\begin{matrix} a_{11} & a_{12} \\ a_{21} & a_{22} \end{matrix}$ | $\begin{matrix} \dfrac{b_{22}}{\Delta^b} & \dfrac{b_{12}}{\Delta^b} \\[6pt] \dfrac{b_{21}}{\Delta^b} & \dfrac{b_{11}}{\Delta^b} \end{matrix}$ |
| $[b]$ | $\begin{matrix} \dfrac{z_{22}}{z_{12}} & \dfrac{\Delta^z}{z_{12}} \\[6pt] \dfrac{1}{z_{12}} & \dfrac{z_{11}}{z_{12}} \end{matrix}$ | $\begin{matrix} \dfrac{-y_{11}}{y_{12}} & \dfrac{-1}{y_{12}} \\[6pt] \dfrac{-\Delta^y}{y_{12}} & \dfrac{-y_{22}}{y_{12}} \end{matrix}$ | $\begin{matrix} \dfrac{1}{h_{12}} & \dfrac{h_{11}}{h_{12}} \\[6pt] \dfrac{h_{22}}{h_{12}} & \dfrac{\Delta^h}{h_{12}} \end{matrix}$ | $\begin{matrix} -\dfrac{\Delta^g}{g_{12}} & -\dfrac{g_{22}}{g_{12}} \\[6pt] -\dfrac{g_{11}}{g_{12}} & -\dfrac{1}{g_{12}} \end{matrix}$ | $\begin{matrix} \dfrac{a_{22}}{\Delta^a} & \dfrac{a_{12}}{\Delta^a} \\[6pt] \dfrac{a_{21}}{\Delta^a} & \dfrac{a_{11}}{\Delta^a} \end{matrix}$ | $\begin{matrix} b_{11} & b_{12} \\ b_{21} & b_{22} \end{matrix}$ |

By permission: R. F. Shea, *Principles of Transistor Circuits*, John Wiley & Sons, 1953.

## Determinant Interrelations

| To \ From → | $\Delta^z$ | $\Delta^y$ | $\Delta^h$ | $\Delta^g$ | $\Delta^a$ | $\Delta^b$ |
|---|---|---|---|---|---|---|
| $\Delta^z$ | $\Delta^z$ | $\dfrac{1}{\Delta^y}$ | $\dfrac{h_{11}}{h_{22}}$ | $\dfrac{g_{22}}{g_{11}}$ | $\dfrac{a_{12}}{a_{21}}$ | $\dfrac{b_{12}}{b_{21}}$ |
| $\Delta^y$ | $\dfrac{1}{\Delta^z}$ | $\Delta^y$ | $\dfrac{h_{22}}{h_{11}}$ | $\dfrac{g_{11}}{g_{22}}$ | $\dfrac{a_{21}}{a_{12}}$ | $\dfrac{b_{21}}{b_{12}}$ |
| $\Delta^h$ | $\dfrac{z_{11}}{z_{22}}$ | $\dfrac{y_{22}}{y_{11}}$ | $\Delta^h$ | $\dfrac{1}{\Delta^g}$ | $\dfrac{a_{11}}{a_{22}}$ | $\dfrac{b_{22}}{b_{11}}$ |
| $\Delta^g$ | $\dfrac{z_{22}}{z_{11}}$ | $\dfrac{y_{11}}{y_{22}}$ | $\dfrac{1}{\Delta^h}$ | $\Delta^g$ | $\dfrac{a_{22}}{a_{11}}$ | $\dfrac{b_{11}}{b_{22}}$ |
| $\Delta^a$ | $\dfrac{z_{12}}{z_{21}}$ | $\dfrac{y_{12}}{y_{21}}$ | $-\dfrac{h_{12}}{h_{21}}$ | $-\dfrac{g_{12}}{g_{21}}$ | $\Delta^a$ | $\dfrac{1}{\Delta_b}$ |
| $\Delta^b$ | $\dfrac{z_{21}}{z_{12}}$ | $\dfrac{y_{21}}{y_{12}}$ | $-\dfrac{h_{21}}{h_{12}}$ | $-\dfrac{g_{21}}{g_{12}}$ | $\dfrac{1}{\Delta^a}$ | $\Delta^b$ |

By permission: R. F. Shea, *Principles of Transistor Circuits*, John Wiley & Sons, 1953.

# Answers to Odd-Numbered Problems

◆ ◆ ◆ ◆ ◆ ◆ ◆ ◆ ◆ ◆ ◆ ◆ ◆ ◆ ◆ ◆ ◆ ◆ ◆ ◆ ◆ ◆ ◆ ◆ ◆

The answers to the problems which have been marked with an asterisk * have been obtained graphically and are subject to variation. All answers have been obtained by means of a slide rule.

**Chapter 2.** **3.** 317.5 ohms at 7.88 watts, 107.5 to 152.5 ma. **5.** 41.6 ma, 18.5 ma, 5.2 ma.

**Chapter 3.** **3.** $i_b = 0.0333(37.5E_c + E_b)^{1.356}$ ma, 17 ma.

**Chapter 6.** **1.** 17.31 watts. **3.** 360 volts. **5.** 12.2 mh. **7.** 273 $\mu\mu$f. **9.** 0.0868 $\mu$f. **11.** 59 $\mu\mu$f.

**Chapter 7.** **1.** At 396 kc 0.84 amperes, 21 volts; at 2 Mc 0.29 amperes, 29 volts. **3.** 51.5 $\mu\mu$f, 52,600 ohms. **5.** 212,000 ohms, 9.4 kc. **7.** $0.908 - j13.72$ ma. **9.** $0.485 - j0.028$ ma. **11.** 0.808, 0.695 ampere. **13.** 28.4 volts, 40.67 volts, 1.136 amperes. **15.** 9.68 volts, 65.8 ohms. **17.** 0.2475 ampere, 58.5 ohms. **19.** 0.356 watt. **21.** $h_{11}$ 58.7 ohms, $h_{12}$ 0.072, $h_{21}$ 0.072, $h_{22}$ 0.0151 mho.

**Chapter 8.** **1.** (a) 3.423, (b) 2.1206, (c) 5.879, (d) 0.1644, (e) 18.468, (f) $-2.638$, (g) $-0.0584$, (h) $-1.204$, (i) $-1.329$, (j) $-4.0755$. **3.** 3.26 volts. **5.** 0.0025 mw, 6.32 mv. **7.** $-3.98$ db. **9.** $+66.32$ db. **11.** 118.2 mw, $+12.95$ db. **13.** 50 watts, $+47.0$ VU. **15.** 0.643 mv, $+98.6$ db.

**Chapter 9.** **1.** 293 volts, 29.3 ma, 121%, 21.1 watts, 29.9 volt-amperes. **3.** 586 volts, 58.6 ma, 48.2%, 42.2 watts, 42.2 volt-amperes. **5.** ($E_c$ volts, $I_b$ ma), $(-15.6, 10.7), (-10.3, 18.7), (0, 21.5), (-15.6, 0), (-20, 0)$.

**Chapter 10.** **1.** 19.65. **3.** 27.6. **5.** 3.75, 15.1. *7. (Bias at $-8.5$ volts), assume screen current 2 ma, 2125 ohms, (using Eq. 10–6, 2.42 watts, 35.7%, 14.4$A_e$,

**613**

245 volts), (using Eq. 10–10, 2.5 watts, 32.4%, 14.3$A_e$, 242 volts).     *9. 6000 $\mu$mhos, 20,000 ohms, 110$\mu$.     *11. 9.4%.

**Chapter 11.**     *1. Bias at 4 ma, 0.95, 14.5 mw, 46.1%, 23.3%.     3. 126.5 ohms, 834,000 ohms, 456$A_e$, $-0.964A_i$, $-439A_p$.     5. 79.4 ohms, 290,000 ohms, 1540$A_e$, $-0.919A_i$, $-1412A_p$.     *7. Bias at 75 $\mu$a, 47.6, 12.7 mw, 40.5%, 19.3%.     9. 47.3$A_i$, $-180A_e$, $-8525A_p$, 2620 ohms, 112,500 ohms.     11. 5450 ohms, 327,000 ohms, 28.25$A_i$, $-62A_e$, $-1755A_p$.     13. 102 ohms, 955,000 ohms, $-31.8A_i$, 1.00$A_e$, $-31.8A_p$.     *15. $R_1 + R_B = 213,500$ ohms.     *17. $R_1 + R_B = 133,300$ ohms.

**Chapter 12.**     1. 0.0204 ampere, $\frac{1}{900}$.     3. 4020, 387, 127, 49, 40.     *5. Assume screen current 3 ma, 211 ohms: using Eq. 10–6, 7.80 watts, 20.4 watts, 38.2%, using Eq. 10–10, 8.43 watts, 23.1 watts, 36.5%.     *7. Assume screen current 5 ma, 95 ohms: using Eq. 10–6, 5.24 watts, 25 watts, 20.9%, using Eq. 10–10, 5.7 watts, 25.5 watts, 22.8%.     9. Gain 84.61 db (9650 $\times$ 30,000), 68.3 $\times$ 10$^{-12}$ watts, 0.566 volts, 61.35 $\times$ 10$^{-6}$ volts, 2.86, 1/6.6, 1/47.2.

**Chapter 13.**     3. 17.7, 15.4, 14.8, 65.5.     5. 20.6 and 116 kc, 201 and 58.3 kc, 31.7 and 348 kc, 66.7 and 39.2 kc.     *7. Bias at $-2$ volts, 1430 ohms, 37, 148 volts.     9. 36.5 kc, 5 kc, 84.1 kc, 0.64 kc.     11. Gain $+66.26$ db (3650 $\times$ 1162), $-13.43$ db at 10 cps and $-10.89$ db at 20 kc down from midband gain.     13. 238, 238, 406 ohms.

**Chapter 15.**     *1. With bias at $-1$ volt, 370 ohms, 2,000 ohms, 98,000 ohms.

**Chapter 16.**     *1. 0.32 ampere $I_b$, 0.0596 ampere $I_c$, 536 watts dissipation, 3624 watts output, 19,200 ohms load, 105 watts grid dissipation, 18.65$A_p$.     *3. Assume $E_{p,\max}$ 225 volts and $E_{g,\max}$ 95 volts, 350 mw (9.72 ma $I_b$).

**Chapter 17.**     1. (0%, 25.2), (5%, 11.2), (20%, 4.2).     3. (5%, 11,120), (10%, 35,200), (20%, 120,800).     5. 17.     7. 29.8.

**Chapter 21.**     1. 680 cps.     3. 57.9 kc.     5. 159 cps, 136 cps, 13.5 kc, 11.6 kc.

**Chapter 22.**     1. 369, 13.85 kc.     3. 41.9, 306 kc.

**Chapter 23.**     1. 3245 cycles.     3. 12.     5. 108.     7. 300.     9. 1.19, 1.23, 1.28, 1.36, 1.45.     11. 13.13 kc, 9.4, 26.26.     13. 0.711, 1.118, 1.518, 1.925, 2.325; 0.775, 1.778, 2.795, 3.795, 4.813, 5.813.

**Chapter 24.**     *1. 59%.

# Index

**615**